BIOMEMBRANE
STRUCTURE AND FUNCTION

TOPICS IN MOLECULAR
AND STRUCTURAL BIOLOGY

Series Editors:
Watson Fuller, University of Keele
Stephen Neidle, King's College University of London

1 S. Neidle (ed.)
Topics in Nucleic Acid Structure, Part 1

2 S. Neidle (ed.)
Topics in Nucleic Acid Structure, Part 2

3 S. Neidle/M. J. Waring (eds)
Molecular Aspects of Anti-Cancer Drug Action

4 D. Chapman (ed.)
Biomembrane Structure and Function

verlag
chemie

Weinheim
Deerfield Beach, Florida
Basel

BIOMEMBRANE STRUCTURE AND FUNCTION

edited by

DENNIS CHAPMAN

University of London

verlag chemie

Weinheim
Deerfield Beach, Florida
Basel

Dennis Chapman, M.D.
Professor of Biophysical Chemistry
Royal Free Hospital School of Medicine
University of London
Rowland Hill Street
London NW3
UK

CIP–Kurztitelaufnahme der Deutschen Bibliothek

Biomembrane structure and function/ed. by Dennis
Chapman. – Weinheim; Deerfield Beach, Florida;
Basel: Verlag Chemie, 1984.
  (Topics in molecular and structural biology; 4)
  ISBN 3–527–26134–6 (Weinheim . . .)
  ISBN 0–89573–208–4 (Deerfield Beach, Florida)
NE: Chapman, Dennis [Hrsg.]; GT

© The Contributors 1984
Published in North America and Continental Europe
by Verlag Chemie GmbH, D-6940 Weinheim
First published 1984 outside North America and
Continental Europe by The Macmillan Press, London
and Basingstoke

Typeset by RDL Artset Ltd, Sutton, Surrey, England
Printed in Great Britain

Contents

The Contributors

R. L. Amey
Department of Chemistry
Occidental College
1600 Campus Road
Los Angeles
California 90041
USA

D. Bach
Department of Membrane Research
The Weizmann Institute of Science
76100 Rehovot
Israel

D. Chapman
Department of Biochemistry and
Chemistry
Royal Free Hospital School of
Medicine
University of London
Rowland Hill Street
London NW3 2PF
UK

W. Hoffmann
NUKEM GmbH
Postfach 11 00 80
D-6450 Hanau 11
Federal Republic of Germany

G. Inesi
Department of Biological Chemistry
University of Maryland
Baltimore
Maryland
USA

M. Kurzmack
Department of Biological Chemistry
University of Maryland
Baltimore
Maryland
USA

J. Li
Department of Biochemistry
College of Physicians and
Surgeons of Columbia University
630 West 168th Street
New York
NY 10032
USA

L. Makowski
Department of Biochemistry
College of Physicians and
Surgeons of Columbia University
630 West 168th Street
New York
NY 10032
USA

D. A. Pink
   Theoretical Physics Institute
   St. Francis Xavier University
   Antigonish
   Nova Scotia
   Canada B2G 1CO

C. J. Restall
   Department of Biochemistry and
   Chemistry
   Royal Free Hospital School of
   Medicine
   University of London
   Rowland Hill Street
   London NW3 2PF
   UK

S. P. Verma
   Tufts-New England Medical Center
   Therapeutic Radiology Department
   Radiobiology Division
   171 Harrison Avenue
   Boston
   MA 02111
   USA

D. F. H. Wallach
   Tufts-New England Medical Center
   Therapeutic Radiology Department
   Radiobiology Division
   171 Harrison Avenue
   Boston
   MA 02111
   USA

Preface

The application of physical techniques to biology has revolutionised much of our thinking and attitudes. Techniques such as X-ray diffraction and crystallographic methods have been particularly outstanding, as seen in studies of nucleic acids and proteins. This is illustrated in the first volume in the present series on Topics in Nucleic Acid Structure.

The present volume is devoted to the application of some selected physical techniques to model and natural biomembranes. Only a few of the many available physical techniques are presented but they are topical and timely.

Understanding the structure and function of biomembranes has already benefited from the application of physical methods and a wide range of techniques have been, and are still being, applied. In the 1960s a strong concentration occurred, centred on consideration of the lipid organisation of biomembrane structures. These considerations were resolved by the application of calorimetric methods applied first to model biomembranes and then to natural biomembranes. This indicated the existence of extensive regions of lipid able to undergo a cooperative melting behaviour. It became clear that it supported the existence of a lipid bilayer structure inside which intrinsic proteins were situated rather than the "sandwich" type structure, previously suggested. Dr Bach, in Chapter 1, reviews studies using calorimetry on model and natural biomembranes.

As knowledge began to accumulate, and a consensus of opinion was reached about the lipid matrix, so concepts such as fluidity, phase transitions and the dynamics of biomembranes developed. At the same time, new approaches were made with electron microscope methods. In particular, freeze fracture techniques were developed and marked improvements were made using the negative staining techniques. The application of these methods now gives us a much better understanding of the way in which membrane proteins are situated within the lipid matrix, and provides information about the organisation of the protein helices, the funnel shape present in gap junction channels, and so on. The application of electron microscope and X-ray diffraction methods to the study of biomembrane stucture showing these many applications is reviewed by Dr Makowski and Dr Li in Chapter 2.

Various spectroscopic methods have been applied to biomembrane structures and a most popular technique at the present time makes use of difference spectroscopy. Thus infrared spectroscopy used in the difference manner, either with a data station or using Fourier Transform methods, is proving of great value in overcoming the problem of water absorption in the infrared region. The study of conformational changes in membrane proteins under triggering conditions say by light or Ca ions, etc., is being studied using this new development of infrared spectroscopy. This is reviewed in Chapter 4 by Amey and Chapman. The chapter on Raman spectroscopy by Verma and Wallach (Chapter 3) is an important complementary technique to infrared spectroscopy, useful for studying lipid and protein organisation. Both Chapters 3 and 4 indicate the way in which detailed information concerning protein conformational changes and protein-lipid perturbations may be obtained.

The fact that a fluid lipid bilayer forms the matrix for many biomembrane structures, raises questions concerning the mobility and dynamics of the membrane protein. Spectroscopic methods using triplet probes have been devised for measuring the rotational diffusion of membrane proteins whilst optical methods have been devised using fluorescent bleaching for measuring lateral diffusion. The relation between protein dynamics and enzyme function and immunology function is described by Hoffmann and Restall in Chapter 5.

The application of theoretical methods to studies of model and natural biomembranes serving to rationalise and to provide insight into the experimental data, has developed and become extremely sophisticated. Studies of lipid phase transitions, lipid-protein interactions and phase diagrams of model and natural biomembranes are described and illustrated by Pink in Chapter 6.

In the final chapter, 7, Drs Inesi and Kurzmack discuss biochemical and biophysical studies of the Ca^{2+}-dependent ATPase of sarcoplasmic reticulum and show the present situation with regard to the manner in which this important pump protein operates. The application of electron spin resonance spectroscopy to the study of the conformational changes of the protein is indicated.

There are many other important physical techniques which could have been included in this selection of topics on biomembrane structure. It is hoped that the present selection is both timely and stimulating.

Dennis Chapman

1

Calorimetric studies of model and natural biomembranes

Diana Bach
Department of Membrane Research,
The Weizmann Institute of Science,
76100 Rehovot, Israel

ABBREVIATIONS

DSC, differential scanning calorimetry; DTA, differential thermal analysis; T_c, transition temperature; T_m, temperature of the midpoint of transition; ΔH, enthalpy of transition; ΔS, entropy of transition; DPL or DPPC, dipalmitoyl phosphatidylcholine; DPPE, dipalmitoyl phosphatidylethanolamine; DPPS, dipalmitoyl phosphatidylserine; DPPG, dipalmitoyl phosphatidylglycerol; DPPA, dipalmitoyl phosphatidic acid; SP, sphingomyelin; PC, phosphatidylcholine lecithin; DSL, distearoyl lecithin; DML, dimyristoyl lecithin; PS, phosphatidylserine.

INTRODUCTION

Biomembrane research was initiated many years ago, when it was recognised that cells possess a selectively permeable barrier determining the diffusion of substances from the inside to the outside of cells and vice versa. Over the years, a vast amount of research has been carried out in an attempt to evaluate the structure of these biomembranes and to correlate their structure with their functions.

Biomembranes are composed of proteins, lipids and carbohydrates (glyco-lipids and glycoproteins) and many different models for their assembly have been proposed. One of the oldest models assumes that the lipids of the membranes are mainly in the bilayer configuration with their polar heads at the membrane surface and their non-polar tails pointing towards the membrane interior. Based on various experimental approaches, it is now generally believed that the lipids in the membranes are indeed in a bilayer configuration. The proteins are either located on the surface of the bilayer (extrinsic proteins) or embedded to various degrees in the lipid matrix (intrinsic proteins). The importance of the lipid layer in maintaining membrane structure and its functions was realised quite early and has resulted in intensive investigation into the lipid properties. A number of physicochemical techniques were used in these studies.

Chapman and coworkers, in their pioneering work, have shown that the phospholipids exhibit thermotropic mesomorphism; when heated they undergo a number of phase changes before reaching the capillary melting point. This formed the basis for the calorimetric studies of lipids and biomembranes. As the phospholipids found in natural membranes are very complex, due to mixtures of different lipids being located in the same membrane, and as there is a distribution of fatty acyl residues even within the same molecule, the physicochemical research of pure lipids and their interaction with various compounds (ions, drugs, proteins) was initiated on synthetic, well-defined phospholipids.

In this chapter we shall describe the principles of the technique of differential scanning calorimetry, present the data showing the thermotropic properties of pure and modified lipids and, finally, we shall review the melting properties of the biomembranes. Examples showing the correlation between the melting properties of the biomembranes and their function will also be presented.

DIFFERENTIAL SCANNING CALORIMETRY AND DIFFERENTIAL THERMAL ANALYSIS

Techniques and instruments

Calorimetry is a thermodynamic technique and as such is based only on changes in the intrinsic parameters and does not use any of the probes used in other techniques (for example, fluorescence).

In lipid and biomembrane research, there are two main calorimetric techniques used: differential thermal analysis (DTA), and differential scanning calorimetry (DSC).

In DTA the temperature difference ΔT, between the sample and an inert reference material is measured as both are heated or cooled at the programmed rate. A plot of ΔT as a function of temperature is thus obtained. ΔT remains at zero or a constant when no phase transition in the sample takes place; then it increases as the phase transition begins and decreases at the end of the transition. As there is no direct relationship between the area under a DTA curve and the heat of transition, DTA is now seldom used in lipid research and has been replaced by a more sophisticated technique, differential scanning calorimetry (DSC).

In DSC the sample and an inert reference are heated independently in such a way that their temperatures remain equal. In the absence of phase transition the differential heat flow between the sample and reference is zero or constant. As phase transition takes place, heat has to be applied to or withdrawn from the sample in order to maintain the same temperature in both sample and reference compartments. The differential heat flow is recorded as a function of temperature and results in a peak-shaped trace. The term "scanning" implies that the temperature of both sample and reference is varied at a programmed rate.

The most popular instruments commercially available are: DSC-1 and DSC-2 (Perkin Elmer Corporation, Norwalk, Conn., USA); DuPont 990 Thermal Analyzer with cell base II and DSC cell (DuPont Corporation, Wilmington, Delaware, USA); Privalov's (Privalov *et al.*, 1975) adiabatic differential scanning calorimeter, trade mark DASM-IM (Academy Sciences of USSR, Moscow, USSR); Brandts' calorimeter (Krishnan and Brandts, 1978) Microcal 1 (Amerhest, Mass., USA).

For the Perkin Elmer instruments calibration of temperature and heat flow scales using substances of known thermal properties is required. The DuPont instrument is precalibrated, so no daily calibration is needed. In both instruments solid samples are examined as compressed discs encapsulated in aluminium or gold pans. Volatile samples are sealed into aluminium pans of 20-μl or 80-μl capacity (Perkin Elmer DSC-2). The sample atmosphere has to be dynamic with a purge gas (nitrogen or helium) flowing through the sample chambers continuously. In the other two instruments (DASM-IM and Microcal 1) the cells (both sample and reference) are surrounded by an adiabatic shield, the temperature of which follows that of the cells. According to Privalov or Brandts, respectively, these instruments have very high stability of the base line, enabling the use of high volumes of dilute samples (1 ml) and very low scanning rates.

Evaluation of experimental data

The transition temperature, T_c
The transition temperature corresponds to the point of departure of the thermogram from the base line. This is strictly true for sharp, well-defined transitions but, in the case of broad transitions, different methods of extrapolation have to be used.

The temperature of the midpoint of transition, T_m
The temperature of the middle of the peak is denoted by T_m.

The enthalpy of transition, ΔH
The area of the transition peak gives the enthalpy of transition, ΔH, per weight of material in the sample pan.

DuPont's new 1090 Thermal Analysis System signals the industry's first successful effort at digital data acquisition. A self-contained microprocessor with dual floppy discs permits recording a run at highest sensitivity for later computer analysis whilst displaying the results in real time at any desired sensitivity level.

The entropy of transition, ΔS

For a reversible two-state process $A \rightleftharpoons B$ the change in entropy is given by:

$$\Delta S = [q(\text{rev})]/T \tag{1}$$

where q is the heat absorbed, T is temperature expressed in K. However,

$$\Delta G° = \Delta H° - T\Delta S \tag{2}$$

where $\Delta G°$ is the free energy change. At T_m, $\Delta G = 0$. So,

$$\Delta S = \Delta H/T_m \tag{3}$$

From the measured enthalpy of transition the entropy of transition can be calculated.

Cooperative unit

For a pure, synthetic phospholipid the phase transition can be described as a two-state process $A \rightleftharpoons B$. For such a two-state process, the term "cooperative unit" can be used to define the size of the molecular aggregate over which the motion of the molecules undergoing phase transition is transmitted. The enthalpy of phase change for a two-state process is given by the van't Hoff formula:

$$\Delta H_{VH} = (4RT^2{}_m)/(T_2 - T_1) \tag{4}$$

The ratio of van't Hoff enthalpy to the enthalpy obtained from the calorimetric peak gives the molecular weight of the unit undergoing melting (Hinz and Sturtevant, 1972b); dividing this number by the molecular weight of the lipid undergoing transition, the size of the cooperative unit is obtained. For sharp transitions the cooperative units are large, and the size decreases as the width of the transition increases. However, this treatment is only an approximate one as, even in the simplest cases, the transition is not a true two-state process.

THERMOTROPIC PROPERTIES OF AQUEOUS LIPID DISPERSIONS

The lipids that occur in biomembranes can be divided into two main classes: (1) phospholipids and (2) glycolipids (devoid of phosphorus). The phospholipids are either derivatives of glycerol (lecithins, phosphatidylethanolamines, phosphatidylserines, cardiolipins, phosphatidylinositols) or derivatives of sphingosine-sphingomyelin. The glycolipids, which do not contain a phosphate group, are also derivatives of sphingosine and can be divided into three subclasses: cerebrosides (or other neutral glycolipids), sulphatides and gangliosides. Most mammalian membranes also contain another important lipid, cholesterol. The chemical formulae of the most common lipids are presented in Figure 1.1.

Phospholipids

Structural factors determining thermotropic properties

When an anhydrous saturated phospholipid is heated from room temperature up

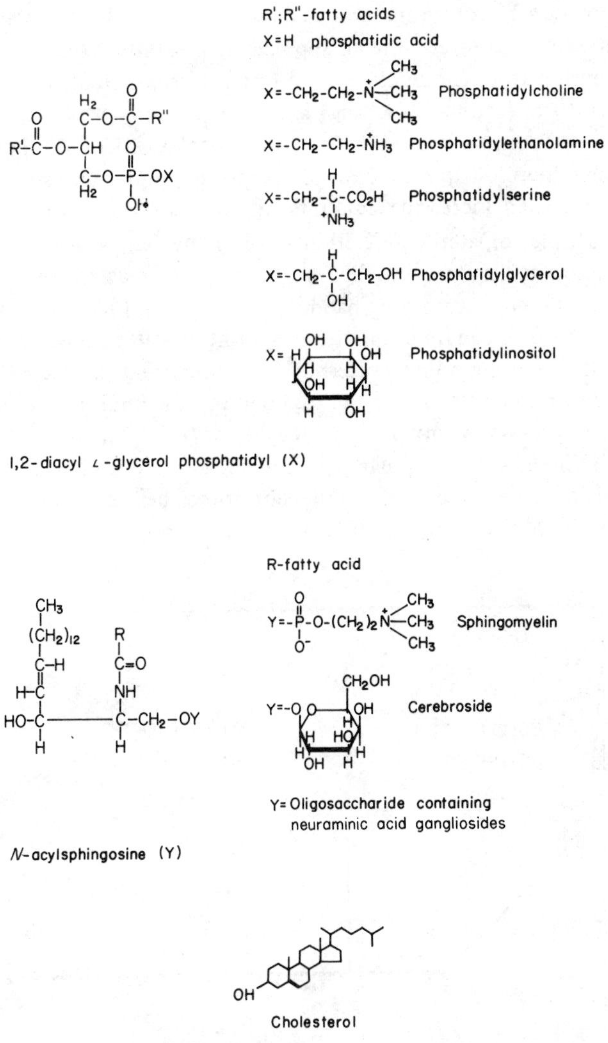

R';R"-fatty acids

X=H phosphatidic acid

X=-CH₂-CH₂-Ṅ—CH₃ Phosphatidylcholine

X=-CH₂-CH₂-ṄH₃ Phosphatidylethanolamine

X=-CH₂-C-CO₂H Phosphatidylserine

X=-CH₂-C-CH₂-OH Phosphatidylglycerol

X= Phosphatidylinositol

1,2-diacyl ∟-glycerol phosphatidyl (X)

R-fatty acid

Y=-P-O-(CH₂)₂Ṅ—CH₃ Sphingomyelin

Y=-O Cerebroside

Y= Oligosaccharide containing neuraminic acid gangliosides

N-acylsphingosine (Y)

Cholesterol

Figure 1.1 Schematic chemical structures of the major membrane lipids

to the capillary melting point, several thermotropic phase changes occur (Chapman and Collin, 1965). Thermotropic mesomorphism indicates that these compounds do not pass directly from a crystalline state to an isotropic liquid, but that, at intermediate temperatures, they exist in a liquid–crystalline state. The transitions from crystalline to a liquid–crystalline state and from liquid–crystalline to an isotropic liquid are endothermic processes – processes accompanied by an absorption of heat. In the crystalline state, the hydrocarbon chains of the phospholipids are in a fully extended, all-*trans* configuration. At the first transition (transformation to the liquid–crystalline state) the hydrocarbon chains "melt", their mobility increases, they are no longer in the fully extended state, the number of *gauche* conformations increases and the chains display "kinks". The chain "melting" requires quite an appreciable investment of energy, whereas the transformation from the liquid crystal to an isotropic fluid, which occurs at higher temperatures (capillary melting) is accompanied by small changes in the enthalpy and entropy, as it involves only the breakdown of the polar lattice.

In addition to thermotropic mesomorphism, phospholipids also show lyotropic mesomorphism. When increasing amounts of water are added to dry phospholipids (for example, dipalmitoyl lecithin (DPL)) the temperature of the transition, crystalline to liquid–crystalline state, drops to reach a certain limiting value at about 20 per cent water (Chapman *et al.*, 1967). Figure 1.2 presents the phase diagram for DPL as a function of the amount of water added. The quantity of water at the limiting value corresponds to about 10 molecules water per molecule of phospholipid and it is tightly bound to the lipid. It does not freeze, even when the lipid–water mixure is cooled below $0°C$. The bound water forms a structure associated with the polar groups of the lipid, leading to a "loosening" of the lattice, or a decrease of the dispersion forces between the hydrocarbon chains, resulting in a downward shift of the melting temperature. As only a

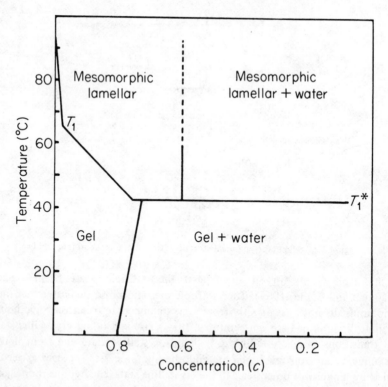

Figure 1.2 Phase diagram of the 1,2-dipalmitoyl-L-phosphatidylcholine/water system (from Chapman *et al.*, 1967)

certain amount of water can be bound, the attractive forces between the hydro-carbon chains are still high and an appreciable amount of energy has to be invested to induce melting. The amount of bound water is not the same for all phospholipids, but depends on the charge and type of the polar head group (Cevc *et al.*, 1981). Above the melting temperature, in the presence of an excess of water, the phospholipid molecules are arranged in bilayers separated by layers of water (mesomorphic lamellar phase + water). Above the phase transition temperature, not only the mobility of the hydrocarbon chains increases, but also the bilayer becomes thinner and the area per lipid molecule increases. As water has such a strong effect on the thermotropic properties of lipids, and as membranes are usually in an aqueous milieu, in the following we shall be dis-cussing only the properties of lipids or membranes dispersed in an excess of water. The influences of different structural factors will be presented.

Figure 1.3 shows the thermograms for a series of saturated lecithins differing in the lengths of the fatty acid residues. As seen from Figure 1.3, increasing the chain lengths causes an increase in the temperature, enthalpy and entropy of melting (Table 1.1). For a series of fully saturated lecithins, a difference of 2 kcal mol^{-1} in the melting enthalpy for a chain length difference of two methylene groups is found. The entropy change presented in Table 1.1 (when recalculated per methylene group) is much smaller than the entropy gain obtained during melting of the corresponding *n*-alkanes, triglycerides or fatty acids (Phillips *et al.*, 1969), indicating that in the liquid–crystalline state chain fluidity is lower than that in the liquid alkanes. This effect stems from the restriction of movement of the hydrocarbon chains of the lecithins due to one end of the chain being bound by an ester linkage to the glycerol backbone and also from interactions between chains.

The transition temperature of phospholipids depends not only on the length of the hydrocarbon chains, but is also a function of the degree of saturation and of the type of the polar head group (Chapman *et al.*, 1966). The presence of a double bond in the fatty acyl residues causes a decrease of T_c, a *cis* double bond having greater effect than a *trans* double bond. The position of the double bond on the hydrocarbon chain also influences the thermotropic properties (Barton and Gunstone, 1975). Mixed chain lecithins have melting temperatures in between those of the corresponding symmetric-chain phosphatidylcholines. However, for saturated and also unsaturated mixed fatty acyl chain lecithins, the thermotropic properties depend also on the position of each of the hydro-carbon residues on the glycerol backbone (Keough and Davis, 1979; Chen and Sturtevant, 1981; Stumpel *et al.*, 1981; Davis *et al.*, 1981; Mason *et al.*, 1981). When the melting temperatures of the nonsymmetric chain lecithins, with the same fatty acyl residues but at different positions on the glycerol backbone (1 or 2), are compared the phosphatidylcholine with the longer chain at position 1 will have the lower transition temperatures. This is due to the non-equivalent bending of the two chains that causes the terminal methyl groups of the two acyl chains to be in different positions, resulting in packing faults in the bilayer.

Table 1.1   Heats and temperatures of transition for 1,2-diacyl-L-phosphatidylcholine–water systems (Chapman et al., 1967)

1,2-diacyl-phosphatidylcholine	Limiting transition temperature (T_c) (°C)	Heat absorbed at T_c $(kcal\ mol^{-1})$ phospholipid	Entropy change at T_c $(cal\ K^{-1}\ mol^{-1})$	Temperature of pretransition peak (°C)
Dibehenoyl	75	14.9	42.8	75
Distearoyl	58	10.70	32.4	56
Dipalmitoyl	41	8.65	27.6	35
Dimyristoyl	23	6.65	22.4	14
Dilauroyl	0	—	—	—
	(under the ice peak)			
Dioleoyl	−22	7.6	30.3	—
Egg yolk	−15/−7	—	—	—

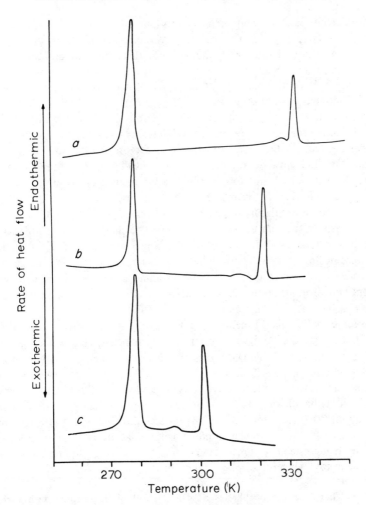

Figure 1.3 Differential scanning calorimeter heating curves for some 1,2-diacyl-phosphatidylcholine–water sytems for distearoyl (*a*) dipalmitoyl (*b*) and dimyristoyl (*c*) derivatives. The peak due to ice formation at 0°C is shown (from Chapman *et al.*, 1967)

In phospholipids the hydrocarbon residues are bound to the glycerol backbone by either ester or ether linkages. The type of bond influences the melting temperature. It was found (Vaughan and Keough, 1974) that the di-ether derivatives have higher transition temperatures than the di-ester ones, probably due to tighter packing. The thermotropic properties of lecithins with an odd number of residues in the hydrocarbon chains were also investigated. The data show that the main melting temperature of phosphatidylcholines with an odd number of residues in the acyl chains varies with the chain lengths similarly to those with an even number of residues (Silvius *et al.*, 1979).

Natural lecithins (for example, egg lecithin, see Table 1.1) are usually mixtures of different fatty acyl chains; that is why their melting peaks will be much broader than those of the corresponding synthetic compounds and their melting temperatures will be between those of the lecithins with two symmetrical fatty acyl residues. Recently, Santaren *et al.* (1981) studied the thermotropic properties of chick embryo lecithins. Phosphatidylcholines from liver, brain and lung were investigated. The lipids of the lung were found to have the highest T_m at $21°C$, reflecting the high degree of saturation (40 per cent) of this lecithin.

Having discussed the different structural factors related to the fatty acid residues, we shall show the effect of the polar head groups on the thermotropic properties. The polar head groups influence the melting behaviour indirectly by changing the packing in the bilayers. These groups can interact through both inter- and intramolecular hydrogen bonds, increasing stability and causing shift of the transition temperature to higher values. The charged polar groups can also undergo ionisation as a function of *p*H, causing a decreasing in T_c. As the area per molecule in the liquid–crystalline state is larger than in the gel state, the electrostatic repulsions in the liquid–crystalline state are diminished with a concomitant drop in melting temperature. The effect of the charge can be seen by comparing the melting temperatures of DPPS at various *p*H values. The zwitterionic DPPS (*p*H 1) melts at $65°C$, having one negative charge at $55°C$ (*p*H 7), whereas the lipid with two negative charges (*p*H 13) melts at $32°C$. Table 1.2 summarises the DSC data for different dipalmitoyl phospholipids differing only in the polar head group.

At neutral *p*Hs both dipalmitoyl phosphatidylcholine (DPL) and dipalmitoyl phosphatidylethanolamine (DPPE) are zwitterions, but in spite of this DPPE melts about $20°$ higher than DPL. This reflects the ability of DPPE to interact intermolecularly via hydrogen bonding with adjacent DPPE molecules, thus achieving higher stability. Protonated forms of dipalmitoyl phosphatidylserine and dipalmitoyl glycerol display higher melting temperatures than the nega-

Table 1.2 Thermotropic properties of dipalmitoyl phospholipids with various head groups

Type of lipid	T_c (°C)	ΔH (kcal mol^{-1})	*p*H	Reference
DPL	41	8.6		Chapman *et al.* (1967)
DPPE	63	8.8		Wilkinson and Nagle (1981)
DPPS	32	8.0	13	
DPPS	55	8.9	7	MacDonald *et al.* (1976)
DPPS	72	~9	3	Cevc *et al.* (1981)
DPPS	65	8.5	1	
DPPG	41	7.9	7	Sacre *et al.* (1979)
DPPG	61		2	Jacobson and Papahadjopoulos (1975)
DPPA	67	5.2	6.5	Jacobson and Papahadjopoulos (1975)
DPPA	58	2.9	9.1	

tively charged ones, as the introduction of charge lowers the T_c. However, the negatively charged DPPS melts even at higher temperatures than the zwitterionic DPL, showing that the ability to interact by hydrogen bonds (which increases stability) counteracts to some extent the repulsive interactions introduced by the negative charge. This effect is even more pronounced in the case of dipalmitoyl phosphatidic acid, where two negative charges have quite a small influence on T_c compared to a single-charged acid.

At this point it is worth mentioning that not only do some phosphatidylethanolamines undergo the gel to liquid–crystal transition, but another phase change is also detected: a liquid crystal to hexagonal phase. This transition occurs at higher temperatures and has quite low enthalpy (Cullis and de Kruijff, 1978; Harlos and Eibl, 1981). In contrast to the gel to liquid–crystalline transition, the transition from liquid crystal to hexagonal phase for the ether forms of phosphatidylethanolamines occurs at lower temperatures (Boggs *et al.*, 1981a). This shows that the introduction of ether linkages causes some destabilisation of the hexagonal phase.

As mentioned previously, biological membranes also contain another phospholipid, sphingomyelin, which is an important constituent of many biomembranes. Sphingomyelins are derivatives of sphingosine, bound by the amide bond to fatty acids. The acyl residue is usually a different length to the sphingosine residue, in contrast to lecithins with identical fatty acyl residues where both chains are of equal length. Due to the presence of hydroxyl and amide groups in the molecule, the sphingomyelin molecules are involved in extensive hydrogen bonding. These structural differences mean that sphingomyelins differ in their thermotropic properties from lecithins, despite the fact that both possess a phosphocholine group.

The thermotropic behaviour of synthetic and natural sphingomyelins has been investigated by several groups (Oldfield and Chapman, 1972; Shipley *et al.*, 1974; Barenholz *et al.*, 1976; Demel *et al.*, 1977; Calhoun and Shipley, 1979a,b; Estep *et al.*, 1980). Shipley *et al.* (1974) investigated the influence of the degree of hydration on the melting behaviour of sphingomyelins (SP). They found that the DSC profiles of SP show the same dependence on the water content as those of phosphatidylcholine lecithin (PC). However, the thermograms of natural sphingomyelins are very complex. The range of melting is broad (25–45°C) and the melting points are higher than those of the corresponding lecithins due to extensive hydrogen bonding. The main endothermic peak has been shown to be composed of at least two peaks (Oldfield and Chapman, 1972; Shipley *et al.*, 1974; Barenholz *et al.*, 1976). Natural SP from different sources and different tissues show significant variability in their melting properties (Calhoun and Shipley, 1979b). The synthetic SP (stearoyl sphingomyelin) exhibits only one sharp endothermic peak (Estep *et al.*, 1980), in contrast to the split peak in the natural phospholipid; however, when the material is quickly cooled and reheated the endotherm is preceded by an exothermic peak, indicating the existence of a metastable gel phase which transforms very slowly to a stable gel phase. The transformation metastable gel to stable gel can be speeded up by heating and the process is accompanied by a release of heat producing the exothermic peak; the stable gel undergoes, at higher temperature, the usual gel to liquid–crystal transition, involving a change in the hydrocarbon chains.

Pretransition(s) in synthetic phospholipids

Synthetic phosphatidylcholines, when heated, exhibit a small endothermic transition at temperatures lower than that at which the main peak occurs (Figure 1.3). The origin of this pretransition was discussed by Rand *et al.* (1975) and by Janiak *et al.* (1976). Rand *et al.* (1975) claim that at temperatures below that of pretransition the hydrocarbon chains are tilted with respect to the plane of the bilayer and at the pretransition temperature the chains transform to a perpendicular position. On the other hand, Janiak *et al.* (1976) suggest that pretransition is associated with a structural transformation in the choline head groups. Pretransition is a very slow process, as was found by kinetic measurements (Lentz *et al.*, 1978; Cho *et al.*, 1981). Recently, it was shown that an additional transition can be detected in DPL thermograms (Chen *et al.*, 1980; Fuldner, 1981). This third transition appears at about 17°C, its kinetics are extremely slow as the transition shows up only when the liposomes are kept at 4°C for several days. Pretransition was also detected in a synthetic phosphatidylethanolamine (Stumpel *et al.*, 1980) and in dipalmitoyl phosphatidylserine (Cevc *et al.*, 1981), but only at $pH > 13$.

Effect of sonication

When phospholipids are dispersed in water above their transition temperatures, big multilamellar liposomes are formed. Sonication breaks these liposomes to single lamellar small vesicles. Sonicated liposomes are used extensively as models for biological membranes; however, due to small size and high degree of curvature, their thermotropic properties differ from those of the unsonicated aqueous dispersion (Sturtevant, 1974; Melchior and Steim, 1976; Suurkuusk *et al.*, 1976; Sternberg *et al.*, 1977; Portis *et al.*, 1979). The thermograms of sonicated DPL do not show the pretransition, the main transition is shifted to lower temperatures and the peak is broadened as the cooperativity of the transition drops. However, with time the melting temperature shifts back to higher values (Suurkuusk *et al.*, 1976), although the pretransition does not reappear. This upward shift of T_c is probably due to fusion of small vesicles, forming larger ones. The decrease in T_c caused by sonication has also been detected in natural phospholipids (Portis *et al.*, 1979).

Mixing, phase separation and fusion

Differential scanning calorimetry can be used to investigate the mixing of various phospholipids. Phospholipids that mix ideally will display only one thermotropic peak if they have previously been dissolved in organic solvent; mixed together, the solvent evaporates and the lipids disperse in an excess of water. The endo-thermic peak will appear at temperatures in between those of the pure compo-nents, but the transition will be wider than that for the pure lipids. If no complete mixing in the organic solvents is taking place, phase separation occurs, as evidenced by the appearance of two separate peaks in the thermograms. Ladbrooke and Chapman (1969) were the first to investigate mixing and phase separation in synthetic phospholipids. Mixtures of distearoyl lecithin plus dipal-mitoyl lecithin and of distearoyl lecithin plus dimyristoyl lecithin were investi-gated. From the calorimetric measurements phase diagrams were constructed by plotting the temperatures of the onset or termination of the transition as a function of the composition. Figure 1.4 presents the phase diagrams for different binary mixtures. As seen from Figure 1.4*a*, DSL + DPL shows co-crystallisation and ideal mixing, whereas for DSL + DML (Figure 1.4*b*) a monotectic behaviour was found, with limited solid solution formation. These data show that if the lecithins differ by only two carbon atoms on each acyl chain ideal mixing can occur, whereas if the fatty acid residues differ considerably no mixing takes

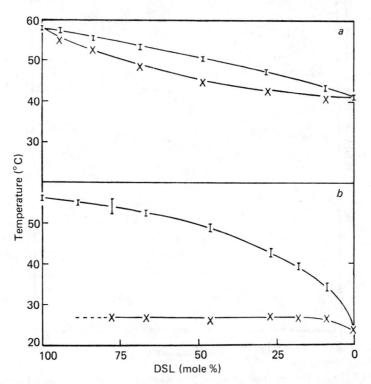

Figure 1.4 Temperature composition diagrams for binary mixtures of saturated lecithins dispersed in excess (50 wt per cent) water. *a*, 1,2-distearoyl lecithin–1,2-dipalmitoyl lecithin–water system (DSL–DPL); *b*, 1,2-distearoyl lecithin–1,2-dimyristoyl lecithin–water systems (DLS–DML). X, onset temperature from DSC heating curve, I, onset tem-perature from DSC cooling curve (from Ladbrooke and Chapman, 1969)

place and separate peaks are obtained. Figure 1.5 presents thermograms for different mixtures of DPL and PS. As natural phospholipids have a distribution of fatty acyl chains, their transition profiles are broad, as seen in the case of bovine brain phosphatidylserine (PS, Figure 1.5*a*). The thermograms of the mixtures of DPL + PS show only one broad peak with a transition temperature

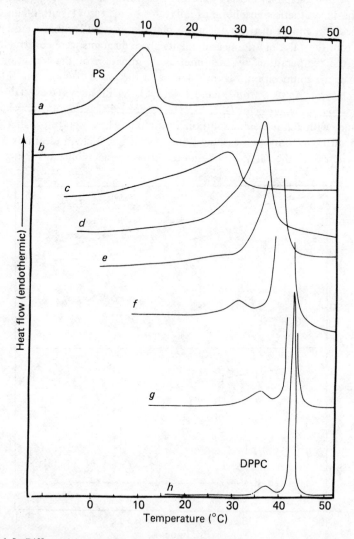

Figure 1.5 Differential scanning calorimetry of multilamellar vesicles composed of bovine brain phosphatidylserine (PS) and dipalmitoyl phosphatidylcholine (DPPC) and various mixtures suspended in 0.1 M NaCl buffer. *a*, Pure phosphatidylserine; *b*, 90 per cent phosphatidylserine/10 per cent phosphatidylcholine; *c*, 50 per cent respectively; *d*, 30 per cent; *e*, 20 per cent, *f*, 10 per cent; *g*, 3 per cent; *h*, pure phosphatidylcholine (from Stewart *et al.*, 1979)

in between those of the pure components, indicating almost complete mixing of the two lipids.

Various binary mixtures of phospholipids have been investigated by DSC and phase diagrams constructed for the following: dioleoyl lecithin + saturated lecithins (Phillips *et al.*, 1970); binary mixtures of synthetic lecithins (Mabrey and Sturtevant, 1976); DPL + mixed acyl chains of unsaturated lecithins (Davis *et al.*, 1980); DPL + DPPE (Chapman *et al.*, 1974; Blume and Ackerman, 1974). Based on these studies it can be concluded that: (1) phospholipids with the same head group, but differing slightly in the number of fatty acyl residues, will be completely miscible; (2) with the same fatty acyl chains, but different head groups, complete miscibility in the liquid–crystalline state is taking place with limited miscibility in the gel phase; and (3) phospholipids differing in the head groups and in the fatty acyl residues show different degrees of miscibility and, depending on the structure and composition, the phase diagrams can become very complex.

Mixtures of sphingomyelin and egg lecithin are miscible at all ratios in the liquid–crystalline state, but above 33 mol % SP separation of the lipids in the gel state takes place (Untracht and Shipley, 1977).

DSC was also used to detect fusion between different populations of vesicles (Papahadjopoulos *et al.*, 1974; 1976a,b; Mason *et al.*, 1980). When two aqueous dispersions of different species of phospholipids are mixed and the thermograms run immediately, two distinct peaks will be obtained that correspond to the thermograms of the pure components. With time, one of two processes may occur: (1) mixing caused by diffusion of one phospholipid species into the other, when one peak will diminish in size and finally disappear; or (2) fusion of the vesicles, where the two peaks will merge and one peak at a temperature between those of the former two peaks will be obtained. Various compounds induce fusion of vesicles, for example Ca^{2+} (Papahadjopoulos *et al.*, 1976b), alkyl bromides (Mason *et al.*, 1980), and proteins (Banerjee *et al.*, 1981).

Effect of cholesterol
The fact that cholesterol is present in almost all biological membranes has led to intensive investigation of its interaction with other lipids. Already in 1968 Ladbrooke *et al.* (1968b) had shown that the addition of cholesterol to dipalmitoyl lecithin causes disappearance of pretransition, broadening of the main peak and a decrease in size at higher cholesterol concentrations; finally at 1:1 molar ratio of cholesterol to DPL no transition is detected. However, Hinz and Sturtevant (1972a) reported that enthalpy of melting of DML or DPL vanishes by 33 mol % cholesterol.

Cholesterol has a similar effect on the thermotropic properties of other saturated or unsaturated lecithins and on sphingomyelins (Oldfield and Chapman, 1972), as it has on DPL. Cholesterol acts as a "spacer" in phospholipid bilayers: it lowers the cohesive forces between the hydrocarbon chains, prevents their crystallisation and increases the fluidity of the bilayers in the gel

state. The effect of cholesterol on mixtures of phospholipids differing in thermotropic properties has been investigated (Van Dijck, 1979). From the decrease
of the size of the peak due to interaction, it was concluded that the affinity of
cholesterol to phospholipids is in the following order: sphingomyelin $\gg$ phosphatidylserine,   phosphatidylglycerol $>$ phosphatidylcholine $\gg$ phosphatidylethanolamine. However, Calhoun and Shipley (1979) and Blume (1980) claim
that cholesterol does not show preferential affinity for either component in
mixtures of SP + DML or PE + PC, respectively.

The effect of cholesterol on the thermotropic properties of single phospholipids (DML, DPL, SP) was reinvestigated recently using high sensitivity, slow
scanning rate calorimeters (Mabrey *et al.*, 1978; Estep *et al.*, 1978; Estep *et al.*,
1979). Below 20 mol % cholesterol the thermograms can be resolved into two
peaks, a narrow one and a broad one. However, above 20 mole % cholesterol
only the broad peak is seen and that also vanishes at 50 mol % cholesterol. At
low cholesterol contents it is probable that two immiscible solid phases differing
in cholesterol content coexist, giving rise to two peaks, whereas at intermediate
concentrations only one phase is found (broad peak). Figure 1.6 presents the
thermograms of DPL–cholesterol mixtures and shows the dependence of the
melting temperatures and enthalpies of the two peaks on the cholesterol content.

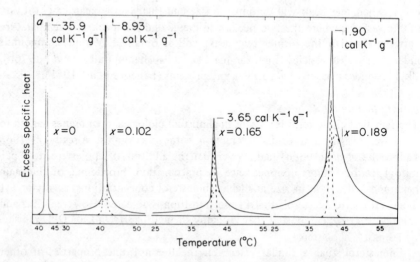

Figure 1.6 *a*, Calorimetric scans for various DPPC–cholesterol mixtures in multilamellar
suspension. *x* Is the mole fraction of cholesterol in the bilayer and the maximum excess
specific heat is given for each suspension. The solid curves are those observed and dashed
curves represent the decomposition of the observed curves into component curves

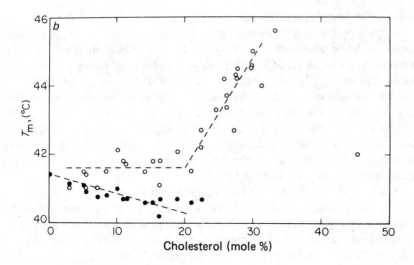

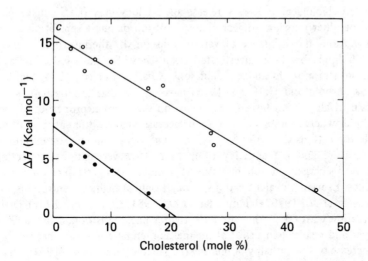

Figure 1.6 *b* The variation with cholesterol content of the temperature of maximum excess specific heat for the narrow peak (●) and the broad peak (○) into which the observed curves for DPPC–cholesterol mixtures can be resolved *c*, The variation with cholesterol content of the enthalpies obtained by integration of the narrow peak (●) and the broad peak (○) into which the observed excess specific heat curves for DPPC–cholesterol mixtures can be resolved (Mabrey *et al.*, 1978)

Effect of lysolecithin and fatty acids

The effect of lysolecithin on the thermotropic properties of DPL was investigated by Klopfenstein *et al.* (1974). Addition of lysolecithin causes a small
drop in the temperature and the enthalpy of melting of the lipid. On the other
hand, synthetic lysolecithin analogue interacting with a mixture of DPPE + DPL
(which has only one melting peak) causes lateral phase separation of the lipids
as evidenced from the splitting of the peak into three peaks (Blume *et al.*, 1976).

  Lysolecithin, which in aqueous solutions exists as micelles, associates with
fatty acids to form bilayers, the melting properties of which differ from those of
lysolecithin, the properties of the latter approaching those of the homologous
phospholipids (Jain and De Haas, 1981).

  Addition of palmitic acid to DPL (Mabrey and Sturtevant, 1977) or myristic
acid to DML (Kantor *et al.*, 1977) shifts the melting temperature of the phospholipids to higher values, probably due to the decrease of the destabilising
crowding of the phosphatidylcholine head groups. Generally, saturated fatty
acids of 12 to 18 carbon atoms raise the melting temperature, whereas fatty
acids of shorter chains lower it. Very long fatty acids mainly influence the
enthalpy of melting (Eliasz *et al.*, 1976; Usher *et al.*, 1978).

Effect of ions

In many biological processes release of calcium ions (Ca^{2+}) takes place. As
Ca^{2+} or other ions may trigger phase transition or phase separation at constant
temperature, the influence of various ions on the thermotropic properties of
phospholipids has been investigated extensively. Studies of the interaction of
DPL with mono-, di- and trivalent ions (Chapman *et al.*, 1974; Simon *et al.*,
1975a; Arnold and Hoffman, 1976) have shown that monovalent cations and
certain divalent ones have no influence on the thermal properties of the phospholipid, whereas anions CNS^-, I^- or acetate increase the enthalpy of melting,
while the cations Ca^{2+}, Cd^{2+}, UO_2^{2+} and La^{3+} cause an increase in both melting
temperature and the enthalpy of melting. However, cations interacting with
negatively-charged phospholipids exert a much stronger effect on the melting
profiles. Even monovalent cations, though only at high concentrations, raise the
T_c (Sacre *et al.*, 1979; Hammoudah *et al.*, 1981; Cevc *et al.*, 1981). Due to the
interaction with Ca^{2+}, Mg^{2+} or La^{3+} tighter packing is obtained, stabilising the
bilayer and resulting in a shift of the melting temperature to higher values and in
an increase of the enthalpy of melting (Papahadjopoulos *et al.*, 1973; Ververgaert
et al., 1975; van Dijck *et al.*, 1975; Jacobson and Papahadjopoulos, 1975;
Newton *et al.*, 1978; Papahadjopoulos, 1977; van Dijck *et al.*, 1978; Liao and
Prestegard, 1981; Hammoudah *et al.*, 1981). The effect of Ca^{2+} on the thermotropic properties of negatively-charged lipids is much stronger than that produced by similar concentrations of Mg^{2+} (Newton *et al.*, 1978); at very high
concentrations of the cation the melting peak is shifted to temperatures above
$100°C$. On the other hand, due to the interaction of Mg^{2+}, with synthetic
phosphatidylglycerols (Ververgaert *et al.*, 1975; van Dijck *et al.*, 1975) meta-

stable phase is formed, as discerned by the appearance of an exothermic peak preceding the endothermic one. Addition of Ca^{2+} to mixtures of negatively-charged phospholipids with zwitterionic phospholipids, which display only one melting peak (in the absence of calcium), induces lateral phase separation due to higher affinity of Ca^{2+} for negatively-charged lipids. The original peak disappears and another one characteristic of the zwitterionic lipid is seen (Papahadjopoulos, 1977; van Dijck *et al.*, 1978). Ca^{2+} and Mg^{2+} also induce fusion of negatively-charged phospholipids (Papahadjopoulos, 1977). The interaction of ions with negatively-charged lipids is not only a simple electrostatic one, but other specific effects are also taking place.

In an attempt to evaluate how multivalent ions used in NMR studies may perturb the structure of the bilayers, the interaction of phospholipids with multivalent cations has also been investigated (Jain and Wu, 1977).

Modification by drugs and other hydrophobic molecules

Biological membranes are the site of action for many drugs and, as on the way to various intracellular organelles the drugs have to pass through many membranous barriers, the study of the interaction of lipids with drugs has evoked huge interest. Here we will summarise the studies involved with the influence of drugs on the thermotropic properties of lipids and also discuss the perturbing effect exerted by other hydrophobic molecules used as probes in spectroscopic techniques.

Drugs modify the melting behaviour of phospholipids to different degrees; for example, antibiotics — gramicidin A, polymyxin B (Chapman *et al.*, 1974; Pache *et al.*, 1972) — remove the transition in a similar way that cholesterol does. On the other hand, antidepressant drug molecules, for example desipiramine (Cater *et al.*, 1974), shift the transition temperature of DPL to lower values and cause phase separation (appearance of two peaks) at higher concentrations. Other compounds of completely different structure, such as hashish components (Bach *et al.*, 1976) and juvenile hormone (Barber *et al.*, 1981), have a similar effect on DPL bilayers. Positively-charged drugs, for example the local anaesthetic dibucaine, produce a downward shift of the T_c of negatively-charged bilayers, having an effect on zwitterionic DPL only at much higher concentrations (Papahadjopoulos *et al.*, 1975a). However, Frenzel *et al.* (1978) claim that cationic drugs (phenothiazine and chloropromazine) at very low concentrations remove the pretransition peak of DPL and at higher concentrations lower T_c with almost no change in the heat of melting. Recently, it was reported that mequitazine (related to phenothiazine) also broadens the melting peak and decreases the T_c of zwitterionic liposomes (Ahmed *et al.*, 1980). The effect of the anaesthetic charge and of the phospholipid charge on the anaesthetic–lipid interactions has also been recently reinvestigated (Davis and Low, 1981).

The influence of various drugs on the melting properties of natural lipids — total lipids — from calf brain has been investigated (Bach and Sela, 1981). The local anaesthetic tetracaine and the general anaesthetics ethanol and ketamine were found to shift the melting temperatures to lower values whilst causing almost no change in the enthalpy of melting. However, cannabinoids caused a decrease in the enthalpy of melting whilst affecting only a very small shift in the melting temperature. The effect of cholesterol on these interactions was also assessed.

Corticosteroids are used for treatment of arthritis; it was shown that cortisol-21-palmitate interacts with DPL, removing the pretransition and broadening the main peak (Fildes and Oliver, 1978). The interaction of gaseous anaesthetics with DPL was also investigated, a decrease in T_c and increase in the width (decrease in the degree of the cooperativity of the main transition) without change of the enthalpy of melting were detected (Koehler *et al.*, 1978; Mountcastle *et al.*, 1978). However, DPL interacts with cyclopropane (model for inhalation anaesthetic) and displays two endothermic peaks of lower enthalpy and at lower temperatures than the peak of the pure lipid (Simon *et al.*, 1975b).

Inducers of Friend leukaemic differentiation stabilise the bilayers and increase the melting temperature which is accompanied by the appearance of a new transition at higher temperatures (Lyman *et al.*, 1976).

The interaction of various antitumour drugs with negatively-charged or zwitterionic lipids has been studied by several groups (Juliano and Stamp, 1979; Goldman *et al.*, 1978; Ter-Minassian-Saraga *et al.*, 1981). According to Juliano and Stamp (1979), polar drugs have little effect on the melting properties of DPL, whereas non-polar drugs exert a profound effect. Actinomycin D or vinblastine both broaden the main peak while the former also shifts the T_c of DML (or of DML + PC) to higher values. However, Ter-Minassian-Saraga *et al.* (1981) reported that vinblastine or vincristine at low concentrations decreased the T_c and increased the ΔH of DPL, whereas at very high concentrations an opposite effect was seen. The anthracycline antibiotics – adriamycin and its derivatives – lower the T_c of DPL which is accompanied by a small change of ΔH. But, due to interaction with PS, those antibiotics cause a decrease in the ΔH of the lipid with almost no change in T_m (Goldman *et al.*, 1978).

Eliasz *et al.* (1976) investigated the interaction of a series of alcohols, acids and quaternary ammonium salts with DPL. Various effects were found and correlated with the structure of the compounds.

Alkyl ammonium iodides modify the thermotropic properties of DPL (Frischleder and Gleichman, 1977). Compounds with C^9 and C^{22} chains have the greatest effect in lowering the melting temperature of the phospholipids. The influence of ubiquinones on the thermotropic properties of DPL has been investigated (Alonso *et al.*, 1981) and it was found that at low concentrations ubiquinones only slightly broaden the DPL peak, whereas at very high concentrations a decrease in ΔH is detected. These effects are dependent on the structure of the uniquinone. Localisation of the various uniquinones in the bilayers was proposed.

Polyethylene glycol is used as a fusogenic agent for biomembranes; due to interaction with DPL, an increase in T_c, ΔH and ΔS is found, accompanied by a decrease in the cooperativity of the transition (Tilcock and Fisher, 1979).

As various compounds are used as spectroscopic probes in lipid research, it was of interest to assess what perturbing effects these molecules might have on the lipid bilayers. Using DSC the interaction between various probes and phospholipids was investigated: anthranoyl fatty acid derivatives (Cadenhead *et al.*, 1977), *N*-4-nitrobenz-2-oxa-1,3-diazole gramicidin S (Wu *et al.*, 1978), and merocyanine 540 (Lelkes *et al.*, 1980) were tested. Extensive perturbation of the bilayer structure was found; this serves to emphasise the caution that should be undertaken when using probes in membrane research.

Jain *et al.* (1975, 1976, 1977) investigated the influence of more than a 100 compounds on the thermotropic behaviour of dipalmitoyl lecithin. The compounds investigated were alkanols, local anaesthetics, uncouplers, tranquilisers, inhalation anaesthetics, fatty acids, detergents, organic solvents, ionophores, spin labels and fluorescent membrane probes. Different types of transition profiles were obtained, depending on the location of the compound within the lipid bilayer. Based on various physicochemical studies, the profiles were divided into four classes and the possible location of the perturbant is indicated:

1. Broadening of the peak with an increase or a decrease in the melting temperature $-$ C^1-C^9 methylene.
2. Decrease in size of the main peak at the normal temperature, a smaller peak appears at lower temperatures $-$ glycerol backbone.
3. Shift of the peak to lower temperatures without broadening $-$ C^{10}-C^{16}.
4. Appearance of a new peak at higher temperatures with consequent disappearance of the original peak at higher concentrations of the modifier $-$ phosphorylcholine region.

The localisation of the modifier within the lipid layer is determined by the presence of the polar and apolar groups in the compound and by the geometric arrangements of these groups within the molecule.

Interaction with polypeptides or proteins
The interaction of well-defined phospholipids with polypeptides or proteins was investigated using DSC in an attempt firstly to learn about the lipid–protein interactions in biomembranes on a simpler model and, secondly, to assess how ionophores $-$ peptide molecules $-$ may perturb the structure of the lipid bilayer. Various globular and membranal proteins were investigated. Basic proteins $-$ cytochrome *c*, lysozyme and polypeptide polylysine $-$ cause a decrease in the melting temperature of natural PS (Chapman *et al.*, 1974). The interaction is mainly electrostatic, however, limited penetration of these compounds into the bilayer also occurs.

Papahadjopoulos *et al.* (1975b) investigated the influence of a series of proteins on the thermotropic properties of synthetic phospholipids. The proteins can be divided into three classes according to the effects they exert on the melting profiles of the lipids:

1. Those that cause a decrease in ΔH and T_m (cytochrome c and A_1-myelin basic protein). The primary interaction is an electrostatic one, followed by limited penetration of the protein into the bilayer.
2. Those that have almost no influence on T_m, but cause a decrease in ΔH (proteolipid apoprotein from myelin, the peptide gramicidin A). The interactions are non-polar and the protein embedded into the bilayer perturbs a limited number of lipid molecules leaving the rest of the bilayer unperturbed.
3. Those that cause an increase in ΔH with or without an increase in T_c (ribonuclease, polylysine). The interaction is a pure electrostatic one, involving positively-charged proteins or polypeptides and negatively-charged lipids, that stabilises the bilayer without penetration of the protein into the lipid layer taking place.

The effect the protein exerts on the lipid layer is also a function of the fatty acids in the phospholipids, as it was reported that A_1-myelin basic protein raises the melting temperature of di-C^{12}-PG (Verkleij *et al.*, 1974), but lowers the T_c of PG with longer fatty acyl chains (Papahadjopoulos *et al.*, 1975b).

Boggs and Moscarello (1978) investigated the influence of the hydrophobic protein derived from myelin–lipophilin (N_2 protein) on the thermotropic properties of synthetic lecithins of various chain lengths. Their data agree with the earlier results of Papahadjopoulos *et al.* (1975b), that is, this protein has almost no effect on T_m, but decreases the enthalpy of melting of the lipids. By plotting the enthalpy of melting as a function of the molar ratio protein: lipid (lipophilin:lipid) and extrapolating to $\Delta H = 0$, the number of lipid molecules removed from the transition by one molecule of the protein can be estimated. In the case of the interaction of single lipids with lipophilin, the number of lipid molecules withdrawn from melting is a function of the length of the lipid fatty acyl chains; however, the effect was not evident when mixtures of lipids were used. Lipophilin or myelin basic protein, added to a mixture of acidic and zwitterionic lipids (displaying only one peak), induce phase separation due to preferential binding of the proteins to negatively-charged lipids, determined from the shift of T_m towards the temperature of melting of the zwitterionic lipid (Boggs *et al.*, 1977a,b). Interaction of myelin basic protein with dipalmitoyl phosphatidylglycerol, a negatively-charged lipid, is complex and depends on the phase state of the lipid (Boggs *et al.*, 1981b).

A drop in the enthalpy of melting of the phospholipid with almost no change in T_m or a small shift towards higher temperatures was also detected in the case of interactions with other proteins and polypeptides: glycophorin from red blood cells (MacDonald and MacDonald, 1975; Van Zoelen *et al.*, 1978), serum apolipoproteins (Andrews *et al.*, 1976; Tall *et al.*, 1975; Tall *et al.*, 1977; Gilman *et al.*, 1981; Massey *et al.*, 1981; Pownall *et al.*, 1981), proteolipid apoprotein from myelin (Curatolo *et al.*, 1977a), spectrin from red blood cells (Mombers *et al.*, 1977; 1979), gramicidin A – a peptide acting as an ionophore in lipid bilayers – (Chapman *et al.*, 1974, 1977a), bee venom peptide melithin (Mollay, 1976), basic polypeptide, a copolymer of lysine with phenylalanine (Bach and Miller, 1976), glucagon – hormone peptides – (Epand and Sturtevant, 1981), $(Ca^{2+} + Mg^{2+})$ATPase (Gomez-Fernandez *et al.*, 1979; 1980). However, even the integral proteins can influence ΔH as well as change T_m. The effect depends probably on the type of lipid used and on the specific protein, as can be seen from the following examples: a viral glycoprotein reconstituted into DPPC vesicles causes a reduction of the transition temperature and the enthalpy of melting (Petri *et al.*, 1980); valinomycin, an ionophore (Grell *et al.*, 1975), also lowers the T_m of lipids.

Recently, we have investigated the interaction of an intrinsic protein $(Ca^{2+} + Mg^{2+})$ATPase with both DML and DPL (Gomez-Fernandez *et al.*, 1979; 1980). We shall discuss these results more extensively as an example of lipid–intrinsic protein interactions. The enzyme was delipidated and reactivated by incorporation into DML or DPL vesicles. At low protein to lipid ratios the pretransition peak disappears first. Increasing the protein concentration causes the main peak to broaden and to become smaller; however, almost no change in T_m is found. At very high protein concentrations, the peak almost completely disappears.

The broadening of the peak is due to melting of the lipid in the protein-rich lipid patches being superimposed on that representing the melting of the free unperturbed lipid. The drop in the peak size stems from the perturbing effect the protein has on the neighbouring lipid molecules which prevents their crystallisation. Thermograms of the interactions between DPPC at various concentrations with ATPase are presented in Figure 1.7a. The enthalpy of melting was calculated from the thermograms and is plotted as a function of the molar ratio (ATPase:DPPC) in Figure 1.7b. The decrease in ΔH is a linear function dependent on the amount of protein added (Figure 1.7b). By extrapolating to $\Delta H = 0$, the number of lipid molecules which are withdrawn from the cooperative transition per molecule of ATPase can be obtained. In the case of DPPC–enzyme interaction, this number is 42. Similar plots were drawn for other lipid–protein interactions. The number of lipid molecules withdrawn from the melting process depends on the specific protein and on the type of the lipid used.

Theoretical treatments of the lipid phase transition

As this topic is very extensive and beyond the scope of this chapter, only a few models will be discussed briefly. Whittington and Chapman (1965, 1966) were the first to develop a theoretical treatment for the phase transition of lipids. Long-chain hydrocarbons fixed at one end were used as models and the co-operative nature of the twisting and movement of the CH_2 groups of adjacent chains leading to phase transition was emphasised.

Marčelja (1974) has used a molecular field approximation to investigate different statistical averages over all conformations for a single chain in contact with neighbouring molecules. Jacobs *et al.* (1975) developed a model in which

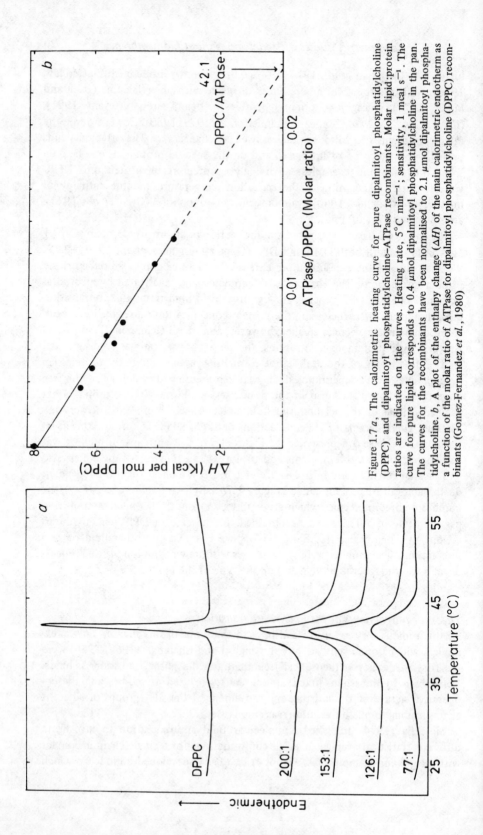

Figure 1.7 a, The calorimetric heating curve for pure dipalmitoyl phosphatidylcholine (DPPC) and dipalmitoyl phosphatidylcholine-ATPase recombinants. Molar lipid:protein ratios are indicated on the curves. Heating rate, 5°C min⁻¹; sensitivity, 1 mcal s⁻¹. The curve for pure lipid corresponds to 0.4 μmol dipalmitoyl phosphatidylcholine in the pan. The curves for the recombinants have been normalised to 2.1 μmol dipalmitoyl phosphatidylcholine. b, A plot of the enthalpy change (ΔH) of the main calorimetric endotherm as a function of the molar ratio of ATPase for dipalmitoyl phosphatidylcholine (DPPC) recombinants (Gomez-Fernandez et al., 1980)

the inter- and intramolecular interactions of the hydrocarbon chains and the influence of head groups on these interactions were taken into account. Freire and Biltonen (1978) used statistical thermodynamics for evaluating the calorimetric data.

A statistical–mechanical treatment was also proposed by Berde *et al.* (1980) to explain the effect head group structure and the degree of chain unsaturation have on the melting behaviour of phospholipids. Scott (1981) derived a theoretical model to account for the pre- and main transitions in DPL. He claims that the pretransition can be seen as nematic to isotropic transition involving the entire lipid molecule. The various theoretical treatments were reviewed recently by Nagle (1980).

Glycosphingolipids

Glycosphingolipids are important constituents of biomembranes. Some diseases (for example, Tay-Sachs, Gaucher) are accompanied by a dramatic increase in the concentration of certain gangliosides or cerebrosides in the cells.

Cerebrosides

Cerebrosides are the simplest sphingoglycolipids as they contain only one sugar, either glucose or galactose. The thermotropic properties of pure ox brain cerebrosides and their mixtures with egg lecithin were investigated by Clowes *et al.* (1971). These cerebrosides contain predominantly long saturated fatty acids linked to C^{18}-sphingosine. Their gel–liquid crystalline phase transition profiles are broad with a midpoint temperature of about $60°C$. Addition of lecithin causes the melting temperature to drop in proportion with the amount of phospholipid added. Cholesterol has a similar effect on the melting properties of cerebrosides as it has on phospholipids; at molar ratio of 1:1 cerebroside: cholesterol, the enthalpy of melting approaches zero (Oldfield and Chapman, 1972).

Bovine brain cerebrosides were fractionated into two fractions, phrenosin and kerasin, and investigated by DSC (Bunow, 1979). The natural cerebrosides and phrenosin have almost the same temperatures and enthalpies of melting ($66°C$ and 7 kcal mol^{-1}), whereas the T_c for kerasin is $72°C$ and $\Delta H = 15.8$ kcal mol^{-1}. Kerasin also exhibits an endotherm at $56°C$ with a lower enthalpy of melting, indicating that in certain conditions this lipid can also exist in a metastable state. The rise in T_c and ΔH of kerasin with respect to phrenosin or unfractionated cerebrosides suggests a higher degree of order in kerasin.

The enthalpies of melting of cerebrosides and sphingomyelins are similar; however, the melting temperatures of cerebrosides are higher. This latter difference stems from the ability of cerebrosides to undergo more extensive hydrogen bonding than sphingomyelins due to the presence of sugar moieties in the glycolipid molecule, which stabilises the gel state further.

Recently, we investigated the thermotropic properties of glucocerebroside from the spleen of a patient with Gaucher disease (Freire *et al.*, 1980). In dry material only one endothermic peak at about 105°C was seen, whereas when dispersed in water the glucocerebroside underwent phase transition at 47°C and at 83°C.

The transition at the higher temperature is endothermic and reflects the melting of the hydrocarbon chains (gel–liquid crystalline transition), whereas the lower one is an exothermic transition and is due to transformation from a metastable gel state to a more ordered gel state. The exothermic transition appears only when the hydrated cerebroside is cooled rapidly from about 90°C. It is not seen if the sample is left for more than 12 hours at room temperature, indicating that at room temperature this transformation is taking place, but at a very slow rate. The synthetic D-erythro-*N*-palmitoyl glucocerebroside shows the same thermotropic behaviour. Ruocco *et al.* (1981) investigated the melting properties of anhydrous and hydrated synthetic *N*-palmitoyl galactocerebroside. In the anhydrous material, three lamellar crystal forms were detected below 143°C and a transition to an isotropic liquid at 180°C, whereas the hydrated cerebroside underwent transitions similar to those of the glucocerebroside.

Gangliosides

Gangliosides are more complex glycolipids than cerebrosides, as their head group contains oligosaccharide chains with varying amounts of the *N*-acetyl and the *N*-glycolyl derivatives of a negatively-charged sugar — neuraminic acid. Gangliosides are divided into subclasses, depending on the number of sugar and neuraminic acid residues. In contrast to phospholipids, when dispersed in aqueous solution they do not form bilayers but associate to form big micelles, due to packing strains introduced by the much higher ratio of the area of the polar head group to the area of the hydrocarbon chains. The thermotropic behaviour of brain gangliosides is very complex (Curatolo *et al.*, 1977b; Bunow and Bunow 1979; Bach and Sela, 1980); their range of transition is wide (0-50°C) and at least two maxima are seen on the melting peak. The maxima appear not only in mixed gangliosides, but also in individual ganglioside species (GM_1, GM_2), so this is an intrinsic property of the molecule and does not reflect mixing of different ganglioside species. The thermotropic properties of gangliosides are influenced not only by the hydrocarbon chain interactions, but also by the polar head groups which are undergoing an extensive, hydrogen bonding. The enthalpy of melting of the mixed bovine brain gangliosides is about 4 kcal mol^{-1} (Bunow and Bunow, 1979; Bach *et al.*, 1982). The melting profiles and the enthalpies of melting of the various gangliosides are strongly influenced by the number and position of the negative charges in the head-group region (Bach *et al.*, 1982).

As the gangliosides act as receptors for different compounds, it was of interest to investigate the influence of various ligands on their thermal properties. Interaction of Tay-Sachs ganglioside and of mixed bovine brain gangliosides with peanut lectin or serotonin was investigated (Bach and Sela, 1980). Peanut lectin or serotonin caused a drop in the melting enthalpy of mixed bovine brain gangliosides, whereas for the human Tay-Sachs ganglioside interaction with lectin elicited no change in the enthalpy of melting while a small increase due to interaction with serotonin was detected. Interaction of synthetic and natural phospholipids with well-defined gangliosides was investigated using DSC (Sillerud *et al.*, 1979; Bunow and Bunow, 1979; Hinz *et al.*, 1981; Bach *et al.*, 1982). Synthetic lipids are completely miscible with gangliosides only at low molar fractions of gangliosides. At higher concentrations their behaviour is very complex due to partial phase separation of the components. However, the ganglioside GM_1, when interacting with egg licithin is completely miscible at practically all ratios (Bach *et al.*, 1982), as assessed by the appearance of only one melting peak in the thermograms (see Figure 1.8). As seen from Figure 1.8, the double peak of the ganglioside merges into one, already at quite high molar fractions of the glycolipid. Progressive addition of egg lecithin causes a shift of the melting peak towards lower temperatures and shortens the range of melting. The measured enthalpy of melting is equal to the calculated enthalpy of the pure components up to about 0.6 molar fraction of the ganglioside, when it starts to rise, giving a maximum at about 0.75 molar fraction of the glycolipid. It would seem that three molecules of ganglioside interacting with one molecule of egg lecithin

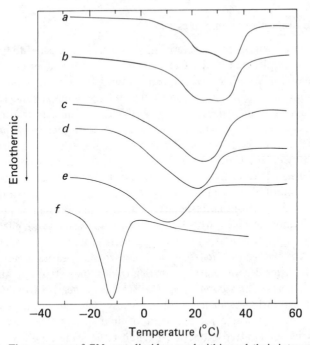

Figure 1.8 Thermograms of GM_1 gangliosides, egg lecithin and their interaction products. x_G, molar fraction of gangliosides; medium, ethylene glycol:salt, 1:1. *a*, $x_G = 1.0$; *b*, $x_G = 0.89$; *c*, $x_G = 0.71$; *d*, $x_G = 0.45$; *e*, $x_G = 0.30$; *f*, $x_G = 0$ (egg lecithin only) (Bach *et al.*, 1982)

gives the most stable structure. In this case, two lipids differing very much in the melting range were mixed, as the T_m of lecithin is about 10° lower than T_c of the gangliosides.

The interaction of cholesterol with GM_1 ganglioside was also investigated (Bach *et al.*, 1982). In contrast to the effect of cholesterol on the enthalpy of melting of phospholipids, at about 30 mol per cent cholesterol, ΔH of the GM_1 ganglioside reaches a plateau, so that even at 1:1 molar ratio ganglioside melting is detected. The different effect of cholesterol on gangliosides to that on phospholipids probably stems from the structural differences of the two lipids in aqueous solution (that is, bilayers as opposed to micelles).

THERMOTROPIC PROPERTIES OF BIOMEMBRANES

In the previous sections we have discussed the thermotropic properties of pure lipids, lipid mixtures and their interaction products with drugs, proteins, peptides. In this section we will summarise the melting properties of biological membranes. Biological membranes are very complex structures, being composed of many lipids and proteins that interact with each other and exert specific effects on the melting behaviour of the membrane they are part of.

Bacterial and other plant membranes

The thermotropic behaviour of bacterial membranes, as compared to mammalian membranes, is simpler due to the fact that bacterial membranes usually do not contain cholesterol. Another advantage in studying bacterial membranes is that it is possible to vary their lipid composition by changing the growing conditions. The bacterium *A. laidlawii* is very easy to handle in this respect and, in addition, lacks a cell wall — hence simpler procedures for membrane preparation can be used. This is why *A. laidlawii* was the first bacterium to be investigated by DSC (Steim *et al.*, 1969). Figure 1.9 presents the thermograms of *Acholeplasma laidlawii* whole cells, membranes and extracted lipids from bacteria grown in different conditions. Trace *d* shows the thermogram of the membranes. Two peaks are seen: the first one corresponds to the gel-liquid crystalline phase transition of the membrane lipids, whereas the second, appearing at a higher temperature, stems from the denaturation of the membrane proteins. This conclusion was drawn after comparing the first scan with subsequent heating scans: the first peak does not alter despite repeated heating cycles, indicating that the process is reversible, whereas the second peak disappears after heating to about 100°C, as protein denaturation is an irreversible process. The transition peaks of the lipids are broad, as expected for a mixture of lipid species. The transition temperature of the lipids after extraction is almost the same as when they are in the membranes. Also, the enthalpy of melting of the lipids in the membranes is about 75 per cent of that of the extracted lipids. When the organisms were grown on saturated fatty acids, the T_c of the lipids shifted to higher values

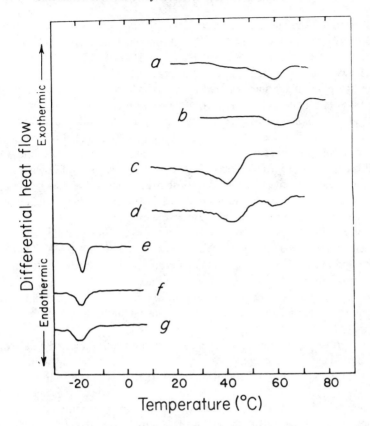

Figure 1.9 Calorimeter scans of *A. laidlawii* lipids, membranes and whole cell. *a*, Total membrane lipids from cells grown in tryptose with added stearate; *b*, membranes from stearate-supplemented tryptose; *c*, total membrane lipids from cells grown in unsupplemented tryptose; *d*, membranes from unsupplemented tryptose; *e*, total membrane lipids from cells grown in tryptose with added oleate; *f*, membranes from oleate-supplemented tryptose; *g*, whole cells from oleate-supplemented tryptose. The first four preparations were suspended in water; for the latter three scans, the solvent was 50 per cent ethylene glycol containing 0.15 M NaCl (Steim *et al.*, 1969)

(Figure 1.9*a,b*), while for bacteria grown on unsaturated acids T_c shifted downwards (Figure 1.9*e,f,g*). As these organisms are able to take up cholesterol from the growth medium, the influence of cholesterol on the melting properties was investigated. Incorporation of cholesterol was found to reduce markedly the enthalpy of melting of the lipids (De Kruijff *et al.*, 1972), analogous to the effect cholesterol has on synthetic phospholipids.

The thermotropic properties of *A. laidlawii* were recently reinvestigated by Silvius *et al.* (1980). By putting defined fatty acids in the culture medium, organisms with homogenous fatty acyl chains in their lipids, were obtained. In this state lipid transitions were much sharper and curves approached the shape of those of the corresponding synthetic lipids.

Phase transitions have also been detected in other bacterial membranes (Steim, 1972; Baldassare *et al.*, 1976; Jackson and Sturtevant, 1977; Ashe and Steim, 1971, Haest *et al.*, 1972; McElhaney and Souza, 1976; Abbas and Card, 1980; Kawada and Nosoh, 1981; Goldfine *et al.*, 1981).

The halophilic bacterium, *Halobacterium halobium*, produces a purple membrane in certain conditions. The thermotropic properties of this membrane were investigated independently by two groups (Jackson and Sturtevant, 1978; Degani *et al.*, 1978). Jackson and Sturtevant (1978) detected no transition in the purple membrane below 70°C, whereas Degani *et al.* (1978) found a small transition at about 35°C. The reason for this difference is not known; however, based on measurements obtained from other physical techniques it seems that the peak at 35°C is not due to a simple gel-liquid crystalline transition of the lipids. That is not surprising for such a rigid membrane.

In yeast protomitochondrial membranes, two endothermic peaks were observed: a very broad transition peak between 307K and 343K due to lipid melting and another one at higher temperatures resulting from the denaturation of the proteins (Bertoli *et al.*, 1974). The extracted lipids undergo melting at lower temperatures (276-305K), indicating that the electrostatic interactions between the lipids and the proteins shifts their melting temperature to higher values.

The thermotropic behaviour of the membranes and extracted lipids of the bread mould *Neurospora crassa* was investigated and correlated with the fatty acyl chain composition of the membranes (Friedman, 1977; Friedman and Glick, 1980).

In spinach chloroplast membranes six endothermic transitions can be seen (Cramer *et al.*, 1981). The shape of the thermograms depends on the ionic strength of the medium and some of the transitions are lost after heating to high temperatures (100°C). The 'A' transition (T_m 42-44°C) was recognised as being associated with Photosystem II, but the origins of the other transitions are not yet known. Below 20°C Cramer *et al.* (1981) detected no transition despite the fact that it had been reported previously (Jursinic and Govindjee, 1977) that in lipid extracts of chloroplasts a small endotherm between 15 and 20°C could be seen.

Mammalian membranes

Most mammalian membranes contain cholesterol and, as cholesterol abolishes the phase transition in model membranes, it was generally believed that at physiological temperatures the lipids in the biomembranes are in a liquid-crystalline state. In the following we will show that in some biomembranes a fraction of the lipids is in the gel state even at physiological temperatures. These membranes either contain a low concentration of cholesterol or, due to the different affinity of cholesterol to various lipids, cholesterol-rich and cholesterol-poor domains coexist.

Myelin, sarcoplasmic reticulum and red blood cells

The calorimetric investigation of mammalian membranes had already been initiated by Chapman as far back as 1968 (Ladbrooke *et al.*, 1968a). Human and ox brain myelins were investigated. No endothermic phase transition was detected in native myelin; however, after drying of the membrane, phase transition was found, probably due to separation of cholesterol from the lipids. After removal of cholesterol from the total lipid extracts, a melting peak was detected. This finding correlates with the very high ratio of cholesterol to lipid (about 1:1 molar ratio) that exists in myelin.

Recently, we have shown that total lipids from calf brain undergo melting in a wide range of temperatures (5-50°C), but here the cholesterol content is much lower – about 16 per cent (Bach *et al.*, 1980). The thermotropic properties of sarcoplasmic reticulum membranes are also influenced by drying. The dry membranes and the extracted lipids undergo transition with a T_m of about 15°C, whereas addition of water shifts the transitions to lower temperatures (Martonosi, 1974).

Human erythrocyte ghosts were also investigated by Ladbrooke *et al.* (1968b). No thermal transitions were detected. A broad endothermic transition was found in the lipids, but only after removal of the cholesterol. The thermotropic properties of human red cell ghosts were reinvestigated using a more sensitive instrument and then four endothermic transitions between 45 and 80°C were seen (Jackson *et al.*, 1973; Brandts *et al.*, 1977). In the lipid extract no phase transition was seen; however, in agreement with previous studies, after removal of cholesterol an endothermic peak appeared. The transitions of the membranes in the 45-80°C region are irreversible, mainly due to denaturation of proteins, however, some proteolipids may be also involved. The influence of *p*H, salt concentration, inhibitors, enzymes and drugs on the melting properties has been investigated (Brandts *et al.*, 1978; Snow *et al.*, 1978; Low and Brandts, 1978; Krishnan and Brandts, 1979; Snow *et al.*, 1981). Based on these data and on other physicochemical measurements, the different peaks have been correlated with various erythrocyte proteins (Lysko *et al.*, 1981).

Microsomes, mitochondria, myocardial membranes and chromaffin granules

The calorimetric properties of rat liver microsomes, rat liver mitochondria and of their extracted lipids were investigated by several groups. Blazyk and Steim (1972) detected two peaks centred at about 0°C and 65°C, in both mitochondria and microsomes. The low-temperature peak is reversible and very broad, as expected for the melting of a mixture of lipids. The second peak is irreversible and stems from protein denaturation. The extracted lipids undergo melting at slightly lower temperatures.

As the liver inner mitochondrial membrane contains very little cholesterol, it was of interest to investigate how enrichment with cholesterol would influence the thermotropic and other properties of this membrane. When the membranes are incubated with DPL-cholesterol liposomes an uptake of cholesterol occurs, causing a decrease in the enthalpy of melting of the modified membrane as compared to the native one (Madden *et al.*, 1980). These results are in agreement with the data obtained on synthetic lipids. The influence of drugs — morphine and alcohol — on the melting profiles of brain mitochondrial lipids was investigated (Hosein *et al.*, 1977, 1980). The lipids were extracted from brains of animals treated *in vivo* with the drug. Application of the drugs *in vivo* caused a shift in the melting temperature to lower values and a decrease in the enthalpy of melting, indicating that those drugs are able to fluidise the membranes.

In recent years, as more sensitive commercially-available instruments have become available, the melting properties of biomembranes have been reinvestigated. It was shown that rat liver microsomes and rat liver mitochondria melt reversibly, also in the range of 18–40°C, with a very low enthalpy of melting, indicating that only a fraction of the lipids is in a crystalline state at these temperatures (Bach *et al.*, 1977; Bach *et al.*, 1978).

In beef heart submitochondrial particles, a reversible lipid transition centred at about 20°C was also detected (Blazyk and Newman, 1980). However, this transition appears only after heating the membranes to 100°C (protein denaturation) or in the extracted lipids. On the other hand, Hackenbrock *et al.* (1976), who investigated whole mitochondria — both inner and outer mitochondrial membranes — did not report the existence of any higher melting temperature lipids in these membranes. Nor were phase transitions detected in liver microsomes of rats fed a normal diet, while they were seen in livers of rats fed a fat-free diet (Mabrey *et al.*, 1977).

Other biomembranes also undergo phase transition at temperatures above room temperature. Chromaffin granule membranes, when heated, undergo a phase transition at 32°C with a very low enthalpy of melting (Bach *et al.*, 1979). The cholesterol content of these membranes is quite high, so that only a small part of the membrane lipid will be in the crystalline state. However, after extraction of cholesterol, an increase in the heat content and shift of the melting peak to higher temperatures are found.

The myocardial membranes of squirrels show an endothermic transition between 15 and 26°C (Charnock *et al.*, 1980). These animals hibernate in winter and, during hibernation, the melting range of these membranes shifts downwards by about 10°. The shift reflects an increase in the linoleic acid content of the membranes during hibernation.

Intestinal plasma membranes and hepatocyte plasma membranes

The thermotropic properties of intestinal plasma membranes have been investigated using a number of different physical techniques (Brasitus *et al.*, 1980; Livingstone and Schachter, 1980). The rat enterocyte was separated into microvillus and basolateral membranes and these were investigated by DSC. Figure 1.10 presents the thermograms of intestinal plasma membranes and of the extracted lipids. The peak at the lower temperature stems from lipid melting as it is reversible and appears also in the extracted lipids. The endotherm is broad and extends above room temperature. The enthalpy of melting is quite low (0.1 cal per g lipid). The second peak at higher temperatures is irreversible and is indicative of protein denaturation. In dry microvillus or basolateral lipids, the peaks become even broader and the enthalpy of melting is much greater than in the hydrated lipids. Endothermic peaks were also detected in rat hepatocyte plasma membranes (Livingstone and Schachter, 1980). The transitions are also broad, encompass the room temperature and the enthalpy of melting is low. As in the hepatocyte membranes the cholesterol content is about 13-17 per cent and its fluidising effect is even more pronounced.

SIGNIFICANCE OF PHASE TRANSITION IN THE BIOMEMBRANES

In the previous sections we have discussed phase transitions in both biomembranes and their models. The data presented evoked a number of questions.

1. What is the distribution of membrane components at the phase transition temperature?
2. How are membrane properties (transport, enzymic activity, etc.) influenced by phase transition?
3. How can phase transition be triggered at constant temperature?

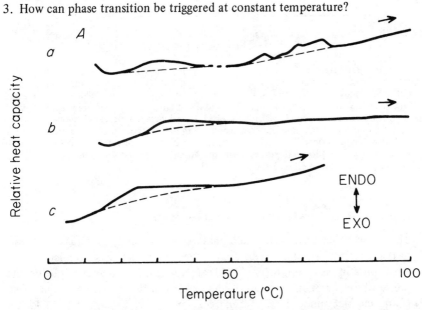

Figure 1.10 *A*, Differential scanning calorimetry heating curves of: *a*, intact microvillus membranes; *b*, the same sample following heating to 100°C, and *c*, hydrated lipids of microvillus membranes. The sample contained 4.5 mg of lipid in *a* and *b* and 3 mg of lipid in *c*. Samples were heated at 5°C min⁻¹. Sensitivity settings for *a* were 0.1 mcal s⁻¹ at temperatures below the dashed curve (that is, in the region of the lipid transition) and 1.0 mcal s⁻¹ at the higher temperatures (in the region of the denaturation endotherms. Sensitivity settings for *b* and *c*, respectively, were 0.1 and 0.2 mcal s⁻¹. Endo and exo represent the directions of endothermic and exothermic transitions

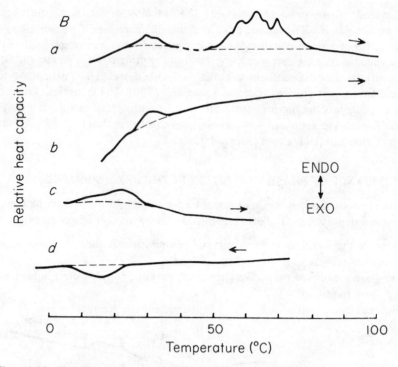

Figure 1.10 *B*, Differential scanning calorimetry heating curves of: *a*, intact basolateral membranes; *b*, the same sample following heating to 100°C; and *c*, hydrated lipids of basolateral membranes. *d*, Shows the cooling curve of the hydrated lipids. The sample in *a* and *b* contained 1.3 mg of lipid and that in *c* and *d* contained 2.3 mg of lipid. Samples were heated or cooled at 5°C min^{-1}. Sensitivity settings for *a* were 0.1 mcal s^{-1} below the dashed curve (in the region of the lipid transition) and 0.2 mcal s^{-1} above the dashed curve (for the denaturation endotherm). The sensitivity setting for *b* was 0.1 mcal s^{-1} and for *c* and *d* it was 0.2 mcal s^{-1}. Endo and exo represent the directions of endothermic and exothermic transitions (from Brasitus *et al.*, 1980)

In the following we will try to answer these points.

1. The effect of phase transition and phase separation on pure lipids or proteins in the presence of lipids can be seen in freeze-fracture electron micrographs. When pure lipids or mixtures of lipids are quenched from above or below the pretransition or main transition temperatures, different structures are seen (Luna and McConnell, 1977). When freeze-fracture is carried out on biological or model membranes containing protein, the surfaces are no longer smooth, but contain particles. It is generally believed that these particles are membrane proteins (Vail *et al.*, 1974). The appearance of the particles can be seen in most membranes, though some do appear to be devoid of these particles. By varying the quenching temperature, phase separation can be induced. When the membranes are quenched from temperatures above the transition

temperature of the lipids, random distribution of the protein particles is seen, whereas quenching from temperatures below T_c causes protein aggregation. This behaviour was seen in model membranes of phospholipid-ATPase (Kleemann and McConnell, 1976; Gomez-Fernandez *et al.*, 1980), lipid-rhodospin (Chen and Hubbell, 1973) and in native membranes of rat liver microsomes (Duppel and Dahl, 1976) and rat liver mitochondria (Hackenbrock *et al.*, 1976). Incorporation of cholesterol into the membranes does prevent aggregation of the protein (Kleemann and McConnell, 1976; Madden *et al.*, 1980).

Chapman *et al.* (1977b) proposed a model of the phase separation of proteins induced by cooling. When membranes are cooled slowly, some of the lipids will start to crystallise. In the case of biological membranes, composed of many lipids, those lipids with higher melting points will crystallise first. The protein molecules will be excluded from the crystallising regions into regions which are still fluid. Depending on the shape of the protein molecules and their concentration, aggregation will be seen. Further increase in protein concentration and cooling might cause additional aggregation thus increasing the protein–protein interactions. The aggregating proteins will trap some lipid molecules and, due to the rigidity of the structure, those lipid molecules would be unable to undergo melting. Only the crystalline lipids produce the endothermic peaks in the calorimeter. The peaks are broad as the proteins influence, to different degrees, the melting of the lipids. The process of protein aggregation, as seen in the micrographs, is a reversible one. Heating the membranes to temperatures above T_c reverts the random distribution of the proteins.

2. The dependence on temperature of enzymic activity of many membrane-bound enzymes is not linear, rather, change in the activation energy at some particular temperature occurs, as discerned by a break in the Arrhenius plots. In many enzymes this behaviour has been attributed to the phase transition of the membrane lipids. Ordering of the lipids will cause aggregation of the proteins, and a change in their microenvironment as the activation energy increases. In some membranes a correlation between the transition temperature of the lipids, as revealed by DSC, and the temperature of the break in the Arrhenius plots was made (De Kruijff *et al.*, 1973; Bach *et al.*, 1977; Brasitus *et al.*, 1979). It is important to note that the amount of lipid in a biological membrane undergoing melting is very small; however, those lipids strongly influence the microenvironment of the enzymes, as revealed by the change in the activation energy of the enzymes.

In the region of phase transition domains of fluid and ordered lipid co-exist. On the boundaries of these domains, structural faults form due to different packing of the lipids in the two phases. The existence of the "packing faults" causes an increase in membrane permeability and facilitates the action of hydrolytic enzymes. Many examples of increased permeability at phase transition temperatures can be cited: the permeability of the probe

Tempo-choline in DML vesicles shows a sharp maximum at the lipid phase transition temperature (Marsh *et al.*, 1976); and the rate of enzymatic hydrolysis of phospholipids is also maximal at the phospholipid phase transition temperature (Op Den Kamp *et al.*, 1975; Strong and Kelly, 1977; Cohen and Barenholz, 1978; Goormaghtigh *et al.*, 1981). Plenty of other references to work showing how membranes' properties are modified in the phase transition region could be made.

3. As shown in the previous sections, metal ions, drugs and other molecules can trigger local phase transition or phase separation at constant temperature. Despite the possibility that these phase changes occur in "microdomains", they may have a profound influence on the properties of the biomembranes. Another point worth mention is the possibility that cholesterol segregates, leaving cholesterol-rich and cholesterol-poor domains; lipids in the cholesterol-poor regions would be able to undergo phase transition.

   Some poikilothermic organisms (marine animals, bacteria, plants and fungi) have an ability to adapt to the environmental temperature by changing their lipid composition (for example, Rahmann, 1976) in such a way that the lipids are in a state of constant fluidity. But even in bacteria that adaptability is limited and growth ceases when more than 50 per cent of the lipids are in the crystalline state (McGarrity and Armstrong, 1981). In mammalian membranes the lipids can be modified to a limited extent by diet (Innis and Clandinin, 1981) or by perfusion *in vitro* with fatty acid solutions (Schroeder and Goh, 1980). All these factors will influence the thermotropic properties of membranes, altering their fluidity and modifying the microenvironment of the membrane proteins.

CONCLUDING REMARKS

In this chapter the papers, which appeared in the literature up to the end of 1981, are reviewed. The field of differential scanning calorimetry has gained extreme popularity in the recent years, as can be judged by the number of papers published. It is believed that in the future many more interesting results will be reported, furthering our knowledge of membrane structure and function.

REFERENCES

Abbas, Ch. A. and Card, G. L. (1980). *Biochim. biophys. Acta*, **602**, 469.
Ahmed, M., Hadgraft, J., Burton, J. S. and Kellaway, I. W. (1980). *Chem. Phys. Lipids*, **27**, 251.
Alonso, A., Gomez-Fernandez, J. C., Aranda, F. J., Belda, F. J. F. and Goni, F. M. (1981). *FEBS Lett.*, **132**, 19.
Andrews, A. L. *et al.* (1976). *Eur. J. Biochem.*, **64**, 549.
Arnold, K. and Hoffman, A. (1976). *Stud. biophys.*, **59**, 139.
Ashe, G. B. and Steim, J. M. (1971). *Biochim. biophys. Acta*, **233**, 810.
Bach, D., Bursuker, I. and Goldman, R. (1977). *Biochim. biophys. Acta*, **469**, 171.
Bach, D., Bursuker, I. and Miller, I. R. (1978). *Experientia*, **34**, 717.

Bach, D. and Miller, I. R. (1976). *Biochim. biophys. Acta*, 433, 13.
Bach, D., Miller, I. R. and Sela, B. (1982). *Biochim. biophys. Acta*, 686, 233.
Bach, D., Raz, A. and Goldman, R. (1976). *Biochim. biophys. Acta*, 436, 889.
Bach, D., Rosenheck, K. and Schneider, A. S. (1979). *Experientia*, 35, 750.
Bach, D. and Sela, B. (1980). *Biochim. biophys. Acta*, 596, 186.
Bach, D. and Sela, B. (1981). *Biochem. Pharmac.*, 30, 1777.
Bach, D., Sela, B. and Miller, I. R. (1980). *Biochem. Pharmac.*, 29, 849.
Baldassare, J. J., Rhinehart, K. B. and Silbert, D. F. (1976). *Biochemistry*, 15, 2986.
Banerjee, S., Vandenbranden, M. and Ruysschaert, J.-M. (1981). *Biochim. biophys. Acta*, 646, 360.
Barber, R. F., McKersie, B. D., Downen, R. G. H. and Thompson, J. E. (1981). *Biochim. biophys. Acta*, 643, 593.
Barenholz, Y., Suurkuusk, Y., Mountcastle, D., Thompson, T. E. and Biltonen, R. L. (1976). *Biochemistry*, 15, 2441.
Barton, P. G. and Gunstone, F. D. (1975). *J. biol. Chem.*, 250, 4470.
Berde, Ch.B., Andersen, H. C. and Hudson, B. S. (1980). *Biochemistry*, 19, 4279.
Bertoli, E., Chapman, D., Griffiths, D. E. and Strach, S. J. (1974). *Biochem. Soc. Trans.*, 2, 964.
Blazyk, J. F. and Newman, J. L. (1980). *Biochim. biophys. Acta*, 600, 1007.
Blazyk, J. F. and Steim, J. M. (1972). *Biochim. biophys. Acta*, 226, 737.
Blume, A. (1980). *Biochemistry*, 19, 4908.
Blume, A. and Ackermann, Th. (1974). *FEBS Lett.*, 43, 71.
Blume, A., Arnold, B. and Weltzien, H. U. (1976). *FEBS Lett.*, 61, 199.
Boggs, J. M. and Moscarello, M. A. (1978). *Biochemistry*, 17, 5734.
Boggs, J. M., Moscarello, M. A. and Papahadjopoulos, D. (1977b). *Biochemistry*, 16, 5420.
Boggs, J. M., Stamp, D., Hughes, D. W. and Deber, C. M. (1981a). *Biochemistry*, 20, 5728.
Boggs, J. M., Stamp, D. and Moscarello, M. A. (1981b). *Biochemistry*, 20, 6066.
Boggs, J. M., Wood, D. D., Moscarello, M. A. and Papahadjopoulos, D. (1977a). *Biochemistry*, 16, 2325.
Brandts, J. F., Erickson, L., Lysko, K., Schwartz, A. T. and Taverna, R. D. (1977). *Biochemistry*, 15, 3450.
Brandts, J. F., Taverna, R. D., Sadasivan, E. and Lysko, K. (1978). *Biochim. biophys. Acta*, 512, 566.
Brasitus, T. A., Schachter, D. and Mamouneas, T. G. (1979). *Biochemistry*, 18, 4137.
Brasitus, T. A., Tall, A. R. and Schachter, D. (1980). *Biochemistry*, 19, 1256.
Bunow, M. R. (1979). *Biochim. biophys. Acta*, 574, 542.
Bunow, M. R. and Bunow, B. (1979). *Biophys. J.*, 27, 325.
Cadenhead, D. A., Kellner, B. M. J., Jacobson, K. and Papahadjopoulos, D. (1977). *Biochemistry*, 16, 5386.
Calhoun, W. I. and Shipley, G. G. (1979a). *Biochemistry*, 18, 1717.
Calhoun, W. I. and Shipley, G. G. (1979b). *Biochim. biophys. Acta*, 555, 436.
Cater, B. A., Chapman, D., Hawes, S. and Saville, J. (1974). *Biochim. biophys. Acta*, 363, 54.
Cevc, G., Watts, A. and Marsh, D. (1981). *Biochemistry*, 20, 4955.
Chapman, D. and Collin, D. T. (1965). *Nature*, 206, 189.
Chapman, D., Cornell, B. A., Eliasz, A. W. and Perry, A. (1977a). *J. molec. Biol.*, 113, 517.
Chapman, D., Cornell, B, A. and Quinn, P. J. (1977b). In *FEBS Symp. no. 42*, (eds G. Semenza and E. Carafoli), Springer-Verlag, Berlin, pp. 72–85.
Chapman, D., Owens, N. F. and Walker, D. A. (1966). *Biochim. biophys. Acta*, 120, 148.
Chapman, D., Urbina, J. and Keough, K. M. (1974). *J. biol. Chem.*, 249, 2512.
Chapman, D., Williams, R. M. and Ladbrooke, B. D. (1967). *Chem. Phys. Lipids*, 1, 445.
Charnock, J. S., Gibson, R. A., McMurchie, E. J. and Raison, J. K. (1980). *Molec. Pharmac.*, 18, 476.
Chen, Y. S. and Hubbell, W. L. (1973). *Expl Eye Res.*, 17, 517.
Chen, S. C. and Sturtevant, J. M. (1981). *Biochemistry*, 20, 713.
Chen, S. C., Sturtevant, J. M. and Gaffney, B. J. (1980). *Proc. natn. Acad. Sci. U.S.A.*, 77, 5060.
Cho, K. C., Choy, C. L. and Young, K. (1981). *Biochim. biophys. Acta*, 663, 14.

Clowes, A. W., Cherry, R. Y. and Chapman, D. (1971). *Biochim. biophys. Acta*, **249**, 301.
Cohen, R. and Barenholz, Y. (1978). *Biochim. biophys. Acta*, **509**, 181.
Cramer, W. A., Whitmarsh, J. and Low, P. S. (1981). *Biochemistry*, **20**, 157.
Cullis, P. R. and de Kruijff, B. (1978). *Biochim. biophys. Acta*, **513**, 31.
Curatolo, W., Sakura, J. D., Small, D. M. and Shipley, G. G. (1977a). *Biochemistry*, **16**, 2313.
Curatolo, W., Small, D. M. and Shipley, G. G. (1977b). *Biochim. biophys. Acta*, **468**, 11.
Davis, S. R. and Low, P. S. (1981). *Biochim. biophys. Acta*, **644**, 157.
Davis, P. J., Coolbear, K. P. and Keough, K. M. W. (1980). *Can. J. Biochem.*, **58**, 851.
Davis, P. J., Fleming, B. D., Coolbear, K. P. and Keough, K. M. W. (1981). *Biochemistry*, **20**, 3633.
Degani, H. *et al.*, In *Energetics and Structure of Halophilic Microorganisms*, (eds S. R. Caplan and M. Ginzburg). Elsevier/North-Holland Biomedical Press, pp. 225–232.
De Kruijff, B., Demel, R. A. and Van Deenen, L. L. M. (1972). *Biochim. biophys. Acta*, **255**, 331.
De Kruijff, B., Van Dijck, P. W. M., Goldbach, R. W., Demel, R. A. and Van Deenen, L. L. M. (1973). *Biochim biophys. Acta*, **330**, 269.
Demel, R. A., Jansen, J. W. C. M., Van Dijck, P. W. M. and Van Deenen, L. L. M. (1977). *Biochim. biophys. Acta*, **465**, 1.
Duppel, W. and Dahl, G. (1976). *Biochim. biophys. Acta*, **426**, 408.
Eliasz, A. W., Chapman, D. and Ewing, D. F. (1976). *Biochim. biophys. Acta*, **448**, 220.
Epand, R. M. and Sturtevant, J. M. (1981). *Biochemistry*, **20**, 4603.
Estep, T. N. *et al.* (1980). *Biochemistry*, **19**, 20.
Estep, T. N., Mountcastle, D. B., Barenholz, Y., Biltonen, R. L. and Thompson, T. E. (1979). *Biochemistry*, **18**, 2112.
Estep, T. N., Mountcastle, D. B., Biltonen, R. L. and Thompson, T. E. (1978). *Biochemistry*, **17**, 1984.
Fildes, F. J. T. and Oliver, J. E. (1978). *J. Pharm. Pharmac.*, **30**, 337.
Freire, E., Bach, D., Correa-Freire, M., Miller, I. R. and Barneholz, Y. (1980). *Biochemistry*, **19**, 3662.
Freire, E. and Biltonen, R. (1978). *Biochim. biophys. Acta*, **514**, 54.
Frenzel, J., Arnold, K. and Nuhn, P. (1978). *Biochim. biophys. Acta*, **507**, 185.
Friedman, K. J. (1977). *J. membrane Biol.*, **32**, 33.
Friedman, K. J. and Glick, D. (1980). *J. membrane Biol.*, **54**, 183.
Frischleder, H. and Gleichman, S. (1977). *Stud. biophys.*, **64**, 95.
Fuldner, H. H. (1981). *Biochemistry*, **20**, 5707.
Gilman, T., Kauffman, J. W. and Pownall, H. J. (1981). *Biochemistry*, **20**, 656.
Goldfine, H., Johnston, N. C. and Phillips, M. C. (1981). *Biochemistry*, **20**, 2908.
Goldman, R., Facchinetti, T., Bach, D., Raz, A. and Shinitzky, M. (1978). *Biochim. biophys. Acta*, **512**, 254.
Gomez-Fernandez, J. C., Goni, F. M., Bach, D., Restall, C. and Chapman, D. (1979). *FEBS Lett.*, **98**, 224.
Gomez-Fernandez, J. C., Goni, F. M., Bach, D., Restall, C. and Chapman, D. (1980). *Biochim. biophys. Acta*, **598**, 502.
Goormaghtigh, E., Van Campendud, M. and Ruysschaert, J.-M. (1981). *Biochem. biophys. Res. Commun.*, **101**, 1410.
Grell, E., Funck, Th. and Eggers, F. (1975). *Membranes*, **3**, 1.
Hackenbrock, Ch. R., Hochli, M. and Chau, R. M. (1976). *Biochim. biophys. Acta*, **455**, 466.
Haest, C. W. M., de Gier, J., van Es, Verkleij, A. J. and van Deenen, L. L. M. (1972). *Biochim. biophys. Acta*, **288**, 43.
Hammoudah, M. M. *et al.*, (1981). *Biochim. biophys. Acta*, **645**, 102.
Harlos, K. and Eibl, H. (1981). *Biochemistry*, **20**, 2888.
Hinz, H.-J., Korner, O. and Nicolau, C. (1981). *Biochim. biophys. Acta*, **643**, 557.
Hinz, H.-J. and Sturtevant, J. M. (1972). *J. biol. Chem.*, **247**, 3697(a); 6071(b).
Hosein, E. A., Lapalme, M. and Vadas, E. B. (1977). *Biochem. biophys. Res. Commun.*, **78**, 194.
Hosein, E. A., Lee, H. and Hoffman, I. (1980). *Can. J. Biochem.*, **58**, 1147.
Innis, S. M. and Clandinin, M. T. (1981). *Biochem. J.*, **193**, 155.

Jackson, W. M., Kostyla, J., Nordin, J. H. and Brandts, J. F. (1973). *Biochemistry*, **12**, 3662.
Jackson, M. B. and Sturtevant, J. M. (1977). *J. biol. Chem.*, **252**, 4749.
Jackson, M. B. and Sturtevant, J. M. (1978). *Biochemistry*, **17**, 911.
Jacobs, R. E., Hudson, B. and Andersen, H. C. (1975). *Proc. natn. Acad. Sci. U.S.A.*, **72**, 3993.
Jacobson, K. and Papahadjopoulos, D. (1975). *Biochemistry*, **14**, 152.
Jain, M. K. and De Haas, G. H. (1981). *Biochim. biophys. Acta*, **642**, 203.
Jain, M. K. and Wu, N. (1977). *J. membrane Biol.*, **34**, 157.
Jain, M. K., Wu, N., Morgan, T. K., Briggs, M. S. and Murray, R. K. (1976). *Chem. Phys. Lipids*, **17**, 71.
Jain, M. K., Wu, N. and Wray, L. V. (1975). *Nature*, **255**, 494.
Janiak, M. J., Small, D. M. and Shipley, G. G. (1976). *Biochemistry*, **15**, 4575.
Juliano, R. L. and Stamp, D. (1979). *Biochim. biophys. Acta*, **586**, 137.
Jursinic, P. and Govindjee (1977). *Photochem. Photobiol.*, **26**, 617.
Kantor, H. L., Mabrey, S., Prestegard, J. H. and Sturtevant, J. M. (1977). *Biochim. biophys. Acta*, **448**, 402.
Kawada, N. and Nosoh, Y. (1981). *FEBS Letts.*, **124**, 15.
Keough, K. M. W. and Davis, P. J. (1979). *Biochemistry*, **18**, 1453.
Kleemann, W. and McConnell, H. M. (1976). *Biochim. biophys. Acta*, **419**, 206.
Klopfenstein, W. E., de Kruijff, B., Verkleij, A. J., Demel, R. A. and van Deenen, L. L. M. (1974). *Chem. Phys. Lipids*, **13**, 215.
Koehler, K. A., Jain, M. K., Stone, E. E., Fossel, E. T. and Koehler, L. S. (1978). *Biochim. biophys. Acta*, **510**, 177.
Krishnan, K. S. and Brandts, J. F. (1978). *Meth. Enzym.*, **49**, 1.
Krishnan, K. S. and Brandts, J. F. (1979). *Molec. Pharmac.*, **16**, 181.
Ladbrooke, B. D. and Chapman, D. (1969). *Chem. Phys. Lipids*, **3**, 304.
Ladbrooke, B. D., Jenkinson, T. J., Kamat, V. B. and Chapman, D. (1968a). *Biochim. biophys. Acta*, **164**, 101.
Ladbrooke, B. D., Williams, R. M. and Chapman, D. (1968b). *Biochim. biophys. Acta*, **150**, 333.
Lelkes, P. I., Bach, D. and Miller, I. R. (1980). *J. membrane Biol.*, **54**, 141.
Lentz, B. R., Freire, E. and Biltonen, R. L. (1978). *Biochemistry*, **17**, 4475.
Liao, M. J. and Prestegard, J. H. (1981). *Biochim. biophys. Acta*, **645**, 149.
Livingstone, C. J. and Schachter, D. (1980). *J. biol. Chem.*, **255**, 10902.
Low, P. S. and Brandts, J. F. (1978). *Arch. Biochem. Biophys.*, **190**, 640.
Luna, E. J. and McConnell, H. M. (1977). *Biochim. biophys. Acta*, **470**, 303.
Lyman, G. H., Papahadjopoulos, D. and Preisler, H. D. (1976). *Biochim. biophys. Acta*, **448**, 460.
Lysko, K. A., Carlson, R., Taverna, R., Snow, J. and Brandts, J. F. (1981). *Biochemistry*, **20**, 5570.
Mabrey, S., Mateo, P. L. and Sturtevant, J. M. (1978). *Biochemistry*, **17**, 2464.
Mabrey, S., Powis, G., Schenkman, J. B. and Tritton, T. R. (1977). *J. biol. Chem.*, **252**, 2929.
Mabrey, S. and Sturtevant, J. (1976). *Proc. natn. Acad. Sci. U.S.A.*, **73**, 3862.
Mabrey, S. and Sturtevant, J. M. (1977). *Biochim. biophys. Acta*, **448**, 444.
MacDonald, R. I. and MacDonald, R. C. (1975). *J. biol. Chem.*, **250**, 9206.
MacDonald, R. C., Simon, S. A. and Baer, E. (1976). *Biochemistry*, **15**, 885.
Madden, T. D., Vigo, C., Bruckdorfer, K. R. and Chapman, D. (1980). *Biochim. biophys. Acta*, **599**, 528.
Marcelja, S. (1974). *Biochim. biophys. Acta*, **367**, 165.
Marsh, D., Watts, A. and Knowles, P. F. (1976). *Biochemistry*, **15**, 3570.
Martonosi, M. A. (1974). *FEBS Lett.*, **47**, 327.
Mason, J. T., Huang, Ch. and Biltonen, R. L. (1981). *Biochemistry*, **20**, 6086.
Mason, W. T., Lane, N. J., Miller, N. G. A. and Bangham, A. D. (1980). *J. membrane Biol.*, **55**, 69.
Massey, J. B., Gotto, A. M. and Pownall, H. J. (1981). *Biochemistry*, **20**, 1575.
McElhaney, R. N. and Souza, K. A. (1976). *Biochim. biophys. Acta*, **443**, 348.

McGarrity, J. T. and Armstrong, J. B. (1981). *Can. J. Microbiol.*, **27**, 835.

Melchior, D. L. and Steim, J. M. (1976). *A. Rev. Biophys. Bioengng.*, **5**, 205.

Mollay, Ch. (1976). *FEBS Lett.*, **64**, 65.

Mombers, C., van Dijck, P. W. M., van Deenen, L. L. M., De Gier, J. and Verkleij, A. J. (1977). *Biochim. biophys. Acta*, **470**, 152.

Mombers, C., Verkleij, A. J., De Gier, J. and van Deenen, L. L. M. (1979). *Biochim. biophys. Acta*, **551**, 271.

Mountcastle, D. B., Biltonen, R. L. and Halsey, M. J. (1978). *Proc. Natn. Acad. Sci. U.S.A.*, **75**, 4906.

Nagle, J. F. (1980). *Ann. Rev. Phys. Chem.*, **31**, 157.

Newton, C., Pangborn, W., Nir, S. and Papahadjopoulos, D. (1978). *Biochim. biophys. Acta*, **506**, 281.

Oldfield, E. and Chapman, D. (1972). *FEBS Lett.*, **21**, 303.

Op Den Kamp, J. A. F., Kauerz, M. Th. and Van Deenen, L. L. M. (1975). *Biochim. biophys. Acta*, **406**, 169.

Pache, W., Chapman, D. and Hillaby, R. (1972). *Biochim. biophys. Acta*, **255**, 358.

Papahadjopoulos, D. (1977). *J. Coll. Interface Sci.*, **58**, 459.

Papahadjopoulos, D., Hui, S., Vail, W. J. and Poste, G. (1976a). *Biochim. biophys. Acta*, **448**, 245.

Papahadjopoulos, D., Jacobson, K., Poste, G. and Shepherd, G. (1975a). *Biochim. biophys. Acta*, **394**, 504.

Papahadjopoulos, D., Moscarello, M., Eylar, E. H. and Isac, T. (1975b). *Biochim. biophys. Acta*, **401**, 317.

Papahadjopoulos, D., Poste, G. and Schaeffer, B. E. (1973). *Biochim. biophys. Acta*, **323**, 23.

Papahadjopoulos, D., Poste, G., Schaeffer, B. E. and Vail, W. J. (1974). *Biochim. biophys. Acta*, **352**, 10.

Papahadjopoulos, D., Vail, W. J., Pangborn, W. A. and Poste, G. (1976b). *Biochim. biophys. Acta*, **448**, 265.

Petri, W. A. *et al.* (1980). *Biochemistry*, **19**, 3088.

Phillips, M. C., Ladbrooke, B. D. and Chapman, D. (1970). *Biochim. biophys. Acta*, **193**, 35.

Phillips, M. C., Williams, R. M. and Chapman, D. (1969). *Chem. Phys. Lipids*, **3**, 234.

Portis, A., Newton, C., Pangborn, W. and Papahadjopoulos, D. (1979). *Biochemistry*, **18**, 780.

Pownall, H. J., Massey, J. B., Hsu, F.-J. and Gotto, A. M. (1981). *Can. J. Biochem.*, **59**, 700.

Privalov, P. L., Plotnikov, V. V. and Filimonov, V. V. (1975). *J. Thermodynamics*, **7**, 41.

Rahmann, H. (1976). In *Ganglioside Function* (eds G. Porcellati, B. Ceccarelli and G. Tettamanti). Plenum, New York, pp. 151–161.

Rand, R. P., Chapman, D. and Larsson, K. (1975). *Biophys. J.*, **15**, 1117.

Ruocco, M. J. *et al.* (1981). *Biochemistry*, **20**, 5957.

Sacre, M. M., Hoffmann, W., Turner, M., Tocanne, J. F. and Chapman, D. (1979). *Chem. Phys. Lipids*, **25**, 69.

Santaren, J. F., Rico, M. and Ribera, A. (1981). *Chem. Phys. Lipids*, **29**, 147.

Schroeder, F. and Goh, E. H. (1980). *Chem. Phys. Lipids*, **26**, 207.

Scott, H. L. (1981). *Biochim. biophys. Acta*, **643**, 161.

Shipley, G. G., Avecilla, L. S. and Small, D. M. (1974). *J. Lipid Res.*, **15**, 124.

Sillerud, L. O., Schafer, D. E., Yu, R. K. and Konigsberg, W. H. (1979). *J. biol. Chem.*, **254**, 10876.

Silvius, J. R., Mak, N. and McElhaney, R. W. (1980). *Biochim. biophys. Acta*, **597**, 199.

Silvius, J. R., Read, B. D. and McElhaney, R. W. (1979). *Biochim. biophys. Acta*, **555**, 175.

Simon, S. A., Lis, L. J., Kauffman, J. W. and MacDonald, R. C. (1975a). *Biochim. biophys. Acta*, **375**, 317.

Simon, S. A., MacDonald, R. C. and Bennett, P. B. (1975b). *Biochem. biophys. Res. Commun.*, **67**, 988.

Snow, J. W., Brandts, J. F. and Low, P. S. (1978). *Biochim. biophys. Acta*, **512**, 579–591.

Snow, J. W., Vincentelli, J. and Brandts, J. F. (1981). *Biochim. biophys. Acta*, **642**, 418.

Steim, J. M. (1972). *Proc. Eur. Biochem. Soc.*, 8th Meeting, 3.

Steim, J. M., Tourtellotte, M. E., Reinert, J. C., McElhaney, R. N. and Rader, R. L. (1969). *Proc. natn. Acad. Sci. U.S.A.*, **63**, 104.

Sternberg, B. *et al.* (1977). *Stud. biophys.*, **64**, 53.
Stewart, T. P., Hui, S. W., Portis, A. R. and Papahadjopoulos, D. (1979). *Biochim. biophys. Acta*, **556**, 1.
Strong, P. N. and Kelly, R. B. (1977). *Biochim. biophys. Acta*, **469**, 231.
Stumpel, J., Harlos, K. and Eibl, H. (1980). *Biochim. biophys. Acta*, **599**, 464.
Stumpel, J., Nicksch, A. and Eibl, H. (1981). *Biochemistry*, **20**, 662.
Sturtevant, J. (1974). *A. Rev. Biophys. Bioengng*, **3**, 35.
Suurkuusk, J., Lentz, B. R., Barenholz, Y., Biltonen, R. L. and Thompson, T. E. (1976). *Biochemistry*, **15**, 1393.
Tall, A. R., Small, D. M., Deckelbaum, R. J. and Shipley, G. G. (1977). *J. biol. Chem.*, **252**, 4701.
Tall, A. R., Small, D. M., Shipley, G. G. and Lees, R. S. (1975). *Proc. natn. Acad. Sci. U.S.A.*, **72**, 4940.
Ter-Minassian-Saraga, L., Maldemont, G., Hort-Legrand, C. and Metral, S. (1981). *Biochem. Pharmac.*, **30**, 411.
Tilcock, C. P. S. and Fisher, D. (1979). *Biochim. biophys. Acta*, **557**, 53.
Untracht, S. H. and Shipley, G. G. (1977). *J. biol. Chem.*, **252**, 4449.
Usher, J. R., Epand, R. M. and Papahadjopoulos, D. (1978). *Chem. Phys. Lipids*, **22**, 245.
Vail, W. J., Papahadjopoulos, D. and Moscarello, M. A. (1974). *Biochim. biophys. Acta*, **345**, 463.
Van Dijck, P. W. M. (1979). *Biochim. biophys. Acta*, **555**, 89.
Van Dijck, P. W. M., De Kruijff, B., Verkleij, A. J., Van Deenen, L. L. M. and De Gier, J. (1978). *Biochim. biophys. Acta*, **512**, 84.
Van Dijck, P. W. M., Ververgaert, P. H. J. Th., Verkleij, A. J., Van Deenen, L. L. M. and De Gier, J. (1975). *Biochim. biophys. Acta*, **406**, 465.
Van Zoelen, E. J. J., Van Dijck, P. W. M., De Kruijff, B., Verkleij, A. J. and Van Deenen, L. L. M. (1978). *Biochim. biophys. Acta*, **514**, 9.
Vaughan, D. J. and Keough, K. M. (1974). *FEBS Lett.*, **47**, 158.
Verkleij, A. J., De Kruijff, B., Ververgaert, P. H. J. Th., Tocanne, J. F. and Van Deenen, L. L. M. (1974). *Biochim. biophys. Acta*, **339**, 432.
Ververgaert, P. H. J. Th., De Kruijff, B., Verkleij, A. J., Tocanne, J. F. and Van Deenen, L. L. M. (1975). *Chem. Phys. Lipids*, **14**, 97.
Whittington, S. G. and Chapman, D. (1965). *Trans. Faraday Soc.*, **61**, 2656.
Whittington, S. G. and Chapman, D. (1966). *Trans. Faraday Soc.*, **62**, 3319.
Wilkinson, D. A. and Nagle, J. F. (1981). *Biochemistry*, **20**, 187.
Wu, E.-S., Jacobson, K., Szoka, F. and Portis, A. (1978). *Biochemistry*, **17**, 5543.

2

X-ray diffraction and electron microscope studies of the molecular structure of biological membranes

Lee Makowski and Jade Li, Department of Biochemistry, College of
Physicians and Surgeons of Columbia University, 630 West 168th Street,
New York, NY 10032, USA

INTRODUCTION

Biological membranes are thin, sheet-like structures composed of a well-defined but usually heterogeneous mixture of proteins, lipids and carbohydrates. Studies aimed at understanding the structural basis of membrane function focus on obtaining images of each membrane component at the highest possible resolution and on determining the spatial relationships among the components in the intact membrane. Detailed structural studies usually require chemically homogeneous specimens which exhibit a high degree of spatial order. For this reason, most membranes in their native state are not satisfactory subjects for high resolution structural studies.

The only proven method of determining the structure of a macromolecule to atomic resolution is by X-ray crystallography. Unfortunately, membrane components have, so far, been particularly resistant to attempts made to crystallise them. Several lipids have been crystallised and their high resolution structure determined, but to date we know of only two integral membrane proteins, matrix porin (Garavito and Rosenbusch, 1980) and reaction centre from *Rhodopseudomonas viridis* (Michel, 1982), that have been crystallised in forms suitable for high resolution X-ray crystallography. The problem of obtaining crystals is undoubtedly related to the fact that integral membrane components are in contact with both polar and non-polar phases in the intact membrane. To maintain the native conformation of a membrane protein it will be necessary to reproduce this bipolar environment in the crystal. The lack of three-dimensional crystals is the major reason why structural studies of membrane proteins have lagged behind comparable studies of soluble proteins. However, the production of small crystals of several integral membrane proteins holds promise that successful techniques for their crystallisation may soon be developed. Once this has been done we may anticipate that the high resolution structural detail which can be attained by X-ray crystallography will provide substantial insights into the molecular mechanisms operating during the functioning of membrane proteins, such as those that act as pumps, channels or receptors.

In the absence of three-dimensional crystals, a great deal of effort has been put into the study of two-dimensional arrays of membrane proteins. Some of these arrays appear to occur naturally while others have been induced by the reconstitution of isolated membrane components. Studies of these two-dimensional arrays have resulted in the most detailed images of integral membrane proteins that have been produced to date. The three-dimensional analysis of purple membrane structure to 7Å resolution using image analysis of electron micrographs of unstained samples (Unwin and Henderson, 1975; Henderson and Unwin, 1975) is a milestone in the study of membrane structure. The extensive, stable, highly ordered crystalline array of bacteriorhodopsin in the purple membrane has so far proved unique in its suitability for high-resolution, three-dimensional reconstruction by electron microscopy. Comparable analyses of other membranes have yet to be produced. There are several reasons for this. Most membrane arrays are smaller and more disordered than the purple membrane lattice. Disorder in a lattice can limit the resolution of a structural study. Furthermore, negative stain must be used to preserve the structure of many membranes during electron microscopy, and the intrinsic properties of the stains limit the attainable resolution to 15–20Å. Nevertheless, analysis of electron micrographs has resulted in the production of a number of detailed two-dimensional projections and three-dimensional reconstructions of the structure of membrane components ordered in two-dimensional arrays. These arrays can also be studied by X-ray diffraction to determine the one-dimensional distribution of electron density in the direction perpendicular to the membrane plane (often referred to as the membrane profile). As these membrane arrays have a well-defined protein composition, the electron density profile can often be interpreted unambiguously in terms of the disposition of the proteins within the membrane. Analysis of the membrane profile can provide information that is unobtainable from electron microscopy even when a three-dimensional reconstruction has been made. It is also possible to produce a three-dimensional electron density map by analysis of the X-ray diffraction from these membrane arrays.

In some cases, membranes which are enriched for, or contain only a single, protein species can be prepared; however, a two-dimensional array cannot be induced to form. Membrane preparations of this kind include sarcoplasmic reticulum vesicles and acetylcholine receptor-enriched membranes. Analysis of X-ray diffraction from these membranes can be used to determine the membrane profile which may be interpreted in terms of the positioning of the proteins relative to the lipid bilayer. Electron microscopy of negatively-stained membranes can also provide important structural information in the absence of a lattice, but the production of a three-dimensional reconstruction based on electron micrographs of a membrane lacking a two-dimensional array may be exceedingly difficult.

X-ray diffraction can be used to determine the electron density profile of any membrane, including intact membranes with heterogeneous protein composition. The resulting profile represents an average of contributions from all the membrane components, making its interpretation in terms of the chemical constituents of the membrane more difficult than when only a single protein species is present. However, electron density profiles have greatly enhanced our knowledge of the structures of intact membranes, such as those in myelin. Myelin was the first membrane structure to be studied using X-ray diffraction (Schmitt *et al.*, 1935). The relatively high degree of order with which the myelin membranes are stacked into a one-dimensional spiral lattice has made possible the determination of the myelin membrane profile to 10Å resolution (Caspar and Kirschner, 1971). Membrane profiles have now been derived for many lipid bilayers and membranes and constitute a substantial reservoir of knowledge about the organisation of lipids and proteins in membranes.

In the structural studies described here it should become apparent that the intrinsic spatial disorder and chemical heterogeneity of most membranes has had a profound effect on the choice of strategies and methods of structural analysis. Often, the most powerful approach to these problems has been the coordinated use of both X-ray diffraction and electron microscopy. The information that can be obtained using the two techniques are highly complementary. The coordinated use of both methods will always provide more information than can be obtained by the use of either one alone.

At the resolution that X-ray diffraction and electron microscope studies have so far attained, membranes have been shown to be very diverse in their structural organisation. Nevertheless, patterns are emerging that indicate the common occurrence of some structural features in membranes from widely disparate sources. The studies reviewed here demonstrate both the variety and the patterns of structural organisation in membranes.

SCOPE

X-ray diffraction and electron microscopy have been applied extensively to the study of cell membranes. We limit this review to a discussion of studies aimed at elucidating the detailed molecular structure of membrane components. Electron microscopy of negatively-stained or, in exceptional cases, unstained membrane structures has generally been aimed at obtaining detailed structural information. Occasionally, electron microscopy of freeze-fractured or heavy metal-shadowed specimens has also been used for this purpose. These studies, as well as most of the X-ray diffraction studies, are the subject of this chapter. Other methods for the analysis of membrane structure, in particular neutron diffraction, are reviewed in other chapters of this book.

The first part of this chapter briefly reviews diffraction theory and some of the experimental considerations necessary for X-ray diffraction and electron microscopy. Also, aspects of membrane structure that are particularly relevant to the application of X-ray diffraction and electron microscopy are discussed. The second part of the chapter reviews structural studies of particular membranes and membrane components. As lipid structure must be considered in the study of all membranes, studies on model systems — lipid crystals, lipid–water liquid crystals, and lipid–protein–water systems — are considered first. The studies on membranes and membrane proteins are described, beginning with those membranes with no spatial ordering of components in the membrane plane. Studies on membrane specimens containing two-dimensional arrays are considered next, followed by descriptions of the results of crystallographic studies on two membrane-related proteins. In describing the X-ray diffraction and electron microscope studies on specific systems we have included some information about function and biochemical composition. Only when this information is taken into account will the significance of the structural studies become clear. For this reason we have chosen to describe a few membrane systems in detail rather than give a comprehensive review and we simply attempt to provide a clear view of the state of the art and the advantages and limitations of existing techniques.

STRUCTURAL METHODS

Structural analysis

X rays and electrons

X rays are electromagnetic waves with wavelengths of the order of 1 Å. Because they interact relatively weakly with biological materials, samples for X-ray diffraction must be between 0.1 and 1.0 mm in diameter and contain a high concentration of the structure of interest to obtain detectable diffraction. However, the sample can be hydrated and at essentially physiological conditions. X rays scatter almost exclusively from electrons and analysis of X-ray diffraction data gives direct information only about the distribution of electrons, or electron density in the specimen. To understand the structural organisation of a diffracting object, the electron density must be interpreted in terms of the chemical constituents.

Electrons are deBroglie or particle waves that diffract from matter in a manner analogous to that of X rays. However, electrons are charged particles that interact very strongly with matter and, unlike X rays, can only be used in a vacuum for studying samples not more than a few hundred angstroms thick. In an electron microscope, electrons with wavelengths of the order of 10^{-2} Å are usually used. Because electrons diffract from both the nuclei and the electrons of the atoms in the specimen, the scattering power of chemical groups for electrons differs from that for X rays. However, for most atoms in biological materials, those with high scattering potential for electrons also tend to have a high scattering density for X rays.

Although X rays and electrons interact with matter rather differently, their diffraction can be considered by the same geometric theory. In the experiments considered here, both X rays and electrons scatter elastically from the structure of interest: that is, the scattered radiation has the same wavelength as the incident radiation. The diffraction pattern is formed by the interference of waves (X rays or electrons) that have scattered from one point in the specimen with those waves that have scattered from all other points. Electron microscopes use magnetic lenses to recombine the diffracted electrons into an image. Lenses for the focusing of X rays do not exist and the phase plates used to focus X rays in X-ray microscopes have not attained resolutions better than about 1,000 Å. Thus, computational methods must be used to combine the information from X-ray reflections into an image of the scattering object.

Here we outline briefly the geometric theory of diffraction with special emphasis on issues of importance in the understanding and interpretation of structural studies on membranes. There are many texts that describe X-ray diffraction (for example, Compton and Allison, 1935; Lipson and Cochran, 1953; Guinier, 1963; James, 1958) and electron microscopy (Meek, 1973) and an excellent short introduction to diffraction theory is given in Holmes and Blow (1965). More detailed discussion of the issues involved in the analysis of X-ray diffraction from membranes is given by Franks and Levine (1981).

Formation of the diffraction pattern

The scattering of waves − be they X rays or electrons − from an infinitely small point scattering centre will always be independent of scattering angle (with some necessary but, in this context unimportant, geometric corrections for experimental details, such as polarisation of the incident beam). When a second point scatterer is introduced the diffraction becomes dependent on scattering angle because of interference between the waves scattered from the two points. As shown in Figure 2.1, the pathlength from radiation source to detector will be slightly greater for a wave scattered from one point than for a wave scattered from the other. When the scattering angle, 2θ, is such that the pathlength difference for the two waves is equal to the wavelength of the radiation (or an integral multiple of the wavelength), the two scattered waves will be in phase and the scattering from the two points will interfere constructively resulting in maximum in the observed intensity. At points between maxima, interference will lessen the intensity and there will be minima at points where the two waves are exactly out of phase and interfere destructively.

Diffraction can also be thought of as reflection from planes of scattering density. As shown in Figure 2.1b, waves reflected from two planes separated by a distance d will interfere constructively to produce intensity maxima at all scattering angles 2θ for which

$$1/d = 2\sin\theta/n\lambda \qquad (1)$$

where λ is the wavelength of the scattered radiation and n is any integer. This is an exceedingly important relationship as it allows any diffraction peak to be immediately identified as arising from scattering features a distance d apart. For two planes separated by less than half the wavelength of the incident radiation ($d < \lambda/2$), no scattering maxima are observed (sin θ cannot be greater than unity; therefore, for $d < \lambda/2$ there are no solutions to equation (1)). This is a reflection of the well known fact that structural details that are small compared to the wavelength of the incident radiation cannot be resolved using that radiation.

Equation 1 is usually referred to as Bragg's law. As the distance, d, between scattering planes in the specimen gets smaller, the angle between scattering maxima gets larger. Diffraction at relatively large scattering angles corresponds to relatively small structural details. This reciprocal relationship between distances in the specimen and distances in the diffraction pattern has led to the use of the terms 'real space', corresponding to coordinates of details in the structure, and 'reciprocal space', which is the three-dimensional space of all possible scattering

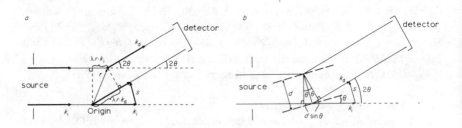

Figure 2.1 Bragg's law. In a diffraction experiment, the incident wave can be represented by a vector, k_j, of modulus $1/\lambda$ pointing in the direction of propagation. The diffracted wave also has a wavelength and can be represented by a vector, k_d, of length identical to k_j. The scattering vector, s, is defined as the difference: $s = k_d - k_j$. The angle of scattering is the angle between k_d and k_j, usually designated 2θ. The relationship between these vectors is shown in a. The pathlength difference, Δ, between a wave scattered by a particle at the origin and a particle at a position r is $\Delta = \lambda r \cdot k_d - \lambda r \cdot k_j = \lambda r \cdot (k_d - k_j) = \lambda(r \cdot s)$. This means that one of the two scattered waves is phase-shifted relative to the other by an amount $2\pi\Delta/\lambda = 2\pi r \cdot s$. The waves scattered from the two points will interfere constructively to form diffraction maxima at all scattering angles for which the phase shift is an integral multiple of 2π, or wherever the pathlength difference is an integral multiple of λ. Diffraction can also be thought of as the reflection from planes of scattering density (b). In b, two planes of scattering density separated by a distance d are indicated by broken lines. The pathlength difference for waves reflected from the two planes is $2d\sin\theta$. For constructive interference, $n\lambda = 2d\sin\theta$ for any integer n

vectors. The scattering vector, s, is defined as the difference between the wave vectors of the incident, k_i, and diffracted, k_d, waves. As shown in Figure 2.1,

$$s = k_d - k_i \qquad (|s| = 1/d) \qquad (2)$$

where the wave vectors k_d and k_i are simply vectors of length $1/\lambda$ pointing in the direction of propagation of the diffracted and incident radiation, respectively.

As in a diffraction experiment scattering is elastic, the incident and diffracted wave vectors have the same length. Consequently, for a particular orientation of the sample relative to the incident beam, diffraction can only be observed for those vectors **s** falling on the surface of a sphere, called the Ewald sphere. To collect diffraction data for other scattering vectors, **s**, the specimen must be rotated relative to the direction of the incident radiation, as shown in Figure 2.2. In reciprocal space, the Ewald sphere is positioned with one point of its surface at the origin. This is required by the relationship between $\mathbf{k}_d$ and $\mathbf{k}_i$ in equation 2 and the fact that the origin of reciprocal space is the origin of the scattering vector. By collecting data at several or, more often, many different orientations of the specimen, the intensity can be observed for all possible scattering vectors, **s**.

The dimensions of the coordinates of reciprocal space are Å^{-1}. Thus, the position of a reflection in reciprocal space is referred to as falling at, for instance, a spacing of $0.1\,\text{Å}^{-1}$, or $10\,\text{Å}$ spacing. This reflection would arise from structural features $10\,\text{Å}$ apart in the specimen and, if the incident radiation was CuK_α X rays ($\lambda = 1.54\,\text{Å}$), it would fall at a scattering angle, 2θ, of about $9°$ (from Bragg's law setting $n = 1$). If a structural study results in an electron density map derived by using all the diffracted intensity out to $0.1\,\text{Å}^{-1}$ (or $10\,\text{Å}$) spacing in reciprocal space, but no further, the resolution of the electron density map is said to be $10\,\text{Å}$.

Fourier transforms

To use the diffracted intensities to obtain a scattering density map, it is necessary to develop a quantitative relationship between the diffraction pattern and the structure. The fundamental result is that the scattered intensity in reciprocal space (that is, the diffraction pattern) corresponds to the square of the Fourier transform of the scattering density distribution in real space (that is, the structure). The analysis of all diffraction data is based on this simple mathematical insight.

Fourier analysis involves the decomposition of a scattering density distribution into a sum of sinusoidal waves, or fringes. In a Fourier synthesis these waves, or sets of fringes, are recombined to form the scattering density distribution. Given a large enough number of sinusoidal waves, their sum can be made to approximate a scattering density distribution with great accuracy. Each sinusoidal wave is characterised by its wavelength, direction, amplitude and phase. To reconstruct a scattering density distribution, it is necessary to determine these four properties of each sinusoid and add all the sinusoids together. This is a powerful approach to the problem of analysing diffraction data because the process of diffraction is analogous to Fourier analysis: each set of sinusoidal fringes in a scattering density distribution gives rise to a pair of diffraction spots at a distinct place in reciprocal space (the diffracted intensities at $\pm\mathbf{s}$ are identical when no absorption occurs). The diffracted waves act as though they reflect from the sinusoidal fringes according to Bragg's law. The positions of reflections in reciprocal space indicate the direc-

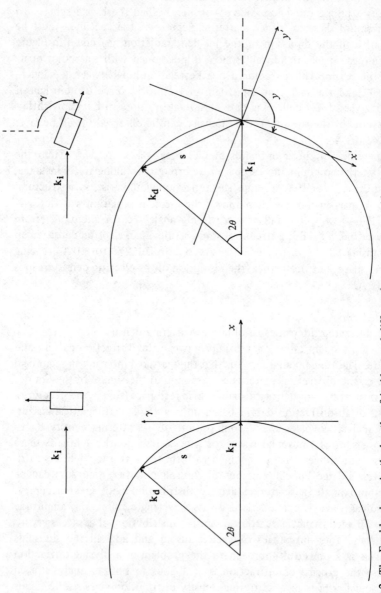

Figure 2.2   The Ewald sphere. As the lengths of incident and diffracted wave vectors are identical in a diffraction experiment, for any one orientation of the specimen relative to the incident radiation, the diffracted intensities can only be measured for values of the scattering vector, s, that fall on the surface of a sphere. Rotation of the specimen relative to the incident beam has the effect of rotating the coordinates of reciprocal space relative to the incident wave vector, k_i. For incident wave vectors k_i and k_i, intensities can be measured for scattering vectors falling on the two Ewald spheres drawn

tion and wavelength of the sinusoidal fringe using Bragg's law as derived in Figure 2.1b. For instance, a reflection falling at a spacing of 0.1 Å^{-1} corresponds to a sinusoidal wave with a wavelength of 10 Å. The amplitude of the fringe is directly proportional to the square root of the intensity. The only piece of information not directly obtainable is the phase. The phase refers to the distance of the fringe's maxima from some arbitrary reference point or origin. If a sinusoid is shifted by a distance equal to one-half of its wavelength moving all of its maxima into the positions previously held by its minima, its phase will have been shifted by 180°, or π radians. The inability to measure directly the phase of the sinusoids making up a scattering density distribution presents a serious ambiguity in the interpretation of diffraction data referred to as the 'phase problem'.

Figure 2.3 shows a one-dimensional example of these concepts. The small-angle diffraction pattern from myelin contains five pairs of reflections at spacings of $n/171$ Å^{-1} for $n = 1\text{-}5$. The reflection at a spacing of $n/171$ Å^{-1} corresponds to a sinusoid of wavelength $171/n$ Å. When these five sinusoids are properly phased and assigned amplitudes corresponding to the measured intensities, they can be added together to form an electron density profile for myelin at a resolution of $171/5$ Å or about 34 Å.

Formally, the quantitative relationship between diffracted intensity, $I(s)$, in reciprocal space and scattering density, $\rho(\mathbf{r})$, where $\mathbf{r}$ is the vector defining the real space position, can be expressed as follows: The inverse Fourier transform of the scattering density is a complex function in reciprocal space referred to as the scattering amplitude, $F(\mathbf{s})$, where

$$F(\mathbf{s}) = \int \rho(\mathbf{r}) \exp(2\pi i \mathbf{r} \cdot \mathbf{s}) \, d\mathbf{r} \tag{3}$$

The diffracted intensity is related to the amplitude by

$$I(s) = F(\mathbf{s}) F^*(\mathbf{s}) = |F(\mathbf{s})|^2 \tag{4}$$

where $F^*(\mathbf{s})$ is the complex conjugate of $F(\mathbf{s})$. The scattering amplitude, $F(\mathbf{s})$, is a complex number characterised by a modulus, $|F(\mathbf{s})|$ and a phase, $\phi(\mathbf{s})$,

$$F(\mathbf{s}) = |F(\mathbf{s})| \exp(i\phi(\mathbf{s})). \tag{5}$$

In the measurement of the diffracted intensity, all information about the phase, $\phi(\mathbf{s})$, is lost. This is equivalent to losing the information about the relative positions (phases) of the sinusoidal fringes in real space.

Methods, some direct and some indirect, exist for determining the phases of the scattering amplitudes. Once the phases are determined, the scattering density distribution can be reconstructed from the complex amplitudes by a Fourier transform,

$$\rho(\mathbf{r}) = \int F(\mathbf{s}) \exp(-2\pi i \mathbf{r} \cdot \mathbf{s}) \, d\mathbf{s} \tag{6}$$

Calculation of this integral is exactly equivalent to summing all the sinusoidal fringes making up the scattering density to reconstruct an image of the structure.

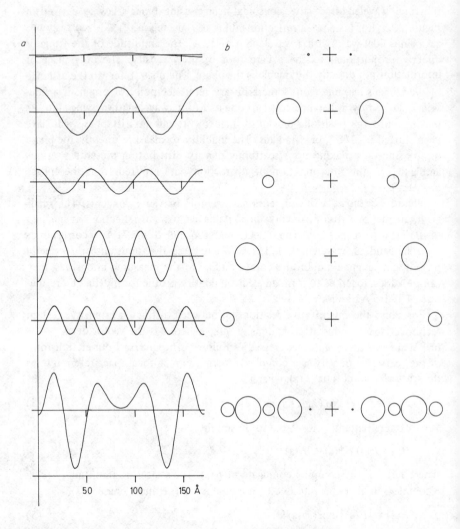

Figure 2.3 Construction of a low-resolution electron density profile of myelin. The top five drawings of *b* show the relative positions of the first five reflections in diffraction from native myelin, with their relative intensities indicated by the diameter of the circles. The graphs, *a*, are of the sinusoidal fringes corresponding to the five reflections. Each reflection has been assigned a phase of 0 or π radians. No other phase choices are possible as the myelin membrane pair is centrosymmetric. Those fringes that have been assigned a phase of 0 have a maximum at the origin. Those with a phase of π have a minimum at the origin. The sum of the five sinusoidal fringes is the low resolution myelin electron density profile shown in the lowermost plot. Data and phases used in constructing this plot are from Kirschner (1971)

In electron microscopy the phase problem is solved by using a lens to recombine the diffracted beams into an image. The lens is, in essence, performing a Fourier transform. The phase information is not lost because it is contained in the relative arrival times of the diffracted waves. Only when the intensity is measured — which requires averaging over time — is the phase information lost. As conventional lenses cannot be constructed for use with X rays we are obliged to measure the scattered intensities and use indirect means for obtaining phases.

Convolution

Although the preceding concepts and formulae are general, they provide little insight into the form that diffraction from membranes might actually take. It is often difficult to think about diffraction by complex objects in terms of the decomposition of the scattering density into a set of sinusoidal fringes. The concept of convolution provides a powerful way of dealing with problems of this kind.

Convolution is best introduced by an example. Figure 2.4*a* demonstrates the convolution of the letter 'C' with a two-dimensional lattice of points. The result is a two-dimensional array of the letter 'C'. The operation can be defined

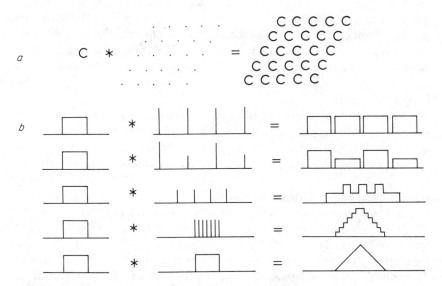

Figure 5.4 Convolution. *a*, The convolution of an array of points with the letter 'C'; *b* demonstrates several one-dimensional convolutions. In these graphs, a spike is used to represent a singular point or δ function. A convolution of a box function with an array of δ functions is an array of boxes. The box function is multiplied by the amplitude of the δ function in the convolution. If the δ functions are too close together, the images of the box functions will overlap in the convolution. This allows the convolution of two continuous functions to be approximated by the convolution of a continuous function and a series of closely spaced δ functions. For instance, the convolution of a box function with a set of closely spaced δ functions is a triangular-shaped function. The convolution of a box function with a box function is a triangle function

as taking the origin of one function (the letter 'C') and placing it at each non-zero point of the second function (the lattice). Each time the first function is placed at a point of the second function, it is multiplied by the value of the second function at that point. The results of all such simple operations are summed to give the result of the convolution operation. In mathematical terms, the convolution of $f(u)$ and $g(u)$ can be expressed as

$$f(u)*g(u) = [f*g](u) = \int f(u-r)g(r)\mathrm{d}r \tag{7}$$

where $*$ denotes the covolution operation.

Figure 2.4*b* gives several one-dimensional examples of convolution. A box function convoluted with a lattice produces a lattice of box functions. If the distance between lattice points is smaller than the box, then the images of the box overlap in the convolution. If the points (or δ functions) are very close together they approximate a continuous function and it is sometimes useful to visualise the convolution of two continuous functions as the convolution of a continuous function with a set of closely spaced, weighted δ functions.

The usefulness of this operation is wholly dependent on the convolution theorem, which states: the Fourier transform of the convolution of two functions is equal to the product of their Fourier transforms and, conversely, the Fourier transform of the product of two functions is equal to the convolution of their Fourier transforms. In other words, a convolution in real space corresponds to a multiplication in reciprocal space. The treatment of both reciprocal lattices and disorder in the following sections are based on this theorem.

Reciprocal lattices

The Fourier transform of an infinite, perfect lattice of geometric points in real space is an infinite perfect lattice of points in reciprocal space. Reciprocal lattices are the Fourier transforms of real space lattices. They exhibit the same symmetry as the real space lattice and have lattice constants that are inversely proportional to those of the real space lattice. In one dimension there is only a single kind of regular lattice — an equally spaced set of points. An infinite, one-dimensional lattice of points with a lattice constant d has, as its one-dimensional Fourier transform, an infinite lattice with a lattice constant of $1/d$. This is its reciprocal lattice. By the convolution theorem, a one-dimensional lattice of identical objects will have, as its Fourier transform, the product of the one-dimensional reciprocal lattice with the Fourier transform of the object. It will be non-zero only at the reciprocal lattice points. At those points it will be proportional to the Fourier transform of the object.

In two dimensions there are five types of reciprocal lattice — oblique, rectangular, centred rectangular, square and hexagonal. These lattices are shown, along with their reciprocal lattices, in Figure 2.5. A two-dimensional array of molecules will have specific symmetry elements defining the geometric relationships among the molecules in the lattice. These will include not only the translational elements of the lattice but also rotational axes perpendicular

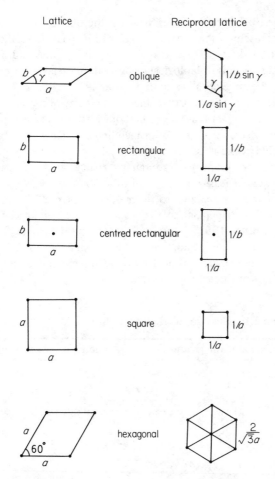

Figure 2.5 Two-dimensional lattices and their reciprocal lattices. The lattices on the left represent the five possible two-dimensional lattices. The corresponding reciprocal lattices are on the right

to the lattice plane and two-fold rotational or screw axes in the plane of the lattice. The sets of possible symmetry elements for membrane specimens are those of the two-sided plane groups (Holser, 1958) described in the next section.

Symmetry

The symmetry of a crystal is the first absolutely essential piece of information that must be obtained in a structural study. Not only does it provide information about the packing and molecular interactions in the crystal, it is also necessary for the interpretation of any structural data. The symmetry of a three-dimensional crystal of a protein or naturally occurring membrane lipid must be described by one of the 65 enantiomorphic space groups; in other words, by one of the space groups in which the only symmetry operations are rotation and translation (International Tables for X-ray Crystallography, 1969; Eisenberg and Crothers, 1979). Mirror planes, glide planes and inversion points cannot occur in crystals of biological macromolecules having asymmetric carbon atoms all with the same absolute configuration.

The possible symmetries of a two-dimensional array of molecules are described by the plane groups. Since, as will be described below, reconstituted membranes may include molecules that face both membrane surfaces, their symmetry may include two-fold rotation or screw axes parallel to the membrane surface. The symmetry of a membrane pair containing lattices in both membranes must necessarily include at least one two-fold rotation or screw axis halfway between the two membranes and parallel to the membrane planes. The plane groups that include two-fold axes parallel to the plane are referred to as the 'two-sided' plane groups (Holser, 1958) of which 17 are enantiomorphic. The 17 enantiomorphic two-sided plane groups are listed in Table 2.1 using the notation of Holser (1958). All two-dimensional arrays of membrane components must be arranged with one of these 17 symmetries.

Table 2.1   The two-sided plane groups

Two-sided plane group	Symmetry of the projection
p1	p1
p21	p2
p12	pm
$p12_1$	pg
c12	cm
p222	pmm
$p222_1$	pmg
$p22_12_1$	pgg
c222	cmm
p4	p4
p422	p4m
$p42_12$	p4g
p3	p3
p312	p3m1
p321	p31m
p6	p6
p622	p6m

There are 80 two-sided plane groups in all, of which 17 contain only rotation, translation or screw-axis symmetry elements. All the others contain inversion centres or mirror or glide planes not allowed in arrays of biological molecules containing asymmetric carbon atoms.

Cell type is indicated by a small letter p or c (primitive or centred). The axis perpendicular to the plane is always chosen as the z axis and symmetry along this axis is described by the first symbol following the cell type (after Holser, 1958)

Electron micrographs of membranes taken with the plane of the membrane perpendicular to the incident electron beam are, to a close approximation, two-dimensional projections of the membrane structure. In these projections, two-fold axes parallel to the membrane plane become mirror lines and two-fold screw axes parallel to the membrane become glide lines. Thus, electron micrographs of membrane lattices can take on the symmetry of any one of the 17 two-dimensional plane groups. The symmetry of the electron micrograph uniquely indicates the symmetry of the membrane structure. If there are mirror-reflection lines in the electron micrograph, they indicate that there are two-fold axes in the membrane plane that are parallel to the observed mirror lines. Glide-reflection lines in the micrograph indicate the presence of two-fold screw axes parallel to the glide lines in the membrane plane. If there are no mirror or glide lines in the electron micrograph, then the symmetry of the membrane array is the same as that of the micrograph. Some care must be taken in the use of electron micrographs for the determination of symmetry as it is possible that some symmetry elements of an array will become apparent only at relatively high resolution.

Fourier transforms of membrane specimens

The previous sections considered two-dimensional reciprocal lattices. However, to obtain the three-dimensional structure of a membrane, it is necessary to consider what the form of diffraction from a membrane will be in three dimensions. Since most membrane specimens do not form three-dimensional crystals, their Fourier transforms are not necessarily limited to discrete sets of points in reciprocal space.

Many X-ray diffraction studies are carried out on membranes which do not have an ordered two-dimensional lattice. The Fourier transform of a structure of this kind is concentrated along, although not restricted to, a single line in reciprocal space in the direction corresponding to that perpendicular to the membrane plane. This line is referred to as the meridian. The amplitudes on the meridian correspond to the Fourier transform of the average scattering density in the direction perpendicular to the membrane plane. This scattering density distribution or density profile is, strictly, the projection of the scattering density in the specimen onto the line perpendicular to the membrane plane. When the membranes in the specimen scatter independently (that is, when they are not stacked in an ordered fashion) the intensities can be measured as a continuous distribution along the meridian, as illustrated in Figure 2.6a. When the membranes in the specimen are stacked into a lamellar lattice with a lattice constant d, the meridional intensity is 'sampled' at the reciprocal lattice points falling at intervals of $1/d$ along the meridian. That is, observable intensity occurs only at the positions of the reciprocal lattice points. The scattering amplitudes at these Bragg reflections are referred to as structure factors. The Fourier transform of the amplitudes at these Bragg reflections is the scattering density profile averaged over all the 'unit cells' or repeating units of the lamellar lattice. Membranes lacking order in their plane cannot generally be used to determine the three-

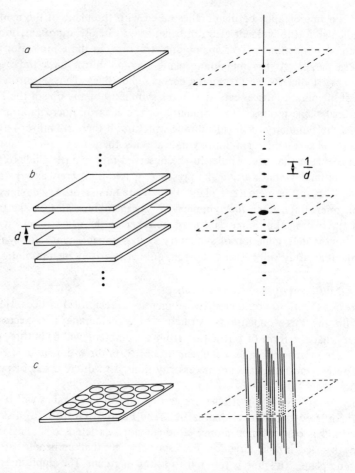

Figure 2.6 Fourier transforms of membrane specimens. *a*, The Fourier transform of a membrane with no order in the membrane plane will be confined to a single line in reciprocal space perpendicular to the membrane and referred to as the meridian. *b*, A stack of membranes without surface lattices will also show diffraction only on the meridian. However, because of the membrane stacking, diffraction will be limited to the Bragg reflections spaced at intervals reciprocal to the real space lattice constant. *c*, The Fourier transform of a two-dimensional lattice is the set of lattice lines perpendicular to the lattice and located at the positions of the reciprocal lattice points of the two-dimensional lattice

dimensional structure of any structural units within the membrane. X-ray diffraction patterns from these membranes exhibit strong diffraction only along the meridian. Intensity in the remainder of the diffraction pattern is weak and diffuse and not amenable to detailed analysis. The situation is very different in diffraction from membranes containing well ordered two-dimensional lattices.

The Fourier transform of a two-dimensional lattice is made up of a set of lattice lines parallel to and including the meridian as shown in Figure 2.6*c*.

Because of the limited spatial extent of a membrane perpendicular to its plane, the Fourier transform along each lattice line is continuous. The lattice lines are arranged on the two-dimensional reciprocal lattice of the membrane lattice. Once the amplitudes along all lattice lines are known, they can be combined in a Fourier synthesis to construct a three-dimensional image of the repeating unit of the membrane array. Much effort has been expended in both X-ray diffraction and electron microscope experiments to measure the scattering amplitudes along these lattice lines.

Disorder

Any physical process that results in differences in structure among scattering units or among unit cells in a lattice can be included under the heading of disorder. Thus disorder can be static or dynamic (for example, thermal). It can involve differences in the structure of single molecules or just differences in the spacings between molecules in a lattice. It can be caused by thermal motion, contamination, polymorphism in the structure, damage to some of the scattering units or intrinsic weakness in the forces binding together a structure. Disorder in membrane specimens reduces the amount of information that can be extracted from structural studies by limiting the resolution of observable intensities and by rendering ambiguous the interpretation of measurable intensities. Disorder can take on many forms, each of which will exhibit itself somewhat differently in the diffraction data. However, a simple discussion of disorder in one dimension should serve as a basis for thinking about more complex forms.

A perfectly ordered crystal structure can be decomposed into a set of sinusoidal fringes with wavelengths that are integral fractions of the unit cell size. In one dimension, a structure arranged on a lattice with a lattice constant d can be decomposed into sinusoids with wavelengths of d/n, where n is any integer, as demonstrated for myelin in Figure 2.3. Each sinusoid corresponds to a pair of reflections falling on the crystal reciprocal lattice. When disorder of any kind is introduced into the lattice two linked phenomena occur: sinusoids with wavelengths other than those with the lattice periodicity become necessary in the decomposition of the crystal structure; and the sinusoidal fringes with wavelengths corresponding to the crystal periodicity decrease in amplitude. In reciprocal space this corresponds to the appearance of intensity between the Bragg lattice reflections and a decrease in the intensity of the Bragg reflections. The effect of disorder is greater on high resolution reflections than it is on low resolution reflections. This is intuitively reasonable as a small degree of disorder should not affect a low resolution image of an object.

In lattices where there is short-range disorder but long-range order (that is, where in spite of variation in the distances between adjacent scattering units the lattice repeat is preserved over many unit cells) the Bragg reflections remain sharp with a width corresponding to the reciprocal of the distance over which the lattice repeat is maintained. Many two- and three-dimensional arrays exhibit long-range order. One-dimensional arrays often do not and the loss of long-range order causes a dramatic increase in the width of the Bragg reflections. In highly disordered lamellar arrays such as those found in retinal rod outer segments or chloroplasts the 'incoherent' scattering due to differences among the unit cells can become comparable in intensity to the 'coherent' intensity corresponding to the average unit cell structure. Furthermore, the Bragg reflections may become sufficiently broad to make an estimation of their intensity difficult.

A useful model for disorder can be constructed by replacing every point scatterer in an object by a gaussian with a half-width determined by the degree of disorder; the greater the disorder, the greater the half-width of the gaussian. The image constructed by such an operation might be thought of as a time-averaged image of the disordered molecule. The gaussians represent the probability of a given scattering point being some distance from its average position in the structure. The replacement of each point by a gaussian is equivalent to the convolution of the object by a gaussian, and its diffraction pattern can be predicted by the convolution theorem. The Fourier transform of a gaussian in real space is a gaussian in reciprocal space having a half-width inversely proportional to the half-width of the first gaussian. By the convolution theorem, the Fourier transform of the disordered object is equal to the Fourier transform of the ideally ordered object multiplied by the gaussian in reciprocal space. As gaussian has its maximum at the origin and decreases monotonically with increasing distance from the origin, multiplication by the gaussian will lessen the amplitude of the higher-order terms relative to the lower-order terms. Thus, disorder results in the weakening of diffraction at high angles.

In high resolution crystallographic studies, each atom in a molecule is replaced by a gaussian of different half-width, as determined by model building. The width is often reported in terms of a 'temperature-factor' or thermal parameter. Differences in the thermal parameters of different atoms allow a measure of the relative disorder in different parts of a molecule to be made. These factors have been derived, for instance, in the crystallographic analyses of lipid crystals and allow the regions of greater or lesser disorder to be identified in these molecular crystals.

In the analysis of diffraction from the disordered crystal, the Fourier transform of the observed amplitudes at the Bragg reflections produces an image of the unit cell that corresponds to the average image of the contents of all the unit cells. If identical scattering units are disordered so that they fall at slightly different places in each unit cell, this average image will be blurred. This blurring results in a loss of detail analogous to that produced by the convolution of a structure with a gaussian. When the structures of the scattering units in each unit cell are slightly different, for instance in electron micrographs of negatively stained crystalline arrays, the filtering of intensity between the Bragg reflections results in an averaging of all the microheterogeneities of structure in the array.

X-ray diffraction

X-ray apparatus

X-ray diffraction experiments require an intense, collimated, monochromatic beam of radiation directed at a specimen and a means to detect the X-ray scattering from the specimen. X rays are produced either by the bombardment of a metal target (usually copper) by electrons using an accelerating voltage of 30–50 kV or, occasionally, by a synchrotron source. The most common source of X rays is the K_α line of copper (CuK_α) with a wavelength of 1.54 Å. A point or line source of X rays is defined and collimated by one of a variety of possible schemes using either pinholes or slits. A point-focus camera is essential when diffraction in more than one dimension is of interest, but a line focus allows the use of greater intensity when only one-dimensional information is to be obtained. Monochromation is achieved by a crystal monochromator or absorption filters. The X ray beam can be focused by using a bent crystal monochromator or bent mirrors. X rays will reflect from mirrors (glass optical flats usually coated with nickel) when they are incident at grazing angles below the critical angle for total external reflection (about 14 minutes of arc). Optimisation of camera parameters for small-angle scattering has been discussed previously (for example, Huxley and Brown, 1967; Harrison, 1969; Witz, 1969).

Because X rays do not scatter too strongly in air, some of the radiation path can be in air. However, background scattering is reduced if most of the radiation path is within a vacuum or helium chamber. The direct beam is absorbed, after it passes through the specimen, by a small lead beam stop. This avoids fogging of the film by secondary scattering or damage to the detector.

The optimum size of a biological sample for X-ray diffraction is about 0.5–1.0 mm thick. A smaller sample will give rise to weaker scattering while a larger sample will absorb too much of the scattered radiation. Membrane samples can be kept hydrated by placing them in thin-walled glass or quartz capillaries or in a thin specimen chamber with plastic or berylium windows.

X rays are detected either by film or a position-sensitive detector. For membrane systems which diffract in more than one dimension, film has the advantage of being able to record all detectable diffraction in a single exposure. The disadvantages of film include a fairly high background level and a limited dynamic range. The most intense reflections in a diffraction pattern from a membrane may be several orders of magnitude stronger than the weakest reflections. The only way that reflections with such dramatically different intensities can be simultaneously recorded with film is to stack three to six films, one behind the other, in a film pack. Each film absorbs about 70 per cent of the radiation incident on it and the subsequent films can then record stronger reflections without overexposure. Data on the films must then be densitometered and scaled to one another.

One-dimensional data is often recorded using a one-dimensional position-sensitive detector. These detectors can lower the time required to collect data by more than an order of magnitude compared to film. They also have an essentially unlimited dynamic range (although counting rates are limited) and a very low background level. The major drawbacks of position-sensitive detectors are that they have a lower point-to-point resolution than film and that they create some problems for the storage of large quantities of raw data. Film is a good, though not ideal, data storage medium. Two-dimensional detectors also exist but are expensive and not widely used.

Intensities measured by any method must be corrected for several geometric factors, such as disorientation in the specimen, the Lorentz factor which involves a calculation of how much of the intensity in reciprocal space is intersected by the Ewald sphere, and polarisation.

X-ray specimens

Specimen preparation for diffraction experiments is one of the most important aspects of the experiment. It is obviously crucial to maintain the structural integrity of the molecular system of interest and to minimise heterogeneities or contamination. But other properties of the specimen — in particular, its degree of orientation and order — are also important. Unfortunately, few generalisations can be made about specimen preparation as the details vary greatly among different membrane systems.

There are four basic kinds of specimens defined by their degree of order and orientation. The simplest membrane specimen is a solution or dispersion of membrane sheets or vesicles with no orientation relative to the X-ray beam. These specimens give rise to circularly symmetric diffraction patterns. If there is order in the membrane plane, diffraction from those features will be superimposed on the meridional diffraction and the measured intensity will represent a spherical average of the intensity distribution in reciprocal space. Figure 2.7a is a diffraction pattern from a disoriented pellet of bacteriophage $\phi6$, a lipid-containing virus. The lipid in the virus forms a bilayer enveloping the capsid. The spacing of the rings in the diffraction pattern correspond to the reciprocal of the diameter of the viral envelope, about 660 Å.

The second type of specimen is an orientated lamellar stack of membranes with no order in the membrane plane. When the X-ray beam is incident parallel to the membrane surfaces, the meridional diffraction corresponding to the membrane profile is observed in a direction perpendicular to the membrane planes. This is by far the most common type of specimen for structural studies by X-ray diffraction. The lamellar stack may be a highly ordered, one-dimensional array or it may exhibit almost no spatial order in the stacking of the membranes. Figure 2.7b is a diffraction pattern from an orientated sample of thylakoids in which there is only partial stacking of the orientated membranes.

The third type of membrane specimen is an orientated lamellar stack of membranes that contain two-dimensional lattices. Diffracted intensities can be measured along lattice lines in diffraction from these specimens so that, in principle, three-dimensional information can be obtained. These specimens differ

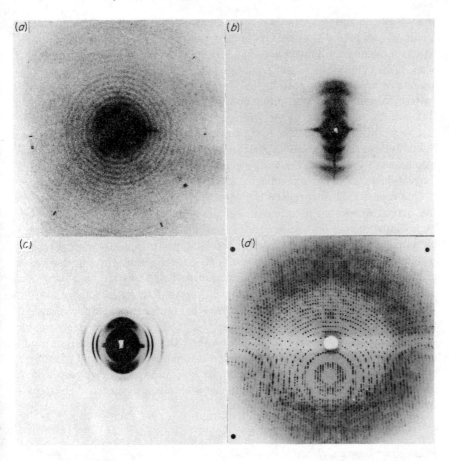

Figure 2.7 X-ray diffraction patterns from membranes. *a*, Diffraction pattern from the lipid-containing bacteriophage $\phi6$. The rings are spaced at intervals of 1/660 Å^{-1}, corresponding to the diameter of the viral envelope. The maximum radius of $\phi6$ is about 380 Å (Makowski and Mindich, unpublished data). *b*, Diffraction pattern of lamellar arrays of thylakoids from the grana fraction of *Heleconia harrisii*. The strong second-order reflection is due to the close appression of the outer surface of thylakoids in the presence of Mg^{2+} ions (Li, 1978). *c*, Diffraction pattern from an orientated pellet of gap junctions. The strong reflections above and below the beam stop are from the continuous diffraction along the meridian. The sharp reflections to the right and left of the centre of the diffraction pattern are equatorial reflections that index on a hexagonal lattice with lattice constant of 82 Å (Makowski, Caspar, Goodenough and Phillips, unpublished data). *d*, Diffraction pattern from a crystal of the photosynthetic reaction centre from *Rhodopseudomonas viridis* (Michel, 1982). The reaction centres are arranged in a tetragonal crystal lattice with dimensions of 223 Å × 223 Å × 114 Å. The asymmetric unit probably contains two copies of the reaction centre complex (from Michel, 1982)

from three-dimensional crystals in that each membrane may be randomly rotated about an axis perpendicular to its surface. Because of this, the measured intensities represent a cylindrical average of the intensity distribution in reciprocal space. This cylindrical averaging will cause the lattice lines at the same reciprocal spacing to superimpose, possibly limiting the attainable resolution. A diffraction pattern from an orientated pellet of gap junctions is shown in Figure 2.7c. In this pattern, in addition to the strong meridional diffraction, sharp reflections can be seen along the equator (the plane perpendicular to the meridian) due to the two-dimensional hexagonal lattice of morphological units in the gap-junction membranes. Above and below the equatorial reflections there are very weak diffraction maxima corresponding to subsidiary maxima along the lattice lines.

The fourth kind of specimen is a crystal. By taking diffraction patterns with the crystal orientated in different ways relative to the X-ray beam, a three-dimensional set of intensities can be collected. Analysis of these diffraction patterns is the only proven method for obtaining electron density maps of macromolecules at atomic resolution. However, only a few membrane proteins have been crystallised. Figure 2.7d shows a diffraction pattern from a three-dimensional crystal of the photosynthetic reaction centre from *Rhodopseudomonas viridis*. This is a rotation photograph, which means that during the exposure the crystal was rotated slowly through, in this case, 1° of arc around a crystallographic axis. This causes a sweeping of the Ewald sphere through reciprocal space resulting in the recording of many more reflections than would appear if the crystal were stationary. The number of reflections is indicative of the vast amount of structural information that can be obtained when three-dimensional crystals are obtained.

Phasing meridional diffraction

The phasing of meridional diffraction data from membranes is a special topic with problems distinct from those associated with the interpretation of any other types of diffraction data. Isomorphous replacement, the principal method used for phasing data from protein crystals (Blundell and Johnson, 1976) has seldom been used successfully on a membrane system (see, however, Franks *et al.*, 1978). This may be because it is difficult to prepare isomorphous membrane derivatives with specifically bound heavy atoms. Furthermore, specimens with very different degrees of disorder in the lamellar stacking of membranes may require different methods of data analysis. A diffraction pattern from a membrane system may consist of only a dozen reflections or less. Nevertheless, long controversies about the phasing of membrane diffraction data have littered the journals with conflicting membrane profiles. We believe that the issues involved in these controversies are now largely resolved.

Two main facts greatly simplify the phasing of meridional diffraction from membranes. The first is that many membranes are centrosymmetric in meridional projection or occur in centrosymmetric pairs. This makes the phasing of intensities much simpler as it restricts the meridional scattering amplitude to being a real function; the phase problem, which normally requires the determination of a phase between 0 and 2π radians is reduced to a sign choice; $F(x) = \pm |F(x)|$ (or equivalently, to phase choice restricted to be either 0 or π radians). The second fact is that the electron density profiles of many lipid bilayers are now well established. The lipid bilayer portion of a membrane is responsible for a considerable fraction of the meridional intensity in diffraction patterns from most membranes because of the great contrast between the high electron density of the lipid polar head groups and the low electron density of the hydrocarbon chains. All membrane electron density profiles are likely to contain some features corresponding to the lipid bilayer portion of the structure. If the calculated electron density profile of a membrane is inconsistent with what is known about lipid bilayers, it must be treated with suspicion.

We present here only a brief discussion of the issues and methods that have been used to phase meridional scattering from centrosymmetric membranes or membrane pairs. For a more thorough treatment of these problems, see Franks and Levine (1981). For a discussion of the phasing of diffraction from non-centrosymmetric membranes see Stroud and Agard (1979) and Makowski (1981).

For a membrane or membrane pair that is centrosymmetric in meridional projection (that is, $\rho(x) = \rho(-x)$) the phase problem is reduced to a sign problem. We consider two cases: a completely disordered membrane specimen from which diffracted intensity can be measured continuously at all points along the meridian; and a completely ordered lamellar array from which diffracted intensity can only be measured at the crystal lattice positions.

In the special case where a continuous intensity distribution, $I(S)$, can be measured at all points, S, out to some resolution limit along the meridian, the diffraction data can, in principle, be use to determine uniquely the phases if the scattering object is centrosymmetric (Hosemann and Bagchi, 1962). Because the scattering amplitude is a real function, its phases can change only at the zeros of intensity. If all the zeros of a continuous intensity distribution from a centrosymmetric structure can be observed, then phasing amounts to distinguishing whether or not the phase changes at each zero. In many cases this can be done without ambiguity. Bragg and Perutz (1952) have demonstrated that, in centrosymmetric projections, peaks of intensity must be of opposite sign if they are closer than $(2/d)\text{Å}^{-1}$, where d is the spatial extent of the structure. This criterion will resolve most phasing ambiguities where continuous intensity is recorded. Extended regions of low intensity will often make the phasing more difficult or produce ambiguities that can only be resolved by additional data (for example, Dupont, Harrison and Hasselbach, 1973; Franks, 1976; Makowski *et al.*, 1977) or by constraints based on structural analogies (Caspar and Kirschner, 1971) or by non-diffraction data.

For the case of a very highly ordered one-dimensional array of membranes, diffraction will only be observed at the Bragg reflections. Because the intensity will be negligible in the region between the crystal reflections, the positions

of the zeros of the continuous intensity distribution will not be directly observable. This problem can be overcome if the positions of the Bragg reflections can
be varied by changing the lattice constant of the diffracting array without changing the structure of the scattering units. This can often be accomplished by
varying the activity of water to alter the width of the aqueous layers between
the membranes of the array. The intensities of a Bragg reflection are proportional
to the intensity from a single scattering unit at the position of the reflection.
Changes in the positions of the reflections will result in changes in their intensities as the Fourier transform of the scattering unit varies with position in
reciprocal space. By collecting diffraction data from lattices containing the same
scattering units but with different lattice constants (different distances between
the scattering units) it is possible to map out the continuous intensity distribution of a single scattering unit (Bragg and Perutz, 1952; Finean and Burge, 1963).
The intensity distribution mapped out in this way is proportional to the square
of the Fourier transform of a single unit cell.

Figure 2.8 shows a set of intensities observed at different swelling stages of
a lamellar array of lecithin:cholesterol bilayers (Franks, 1976). The spacing
between adjacent bilayers varied from 52.5 to 58.9 Å as the relative humidity
was varied. This allowed a continuous intensity distribution to be mapped out
and, although there are gaps in the data, the positions of most zeros of the
intensity are clear. At high resolution, a single phase ambiguity remained due

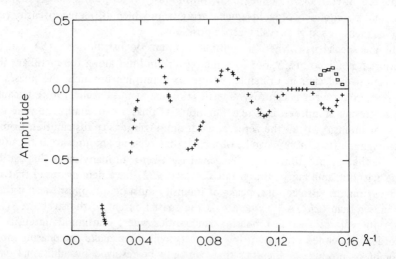

Figure 2.8 Amplitudes with assigned phases for Bragg reflections from a swelling series of
lamellar arrays of a mixture of egg lecithin and 40 per cent (molar) cholesterol in water. The
amplitudes from the crystalline arrays with different lattice constants fall at different points
in reciprocal space and consequently map out the Fourier transform of a single bilayer. The
amplitudes can be unambiguously phased out to 0.13 A^{-1}. Beyond that, the data are
consistent with two possible phase choices. However, the phase choice marked by squares
is not consistent with the expected behaviour of lipid bilayers at different relative humidities
as discussed in the text (from Franks, 1976)

to an extended region of very low intensity. The phase ambiguity was resolved by calculating the electron density profiles for the two possible phase choices and comparing profiles calculated from intensities collected when the specimen was at different relative humidities. Comparisons using the phase choice marked by squares in Figure 2.8 indicated that, if this phase choice was correct, the bilayer structure must be changing as a function of relative humidity. For the phase choice marked by crosses, the only apparent change in bilayer structure as relative humidity increased was a slight increase in disorder. As increase of disorder with increasing humidity has been observed in other bilayers (for instance, see Figure 2.15), these comparisons strongly suggest that the correct phase choice is the one marked by crosses in Figure 2.8.

When membrane pairs are being studied, there may be additional problems in the application of the swelling method. There are two distinct aqueous regions in a lamellar stack of membrane pairs: the region between the pairs and the region between the membranes of a single pair. The swelling method requires that the structure of the scattering unit (in this case a membrane pair) remain approximately constant as the lattice constant changes. If the thicknesses of both aqueous regions change as a function of relative humidity, this criterion is not fulfilled and the method will fail. In studies of sarcoplasmic reticulum membrane vesicles, Dupont, Harrison and Hasselbach (1973) discovered that at relatively low humidities one of the intermembrane spaces was changing thickness and at higher humidities, the other aqueous region was changing thickness. This observation allowed the swelling data to be broken into two sets, each of which could be used independently to solve for the phases.

A more serious problem occurs when swelling of membrane pairs disorders the entire array (for example, Worthington and McIntosh, 1974). In this case, misinterpretation of the data in terms of membrane pairs rather than single membranes can lead to serious errors in the derived electron density profiles (Blaurock, 1976).

Analysis of diffraction from partially ordered lamellar arrays of membranes has been pursued by a number of groups because a large number of membrane arrays are only partially ordered. Several different approaches have been taken (Schwartz *et al.*, 1975; Blaurock and Nelander, 1976; Makowski *et al.*, 1977; Li, 1978; Nelander and Blaurock, 1978). The choice of approach depends on the degree and nature of the disorder. The results of these analyses can include not only an electron density profile for the membrane but a measure of the variability in the spacings between membranes and, in the case of membrane pairs, the variability in the thicknesses of both aqueous regions.

Secondary structure
X-ray diffraction can be used to estimate the proportion of the membrane proteins in an α-helical or β-sheet conformation, and to indicate the average orientation of these structures relative to the membrane plane. Information

about the conformation and packing of the lipid hydrocarbon chains can also be obtained.

α Helices are regular helical structures with a packing diameter of about 10 Å, a pitch of 5.4 Å and an axial spacing between amino acid residues of about 1.5 Å. The axial repeat of α helices arranged in a coiled-coil configuration may be as low as 5.1 Å (Crick, 1953). Because of these spatial periodicities, diffraction from α helices is very strong at 10 Å spacing in the direction perpendicular to their axes, at 5.1 to 5.4 Å spacing in the direction parallel to their axes, and at 1.5 Å spacing also in the direction parallel to the α-helical axes. The 1.5 Å reflection is relatively difficult to observe and diffraction at 10 Å also arises from β sheets. However, intense diffraction at 5.1 to 5.4 Å is a strong diagnostic for α helices. Observation of diffraction of X rays at 5.1 Å spacing near the meridian and at 10 Å near the equator was the first indication that bacteriorhodopsin contained a high proportion of α helices orientated approximately perpendicular to the membrane plane (Henderson, 1975).

β Sheets give rise to strong scattering at 10 Å spacing. This scattering arises from the stacking of the sheets about 10 Å apart. β Sheets also scatter strongly at 4.7 Å spacing, corresponding to the distance between peptide chains in a single sheet. The observation of diffraction at 4.7 Å spacing near the equator in diffraction from a membrane system cannot be taken as an unambiguous indicator of β-sheet structure as lipids in the liquid crystalline phase exhibit strong diffraction at about 4.7 Å spacing in the equatorial direction (the direction parallel to the membrane plane). In diffraction patterns from gap junctions (Makowski *et al.*, 1982) strong diffraction at 4.7 Å spacing was observed near the meridian along with intense scatter at 10 Å spacing on the equator. As the 4.7 Å scatter on the meridian is unlikely to be due to lipids, these observations suggest the presence of β-sheet structure in the gap junctions with the peptide chains running parallel to the membrane surface and the sheets lying perpendicular to the membrane plane.

Electron microscopy

Electron microscopes

Electron microscopes typically use electrons accelerated by 80,000 volts for imaging. Electrons of this energy have a wavelength of about 0.04 Å. This wavelength is small enough to resolve the minutest details of biological structure. The resolution of an electron microscope is limited, however, not by the wavelength of the electrons, but by the quality of electron lenses which are, by optical standards, relatively poor. This problem is overcome by the use of small apertures to maintain high image quality. The resolution limit of a contemporary high resolution electron microscope is of the order of 1 Å.

The major problem in the use of electrons for imaging of biological structures is that they interact very strongly with matter. In air, electrons scatter and are absorbed such that, in an electron microscope, the entire electron path, including specimen, must be kept in a vacuum. Although purple membrane seems able to maintain its structure at very low relative humidities with only a slight decrease in lattice constant (Henderson, 1975; Rogan and Zaccai, 1981) and increase in disorder (Blaurock 1975), most biological samples are not particularly happy about being placed in a vacuum and some means of structural preservation is necessary. Furthermore, electrons are ionising particles and at electron doses commonly used for imaging (> 10 e/Å^2), they will completely decompose a protein. This makes the imaging of biological macromolecules using electrons somewhat difficult.

Usually a biological structure is used as a template for the deposition or binding of a heavy metal stain or for the casting of a carbon and heavy metal replica by shadowing. Most electron micrographs are actually images of the deposited stain. The recent analysis of bacteriorhodopsin structure using unstained specimens (Unwin and Henderson, 1975; Henderson and Unwin, 1975) is one of the few exceptions. The successful application of that technique to other membrane structures will depend on the development of methods to produce very large, well-ordered, two-dimensional crystals of molecules that are stable when embedded in glucose or some other involatile fluid and placed in a vacuum. One technique that shows some promise is the use of frozen specimens which are maintained at liquid nitrogen (or in some cases liquid helium) temperatures during imaging (for example, Taylor and Glaeser, 1976; Hui, 1977; Hayward and Glaeser, 1980). Ice crystals do not form in rapidly frozen specimens and amorphous ice seems to sublime very slowly from a specimen kept at low temperatures. Furthermore, specimen damage is very much reduced at low temperatures.

Negative stain

Most of the electron microscope results reviewed here were obtained using negatively-stained specimens. One of the most common ways of preparing a negatively-stained specimen (for example, Huxley and Zubay, 1960) is as follows. A drop of dilute specimen solution is applied to the support film on the grid and the excess specimen not attached to the grid is washed off. A few drops of stain (usually a dilute solution of a heavy metal salt such as uranyl acetate or phosphotungstate) are applied and excess stain is removed by blotting with filter paper. A great number of variations on this technique have been used. The goal of these techniques is to induce the stain to form the tightest possible coating around the structure while causing the least structural distortion.

Electron micrographs of negatively-stained specimens usually indicate only the distribution of the stain coating the specimen and contain no features originating from the biological molecules themselves. A structure is visualised as a characteristic distribution of stain. Stain excluding features on the two sides of a membrane are superimposed in an electron micrograph and from the micrograph it is impossible to determine the level in the membrane from which each feature originates. The faithfulness of the image of the structure obtained in this way depends on the extent to which structural integrity has been maintained during preparation and drying and the degree of crystallinity of the stain.

The amount of distortion caused by drying the specimen down on the grid and placing in a vacuum seems to vary depending on the structure. Comparison of images of tomato bushy stunt virus calculated from X-ray diffraction of single crystals and electron microscopy of negatively-stained particles showed that the two methods resulted in similar images of the virus particles at 28 Å resolution. The major differences in the two images were due to variable penetration of stain around some of the external features of the particles and positive staining of portions of the RNA (Harrison and Jack, 1975; Jack, Harrison and Crowther, 1975). The structure of immunoglobulin G Dob in negatively-stained microcrystals at 20 Å resolution showed remarkably good correlation to the known structure solved by X-ray crystallography (Steven and Navia, 1980). However, gap junctions (Unwin and Zampighi, 1980) and a number of other structures have been shown to flatten somewhat on the grid, presumably as a result of surface forces during drying.

The amount of detail preserved in negative stain is maximised if the stain remains completely amorphous. Negative stains appear to crystallise when exposed to the electron beam (Zingsheim and Bachmann, 1971) and the resolution limit of the method must be limited by the grain size of the stain crystals. Figure 2.9 includes images of gap junctions taken at two different electron doses. Comparison of these images indicates that the stain around the morphological units in the gap junction lattice undergoes a gross movement in response to irradiation by electrons. By maintaining low electron doses, higher resolution details can be observed in micrographs of negatively-stained specimens (Williams and Fisher, 1970). However, structural details at resolutions of better than about 18 Å are seldom, if ever, observed in micrographs of negatively-stained specimens.

Filtered images

Images produced by an electron microscope are, to a very good approximation, projections of the three-dimensional structures being imaged. This means that features at the top, bottom and through the structure are superimposed by the imaging process. A single micrograph does not, in general, contain sufficient information for the reconstruction of the three-dimensional structure of a membrane. However, a great deal of information is often contained in the projection.

In the preparative, staining and imaging processes, biological macromolecules are exposed to conditions which may cause random alterations in their structure or variations in the distribution of stain surrounding them. If the molecules are in a two-dimensionl lattice, the features introduced by the processes required to obtain an electron micrograph are often different in each unit cell and can be filtered out. The rationale for the filtering process is that any structural features that are common to all members of the array are likely to be biologically relevant

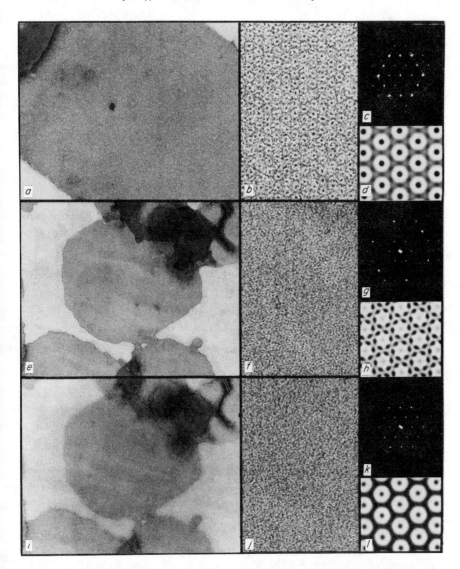

Figure 2.9 Computer filtering of electron micrographs of gap junctions. Top figure is of a micrograph of gap junctions at normal electron doses. The middle figure is a micrograph taken at low dose. The bottom figure is a high dose image of the same gap junction plaque as the middle figure taken after the low dose micrograph is taken. a, e And i are two plaques of isolated gap junctions from mouse liver. b, f And j are enlarged highly ordered portions of these plaques. c, g And k are the computed diffraction patterns of these highly ordered regions. The filtered images of the micrographs (d, h, l) taken at normal and low dose are grossly different, indicating a general redistribution of stain in response to electron irradiation (from Baker et al., 1983)

and any features that vary from unit cell to unit cell in the array are likely to have been induced. When the molecules are in a lattice, the features common to all unit cells will give rise to periodicities in the image. The variations in the structures of the unit cells will not have the periodicity of the lattice. If a Fourier transform of a lattice is calculated, periodic features will contribute to sharp peaks corresponding to Bragg reflections, whereas the non-periodic features will contribute to 'noise' in the regions between the Bragg reflections. This noise can be filtered out by photographic superposition of unit cells in a micrograph (Markham *et al.*, 1964) by optical filtering (Klug and DeRosier, 1966) and by computer processing (DeRosier and Klug, 1968).

Optical filtering is carried out using an optical diffractometer where a laser is used to illuminate an electron micrograph which diffracts the laser light. A series of lenses creates a Fraunhofer diffraction pattern and then recombines the light in the diffraction pattern into an image of the original micrograph. If the micrograph is of an ordered, two-dimensional array, the Fraunhofer diffraction pattern will contain sharp Bragg reflections on the reciprocal lattice of the array. Noise is filtered out by placing a mask at the Fraunhofer diffraction plane of the diffractometer. The mask is an opaque sheet with small holes that allow the passage of intensity falling at the positions of the Bragg reflections. The resulting filtered image is a representation of the average of the unit cells in the array.

A similar process can be accomplished in a computer. A micrograph is densitometered and the array of optical densities transferred to a computer. The Fourier transform of the micrograph is then calculated. This Fourier transform corresponds to the optical diffraction pattern, but in the computer the phases are calculated so that the subsequent inverse Fourier transform can be calculated. The amplitudes at the Bragg reflection points are used to recalculate a filtered or average image of the unit cell of the array. In Figure 2.9 an example of computer filtering is shown. These micrographs of gap junctions demonstrate the great improvement in image features that can be attained by filtering.

Average images can also be obtained by photographic superposition (Markham *et al.*, 1964) and computer superposition of images. With the use of computer superposition it is possible to forego the requirement of a highly ordered lattice to obtain an average image (Frank *et al.*, 1978). Superposition methods that do not use ordered arrays rely on the correspondence of common structural details to align images with one another. The reliability with which micrographs can be aligned depends on the signal-to-noise ratio in the original micrographs. Significant improvement of image quality has been achieved using this technique (for example Zingsheim *et al.*, 1980).

Three-dimensional reconstruction

Computer processing of electron micrographs allows the Fourier transform of any micrograph to be calculated. As shown in Figure 2.10 the Fourier transform of a micrograph corresponds to a central section through the three-dimensional Fourier transform of the object being imaged. By changing the tilt angle of the

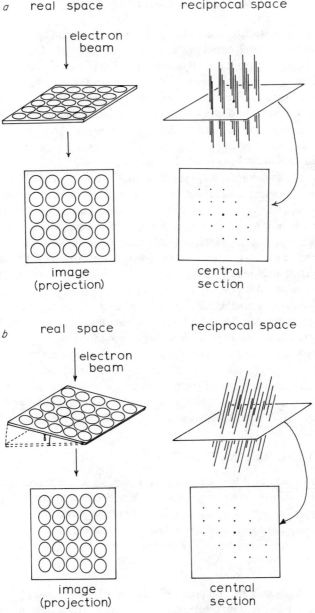

Figure 2.10 The use of a tilting stage for three-dimensional reconstruction. An electron micrograph is (to a close approximation) a two-dimensional projection of the membrane structure. The Fourier transform of a micrograph is a central section of the three-dimensional Fourier transform of the membrane specimen. When the micrograph is taken with the membrane perpendicular to the electron beam (*a*), the corresponding central section is perpendicular to the lattice lines in reciprocal space. When the membrane is tilted relative to the electron beam (*b*), the corresponding central section in reciprocal space is tilted relative to the lattice lines. By taking electron micrographs of the specimen at different tilting angles, the entire three-dimensional Fourier transform of the membrane specimen can be mapped out

specimen in the electron microscope, images corresponding to other central sections of the Fourier transform are obtained. (The Fourier transform of an image is, strictly, a portion of the spherical surface of an Ewald sphere. Because the wavelength of electrons used in electron microscopes is so small compared to resolvable features of biological molecules, the curvature of the Ewald sphere only has to be taken into account in very high resolution studies.) By collecting images of the specimen at many tilt angles an entire three-dimensional set of data in reciprocal space can be obtained. This set of data can be used to calculate a three-dimensional image of the structure by an inverse Fourier transform.

Because tilt angles are usually restricted to between 0° and 60° in an electron microscope, a missing cone of data exists along the meridian out to an angle of about 30° relative to the meridional lattice line. Calculation of density maps from data sets lacking amplitudes within this cone of data will result in elongation of the structural features in a direction perpendicular to the membrane surface. Several methods have been used in attempts to overcome this problem: micrographs of membranes folded over on the grid have been used to estimate meridional amplitudes (Unwin and Zampighi, 1980) and the amplitudes have been extrapolated into the missing cone using density map modification and refinement (Agard and Stroud, 1982). The use of special specimen holders for achieving very large angles of tilt also seems promising, although there are substantial technical problems associated with collecting and processing images of specimens at very high angles of tilt. Since the meridian is the most easily measured part of an X-ray diffraction pattern it may be possible to use X-ray diffraction data, for instance from solvent density change experiments (Harrison and Jack, 1975), to assist in filling in the missing cone.

ASPECTS OF MEMBRANE STRUCTURE

This section is intended to review only those aspects of membrane structure that influence the course of structural studies. Membrane structure has been extensively reviewed and we assume that the properties of most membranes can be described using some variation on the fluid-mosaic model for membrane structure (Singer, 1971; Singer and Nicholson, 1972).

Disorder

Biological membranes are composed principally of proteins and lipids, some of which have covalently bound carbohydrate moieties. The spatial organisation of proteins and lipids in a membrane exhibits some disorder even in most differentiated membranes with homogeneous protein composition. The nature of this disorder profoundly affects structural studies. The disorder of components in the plane of the membrane is very different in form from disorder in the direction perpendicular to the membrane plane. The structural polymorphism and flexibility of lipid molecules is in sharp contrast to the relatively well-defined structures of most membrane proteins; major conformational changes in proteins are likely to correspond to transitions between distinctly different functional states.

Membrane structure is currently thought of in terms of floating (not always freely) membrane proteins in a two-dimensional fluid lipid bilayer (Singer and Nicholson, 1972). In many cases both proteins and lipids are free to diffuse in the membrane plane. During diffusion the components remain orientated relative to the two sides of the membrane. 'Flipping' from one side of the membrane to the other is an unlikely event for a lipid molecule (Rothman and Lenard, 1977; Op den Kamp, 1979) and seldom, if ever, occurs for integral membrane proteins (flipping refers to a change in the polarity of orientation relative to the membrane surfaces as distinct from the translocation of a protein during membrane assembly or secretion). The purpose of many structural studies is to determine the well-defined structure of the proteins that are immersed in the disordered structure of the membrane.

The spatial organisation of membrane components in the membrane plane can take on all possible degrees of order from the essentially complete disorder found in most membranes to the extraordinary crystalline order of the purple membrane. Lipid hydrocarbon chains exhibit two characteristic, temperature-dependent, packing modes: one which is highly ordered and one which is liquid in character. The phase of the lipid molecules can have substantial effect on the distribution of membrane proteins in the membrane plane. Normally, the lipid hydrocarbon chains in a biological membrane are in a fluid, disordered state. The proteins in most membranes are also arranged in a disordered fashion in the membrane plane. However, differentiated regions of some membranes contain specific protein components arranged into a two-dimensional array. In addition, proteins in reconstituted membranes have been induced to form arrays not found *in vivo*. In these arrays, the protein composition of each unit cell is the same. Most of these arrays appear to exhibit a substantial degree of disorder compared to three-dimensional crystals of soluble proteins. X-ray (Henderson, 1975) and electron diffraction (Unwin and Henderson, 1975; Hayward and Stroud, 1981) from purple membrane has been observed out to 3.5 Å spacing but there appears to be an intrinsic disorder in many of the arrays of membrane proteins. The consequence of this is a limitation of the attainable resolution of structural studies on the components in the array.

Disorder of membrane components in the direction perpendicular to the membrane array is probably similar in most membranes, although it may vary in degrees depending on the order of packing of the lipid hydrocarbon chains. The lipids are organised into a bilayer. The amphipathic character of the lipid molecules -- which consist of a hydrophilic polar head group and one or two hydrophobic hydrocarbon chains -- causes the molecules to organise into a thin structure in which the hydrocarbon chains are sandwiched between two layers of polar head groups and are thus sequestered from the aqueous surroundings. The energetically unfavourable interaction between hydrocarbon chains and water is minimised by the maintenance of an ordered arrangement of the lipid molecules in a direction perpendicular to the membrane plane. Presumably, the surface of a membrane protein is divided into hydrophobic and hydrophilic regions that define the positioning of the protein relative to the bilayer. The hydrophobic effect, in spite of its importance for membrane stability (Tanford, 1980), is not strong enough to make the bilayer completely rigid. If there were no disorder in the direction perpendicular to the membrane plane, membranes would be rigid, inflexible sheets. The flexible, fluid behaviour of membranes indicates that their constituents can move in a restricted fashion in a direction perpendicular to the bilayer surface.

The magnitude of the motion of lipids and proteins perpendicular to the membrane surface is probably between one and several angstroms. In most membrane systems X-ray diffraction in the meridional direction is limited to about 10 Å resolution (for example, Franks and Levine, 1981), suggesting that the structure in the direction perpendicular to the membrane plane is not determined to better than 3–4 Å by the forces stabilising the membrane. This does not necessarily mean that adjacent molecules are free to move several angstroms relative to one another; ripples caused by the coordinated motions of adjacent molecules might have a similar effect on the diffraction pattern. In lamellar stacks of lipid bilayers at low levels of hydration it is possible to observe Bragg reflections to much higher resolutions (5–6 Å spacing). Presumably in these tightly packed arrays the motion of molecules perpendicular to the bilayer plane is more restricted.

A second form of disorder perpendicular to the membrane plane is disorder in the stacking of membranes into a lamellar array. Lamellar stacks of membranes occur naturally in retinal rods and chloroplasts and in the spiral array of myelin. The disorder in these one-dimensional arrays is due both to the weakness of forces between adjacent membranes and to variations in those forces over the membrane surfaces. This disorder in stacking may or may not be important for the functioning of the organelles in which it occurs. It does, however, represent a property that may complicate the analysis of structural data or limit the resolution of a structural study. It also represents a probe for the nature of the forces between membranes in a lamellar array and so can potentially provide information about the interactions between closely opposed membranes.

Asymmetry

Intact biological membranes always have a well-defined sidedness: one side will face the inside of a cell or organelle, and the other will face the outside. Transport of molecules across the membrane must be directional and any given receptor, enzymatically active site or immunological determinant is universally found on only one side of a membrane. Thus, in intact membranes, proteins are always arranged asymmetrically relative to the two surfaces of the membrane. Most lipid species are found on both sides of the lipid bilayer, but often at very different concentrations (Bretcher, 1973; Rothman and Lenard, 1977; Op den Kamp, 1979). The origin, maintenance and function of lipid asymmetry are unclear. This intrinsic asymmetry limits the possible symmetries of naturally occurring membrane arrays to one of the five enantiomorphic two-sided plane groups that do not have two-fold rotation or screw axes parallel to the plane; that is, to p1, p2, p3, p4, or p6.

In artificial membrane lattices prepared by detergent treatment of natural membranes or reconstituted from purified membrane components the constituents may be either symmetrically or asymmetrically arranged relative to the two membrane surfaces. For instance, in two-dimensional crystalline arrays of cytochrome oxidase prepared by deoxycholate extraction, half of the molecules 'face' one side of the sheet (there is no continuous bilayer) and half face the other side (Fuller, Capaldi and Henderson, 1979). But cytochrome oxidase has also been prepared by Triton extraction and found to form vesicle crystals (Henderson, Capaldi and Leigh, 1977) in which all the proteins face the same side of the membrane. Thus, arrays of membrane components in reconstituted membranes may exhibit the symmetry of any one of the 17 enantiomorphic two-sided plane groups.

Membrane specimens

Membrane proteins are often classified as integral or peripheral. Integral proteins are those proteins with portions deeply inserted into the lipid bilayer and most, if not all, of these proteins span the lipid bilayer. A large fraction of these proteins are glycosylated. They are largely insoluble in aqueous media and can be dissociated from the membranes only by detergent treatment. Peripheral proteins are associated with the membrane surfaces and can usually be dissociated from the membrane in relatively mild conditions. Peripheral proteins are often soluble.

Figure 2.11 illustrates the schematic dissection of a membrane into the sorts of membrane specimens that can be produced and studied by presently available techniques. Whole membranes can be studied by X-ray diffraction, but the information is usually limited to one dimension and will represent an average of contributions from all the membrane components. To get more detailed information, structural studies must concentrate on particular membrane components isolated from the whole membrane.

Lipids can be isolated and crystallised in three dimensions or studied as lipid–water liquid crystals which are usually one-dimensional lamellar arrays of bilayers with no order in the bilayer plane. Proteins, depending on their disposition relative to the membrane bilayer, must be handled in different ways.

Three-dimensional crystals of integral membrane proteins in association with membrane lipids would be the most suitable specimens for high resolution diffraction studies. In the absence of three-dimensional crystals, two-dimensional arrays are being used in many structural studies. Peripheral membrane proteins are generally soluble and can be crystallised like many cytoplasmic proteins. As these proteins are likely to have a structural organisation similar to soluble proteins they are not considered in detail here. The filamentous, cytoskeletal proteins tend to be very large, as in the case of spectrin from human erythrocyte membranes or clathrin from coated vesicles. They have been difficult to study

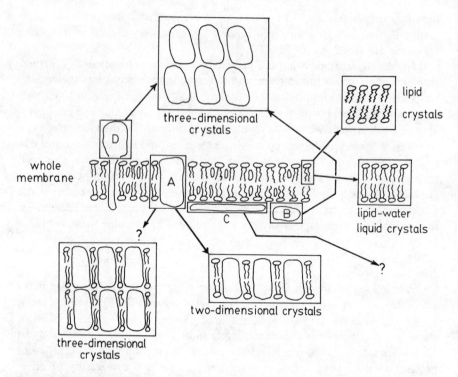

Figure 2.11 Diagram showing how a membrane can be dissected. Phospholipids are represented with an oval for the polar head group connected to two wavy lines corresponding to the hydrocarbon chains. Neutral lipids are small ovals within the bilayer. Proteins are large vague shapes and the centre diagram represents a whole intact membrane. A, integral membrane protein; B, peripheral membrane protein; C, filamentous, cytoskeletal protein which may form a continuous network along one surface of the membrane; D, a protein that traverses the lipid bilayer. The components of a whole membrane must be isolated and arranged into two- or three-dimensional arrays for detailed diffraction analyses of their molecular structure

in detail structurally because of their size, their tendency to form large insoluble networks and because some of them are apparently quite flexible. The representation of the protein labelled 'D' also traverses the lipid bilayer but most of its mass is on one side of the membrane. Treatment with proteases may sometimes separate the large soluble domain intact from the small insoluble domain that traverses the bilayer. In the case of haemagglutinin from influenza virus, the large glycosylated surface domain has been crystallised and a high resolution image of its structure produced (Wilson *et al.*, 1981).

These one-, two- and three-dimensional arrays constitute the types of specimens used most frequently in structural studies on membranes. In addition, detergent micelles containing integral membrane proteins have been studied in solution using small angle X-ray scattering. Several examples of structural studies using each of these specimen types will be considered here.

LIPID MODEL SYSTEMS

As initially proposed by Gorter and Grendel (1928), lipids in biological membranes virtually always occur in a bilayer configuration. Substantial evidence has accumulated to indicate that in most biological membranes the lipid hydrocarbon chains are in a liquid-like arrangement in the bilayer (for early work see Hartley, 1936; Schmitt *et al.*, 1941; Bear *et al.*, 1941). The degree of order of the hydrocarbon chains is variable, however, and depends on the temperature and hydration and on the homogeneity and chemical nature of the lipids involved.

Lipid crystals

The flexibility and conformational polymorphism of lipid molecules has made the growth of three-dimensional lipid crystals relatively difficult. Lipid crystals contain only a single species of lipid (there can be no heterogeneity of hydrocarbon chain length) and have a low water content. Although lipids in biological membranes exist in heterogeneous, highly hydrated lipid bilayers, studies of lipid structure in crystals are relevant to membrane structure because they provide information about the preferred conformations of the lipid molecules. Furthermore, most of the types of intermolecular interactions that are important in determining the structure of lipid crystals will also be important in determining the structure of biological membranes.

X-ray crystallography has been used to solve the structure of a number of lipid crystals to high resolution and the results of some of those analyses are outlined here.

The crystal structure of 1,2-dilauroyl-DL-phosphatidylethanolamine:acetic acid (DLPE) has been studied by X-ray diffraction (Hitchcock *et al.*, 1974; Elder *et al.*, 1977) and the positions and thermal parameters of all the non-hydrogen atoms have been determined. The phospholipids are arranged in bilayers in the crystal with the hydrocarbon chains nearly perpendicular to the bilayer surface. The α fatty acid chain extends further into the bilayer than the β chain as can be seen in the projection in Figure 2.12. This is because the glycerol moiety extends nearly perpendicular to the bilayer surface. The β chain branches at right angles to the glycerol moiety and extends for several angstroms almost parallel to the bilayer surface. This arrangement of the glycerol group has also been observed in crystals of 1,2-dimyristoyl-sn-glycero-3-phosphorylcholine (DMPC) (Pearson and Pascher, 1979) and cerebroside (Pascher and Sundell, 1977). In 2,3-dilauroyl-D-glycerol, the glycerol group is orientated almost parallel to the bilayer plane (Pascher *et al.*, 1981a). Apparently, the attachment of the polar head group alters the orientation of the glycerol moiety so that it is nearly perpendicular to the membrane surface.

In most lipid crystals the hydrocarbon chains appear to be almost hexagonally close packed as can be seen in the projection of the DLPE structure perpendicular to the bilayer surface shown in Figure 2.13. The packing cannot be exactly

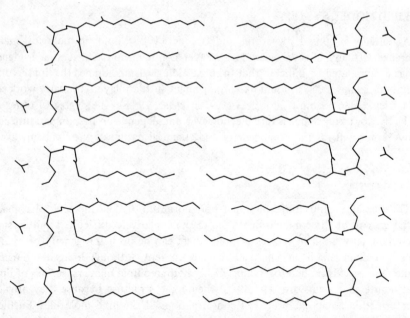

Figure 2.12 1,2-dilauroyl-DL-phosphatidylethanolamine:acetic acid. The intermolecular packing as projected down the *c* axis, approximately parallel to the surface of the bilayer in the crystal (from Elder *et al.*, 1977)

hexagonal because at high resolution the hydrocarbon chains do not closely approximate circular cylinders. The disorder in the hydrocarbon chains, as indicated by the isotropic temperature factors of the carbon atoms, increases with distance from the polar head groups in the crystal (Elder *et al.*, 1977). In the centre of the bilayer, where the ends of the α chains from lipid molecules on opposite sides of the bilayer interdigitate, the disorder is very large. In this region the interatomic distances between carbon atoms on different chains are greater than the sum of the expected van der Waals' radii.

The region of the polar head groups is much more highly ordered. In most lipid crystals these regions are stabilised by a continuous network of hydrogen bonds. In the crystal structure of DMPE (Elder *et al.*, 1977) the phosphatidyl-ethanolamine dipoles are organised into antiparallel strands. In lysophosphatidyl-ethanolamine (Pascher *et al.*, 1981b) the dipoles are orientated parallel to one another in double strands. A continuous network of hydrogen bonds stabilises both of these arrangements. When water molecules are present, they also are seen to hydrogen bond to the lipid polar head groups (Pearson and Pascher, 1979) as do other molecules of hydration such as acetic acid in the crystals of DLPE (Elder *et al.*, 1977). The polar head group dipole appears to be nearly parallel to the bilayer surface in most of these crystals.

In crystals of DMPC (Pearson and Pascher, 1979) the lipids crystallise as stacked bilayers as in the crystals of DLPE, but with the hydrocarbon chains

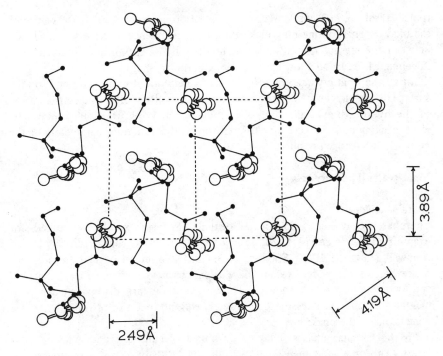

Figure 2.13 1,2-dilauroyl-DL-phosphatidylethanolamine:acetic acid. The crystal structure viewed down the *a* axis, approximately perpendicular to the bilayer surface and parallel to the hydrocarbon chains. Note that the hydrocarbon chains bend slightly. Their packing is not exactly hexagonal because they do not closely resemble circular cylinders at high resolution (from Elder *et al.*, 1977)

tilted by about 12° relative to the bilayer normal. The tilting of the hydrocarbon chains occurs because the phosphatidylcholine head groups require a larger surface area than that taken up by two hydrocarbon chains lying perpendicular to the bilayer surface. The cross-sectional area occupied by polar head groups and hydrocarbon chains can be equal only when the hydrocarbon chains are tilted relative to the bilayer surface. This phenomenon is also observed in liquid crystals of DMPC in water. The molecular conformations of DLPE and DMPC are very similar both in the crystalline and liquid crystalline states (Hauser, *et al.*, 1981). The hydrocarbon chains of DLPE are not tilted in the crystal because the phosphatidylethanolamine head groups do not occupy more than 40 Å^2 on the surface of the crystalline bilayer.

In crystals of both cholesterol monohydrate (Craven, 1976) and anhydrous cholesterol (Shieh *et al.*, 1977) the cholesterol molecules organise into bilayers with the molecular axes approximately but not exactly perpendicular to the bilayer surfaces. In both structures, the hydroxyl groups are hydrogen bonded together in a network stabilising the crystal. In the monohydrate, none of the molecules has a fully extended hydrocarbon chain. Instead, the chain is partially folded, resulting in a condensed, relatively disordered structure at the centre of the bilayer. This folding may make up for the difference in cross-sectional area between the steroid ring system and its short hydrocarbon tail (Rothman and Engelman, 1972), and allow closer packing in the crystal.

In all the lipid crystals the formation of a network of hydrogen bonds on the surface of the bilayer seems to be essential for crystal stability. The configuration of the hydrocarbon chains and ring groups seems to be determined largely by close packing and the necessity to conform to the structural parameters of the network of hydrogen bonds.

Lipid–water liquid crystals

Phase behaviour

The phase behaviour of lipid–water systems has been extensively studied (for example, Tardieu *et al.*, 1973; Ranck *et al.*, 1974; Caron *et al.*, 1974) and reviewed (Luzzati, 1968; Shipley, 1973) but a brief recapitulation is appropriate here. Lipid–water systems have been observed with lamellar, hexagonal and two-dimensional symmetries. These symmetries are distinguished experimentally by the spacings of the X-ray reflections that also provide the lattice dimensions of the phase.

In the lamellar phases, bilayers of lipid molecules alternate with aqueous layers to form a one-dimensional, periodic stack. Many of the two-dimensional phases also consist of bilayer arrangements of lipids separated by water layers. In these phases, the bilayers exhibit periodic, wave-like undulations with periods of 150–400 Å (Tardieu *et al.*, 1973). The hexagonal phases are made up of long cylinders of lipids packed in a two-dimensional hexagonal lattice with interstitial water or, alternatively, of long cylinders of water surrounded by interstitial lipids.

The conformation of lipid hydrocarbon chains has been studied in detail since the discovery of an order–disorder transition in the packing of hydrocarbon chains in many lipid systems (see for example, Chapman, 1965; Luzzati, 1968; Ranck *et al.*, 1974). At temperatures above the order–disorder transition temperature (usually in the range of 0–40° C), the hydrocarbon chains are disordered as in liquid paraffin. This phase is referred to as the liquid crystalline phase. At temperatures below the transition temperature the hydrocarbon chains are packed rigid and parallel (gel phase) and may be either perpendicular to the lamellar surface or tilted at some angle to the surface normal.

A large number of factors influence both the temperature at which the transition takes place and the sharpness of the transition, that is, the range of temperatures over which the transition occurs. Heterogeneous mixtures of lipids tend to have a less well defined, lower transition temperature than homogeneous lipid systems. Longer, more highly saturated hydrocarbon chains seem to stay ordered to higher temperatures than shorter, less saturated chains. Components such as cholesterol, which disrupt the packing of hydrocarbon chains, tend to lower the transition temperature and broaden the range of temperatures over which the transition takes place.

The gel and liquid crystalline phases of the lipid hydrocarbon chains can be distinguished by high-angle X-ray scattering. Hydrocarbon chains in the liquid crystalline phase give rise to a broad, diffuse band of scattering at about 4.6 Å spacing near the equator of the diffraction pattern (Luzzati, 1968; Levine and Wilkins, 1971; Wilkins *et al.*, 1971). In the gel phase the lipids give rise to a strong, sharp reflection at 4.2 Å spacing, corresponding to a two-dimensional hexagonal packing of the chains with a centre-to-centre separation of 4.85 Å. When the hydrocarbon chains are tilted relative to the bilayer surfaces an additional diffuse band of scattering is observed in the region of 3.6–4.1 Å spacing. These phases can also be distinguished by electron diffraction from specimens kept hydrated in the electron microscope by a hydration chamber (Hui *et al.*, 1974; 1975).

Structure of the lamellar phases

X-ray diffraction studies have resulted in electron density profiles for many pure lipid–water systems both in the liquid crystalline and gel phases. As the electron density profiles of most biological membranes are dominated by the strong electron density contrast between the high density lipid polar head groups and the low density hydrocarbon core, these studies of pure lipid systems constitute a basis for the interpretation of the electron density profiles of membranes.

Figure 2.14 shows an electron density profile for a bilayer consisting of lecithin and cholesterol in a molar ratio of 3:2 at 100 per cent relative humidity (Franks, 1976). Many membranes have phospholipid:cholesterol ratios in this range and some of the features of this electron density profile are likely to be found in electron density profiles of most membranes. The principal features of the profile are two electron density peaks, in this case about 44 Å apart, corresponding to the phosphate of the lecithin head groups, and a pronounced minimum in the electron density at the centre of the bilayer due to the lipid hydrocarbon chains, in particular, the terminal methyl groups. The shoulders, about 11 Å from the bilayer centre, are due to cholesterol. Two possible molecular models are shown for the average conformation of lecithin and cholesterol in these bilayers. These models are based on coordinates taken from crystallographic studies of lipid molecules. They are consistent with the X-ray diffraction data and also with neutron diffraction experiments (Worcester and Franks, 1976). The data used to construct the electron density profiles are shown in Figure 2.8. The intensities were phased using swelling experiments. In the lamellar array the bilayers are packed 58.9 Å apart and observable diffraction extended to about 6 Å spacing. A diffuse band of scattering at about 4.7 Å spacing indicated that the hydrocarbon chains are in the disordered, liquid crystalline state.

In the models presented in Figure 2.14 the phosphatidylcholine headgroup is orientated approximately parallel to the membrane plane as suggested by the

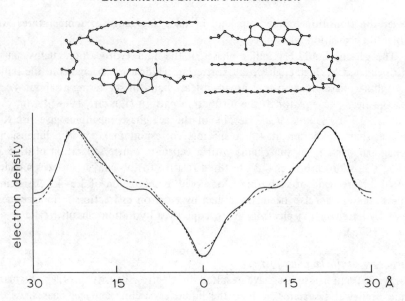

Figure 2.14 Electron density profile of a lecithin:cholesterol bilayer. The molar ratio of lecithin:cholesterol is 3:2 and the bilayer was at 100 per cent relative humidity. The solid curve is that calculated from the X-ray diffraction data. The dashed curves are calculated from the two models drawn above. Two distinct molecular models are presented above, both of which are consistent with the diffraction data. The data, to 6 Å resolution, is not of sufficient resolution to allow a distinction to be made between similar lipid molecule conformations. Indeed, in the bilayer, the molecules may take on a large variety of conformations similar to the ones shown here (from Franks, 1976)

crystallographic studies of L-α-glycerylphosphorylcholine (Abrahamsson and Pascher, 1966) and DLPE (Elder *et al.*, 1977). The close correspondence between the electron density profiles calculated from the models and that obtained from analysis of the diffraction data suggests that the lipid molecules in the fluid lipid bilayers may have average conformations similar to their conformation in single crystals.

The end of the hydrocarbon chain of cholesterol is very close to the centre of the bilayer in the models in Figure 2.14 and the cholesterol hydroxyl oxygen is the same distance from the bilayer surface as the fatty acid ester groups (Franks and Lieb, 1979). This positioning of cholesterol is supported by X-ray diffraction studies of lecithin:cholesterol bilayers containing cholesterol halogenated at C-26 (Franks *et al.*, 1978). McIntosh (1978) has presented results indicating that the cholesterol molecules are at approximately the same distance from the bilayer surface in bilayers of different thicknesses. Electron density profiles were determined for bilayers made up of cholesterol with phosphatidylcholine having hydrocarbon chains containing 12 (dilauroyl), 14 (dimyristoyl), 16 (dipalmitoyl) and 18 (distearoyl) carbons. Features in the electron density profiles identified as due to cholesterol maintain a constant distance from the polar head group peaks, independent of the bilayer width which varied from 38 to 50 Å in these membranes. This result suggests that the position of the cholesterol molecules in these bilayers may be constrained by an energetic requirement for the cholesterol hydroxyl to be at the bilayer surface in order to hydrogen bond to solvent molecules or the polar head groups of other lipid molecules.

Electron density profiles of lipid bilayers in the gel and liquid crystalline states are surprisingly similar. Figure 2.15 compares the electron density profiles of dilauroylphosphatidylcholine (DLPC) bilayers above (*b*) and below (*a*) the phase transition temperature at 50 per cent relative humidity and above the phase transition temperature at 75 per cent relative humidity (*c*) (McIntosh, 1978). In these high resolution (5 Å) profiles the polar head group peaks are resolved into two peaks of electron density or, in the profile of the more disordered bilayer at 75 per cent relative humidity, a peak and a shoulder. The

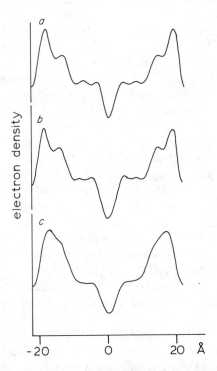

Figure 2.15   Electron density profiles of dilauroylphosphatidylcholine bilayers at 50 per cent relative humidity below (*a*) and above (*b*) the liquid crystal–gel phase transition temperature and at 75 per cent relative humidity above the phase transition temperature (*c*). At 50 per cent relative humidity the profiles of the bilayers above and below the phase transition temperature are almost identical, the major difference being additional evidence for disorder in the bilayer above the transition temperature. The structural change on going from 50 to 75 per cent relative humidity is also largely due to increasing disorder in the bilayer (from McIntosh, 1980)

higher density peak corresponds to the phosphate groups, the lower density peak or shoulder (which is also visible in Figure 2.14) has been attributed to the glyceryl-fatty acid ester groups (Wilkins, 1972). The relative positions of the two head group peaks suggests that the head groups are orientated parallel to the plane of the bilayer in both gel and liquid crystalline states.

Comparison of the electron density profiles in Figure 2.15a and b shows that the width of the DLPC bilayer decreases by about 1 Å on going from the gel state to the relatively less ordered liquid crystalline phase. The width of the low density trough occupied by the terminal methyl groups of the hydrocarbon chains increases slightly, reflecting the chain packing disorder in the liquid crystalline phase. Otherwise, the two profiles are remarkably similar. Larger changes in the profile are observed on going from 50 to 75 per cent relative humidity. Comparison of the profiles in Figure 2.15b and c indicates that there is a substantial increase in the disorder in the liquid crystalline phase bilayers on increasing the relative humidity as well as a 2-Å decrease in the bilayer thickness.

There is no cholesterol in the bilayers represented by the profiles in Figure 2.15 and the steps in the electron density about 11 Å from the centre of the profile in Figure 2.14 are absent from the profile in Figure 2.15c. All other features of the two profiles correspond. The step seen in Figure 2.14, but missing in Figure 2.15c is thus likely to be due to cholesterol. McIntosh (1978) has demonstrated this by adding cholesterol to DLPC bilayers. When this is done, and electron density profiles are calculated, they contain steps that appear very similar to those in Figure 2.14.

In the gel phase, the hydrocarbon chains of some lipids are tilted relative to the bilayer surface just as they are in crystals. For instance, the hydrocarbon chains of dipalmitoylphosphatidylethanolamine (DPPE) are orientated normal to the bilayer plane, whereas those of dipalmitoylphosphatidylcholine (DPPC) are tilted by about 30° relative to the bilayer normal (Tardieu *et al.*, 1973; Ranck *et al.*, 1974; McIntosh, 1980). Addition of *n*-alkane or lanthanum ions to the DPPC bilayers causes the hydrocarbon chains to reorientate perpendicular to the bilayer (McIntosh, 1980). This suggests that the chain tilting can be explained by a simple packing argument (Nagle, 1976; McIntosh, 1980) similar to that put forward to explain the chain tilting in lipid crystals (Hauser *et al.*, 1981): that is, the area per lipid molecule in a bilayer is determined by the properties of the polar head group. In DPPE bilayers the head group requires less than 40 Å^2 on the bilayer surface. As each hydrocarbon chain occupies about 20 Å^2, the two DPPE chains can be perpendicular to the surface without compressing the head groups. The DPPC head groups are larger, requiring more than 40 Å^2 on the bilayer surface. For the hydrocarbon chains to occupy more than 40 Å^2 they must tilt relative to the bilayer surface. Addition of *n*-alkanes to the bilayer adds volume to the hydrocarbon region, allowing the chains to become perpendicular without compression of the polar head groups (McIntosh, 1980). Lanthanum ions apparently bind to the phosphatidylcholine head groups, changing their conformation to reduce the area they occupy on the surface. This also allows the hydrocarbon chains to reorientate perpendicular to the bilayer surface. The similarity of lipid behaviour in lipid crystals and lamellar liquid crystals indicates that the lipid molecules are likely to take on similar conformations in the two sytems.

Stabilising forces
The well-ordered stacking of lipid bilayers in lamellar liquid crystals suggests that there are relatively strong interbilayer forces stabilising the arrays. Three kinds of forces are important in determining the equilibrium separation of two lipid bilayers (for a review, see Rand, 1981): electrostatic and van der Waals' forces between bilayers and the hydrophilic forces between the lipid polar head groups and their water of hydration ('hydration force').

Electrostatic repulsion occurs between any two identically charged structures. These forces can be modified or masked by ions in the aqueous solution between the bilayers. The force of repulsion between two charged planar surfaces is approximately proportional to the product of their surface charge densities and falls off exponentially with a decay constant that, in physiological saline, is about 8 Å (Parsegian, 1973). Electrostatic repulsion is responsible for the indefinite swelling of phases of charged lipids in water with increasing water activity (Gulik-Kryzywicki, Tardieu and Luzzati, 1969). Bilayers composed of neutral, dipolar lipids will swell until they reach a maximum, equilibrium separation. Once the equilibrium separation is reached, as water activity is further increased the uncharged bilayers remain a constant distance apart.

Van der Waals' attraction between bilayers is due to transient electrical and magnetic fields caused by random displacements of charges (Parsegian, 1973). These forces are always attractive. They tend to decay more slowly than electrostatic forces and can be strong enough to stabilise lamellar phases with very large water contents.

The effect exerted by lipid polar group hydration on the separation of bilayers in lamellar arrays is less well understood. Energy is necessary to dehydrate the lipid polar groups of two opposing bilayers as they approach one another closely (LeNeveu *et al.*, 1977). This tends to act as a force keeping two bilayers apart. For bilayer separations of less than 30 Å, this force can be stronger than electrostatic repulsion. Over the range of bilayer separations in which it can be estimated this force is approximately exponential with a decay constant of about 2 Å.

Quantitative measurement and modification of forces between lipid bilayers can be achieved by varying the chemical potential of water in a liquid crystal and measuring the resultant changes in the thicknesses of the lipid and water layers by X-ray diffraction (Parsegian *et al.*, 1979). Water activity can be varied by using hydrostatic pressure, by altering osmotic pressure through the introduction of large solutes, such as dextran, that dehydrate the lipid–water phase without being able to enter it, or by introducing small solute molecules that both alter the water activity and enter the lipid–water phase. For instance, as sucrose concentration is increased and allowed to enter the aqueous region between lecithin bilayers, the bilayer separation first increases and then, at higher sucrose concentrations, decreases (LeNeveu *et al.*, 1977), apparently because the sucrose at low concentrations weakens the van der Waals' attraction between bilayers and then, at higher concentrations, strengthens it. As the weight per cent of dextran in aqueous solution in equilibrium with the lecithin-water liquid phase is increased from 0 to 40 per cent, the activity of water is decreased, causing it to diffuse out of the lamellar phase and decreasing the lamellar repeat of the liquid crystal from 62 to 55 Å. As the lecithin bilayers approach one another closely, a strong repulsion is observed that cannot be explained simply on the basis of electrostatic forces and is apparently associated with the energy required to dehydrate the lipid polar head groups. Addition of small amounts of charged lipids to the neutral egg lecithin bilayers generates an electrostatic repulsion between the bilayers that can be measured quantitatively by this technique (Cowley *et al.*, 1978). When the water layers between these charged bilayers are less than 30 Å wide the hydration force becomes stronger than the electrostatic repulsion. This direct demonstration of the importance of removing water of hydration to achieve close apposition of lipid bilayers may be relevant to an understanding of membrane fusion.

These methods can also be used to measure the deformation of lipid bilayers in response to the applied osmotic forces. As bilayers get closer together the area per lipid molecule decreases and the bilayer thickness increases (Parsegian *et al.*, 1979). The force required to compress the area of a lecithin bilayer by 25 per cent is about 25 dyn cm^{-1}. This lateral compression can actually induce a transition of the hydrocarbon chains from liquid crystalline phase to gel phase at temperatures above the normal order–disorder transition temperature.

Protein–lipid–water model systems

The structure of liquid crystals containing protein, lipid and water has been studied to enumerate the ways in which proteins may interact with lipid bilayers and to observe what effect the presence of proteins may have on lipid structure. These studies are distinct from studies of reconstituted membranes in that they may not correspond to a functional membrane system and may utilise proteins that are not normally associated with membranes. Perhaps the first X-ray diffraction study of such a system was that of Palmer *et al.* (1941) who showed that lamellar structures formed from cephalin and histone and from cephalin and globin had repeat distances 13–15 Å and 7–9 Å greater, respectively, than that of a pure cephalin–water phase. They interpreted this result to indicate that 'the protein occurs as thin, possibly unimolecular, layers intercalated between the bimolecular leaflets of the cephalin'.

More recent studies have shown that the phase behaviour of protein–lipid–water systems is very complex. However, the pattern of protein–lipid interactions seems to be similar in most of the systems that have been studied (Gulik-Krzywicki, 1975). In their study of mixtures of cytochrome *c*, phosphatidyl inositol and water, Gulik-Krzywicki *et al.* (1969) identified two phases with repeat distances (depending on the level of hydration) of 68–78 Å and 91–112 Å. These two phases both contain lipid bilayers of approximately equal thickness. The phase with the smaller repeat has a single layer of protein molecules in the aqueous region between bilayers; in the other phase, two layers of protein molecules are contained in the spaces between bilayers. Similar results were observed (Shipley *et al.*, 1969a; 1969b) in mixtures of cytochrome *c* with phosphatidylcholine and phosphatidylserine. In lysozyme–cardiolipin–water systems, the protein was again found to be mainly intercalated in layers between lipid bilayers (Gulik-Krzywicki *et al.*, 1969). However, in this system, the partial thickness of lipid decreases with the addition of protein. The partial thickness is a measure of the percentage of the lamellar repeating unit occupied by lipid. As this parameter decreases while the actual thickness of the lipid bilayer remains approximately constant, it was concluded that some of the protein was inter-calating into the lipid bilayer.

Myelin basic proteins A1 (from the central nervous system) and P1 (from the peripheral nervous system) were mixed with myelin lipids and water to study the interactions of these proteins with lipid (Mateu *et al.*, 1973). Again, a very complex phase behaviour was observed. One phase had a lamellar repeat distance of 150–180 Å, and included two bilayers in the repeat period. For this to occur, either the two bilayers must be asymmetric and related by a two-fold axis parallel to their surfaces or they must have different structures. Detailed analysis of X-ray diffraction and electron microscope data led to the conclusion that the two bilayers are different: one bilayer contains those phospholipids with their hydrocarbon chains in a liquid-like conformation while the other bilayer con-tains mainly sulphatides with at least part of their hydrocarbon chains in a stiff, hexagonally packed, ordered phase. The protein was located in the aqueous spaces between the bilayers. High temperature or cholesterol melts the ordered sulphatide hydrocarbon chains and the phase exhibiting the long repeat distance is replaced by a phase containing a single bilayer in the repeating unit. This suggests that the ordering of the sulphatide hydrocarbon chains is responsible for the formation of the phase containing two bilayers with different structures.

For the most part, these studies have shown that soluble proteins interact electrostatically with lipid bilayers, binding loosely to their surfaces. Stronger, hydrophobic interactions between protein and lipid must occur when protein is intercalated into the lipid bilayer. This is observed in some conditions even for soluble, non-membrane proteins such as lysozyme.

STRUCTURAL STUDIES ON MEMBRANES

Myelin

The myelin sheath is an assembly of membrane pairs formed by the spiral wrapping of the Schwann or glial cell membrane around nerve cell axons (Geren, 1954). As the myelin membranes usually pack parallel to one another in a periodic array encircling the axon, myelin is one of the few living pieces of tissue from which moderate resolution X-ray diffraction data can be obtained. The myelin sheath functions mainly as an insulator to minimise the movement of ions between the axon cytoplasm and the extracellular medium. The resulting saltatory conduction substantially increases the conduction velocity of the axon (see Aidley, 1971). Lipids make up a relatively large percentage of the dry weight in myelin: 75 per cent in the peripheral nervous system (PNS) and 80 per cent in the central nervous system (CNS) (Norton, 1977). The remainder of the dry weight is protein and glycoprotein. The very low protein-to-lipid ratio in myelin is a reflection of its principal role as an insulator. However, both structural (Caspar *et al.*, 1980) and metabolic (Benjamin and Smith, 1977) studies have shown that myelin is a dynamic molecular system requiring both lipids and proteins for its structural stability. Nerve myelin was the first membrane to be studied using X-ray diffraction (Schmitt *et al.*, 1935) and several reviews have outlined the progress of diffraction studies on myelin since those pioneering studies (see, for example, Shipley, 1973, Kirschner and Caspar, 1977, Franks and Levine, 1981).

There is no regular ordering of myelin components in the plane of the membranes so X-ray diffraction can be used only to obtain an electron density profile. There has been a large number of X-ray diffraction studies of myelin structure. The low resolution diffraction pattern, consisting of five strong reflections has been phased using swelling experiments (Finean and Burge, 1963; Moody, 1963; Blaurock, 1971) to produce an electron density map at about 35 Å resolution. The weaker diffraction which extends out to 10 Å spacing could not be interpreted by this method because of the disorder induced in the membrane array by the swelling. Caspar and Kirschner (1971) reasoned that as the functions of myelin from different nerves and different species are identical, the structures of these myelins must be very similar. In their studies of myelin from frog sciatic, rabbit optic and rabbit sciatic nerves they used this constraint to resolve ambiguities that had previously existed in the phasing of X-ray diffraction from myelin to 10 Å resolution. Alternative interpretations of the diffraction from myelin (McIntosh and Worthington, 1974; Worthington and McIntosh, 1974; Nelander and Blaurock, 1979) now seem unlikely in view of the close correspondence between the electron density profile of myelin and that of myelin lipids (Franks *et al.*, 1982).

The myelin electron density profile as determined by Caspar and Kirschner (1971) is diagrammed in Figure 2.16. The myelin electron density profile has similarities to that of purified egg lecithin and cholesterol bilayers (Figure 2.14). The principal features of this profile are, therefore, due to the myelin lipids as expected from the low protein content. The asymmetry in the bilayer profile is due, at least in part, to asymmetric distribution of lipids between the two halves of the bilayer (see, however, Blaurock and Nelander, 1979; Blaurock, 1981a). The asymmetry in the heights of the 'steps' in the electron density profile, halfway between the polar head group peaks and the minimum at the centre of the

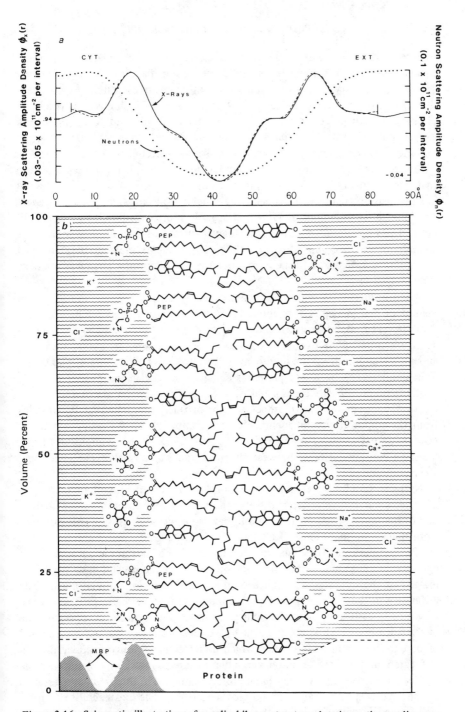

Figure 2.16 Schematic illustration of myelin bilayer structure showing a, the myelin membrane electron density profile from rabbit sciatic (solid line) and rabbit optic nerve (dashed line) and the neutron diffraction profile from sciatic nerve (dotted line); and b, the interpretation of the profile in terms of the arrangement of lipids and proteins in the membrane. The portions of the profile that have been identified with the arrangement of chemical constituents are shown in the drawing below (from Kirschner et al., 1983)

hydrocarbon region suggests that there is about twice as much cholesterol in the extracellular half of the bilayer as in the cytoplasmic half (see also Franks *et al.*, 1982). Asymmetry in the distribution of other membrane lipids is also very likely. Chemical studies indicate that mercuric chloride binds specifically to phosphatidylethanolamine plasmalogen in intact myelin, and X-ray diffraction experiments indicate that the bound mercury is located mainly on the cytoplasmic surface of the myelin membrane bilayer (Kirschner and Ganser, 1982).

In the electron density profile of intact myelin there is no principal feature that can be unambiguously interpreted as due to myelin protein. The data are not inconsistent with protein occupying roughly constant area across the repeat structure, but experience dictates that specific proteins will be located in well-defined positions relative to the lipid bilayer surfaces. However, determining the location of minor components in a chemically complex molecular system such as myelin is difficult and usually requires the use of specific chemical or structural alterations.

When immersed in water the lamellar repeat distance of the sciatic myelin membrane pair increases from about 170 Å to over 270 Å, the swelling occurring almost exclusively in the extracellular space (Blaurock, 1967). When the electron density profile of the swollen myelin is calculated, a shoulder about 30 Å long appears extending from the lipid bilayer out into the swollen extracellular space. This shoulder has been interpreted as being due to the major glycoprotein (P_o protein) of myelin (Blaurock, 1981a; 1981b). The shoulder is not apparent in electron density profiles of intact myelin because interdigitating P_o proteins from the opposing myelin membranes will completely span the approximately 40-Å wide extracellular space and may, in fact, act as spacer molecules maintaining a constant distance between the membranes in normal myelin (Blaurock, 1981b).

Naturally occurring chemical variations are found in mutant myelins. The peripheral nerve myelin from shiverer mutant mouse has been shown to lack one of the myelin basic proteins and to have an electron density profile different from that of normal mouse (Kirschner and Ganser, 1980; Ganser and Kirschner, 1980). Comparison of the electron density profiles of shiverer and normal adult mouse myelin, shown in Figure 2.17, suggests that the myelin basic protein is located at the cytoplasmic surface of the lipid bilayer in normal myelin. The difference in the two membrane profiles suggests that the basic protein may be very closely associated with the lipid polar head groups on the cytoplasmic side of the membrane. This is supported by studies of artificial bilayers composed of myelin lipids and basic protein which indicate that the myelin basic protein is located in the head group layers (Blaurock, 1981a). Electron microscopic studies have also suggested that basic protein is present in the cytoplasmic spaces in the myelin sheath (Peterson and Gruener, 1978). The existence of compact, well-formed myelin sheaths in the absence of myelin basic protein in shiverer mice questions the proposed role of basic proteins as 'structural cement'. However, normal basic protein has been shown to induce the formation of an ordered

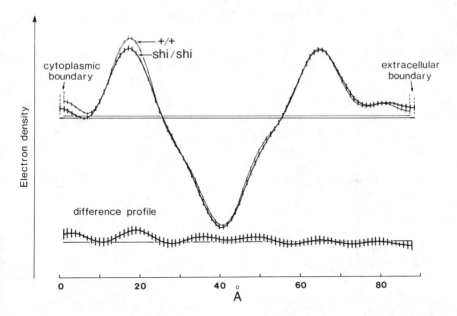

Figure 2.17   Electron density profiles of the myelin membranes in normal (*+/+*) and shiverer (*shi/shi*) mouse sciatic nerves. Vertical bars represent uncertainties in electron density. The only region in which the two profiles are significantly different are at the cytoplasmic polar head group peak and in the thin cytoplasmic aqueous space of the myelin. This suggests that the basic protein, absent in the shiverer mouse myelin, may be present at the cytoplasmic surface of the myelin membranes in normal myelin, possibly tightly associated with the polar head groups of the lipids (from Ganser and Kirschner, 1980)

multilayered arrangement of phosphatidylglycerol vesicles, a property less pronounced in basic protein from multiple sclerosis myelin (Brady *et al.*, 1981a).

Comparative structural studies of myelins from CNS and from PNS and from different species have defined some of the differences in the structures of myelins. As shown in Figure 2.18, the electron density profiles of myelins from different sources are very similar, but some significant differences are apparent (Caspar and Kirschner, 1971). Although the repeat period of rabbit optic nerve is 24 Å less (156 Å compared to 180 Å) than rabbit sciatic nerve myelin, the width of the lipid bilayers as measured by polar head group peak separation is identical in the two myelins. The major structural difference is in the width of the extracellular space between membrane pairs. The chemical origin and functional significance of this structural difference are unclear. Frog sciatic nerve has a spacing of 170 Å, 10 Å less than rabbit sciatic nerve, and a lipid bilayer width 2.8 Å less than in the rabbit myelins. Differences in lipid bilayer widths almost surely reflect differences in the lipid compositions of the two membranes.

X-ray diffraction studies have also been carried out on immature myelins and on myelin from a variety of mutant mice (Kirschner and Sidman, 1976). Myelin from sciatic nerves of quaking mice shows significant elevation of density in the

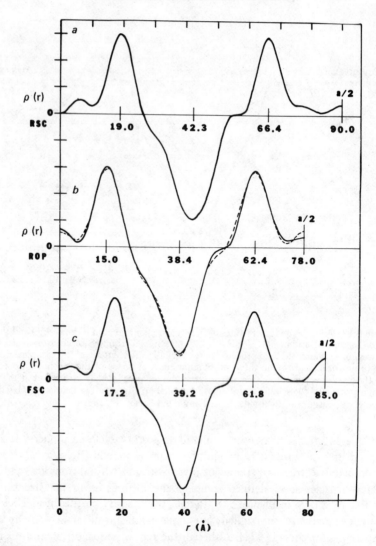

Figure 2.18 Electron density profiles of myelin membranes from rabbit sciatic (*a*), rabbit optic (*b*) and frog sciatic (*c*) nerves. The distance between the polar head group peaks is 47.4 A in both rabbit myelins and 44.6 A in the frog sciatic myelin. The two curves in the middle trace correspond to slightly different treatment of unobserved reflections in the calculations. The electron density profiles from all three sources are strikingly similar in spite of the very different lamellar repeat distances (156–180 Å) (from Caspar and Kirschner, 1971)

extracellular protein-water layer; the membrane bilayer of the more compact phase of the two phases found in trembler mice is about 5 Å thinner than for normal myelin; the bilayer of immature myelin is about 2 Å thinner than that of normal adult myelin. The difference in the bilayers of immature and adult myelin seems to be due to the low cholesterol content of the immature myelin (Franks *et al.*, 1982). Correlation of chemical differences with structural differences among other myelins may further characterise the structure of normal myelin and the source of nerve dysfunction in abnormal myelins.

Characterisation of the myelin structure to 10 Å resolution has provided a basis for studying myelin structure in conditions where nerve conduction is abnormal. The repetitive propagation of action potentials does not seem to affect myelin structure at 11 Å resolution (Padron and Mateu, 1980). At concentrations above about 40 per cent, dimethylsulphoxide (DMSO) is found to produce reversible blockage of nerve conduction and to decrease conduction velocity at lower concentrations (Davis *et al.*, 1967; Sams, 1967; Becker *et al.*, 1969). X-ray diffraction studies (Kirschner and Caspar, 1975) show that at concentrations of 10–40 per cent DMSO the myelin sheath exists partly in its native form and partly in a compacted form with a repeat period two-thirds that of native. At concentrations of DMSO above 40 per cent, the native pattern is no longer observed. Freeze-fracture electron microscopy shows that normally, myelin membranes have numerous intramembrane particles (Pinto da Silva and Miller, 1975) whereas experimentally compacted myelin membranes are particle free (Hollingshead *et al.*, 1981). The compacted and normal myelin phases are contiguous (Kirschner *et al.*, 1979) and most of the intramembranous particles observed in electron micrographs of replicas of freeze-fractured specimens seem to have moved within the plane of the membrane into the regions of the membrane with the larger, native repeat distance. DMSO apparently acts by removing water from between the membranes and in so doing it alters the distribution of proteins in the membrane plane.

Sarcoplasmic reticulum

The sarcoplasmic reticulum (SR) is a complex system of thin channels extending throughout muscle fibres. In the resting state of muscle, the SR is a reservoir of Ca^{2+} ions. A Ca^{2+}-ATPase active transport system maintains a calcium concentration $>10^{-3}$ M inside the SR sacs while the calcium concentration in the cytoplasm of resting muscle fibres is $<10^{-6}$ M. Depolarisation of the muscle cell is transmitted to the interior by the T tubules and results in a sudden release of calcium ions from the SR. The released calcium stimulates muscle contraction. Uptake and sequestering of the calcium by the sarcotubules leads to muscle relaxation. The Ca^{2+}-ATPase active transport system is made up of a 100–120,000 molecular weight (MW) subunit (Inesi and Scales, 1974; Rizzolo *et al.*, 1976) which constitutes about 70 per cent of the protein and which may have a 55,000-MW glycoprotein associated with it. The other major protein of the SR is a calcium-binding protein.

Close vesicles derived from sarcoplasmic reticulum have been isolated and shown to concentrate calcium using ATP as an energy source in conditions similar to those *in vivo* (Haselbach and Makinose, 1961). The inside of these vesicles corresponds to the lumen of the SR; the outside of the vesicles to the muscle cytoplasm. Centrifugation of the SR vesicles onto a mica strip flattens the vesicles and results in lamellar stacks of orientated, centrosymmetric membrane pairs that have been studied using X-ray diffraction. In diffraction from these vesicles, no off-meridional scattering has been observed, indicating that the Ca^{2+}-ATPase molecules are disordered in the membrane plane. The repeating unit of the lamellar stack contains a membrane pair and, depending on the water content, has a meridional repeat of 170–270 Å (Dupont *et al.*, 1973). The diffraction patterns were phased using swelling experiments to map out the continuous transform by measuring the diffracted intensities from specimens with different repeat distances. In this case the swelling series was complicated because at low water contents the distance between vesicles increased with increasing water content, while the distance between membranes of an individual vesicle was nearly constant; at higher water contents the reverse was observed. A swelling experiment requires that the scattering unit has a constant structure for the different lattice constants. Thus, at low water content the membranes from a single vesicle were chosen as the invariant scattering unit; at high water contents the opposed membranes of adjacent vesicles were taken to be the invariant structure. Interpretation of the data as two independent swelling series led to a self-consistent interpretation of the diffraction data (Dupont *et al.*, 1973) and resulted in the electron density profiles shown in Figure 2.19.

The SR membrane electron density profile is asymmetric with a large mass of electron density projecting from the cytoplasmic side of the vesicles. The authors identify this density with the Ca^{2+}-ATPase active transport system. Analysis of the lipid content of the unit cell suggested that 30–40 per cent of the volume of the membrane between lipid polar head groups was probably occupied by protein. This result is consistent with the expectation that the Ca^{2+} transport protein spans the membrane. Although another diffraction study (Worthington and Liu, 1973) contradicted these interpretations, more recent diffraction studies (Herbette, *et al.*, 1977; 1981a; 1981b) have reconfirmed the principal results of Dupont *et al.* (1973). Solution scattering results (Brady *et al.*, 1981b; 1982) are also consistent with these results, indicating that the Ca^{2+}-ATPase is an elongated molecule with an axial ratio of about 4 : 1, projecting mainly from one side of the membrane.

Observation of strong diffraction on the equator at about 10 Å spacing and on the meridian at 5.2 Å spacing (Herbette *et al.*, 1977) suggests that a high proportion of the Ca^{2+}-ATPase is in an α-helical conformation with the α helices being mainly perpendicular to the membrane surface.

Electron micrographs of negatively-stained SR vesicles (Ikemoto *et al.*, 1968; Stewart and MacLennon, 1974) show numerous 40 Å diameter particles on the cytoplasmic side of the membrane. The centre of these particles, seen at the edge of the vesicles, appears to be 30–60 Å from the membrane surface, making them project 50–80 Å into the cytoplasm. These particles correlate with the projec-

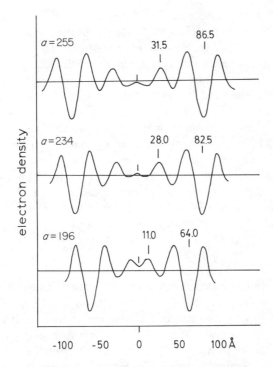

Figure 2.19 Electron density profile of the sarcoplasmic reticulum membrane vesicles calculated at three different water contents, corresponding to lamellar repeat distances of 255, 234 and 196 Å. The origin has been chosen to be half-way between two vesicles so that the vesicle interiors (corresponding to the SR lumen) are at the outside edges of the curves and the centre of the curves correspond to the muscle cell cytoplasm. The lipid bilayers are clearly visible as is additional density about 55 Å from the bilayer centres on the cytoplasmic surfaces. These electron density peaks on the cytoplasmic surfaces of the SR membranes almost certainly correspond to the Ca^{2+}-ATPase and the 40 Å diameter particles seen by electron microscopy of negatively stained SR membranes (from Dupont *et al.*, 1973)

tion of electron density from the cytoplasmic surface in the electron density profiles and are almost surely components of the calcium transport system.

Reconstituted SR vesicles can be formed from deoxycholate solubilised SR proteins and lipids (Meissner and Fleischer, 1974). These vesicles regain some, but not all, of their ATPase activity. Structurally, however, these vesicles no longer exhibit the asymmetry of the isolated SR vesicles; 40 Å diameter particles are seen on both surfaces of the membranes in reconstituted SR vesicles (Saito *et al.*, 1978). Asymmetric vesicles can be obtained in the reconstitution if the molar ratio of lipid to protein is kept above 88 (Herbette *et al.*, 1981a; 1981b). With high lipid-to-protein ratios the reconstituted vesicles accumulate Ca^{2+} in the presence of ATP (Herbette *et al.*, 1981a), just as is observed for the isolated vesicles. X-ray diffraction and electron microscopy both indicate that the vesicles with low protein content are asymmetric with most but probably not all of the Ca^{2+}-ATPase projecting from their external surfaces (Herbette *et al.*, 1981b). At lower lipid:protein ratios the efficiency of Ca^{2+} accumulation in the reconstituted vesicles decreases and both X-ray diffraction and electron microscopy indicate a more symmetric distribution of Ca^{2+}-ATPase on the two sides of the membrane. The mechanism by which lipid:protein ratio affects the symmetry of reconstituted membranes is not understood. Alternatively, the high detergent content associated with the high protein content can perturb the lipid bilayer and facilitate the reassembly of a symmetric membrane from mixed micelles of protein, lipid and detergent is possible that membrane curvature or some aspect of the mechanism of membrane assembly during reconstitution is contributing to the asymmetry. At high protein contents specific protein–protein or protein–lipid interactions at one membrane surface can saturate, forcing additional protein to take on the reverse orientation.

Human erythrocyte membrane

The human erythrocyte membrane is one of the best characterised biological membranes. The methods discussed in this chapter have, however, contributed relatively little to our understanding of this membrane. To date, none of the membrane proteins have been induced to form two-dimensional arrays. Furthermore, spectrin, the major structural protein, is a very large, filamentous, relatively flexible molecule (Shotton, *et al.*, 1979) easily dissociated from the membrane. Thus, in addition to the usual disorder and polymorphism in the conformation of the lipids, there may be an intrinsic polymorphism in the protein structure.

Approximately 52 per cent of the erythrocyte membrane mass is protein (Steck, 1974), 40 per cent is lipid and 8 per cent is carbohydrate (most of which is in the form of small oligomers attached to membrane glycoproteins). About 60 per cent of the membrane protein mass forms a continous network or membrane skeleton on the cytoplasmic surface of the membrane (Lux, 1979; Branton *et al.*, 1981). Most of the remaining proteins, including the Band 3 anion channel, span the membrane. The major proteins in the cytoskeleton are spectrin, actin, ankyrin and Band 4.1. Spectrin makes up about 75 per cent of the mass of the membrane skeleton.

As none of the membrane proteins have been induced to form two-dimensional arrays, X-ray diffraction studies have been limited to a study of the membrane profile. Early diffraction studies (Wilkins *et al.*, 1971; Stamatoff *et al.*, 1975; Pape *et al.*, 1977) used membrane ghosts (haemoglobin-free red cells) prepared in conditions that are now known to displace spectrin from the membrane. Diffraction studies of membranes prepared in such a way as to retain spectrin (McCaughan and Krimm, 1980) have resulted in a low (approximately 40 Å) resolution membrane profile. Because of the limited resolution, no details of the membrane proteins are apparent in the profile. The separation between density peaks in the profile was 48 Å. This is 12 Å larger than that found for extracted red blood cell lipids (Rand and Luzzati, 1968). The magnitude of this difference is difficult to understand. It is possible that protein-lipid interactions or the asymmetric distribution of lipids in the intact membrane might contribute to some increase in thickness. The very limited resolution of the study of intact membranes could also lead to an overestimate of the membrane thickness and this effect might be amplified by the presence of a dense layer of protein at the cytoplasmic membrane surface. Thus, although there appears to be a difference in the thickness of bilayers in the intact erythrocyte membrane and in liquid crystals of isolated erythrocyte lipids, it may not be as dramatic as suggested by comparison of the derived profiles.

The structural organisation of the erythrocyte membrane skeleton has been extensively studied by electron microscopy of freeze-fractured, freeze-etched and heavy metal shadowed specimens. The membrane skeleton retains the size and shape of the intact red cell membrane after the cell is extracted with a non-ionic detergent, removing most of the lipid (Yu *et al.*, 1973; Tilney and Detmers, 1975; Hainfield and Steck, 1977; Sheetz, 1979). In negative stain, the skeleton appears as an anastomosing network of 80-120 Å diameter beaded filaments (Sheetz and Sawyer, 1978). In the membrane skeleton the spectrin is in the form of an $\alpha_2\beta_2$ tetramer made up of two $\alpha\beta$ heterodimers that interact in a head-to-head arrangement (Shotton *et al.*, 1979). The spectrin dimers, when visualised using low angle rotary shadowing (Shotton *et al.*, 1978) appear as two flexible strands, loosely coiled around one another and associated by contacts mainly at each end, as shown in micrographs in Figure 2.20. The dimers are around 970 Å long, the tetramers about 1940 Å.

Spectrin binds to the membrane via ankyrin which interacts with the Band 3 integral protein (Bennett and Stenbuck, 1979). Spectrin tetramers act to cross-link actin filaments (Cohen *et al.*, 1980), whereas spectrin dimers bind to, but do not crosslink, actin filaments. Actin–spectrin interactions are mediated through Band 4.1 protein (Ungewickell *et al.*, 1979) which, in addition to binding actin and spectrin, may act as a secondary membrane attachment protein. The membrane skeleton has been shown to affect the aggregation of membrane particles observed in freeze-fractured specimens (Elgsaeter and Branton, 1974) and spectrin has been shown to cluster on the cytoplasmic surface directly underlying the membrane particle clusters (Shotton *et al.*, 1978). However, much of the membrane protein that can be labelled with fluorescein-isothiocyanate retains mobility in the presence of the spectrin-actin network (Fowler and Branton, 1977; Fowler and Bennett, 1978).

Rod outer segments

Rods are photoreceptor cells in vertebrate retina. The outer segment of the rod cell is a cylinder, microns in diameter and tens of microns long. Throughout its length, membrane-bound discs formed by the infolding and sealing off of the plasma membrane, are stacked with a period of about 300 Å. Roughly

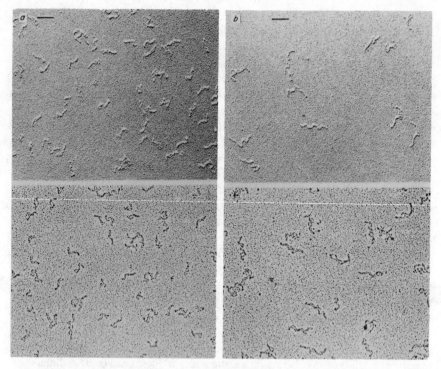

Figure 2.20 Electron micrographs of spectrin dimers (*a*) and tetramers (*b*). The spectrin was visualised using unidirectional shadowing (above) and low-angle rotary shadowing (below) to make the heavy metal replicas (from Shotton *et al.*, 1980). Scale bar: 0.1 μm

one-half of the dry weight of the disc membrane (Bownds *et al.*, 1971) and 95 per cent of the protein weight (McCaslin and Tanford, 1981a) are due to the visual pigment rhodopsin, a protein of approximately 40,000 MW (Hubbard, 1954; McCaslin and Tanford, 1981a) containing covalently bound retinal and carbohydrates.

Visual excitation is initiated in the disc membrane by photoisomerisation of the retinal bound to rhodopsin. Subsequent events lead to a reduction of the Na^+ current flowing from the inner segment region to the outer segment region (Penn and Hagins, 1969) and a hyperpolarisation (hyper-increased polarisation, or increased negative voltage drop relative to the extracellular space) of the rod outer segment (Tomita, 1970). The hyperpolarisation is propagated down the visual pathway. Structural studies have been directed at determining the disposition of the rhodopsin in the disc membrane and at detecting light-induced structural changes corresponding to the conformational changes of rhodopsin and permeability changes in the disc membrane and the plasma membrane.

The quasi-crystalline array of paired disc membranes is responsible for the strong meridional X-ray diffraction observed from the retina in the living eye (Webb, 1972, 1977; Funk *et al.*, 1981), from dissected retina (Grass and

Worthington, 1969, 1972; Corless, 1972; Chabre and Cavaggioni, 1973; Schwartz *et al.*, 1975) and from isolated rod outer segments (Chabre, 1975; Chabre and Cavaggioni, 1975). These patterns show up to 11 Bragg reflections of the disc-stacking period of about 300 Å and the relative peak intensities of the reflections are very consistent among the patterns. Therefore, out to 30 Å resolution the average profile on the disc membrane pair is conserved among the different systems and preparations.

The lamellar reflections are seen to broaden with increasing scattering angles and are well resolved only up to the 7th or 8th order. This indicates a short-range disorder in the absence of long-range order — the disc spacings are variable about the mean period and the variations are accumulated up the stack. Furthermore, well orientated, diffuse intensity, which is present underlying the Bragg reflections, has been observed extending to 8 Å spacing (Blaurock and Wilkins, 1969), resembling the continuous intensity from a single membrane rather than that from a centrosymmetric membrane pair. This shows that the disc membrane separations are variable both across the cytoplasm and across the disc lumen. These variable separations are the source of the disorder of disc spacings and limit the resolution of the disc profile to 30 Å.

In diffraction patterns from the retinae, the small size of the rod outer segment (less than 60 microns long) compared to the normally collimated incident beam makes it difficult to avoid parasitic scattering from other structures. Only when a point focused X-ray beam was used (Blaurock and Wilkins, 1969, 1972; Chabre, 1975; Funk *et al.*, 1981) was it possible to monitor the orientation of the disc membranes and then to separate the orientated scattering from the disc and the unorientated scattering from other structures.

Disc profiles have been calculated using two general procedures: by phasing the amplitudes taken from integrated intensities at shrinkage stages (Blaurock and Wilkins, 1972; Corless, 1972; Chabre, 1975) or by fitting continuous intensities to parameters of the variable membrane separations (Schwartz *et al.*, 1975; Funk *et al.*, 1981). The phase choices obtained by these procedures were generally in agreement. The resultant profiles all show a pair of bilayers with their centres about 88 Å apart. Each bilayer had density peaks about 40 Å apart and a density extension from the cytoplasmic side. Given the high rhodopsin content of disc membranes, this profile can be accounted for by rhodopsin traversing the lipid bilayer and being exposed at both surfaces, particularly the cytoplasmic surface. This disposition is indicated by the biochemical results locating the amino terminus and carbohydrates within the disc and the carboxyl terminus within the cytoplasm (Hargrave *et al.*, 1980; Dratz *et al.*, 1979; Fung and Hubbell, 1978). It is also consistent with the electron microscope finding that antiserum against rhodopsin binds to the surface of isolated cattle discs (Blasie *et al.*, 1969) and that, after freeze fracture, rhodopsin remains attached primarily to the cytoplasmic half of the disc membrane (Corless *et al.*, 1976). Unfortunately, a quantitative description of the relative membrane areas due to the rhodopsin and lipids across the membrane thickness has not been obtained because the calculated disc profiles were not in agreement with regard to the bilayer asymmetry and the peak-to-trough density ratios, even though a consistent structure should be expected on the basis of the diffraction patterns.

The ambiguities in the details of the profile of the disc membrane illustrate the importance of accurate intensities. Incorrect subtraction of background and parasitic scattering can alter the relative intensities of different reflections. Moreover, reflections broadened and not completely resolved due to disorder cannot be adequately represented by discrete integrated intensities. It has been shown that variable membrane separations give rise to an incoherent intensity (Schwartz *et al.*, 1975) which reaches maximum where the transform of the membrane profile is at its extremum at about 40 Å spacing. The membrane profile asymmetry and the depth of the minimum in the centre of the bilayer are particularly sensitive to the shape of the transform in this region (Li, 1978; Nelander and Blaurock, 1978). Difficulties in estimating its contribution may have led to the discrepancies among the reported membrane profiles.

The distribution of rhodopsin in the plane of the disc membrane is more liquid-like than crystalline. This is shown by a broad equatorial band centred at 52 to 57 Å spacing, observed in diffraction from well orientated rod outer segments (Blaurock and Wilkins, 1969) and from isolated, reorientated discs (Chabre, 1975). Additional diffuse intensity at 4.5 Å spacing indicates a fluid state of the membrane lipids over the physiological temperature range (Chabre, 1975).

X-ray intensities at 10.5 Å on the equator (Blaurock and Wilkins, 1969) and at 5 Å on the meridian (Gruner *et al.*, 1978) have shown that rhodopsin contains α-helical segments in a predominantly transmembrane orientation. The helical content of rhodopsin, based on circular dichroism of the detergent-solubilised protein is about 50 per cent (Shichi and Shelton, 1974; Stubbs *et al.*, 1976).

Two light-induced structural changes have been reported from X-ray diffraction. The first, a small shift of electron densities in the disc membrane toward the cytoplasmic surface (Corless, 1972; Chabre, 1975), is only observed in non-physiological total bleaching conditions. Contrast matching experiments in neutron diffraction identified this shift to be a displacement of the membrane protein (Saibel *et al.*, 1976). The second, a transient shrinkage of the disc spacing by 0.5 per cent, is an osmotic effect related to the light modulation of ion permeabilities (Chabre and Cavaggioni, 1973, 1975). The mechanism that leads to the permeability changes, be it by Ca^{2+} release from the disc (Hagins, 1972) or through regulation of cyclic GMP levels (Kühn *et al.*, 1981), is still undetermined.

Two-dimensional crystals of rhodopsin have been obtained (Corless *et al.*, 1982) by treatment of purified frog discs with the non-ionic detergent Tween-80 that removed roughly 50 per cent of the total membrane lipids. Figure 2.21*a* is an electron micrograph of the resultant crystalline sheet. The rhodopsin molecules are organised into an orthorhombic lattice with symmetry $p22_12_1$ (Holser, 1958) and lattice dimensions of 47 ± 1 Å by 151 ± 2 Å. There are two-

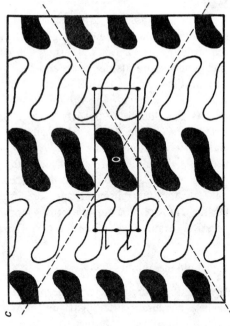

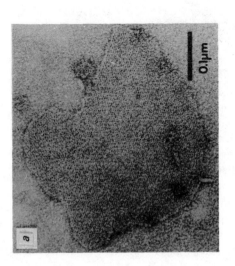

Figure 2.21 Two-dimensional membrane crystal of rhodopsin prepared from the disc membranes of frog retinal rod outer segments by treatment with the detergent Tween-80. *a*, Electron micrograph of a negatively-stained membrane crystal. Its optical diffraction pattern indicates that the lattice is orthorhombic with a unit cell of 47 Å × 151 Å, and $p22_12_1$ symmetry. The screw axes in the membrane plane require bidirectional orientation of the protein molecules in the crystalline sheet. *b*, Contour map of the computer-filtered projection of the stain distribution. Low contours indicate stain exclusion by the portions of the rhodopsin molecules extending above and below the lipid bilayer. Each stain-excluding feature is due to a dimer of protein molecules related by a two-fold axis normal to the plane. *c*, Schematic representation of the arrangement of rhodopsin dimers in the unit cell. Black and white sigmoids distinguish the two orientations relative to the bilayer; •, two-fold rotation axis normal to the plane; ↪, two-fold screw axis lying in the plane (from Corless *et al.*, 1982)

fold axes perpendicular to the sheet and two-fold screw axes in the plane of the sheet and parallel to the a, b edges of the unit cell. The computed projection of the structure in Figure 2.21b shows in each unit cell a sigmoid-shaped, stain-excluding feature at the centre and four such features of the opposite handedness at the corners. In accordance with the $p22_12_1$ symmetry, each sigmoid represents a dimer of the rhodopsin molecule and the alternating handedness reflects the alternating polarity of insertion into the sheet, as required by the screw axes (Figure 2.21c). The sigmoidal shaped feature is 20 to 25 Å wide and 70 to 80 Å long giving $1,323$ Å^2 as the projected area per monomer. Compared to the molecular weight and the specific volume of 0.735 cm^3/g^{-1} of rhodopsin (McCaslin and Tanford, 1981b), this area predicts a molecular height of 71 Å in the transmembrane direction, which would project beyond the bilayer and account for the strong contrast in the electron micrographs of negatively-stained crystalline sheets and disc membranes.

Thylakoid membranes

Thylakoid membranes are the chlorophyll-containing membranes of green plants. In these membranes the "light" reactions of photosynthesis take place catalysed by two photopigment systems operating in series (see Govindjee, 1975). Briefly, the reaction catalysed by photosystem II is associated with oxygen evolution; that catalysed by photosystem I is responsible for NADP reduction; and the electron transfer from photosystem II to photosystem I is coupled to ATP production. The ATP and NADPH produced on these membranes are fuel for the "dark" synthetic reactions taking place in the soluble matrix, called the stroma, of the chloroplast organelle.

Thylakoid membranes are differentiated laterally into stacked and unstacked membranes, called grana and stroma membranes, respectively. The stacked morphology is due to a close apposition, over areas 5,000–8,000 Å in diameter, of the outer surface of successive thylakoids. Freeze-fracture electron micrographs of thylakoids showed that the large (160 Å diameter) intramembrane particles are restricted to the stacked membranes (Goodenough and Staehelin, 1971), where they extend to both membrane surfaces (Miller, 1976; Miller *et al.*, 1976). Fractionation of thylakoid membranes following mechanical or detergent rupture revealed that, whereas grana membranes have both photosystem II and photosystem I activities, the stroma membranes can only carry out photosystem I reactions (Anderson and Boardman, 1966; Sane *et al.*, 1970).

These distinctions are well correlated with the distribution of the two major chlorophyll proteins (Anderson and Levine, 1974), which account for a combined 70 per cent of the thylakoid membrane proteins (Thornber, 1975, 1979). The first is the P700-chlorophyll *a* protein, which contains the reaction centre pigment of photosystem I and is found preferentially in stroma membranes. The second, the chlorophyll *a/b* light-harvesting protein, is the major antenna for photosynthesis, supplying light quanta chiefly to photosystem II. This protein is localised in the grana membranes and studies of thylakoid development suggest that it exists as subunits of the large membrane spanning particles (Armond *et al.*, 1976). Moreover, the light-harvesting protein has been implicated as the stacking factor, because genetic and chemical modifications of it are observed to interfere with thylakoid stacking (Berg *et al.*, 1974; Arntzen *et al.*, 1976; Staehelin *et al.*, 1976; Steinback *et al.*, 1978).

Early X-ray studies of thylakoid membranes (Kreutz, 1970) overlooked the lateral differentiation into two structures. Sadler *et al.* (1973) circumvented this problem by examining thylakoids of the unicellular organism *Euglena gracilis*, which are entirely stacked, two to five at a time, into "discs" analogous to the grana of higher plants. Diffraction patterns from pellets dried at 90 per cent humidity showed five orders of membrane pair reflections, at a period of 165 Å to 174 Å. However, reflections from a separate lipid phase were also present, indicating membrane disintegration due to excessive drying. The electron density profiles calculated using only the thylakoid reflections showed that, of the two aqueous spaces found in each repeat period, the thylakoid lumen is highly variable in width, but the extra-thylakoid membrane separation is relatively invariant. A similar conclusion can be drawn from the diffraction patterns of spinach thylakoids in suspension (Sadler, 1976), where the ionic conditions were chosen to maintain grana formation (Izawa and Good, 1966).

A prerequisite for detailed intensity analysis leading to reliable membrane profiles is specimen homogeneity. For higher plant thylakoid membranes, homogeneity was attained by preparing a pure grana fraction, and by controlling dehydration of the specimen (used to promote membrane orientation) to prevent membrane disintegration and phase separation. Li (1978) purified grana membrane from the shade plants (Bjorkman, 1972), *Heliconia harrisii* and *H. rostrata*, which are adapted to growth in low light intensities and are rich in grana membranes. Electron microscopy confirmed that the close apposition of the extra-thylakoid surfaces was preserved in the X-ray specimens.

Strong meridional X-ray patterns to ~25 Å spacing were observed from pellets of orientated grana membranes. The presence of broad Bragg reflections from membrane pairs together with continuous diffuse scattering indicates variable repeat distance between thylakoid membrane pairs and, within each pair, both variable membrane centre-to-centre separation and a variable thylakoid membrane profile (compare Schwartz *et al.*, 1975, on rod outer segment; Blaurock and Nelander, 1976, on myelin). As the same intensity envelope was observed in thylakoid patterns showing repeat periods ranging from 163 Å to 200 Å, variations in the thylakoid membrane pair profile centred at the extra-thylakoid apposition are, at the resolution of the data, apparently not correlated with variations of the thylakoid repeat. A direct consequence of the non-correlation is that the intensity from the stacked thylakoids is separable into a coherent term equal to the diffraction by stacks of average membrane pairs and an incoherent term equal to the variance of the scattering from differing membrane pairs (Guinier, 1963).

Through iterative refinement, a self-consistent structural solution was determined that specifies both the average thylakoid membrane profile and the structural variabilities (Li, 1978). This model predicted the coherent and incoherent terms of the scattering from thylakoid arrays, which fits the observed continuous intensity to within an R-factor of 5 per cent. Furthermore, the validity of this result was confirmed by Monte Carlo calculations of the total intensity (Li, 1979). These calculations showed that the membrane profile was stringently defined by the data, and placed limits on the range of structural variations present in the stacked thylakoids.

The average electron density profile of stacked thylakoid membranes is shown in Figure 2.22*a*. The membrane contains a bilayer with only 34 Å separating the lipid head groups. This thinness is consistent with the high degree of unsaturation in the lipid acyl chains (Engelman, 1971), where linolenic acid predominates (18:3) (Kates, 1970). Moreover, isolated thylakoid membrane lipids, which consist mainly of monogalactosyl and digalactosyl diglycerides at a 2:1 molar ratio, have been shown by X-ray diffraction to form bilayers in water with a 34 Å partial thickness for the lipids (Rivas and Luzzati, 1969; Shipley *et al.*, 1973).

Based on correlation of the membrane profile with chemical composition of the same grana preparation, it was concluded that proteins are distributed asymmetrically across the bilayer in the stacked thylakoid membranes. This is summarised in the model, Figure 2.22*b*. In the hydrophobic interior 25 per cent of the membrane area is occupied by proteins. This is consistent with the total area of intramembrane particle in electron micrographs of replicas of frozen-fractured grana membranes (Staehelin, 1976), allowing that the diameter of each particle was increased by 30 Å due to deposition of heavy metals in making the replica (Slayter, 1976). The model also shows proteins extending 10 Å beyond the lumen surface over 20 per cent of the membrane area. This is again consistent with electron microscopic observations and supports the notion that the large intramembrane particles and the lumen surface particles observed on replicas of freeze-fractured and etched specimens are two images of the same molecular structure (Staehelin, 1976; Miller, 1976). The chlorophyll *a/b* light-harvesting protein, being the major integral membrane protein of the grana, is the most likely constituent of this structure. Of the extra-thylakoid surface area, 40 per cent is covered by proteins. Both segments of the integral membrane proteins responsible for thylakoid stacking, and the peripheral proteins functioning in photosynthetic electron transport (Anderson, 1975) must contribute to the protein content of this surface.

A more detailed molecular picture of a membrane as chemically complex as the thylakoids is difficult to obtain. However, detailed stereochemical information is obtainable on isolated photosynthetic membrane components by placing them in well-ordered two- and three-dimensional lattices. Studies of two of these systems, the chlorophyll *a/b* light-harvesting protein, and the photosynthetic reaction centre from *Rhodopseudomonas viridis* are described in later sections of this chapter.

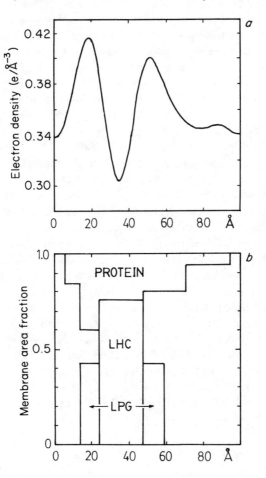

Figure 2.22 The average electron density profile of "stacked' (granal) thylakoid membranes from *Heleconia harrisii* (*a*), and the model of protein and lipid distribution across the membrane (*b*), based on correlation of this profile with the membrane chemical composition. The boundary between thylakoids is at $x = 0$, and the lumen is on the right. LHC, lipid hydrocarbon; LPG, lipid polar groups (from Li, 1978)

Lipid-containing viruses

In electron micrographs of negatively-stained specimens, many lipid-containing viruses appear irregular in structure and heterogeneous in size and shape. A few of the smaller viruses, such as bacteriophage PM2 (Harrison *et al.*, 1971a), appear more regular, but these are exceptions. X-ray and neutron diffraction studies have demonstrated that some of the larger lipid-containing viruses have a more regular structure in solution than the micrographs suggest. These include Sindbis virus (Harrison *et al.*, 1971b), influenza B virus (Mellema *et al.*, 1981), bacteriophage ϕ6 (Makowski and Mindich, unpublished data), the 1,580 Å diameter frog virus 3

(Cuil!el *et al.*, 1979) and vesicular stomatitis virus (Makowski, Fahey and Caspar, unpublished data). Diffraction patterns from solutions or pellets of each of these viruses show a series of sharp rings of intensity with well-defined intervening minima characteristic of a homogeneous population of particles. Figure 2.7*a* shows a diffraction pattern from a pellet of bacteriophage ϕ6. The series of diffraction fringes out to about 30 Å resolution indicates a regularity in the structure of the $\sim$700 Å diameter virus particle that is not evident in electron micrographs. The apparent irregularity and heterogeneity in the images of negatively-stained particles seem to be caused by distortion or collapse of the particles during drying on the electron microscope grid. These distortions have precluded an unambiguous determination of the surface organisation of the virus particles which, for the isometric particles, is expected on theoretical grounds to exhibit icosahedral symmetry (Caspar and Klug, 1962).

As an example of the structural studies on viral membranes, we will consider Sindbis virus in some detail. Sindbis virus is made up of a nucleoprotein core containing RNA and subunits of a single 30,000-MW protein, wrapped by an envelope containing lipid and two distinct protein species, both with molecular weights of about 50,000 (Strauss *et al.*, 1968; Schlesinger *et al.*, 1972). X-ray diffraction patterns from pellets of the approximately spherical sindbis virus particles were used to determine the spherically averaged, radial electron density distribution to 28 Å resolution (Harrison *et al.*, 1971b). This electron density distribution is shown in Figure 2.23. The electron density extends out to a radius of about 350 Å with a pronounced minimum at 232 Å radius. The minimum corresponds to the lipid bilayer which is about 40 Å thick. The virus core is a relatively smooth-surfaced sphere with an outer radius of

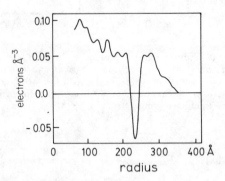

Figure 2.23 Spherically averaged electron density distribution of Sindbis virus. The graph is plotted as a function of radius and the electron density scale is given in electrons Å^{-3} with solvent density taken as zero. The high electron density at radii less than 150 A is due to the viral RNA and core protein. The lipid bilayer is seen as a distinct minimum at about 232 A radius. Density extending to higher radii corresponds to the viral glycoprotein. The poiar head group peaks are not clearly distinguished because of the close juxtaposition of protein components with similar electron density (taken from Harrison *et al.*, 1971)

about 200 Å (Harrison and Sefton, unpublished results; Harrison *et al.*, 1974) which must interact closely with the lipid polar head groups of the bilayer at about 210 Å radius. The electron density extending from the external polar head groups of the bilayer at about 260 Å radius out to the maximum radius of the particle at 350 Å must correspond to the two viral glycoproteins.

The organisation of the viral proteins of Sindbis is not clear in electron micrographs of negatively-stained nucleocapsids (Acheson and Tamm, 1970) or intact virions. There do, however, appear to be several characteristic, reproducible images of the virions indicative of a regular surface structure (Harrison *et al.*, 1974). Chemical analysis of the closely related Semliki forest virus particles (Laine *et al.* 1973) indicates that there are about 240 copies of the nucleocapsid protein and of each of the two glycoproteins. As Semliki forest virus has a radial electron density distribution essentially identical to Sindbis (Harrison and Kaariainen, unpublished data; Harrison *et al.*, 1974) it is possible that the symmetry of both particles is that of a T = 4 icosahedral surface lattice (Caspar and Klug, 1962). The stoichiometry of the particle suggests that both nucleocapsid core and the envelope glycoproteins are arranged with the same symmetry. Thus, the available electron microscope, X-ray diffraction and chemical data are all consistent with a regular arrangement of glycoproteins on a viral surface.

The Semliki forest virus glycoproteins span the viral membrane (Garoff and Simons, 1974; Utermann and Simons, 1974), attached by a hydrophobic region of peptide near the carboxyl terminus (Garoff and Soderlund, 1978). The assembly of the virus by a budding process during which the pre-assembled viral capsid is enclosed by a region of the host cell membrane containing the viral glycoproteins but few, if any, host proteins suggest that specific interactions may be occurring between the viral core proteins and the viral glycoproteins. This could result in 1:1 stoichiometry and identical symmetries of the core and envelope proteins. However, the symmetry of the core may not always be reproduced by the envelope proteins. In vesicular stomatitus virus, another animal virus that assembles by budding (but which is bullet-shape rather than isometric), the surface glycoprotein is also anchored to the membrane by a carboxyl terminal region of hydrophobic amino acid residues (Rose *et al.*, 1980). For this virus, the ratio of matrix protein to glycoprotein is not always constant and the glycoprotein is not strictly essential for assembly (Lodish *et al.*, 1980). Thus, although here is a potential for the symmetric arrangement of envelope glycoproteins in lipid-containing viruses, that potential may not always be realised.

Coated vesicles

Coated vesicles are the vehicles for a large intracellular molecular traffic among the organelles and the plasma membrane (Roth and Porter, 1964; Friend and Farquar, 1967; Heuser and Reese, 1973; Anderson *et al.*, 1977; Rothman and

Fine, 1980). Furthermore, many proteins and peptides that enter cells by receptor-mediated endocytosis are internalised by clustering of receptors in specialised regions of the cell surface called coated pits (Goldstein *et al.*, 1979) that invaginate to form coated vesicles. Both structures are composed of a bilayer structure enveloped by a polygonal protein basket or lattice (Kanaeski and Kadota, 1969; Crowther *et al.*, 1976; Heuser, 1980). The principal constituent of the lattice is the protein clathrin, made up of one heavy chain (180,000 MW) and one of two classes of light chains (molecular weights 33,000 and 36,000) (Pearse, 1975, 1976, 1978; Kirchhausen and Harrison, 1981). Clathrin is anchored to the underlying membrane by interaction with a 110,000-MW protein (Kirchhausen and Harrison, 1981; Unanue *et al.*, 1981). The clathrin coats dissociate reversibly into trimers called triskelions (Ungewickell amd Branton, 1981). Electron micrographs of low-angle rotary-shadowed and negatively-stained triskelions show that they are composed of three curved, apparently flexible arms radiating from a centre. Each arm is about 450 Å long (Ungewickell and Branton, 1981) and there is some reason to believe that they are not coplanar (Kirchhausen and Harrison, 1981).

Coated vesicles range in size from about 450 to several thousand angstroms in diameter (Crowther *et al.*, 1976; Heuser, 1980) and the clathrin coat may extend out from the surface of the enclosed membrane by as much as 200 Å. Computer modelling of electron micrographs of negatively-stained 'empty baskets' — coats without internal vesicles — identified at least three different arrangements of polygonal lattice among the smallest coated vesicles (Crowther *et al.*, 1976). Each arrangement contained 12 pentagons with a variable number of hexagons. The clathrin molecules make up the edges of the polygons. All vertices of the lattice work are at the junctions of three edges, suggesting that each vertex includes the centre of a triskelion (Crowther and Pearse, 1981; Ungelwickell and Branton, 1981). As the triskelion arms are about twice the length of the edges of the polygons, each clathrin molecule may extend along two polygonal edges. The observed arrangements indicate that the clathrin molecules must be flexible as it would be impossible to form these structures in such a way that all the molecules are identically arranged. For instance, there are empty baskets, in which some of the hexagons are flat while others appear puckered (Crowther *et al.*, 1976).

Figure 2.24*a* shows a tilt series of five micrographs of a single empty basket viewed at different tilt angles along with a computer generated gallery of corresponding views (Crowther *et al.*, 1976). The central view is the clearest because of the superposition of the details on the two sides of the basket. Figure 2.24*b* shows several micrographs of replicas of freeze-etched empty baskets (Heuser, 1980). These micrographs appear clearer than those of the negatively-stained specimens because they show only one surface of the basket. The overall arrangement of the polygons in the baskets is, however, more difficult to determine from these micrographs. The image in the centre of the

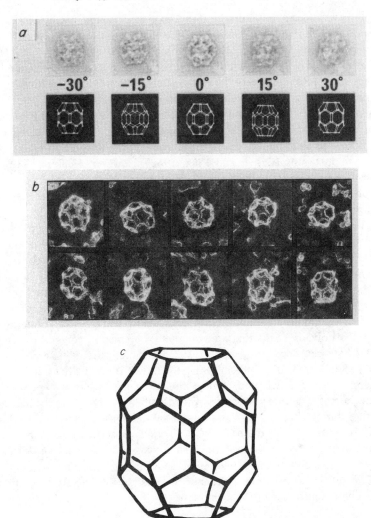

Figure 2.24 *a*, Tilt series of five micrographs of a single negatively-stained 'empty basket' and a set of computer generated images corresponding to the micrographs. The empty basket is a small coated vesicle that has lost its underlying vesicle. The basketwork is composed of 108 clathrin molecules organised along the edges of 12 pentagons and 8 hexagons with 36 trivalent vertices. The features in the centre micrograph are clearest due to superposition of structural features from the top and bottom of the basket (from Crowther *et al.*, 1976). *b*, Electron micrographs of replicas of freeze-etched samples of empty baskets. Although the surface features are clear in these micrographs, a substantial portion of each basket is not visible, making a direct interpretation of the entire organisation of the baskets difficult (from Heuser, 1980). *c*, Diagram of the structural organisation found in some of the small empty baskets of clathrin molecules. The clathrin molecules are arranged to form the edges of 12 pentagons and 8 hexagons. The hexagons on the top and bottom appear flat, whereas those around the barrel appear puckered. This is one of three arrangements found for small empty baskets (drawing from Anderson *et al.*, 1977)

bottom row appears to have the same geometry as the particle in *a* and a diagram of this arrangement is shown in *c*. This is only one of several structural arrangements of clathrin observed in small coated vesicles.

Larger coated vesicles and their precursor coated pits are constructed based on the same local geometry and the same patterns of interactions of the clathrin molecules. Direct analogy to the smaller vesicles would suggest that in the larger ones the clathrin molecules are arranged to form 12 pentagons and a variable number of hexagons (Crowther *et al.*, 1976). Increased curvature of the vesicles should require an increase in the proportion of pentagons relative to hexagons (Caspar and Klug, 1962). However, Heuser (1980), in a study of coated pits with different radii of curvature, noted that the proportion of pentagons observed was smaller than expected and that even sheets with no pentagons exhibited some curvature.

A major unsolved problem in understanding endocytosis is the mechanism by which curvature of the coated pits is increased during invagination. This could occur by the replacement of hexagons by pentagons in the clathrin coat (Kanaseki and Kadota, 1969). However, a pentagon cannot be introduced into the centre of a sheet of hexagons without the rearrangement of an entire section of the basketwork, requiring the breaking and reforming of a large number of intermolecular bonds. This is also true of pentagon–heptagon (regular, seven-sided polygon) pairs that are commonly observed in coated pits (Heuser, 1980). These can occur only at a crystal dislocation, that is, at a pleat in the lattice. Alternatively, it is possible that the lattice is originally assembled with pentagons already distributed among the hexagons. Pentagon–heptagon pairs may be variant structures indicative of the flexibility of clathrin. The increase in curvature during endocytosis could be the natural consequence of the addition of clathrin triskelions to the basketwork. Triskelions seem to interact with one another in such a way as to form a latticework with a curved surface. The energy associated with the binding of additional clathrin molecules to the lattice might act as a source of energy to generate the curvature of the lipid bilayer and the infolding of the membrane.

STRUCTURAL STUDIES ON PLANAR ARRAYS OF MEMBRANE COMPONENTS

Matrix porin

Matrix protein, or matrix porin, is a major protein component of the outer cell membrane of *Escherichia coli* (Rosenbusch, 1974; DiRienzo *et al.*, 1978). It forms extensive two-dimensional hexagonal lattices in the membrane plane (Steven *et al.*, 1977; Rosenbusch *et al.*, 1980), and it was perhaps the first integral membrane protein to have been crystallised in three dimensions in a form suitable for high resolution protein crystallography (Garavito and Rosenbusch, 1980). Matrix porin consists of a single polypeptide species of molecular weight 36,500 (Rosenbusch, 1974). In the outer bacterial membrane these polypeptides appear to be present as trimers. Porin confers a molecular sieve-like permeability to the membrane that allows nonspecific diffusion of molecules of up to 700 MW across the bilayer. When integrated into planar lipid bilayers, porin leads to the formation of voltage inducible, trans-membrane channels approximately 10 Å in diameter (Schindler and Rosenbusch, 1978). These channels seem to exist in two states – open and closed – which coexist in equilibrium with one another in the membrane. In the intact outer bacterial membrane, only about 1 in 20 of the channels may be open at any given time. In planar lipid bilayers the proportion of channels open is strongly dependent on pH and trans-membrane potential. The channels exhibit a high degree of cooperativity among themselves and the minimal inducible unit would seem to be three pores. Apparently, even at very low protein-to-lipid ratios the proteins exist as trimers in the membrane with one channel associated with each monomer.

The function of porin channels, most of which are closed in normal circumstances *in vivo*, is not well understood. Apparently they act as a means by which nutrients can enter the cell. The large excess of closed channels may be an important reserve used in conditions when the cell is starved of nutrients. The *in vivo* regulation of channel permeability has not yet been studied.

In the intact bacterial cell, porin is tightly, but non-covalently, associated with the peptidoglycan layer beneath the outer membrane (Rosenbusch, 1974). The peptidoglycan-associated proteins form relatively small, two-dimensional crystals with hexagonal lattices (Rosenbusch, 1974) that fuse together to form much larger arrays when the peptidoglycan is removed (Steven *et al.*, 1977). The lattice constant of the hexagonal array was estimated to be 77 Å using electron microscopy (Steven *et al.*, 1977) and 81 Å using X-ray diffraction (Rosenbusch *et al.*, 1980). X-ray diffraction patterns show that isolated porin membranes stack with a 46 Å repeat distance (Rosenbusch *et al.*, 1980), indicating that the porin molecules do not project more than a few angstroms above either face of the membrane bilayer. Circular dichroism and infrared spectroscopy indicate that a large fraction of the polypeptide is in a β-sheet conformation (Rosenbusch, 1974).

Figure 2.25 contains two electron micrographs of negatively-stained periodic arrays of matrix porin derived from spheroplasted *E. coli* cells. Optical diffraction patterns of these micrographs extend to the 5th order at 22 Å spacing. Optical and computer filtered images of porin derived from these micrographs are shown in Figure 2.26. These filtered images indicate that the morphological units visible in the micrographs in Figure 2.25 are trimers. Each of the three subunits in the trimer contains a strongly staining feature that has been interpreted as an indentation in the surface at least 20 Å in diameter (Steven *et al.*, 1977). Combined with the physiological results (Schindler and Rosenbusch, 1978) that indicate a minimal diameter of 10 Å for the trans-membrane channel, these electron micrographs suggest that the porin channel may be shaped like a

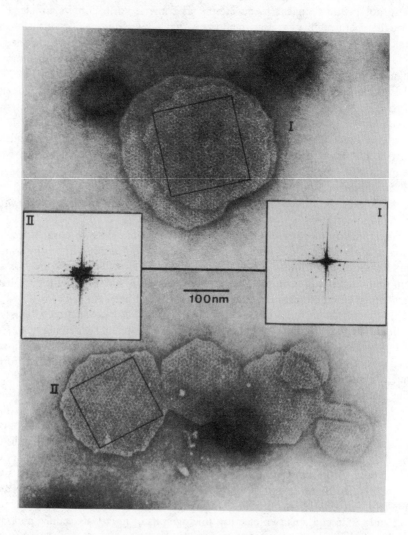

Figure 2.25 Electron micrographs of negatively-stained (2% sodium phosphotungstate) periodic arrays of matrix protein derived from spheroplasted *Escherichia coli* cells by differential heat treatment in SDS. The top micrograph is of two lattices superimposed. The optical diffraction pattern of area I (right inset) shows lattice reflections from two hexagonal lattices rotated relative to one another. The bottom micrograph shows several lattices, fused at their edges. The lattice reflections in the optical diffraction patterns index on a hexagonal lattice with a lattice constant of ~ 77 Å. The repeating units in these lattices do no have any obvious substructure in these unprocessed micrographs (from Steven *et al.*, 1977)

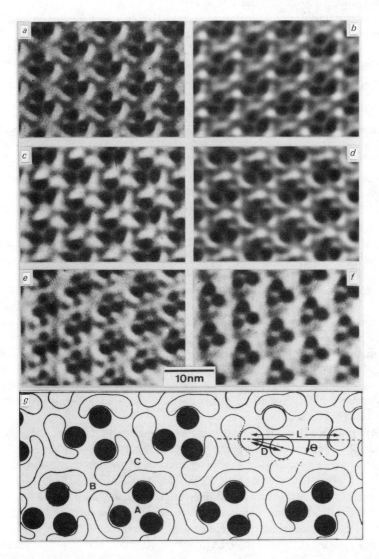

Figure 2.26 Images of matrix porin obtained by optical filtering (*a, c, e, f*) and computer filtering (*b, d*). The optically filtered images in *a* and *c* correspond to the computer generated images in *b* and *d*. The filtered images in *e* and *f* are from less well preserved specimens for comparison. All images indicate that three darkly staining regions are associated with each repeating unit of the lattice. *g* Is a schematic interpretation. The lattice constant, L, is about 77 Å, the centre-to-centre distance between the presumed indentations within a single triplet, D, is about 30 Å. The angle between the lines D and L, designated, in this diagram as θ, is 19° (from Steven *et al.*, 1977)

funnel (Rosenbusch *et al.*, 1980). One funnel-shaped channel is presumed to be associated with each 36,500-MW subunit.

The crystallisation of membrane porin (Garavito and Rosenbusch, 1980) brings with it the promise that a high resolution (~ 4 Å) three-dimensional structure of porin will soon be produced. It also inspires hope that other membrane proteins will soon be crystallised in three dimensions.

Chlorophyll *a/b* light-harvesting protein (LHC)

Roughly 50 per cent of the total protein and 50 per cent of the total chlorophyll, including all of the chlorophyll *b*, in the thylakoid membranes are present in the chlorophyll *a/b* light-harvesting protein (LHC) (Thornber, 1975, 1979). This is a non-covalent association of a 27,000-MW polypeptide with at least three molecules each of chlorophylls *a* and *b*. This integral membrane protein can be purified from pea thylakoid membranes solubilised in the detergent Triton X-100 (Burke *et al.*, 1978). The solubilised pigment protein shows fluorescence and aggregation properties reflecting its functions as antenna pigment and the thylakoid stacking factor (Steinback *et al.*, 1978; Mullet and Arntzen, 1980; McDonnel and Staehelin, 1980).

X-ray diffraction (Li and Hollingshead, 1982) showed that in 10 mM $MgCl_2$, the detergent solubilised LHC aggregates to form sheets, the sheets being stacked regularly at 51 Å repeat distance. Equatorial X-ray reflections indicate a non-crystalline hexagonal close packing, with a centre-to-centre distance of ~ 85 Å. This distance can be correlated with the ~ 80 Å diameter of the particles seen in freeze-fracture micrographs of the aggregates. As the volume of 51 Å tall, 85 Å diameter cylinder can accommodate six to seven copies of the 27,000-MW polypeptide with its associated chlorophylls, these particles represent a multimeric form of the LHC.

When purified LHC is reconstituted into single-walled phosphatidylcholine vesicles, the addition of NaCl above 10 mM or $MgCl_2$ above 2 mM results in its migration and crystallisation in the membrane plane into a two-dimensional hexagonal lattice (Steinback *et al.*, 1978; Mullet and Arntzen, 1980; McDonnel and Staehelin, 1980). In the X-ray diffraction patterns, sharp lattice lines from the hexagonal lattice of 125 Å lattice constant were seen to extend beyond 10 Å spacing on the equator, demonstrating that the LHC lattice is extensive and well-ordered (Li and Hollingshead, 1982). At NaCl or $MgCl_2$ concentrations sufficient for thylakoid stacking (Izawa and Good, 1966), the reconstituted LHC planar lattices become stacked. Freeze-fracture electron microscopy showed that occasionally the stacked lattices on adjacent membranes are aligned with each other, resulting in a small three-dimensional crystal that is contiguous with the pure lipid bilayers (Li and Hollingshead, 1982). X-ray patterns showed that single layers of lattices are stacked, at 70 Å repeat distance and that, generally, stacking is not in register as only the meridian but not the lattice lines are sampled at this period. Compared to the 55 Å repeat in the contiguous lamellar array of lipid bilayers, this 70 Å repeat show that LHC is exposed at the surface of the reconstituted membranes. Compared to the 51 Å repeat of the planar aggregates in the absence of lipids, it shows that LHC protrudes from the membrane surfaces by at least 10 Å.

The two-dimensional lattice of LHC and phospholipids, once freed from the contiguous pure lipid phase, contains protein and lipid at $\sim$4:1 weight ratio (Li, unpublished data). This means that six to seven lipid molecules are packed with every 27,000-MW polypeptide. The volume of the hexagonal unit cell with a 125 Å lattice constant and a 70 Å thickness is sufficient to accommodate 12 copies of this polypeptide and its bound chlorophylls as well as the stated proportion of phospholipid molecules.

Analysis of electron micrographs of the LHC lattice negatively stained with uranyl acetate (Figure 2.27*a*) (Li and Hollingshead, 1982; Li and Henderson, unpublished data) showed that LHC molecules are arranged with p622 symmetry (Holser, 1958). The six-fold axis is perpendicular to the membrane plane and at the middle of the bilayer intersects with six two-fold axes parallel to the membrane. Such symmetry implies that LHC molecules are inserted in bipolar fashion into the membrane lattice and that 12, or multiples of 12, LHC molecules are contained in one unit cell, which is consistent with the chemical analysis.

Three-dimensional image reconstruction of the stained lattice (Figure 2.27*b*) (Li and Henderson, unpublished data), showed on each face of the lattice a lacework formed by trimer and dimer interactions between LHC molecules. The LHC monomer appears about 60 Å tall and about 30 Å in diameter. In side view, LHC trimers of opposite polarity interdigitate in the middle of the 70 Å-thick membrane lattice. Extensive lateral contacts, probably of a hydrophobic nature, exist between LHC molecules for about 35 Å perpendicular to the membrane plane and near one end of the elongated molecule. Thus, the reconstruction shows that the LHC monomer spans the bilayer region of the reconstituted membrane and projects asymmetrically beyond this region, by about 15 Å from one surface and less from the other. This disposition is probably the chief determinant of the total protein distribution across thylakoid membranes (Figure 2.22), of which LHC is the major integral protein constituent.

Bacterial photosynthetic membranes

Bacterial photosynthesis differs from that of green plants considerably: the light reactions are catalysed by only one photopigment system, so electron transport is cyclic; reduced sulphydryl and organic compound replace water as hydrogen donors, so oxygen is not evolved; and the photosynthetic membranes are not enclosed in an organelle. We will discuss diffraction studies of photosynthetic membranes and membrane components of the purple bacteria but not those of the green bacteria (Clayton and Sistrom, 1980). In purple bacteria the photosynthetic apparatus exists in intracytoplasmic membranes of species-specific morphology or, more rarely, in the cytoplasmic membrane (Oelze and Drews, 1972). The photosynthetic components are invariably orientated with the ATPase facing the cytoplasm, and the *c*-type cytochromes facing the vesicle

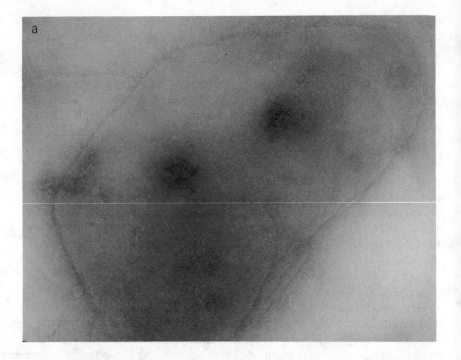

Figure 2.27 Two-dimensional crystalline array of the chlorophyll *a/b* light-harvesting protein prepared by reconstitution of the purified protein from pea with phosphatidyl-choline vesicles in the presence of Mg^{2+} ions. *a*, Negatively-stained crystalline sheet about 1 μm by 2 μm across. Moire patterns appear where two or more sheets are stacked out of register. The lattice has p622 symmetry with a lattice constant of 125 Å. Each unit cell contains 12 protein molecules with 6 to 7 phospholipid molecules per protein molecule. *b*, Three-dimensional model of the LHC membrane lattice obtained by image reconstruction. The model has been sliced vertically through a pair of LHC molecules (dashed outlines) that are related by a two-fold rotation axis in the membrane plane and that make extensive contacts with each other within the bilayer region.

interior or the periplasmic space (Drews, 1978). Isolated photosynthetic membranes form inside-out vesicles, which are called chromatophores.

The photopigment system of purple bacteria, like its plant counterpart, comprises light-harvesting and reaction centre components. The light-harvesting complexes contain 50–70 per cent of the bacteriochlorophyll and 40–50 per cent of the protein in the chromatophore membrane (Loach, 1978; Cohen and Kaplan, 1981a). They have small (7,000–12,000 MW) hydrophobic polypeptides (Tonn *et al.*, 1977; Cuendet and Zuber, 1977; Cohen and Kaplan, 1981b), which are partially exposed at the chromatophore surface (for example, Cuendet *et al.*, 1978). One of these polypeptides, from *Rhodospirillum rubrum*, has been sequenced (Brunisholz *et al.*, 1981).

The reaction centre is the minimal set of (tightly associated) components capable of initiating the conversion of light energy into chemical potential energy. The reaction centre from *Rhodopseudomonas spheroids*, strain R26, purified in the detergent LDAO (Okamura *et al.*, 1974) has a molecular weight of 70,000, consisting of four bacteriochlorophyll *a*, two bacteriopheophytin *a*, one Fe-quinone complex, and another quinone in association with polypeptides of 21,000, 24,000 and 29,000 MW. All the bacterial reaction centres isolated so far have this pigment composition (Loach, 1978), but the protein subunits from different species show no immune cross-reactivity (Clayton and Haselkorn, 1972).

The disposition of the reaction centre protein from *Rps spheroides* (Clayton and Wang, 1971) in the membrane bilayer has been determined by combined X-ray and neutron diffraction studies of reconstituted reaction centre–phospholipid vesicles (Pachence *et al.*, 1979, 1981). The reaction centre was incorporated into the vesicles unidirectionally and in the same polarity as in the isolated chromatophores, that is, with the binding sites for the electron donor, a *c*-type cytochrome, on the outer surface (Pachence *et al.*, 1979). Well-orientated X-ray specimens were prepared from vesicles containing lipid and reaction centre at molar ratios between 150 : 1 and 50 : 1, and X-ray patterns showed nine or more Bragg reflections from membrane pairs at repeats of 125 Å to 138 Å. Except at the highest protein content, the stacking of vesicles was sufficiently ordered that the lamellar reflections were resolved at all scattering angles. For each lipid : protein ratio, the diffraction patterns were phased by maximising the agreement over the membrane portion of the profiles obtained at two slightly different repeat spacings (Stamatoff and Krimm, 1973). However, no constraint was imposed in the phasing for a consistent trend of profile changes over a range of lipid : protein ratios (compare Torbet and Wilkins, 1976).

Figure 2.28*a* shows the electron density profile at 10 Å resolution of the reconstituted reaction centre-vesicle having a lipid : protein molar ratio of 100 : 1, or a weight ratio of 1.1 : 1. Compared to the control phospholipid vesicles, the incorporation of reaction centre protein increased the membrane width from 50 Å to 60 Å and raised the electron density in the centre of the bilayer, indicating that the protein spans the bilayer. The protein confers an asymmetry on the membrane profile which is consistent with its vectorial insertion.

In subsequent neutron diffraction experiments (Pachence *et al.*, 1981), by separately replacing the phospholipid head group or the protein in the recon-stitution system with the corresponding deuterated molecules, the neutron scattering difference profiles due to the protein and to the lipid were deter-mined to 32 Å resolution (Figure 2.28*b,c*). These component profiles indicate that the reaction centre protein has a highly asymmetrical shape with two-thirds of its mass located in the inner leaflet (see below) of the vesicle membrane. Thus it must displace an unequal number of lipid molecules in the two halves of the bilayer. This information was used to decompose the membrane electron density profile obtained from X-ray diffraction (Figure 2.28*a*) into separate profiles of its protein and lipid parts. The result is the model of protein disposition shown in Figure 2.28*d*.

In the reconstituted vesicles the narrow end of the reaction centre protein has been shown to bind cytochrome *c* (Blasie *et al.*, 1982). As cytochrome *c* is known to reduce the reaction centre from the outside of these vesicles (Pachence *et al.*, 1979), and from the interior of the chromatophores *in vivo*, this shows the reaction centre protein is orientated with the wider half embedded in the inner leaflet of the vesicle, analogous to the cytoplasmic half of the chromato-phore membrane. The location of bound cytochrome *c* relative to the vesicle membrane profile was indicated by the difference electron density profile obtained by Fourier transformation from the difference between X-ray ampli-tudes measured in the presence and absence of the cytochrome (Blasie *et al.*, 1982). This location was confirmed when the cobalt atom, in an isomorphous replacement for the Fe atom in the haem of bound cytochrome, was localised by its resonance X-ray scattering signal (Stamatoff and Blasie, 1981).

Recently, the reaction centre from the bacteriochlorophyll *b*-containing *Rhodopseudomonas viridis* has been crystallised in three dimensions (Michel, 1982). A diffraction pattern extending to 3 Å spacing is shown in Figure 2.7*d*. This reaction centre contains pigments and four polypetides of 38,000, 35,000, 28,000 and 24,000 MW. The 38,000 MW subunit probably represents a mem-brane-bound cytochrome *c*; the other three correspond to the three subunits in the bacteriochlorophyll *a*-containing reaction centres (Thornber and Thornber, 1980; Thornber *et al.*, 1980). The complexity of this reaction centre, two copies of which are present in each asymmetric unit of the tetragonal unit cell (Michel, 1982), poses a formidable crystallographic challenge. But solving this structure will provide high-resolution information about the photosynthetic reaction centre and the membrane-bound cytochrome.

The reaction centre and its allotment of light-harvesting complexes can be co-purified in detergent as a photoreceptor complex, which has properties of a photosynthetic unit (Loach, 1978). However, it is advantageous to study the spatial organisation of these components when they are contained in a periodic lattice in the membrane. Order in the chromatophore membrane plane has been reported for *Rps spheroides* and *R. rubrum* (Ueki *et al.*, 1976). From *R. rubrum* chromatophores, equatorial reflections indexing on a hexagonal lattice of 42.6 Å lattice constant have been observed to 7.4 Å spacing. But linewidths indicate the ordered regions to be only 120 Å, or about three unit cells across.

An extensive hexagonal lattice exists in the intracytoplasmic membranes of *Rps viridis* (Giesbrecht and Drews, 1966; Wehrli *et al.*, 1979; Miller, 1979).

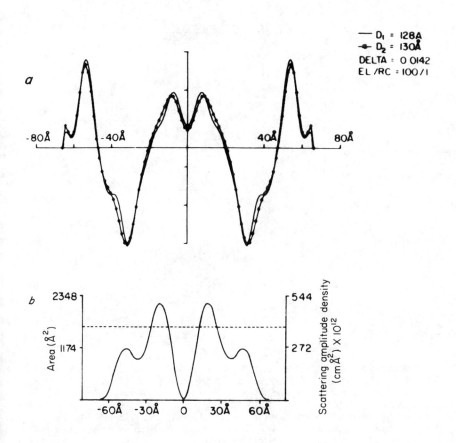

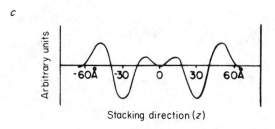

Figure 2.28 *a–c* Legend overleaf.

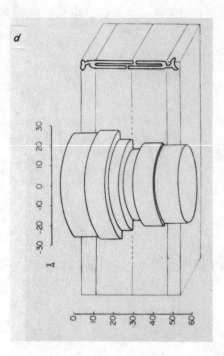

Figure 2.28   (*a–c* overleaf) Disposition of the protein of the bacterial photosynthetic reaction centre from *Rhodopseudomonas spheroides* with respect to the lipid bilayer of the reconstituted vesicle. The centre of the vesicle is at the origin on the *x* axis. The cytochrome *c* binding sites are on the outside of the vesicle. *a*, Electron density profile of the reconstituted vesicle containing lipid and protein at 100:1 molar ratio determined by analysis of X-ray patterns from orientated stacked vesicles. The asymmetrical membrane profile (compared to the symmetrical one for the control lipid vesicles) is correlated with the unidirectional incorporation of the reaction centre protein. *b*, Neutron scattering difference profile due to replacing hydrogenated protein in the vesicles with the deuterated protein (which has a different neutron scattering length). Asymmetry of the difference profile is proportional to the asymmetry of protein cross-sectional areas. *c*, Neutron scattering profile due to the lipid component. Asymmetry is the result of protein displacing unequal numbers of lipid molecules in the two halves of the bilayer. *d*, Schematic representation of the cylindrically averaged structure of the reaction centre protein within the reconstituted membrane. The model is obtained by decomposing the membrane profile in *a* in proportion to the non-uniform cross-sectional areas of its lipid and protein components as shown in *b* and *c* (from Pachence *et al.*, 1979; 1981)

These membranes are stacked, flattened vesicles, and hence are also called thylakoids. Welte *et al.* (1980) reported that a square lattice also occurs in this bacterium, and it has the same lattice constant of 125 ± 8 Å as the hexagonal lattice. Miller (1979) observed the hexagonal lattice on both membrane surfaces and in the membrane interior, by electron microscopy of freeze-fractured and etched, negatively-stained, and thin-sectioned specimens. Freeze-etching microscopy showed that the portion of the repeating unit projecting from the outer thylakoid surface has a larger diameter than that projecting from the inner surface. In the filtered image of the negatively-stained lattice, the repeat unit consists of a strongly stain-excluding circle of ~50 Å diameter, surrounded concentrically by a less strongly stain-excluding, hexagonal shaped area of ~110 Å outer diameter. This image was accounted for by a superposition of the surface relief on the two membrane faces (Miller, 1979).

Miller (1982) recently reconstructed at 33 Å resolution a three-dimensional image of the stain distribution over the *Rps viridis* membrane lattice. Fourier amplitudes along the meridian were obtained from an edge-on view of the folded membrane and included in the reconstruction. Figure 2.29*a* shows the repeating structure in the image. This structure is about 100 Å wide and about 70 Å thick in the central region. A prominent central protrusion of ~50 Å diameter is clearly resolved from the six surrounding, less prominent protrusions of ~30 Å diameter. Figure 2.29*b* shows that, possibly because of stain penetration of the membrane, these features are also well resolved in a section of the three-dimensional image taken along the midplane of the membrane.

Jacob and Miller (1982) have determined the polypeptide composition of the membrane lattice. Of the seven polypeptides resolved by SDS gel electrophoresis, with molecular weights ranging between 11,000 and 44,000, the 11,000 and 16,000-MW species bind bacteriochlorophyll *b* and belong to the light-harvesting complexes; three others correspond to known subunits of the reaction centre (Thornber *et al.*, 1980); and the remaining two are believed to be electron transport components. The two light-harvesting subunits were estimated to be present in six- to ten-fold molar excess to the other five polypeptides. On this basis, Miller (1982) proposed that the central feature in the repeating unit contains the reaction centre and electron carriers, while the six satellite features contain the light-harvesting complexes. The relative volumes of the stain-excluding features seem to be consistent with this assignment.

The polypeptide stoichiometry (Jacob and Miller, 1982) combined with the finite volume of the repeating unit implies that about 50 per cent of the protein mass is not present in six, or multiplies of six, copies per unit cell. By assigning the peptides in low copy numbers to the central structural feature and those present in six-fold excess to the outer features, the contacts of repeating units can have a hexagonal periodicity. However, because polypeptides have no internal rotational symmetry, within each unit the interactions of the peptides in the central feature with those in the outer features cannot be six-fold equivalent. Therefore, the hexagonal symmetry of the *Rps viridis* membrane lattice,

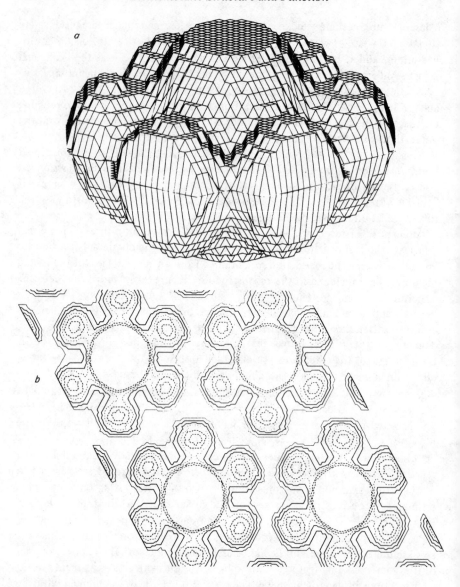

Figure 2.29   Three-dimensional image reconstruction at 33 Å resolution of the stain distribution over the natural membrane lattice in thylakoids of *Rhodopseudomonas viridis*. *a*, Perspective view of the repeating unit. *b*, Section along the midplane of the membrane. The repeating structure is about 100 Å wide in the membrane plane and about 70 Å thick in the central region. It can be clearly resolved into a central component of 50 Å diameter which protrudes well above the thylakoid membrane surface, and six less prominent surrounding components of 30 Å diameter. Based on analysis of the protein stoichiometry of purified membranes, it was proposed that the central component contains the photosynthetic reaction centre and electron carriers while the outer components represent six sets of light-harvesting pigment–protein complexes (from Miller, 1982)

which was used in the image reconstruction (Miller, 1982), is an approximation at low resolution.

Beyond a description of surface topology, the internal structure of the membrane lattice may be determined by X-ray diffraction, or by three-dimensional image reconstruction from micrographs of unstained membranes. Hodapp and Kreutz (1980) have calculated a 35 Å resolution electron density profile of the *Rps viridis* thylakoid. It shows a pair of bilayers closely appressed at the boundary between thylakoids. In addition there is in the centre of the lumen a peak of comparable electron density to the bilayer head group region which was attributed to the lumen solutes concentrated by dehydration of the X-ray specimen. However, the authors pointed out that the large magnitude of this electron density peak may be partly due to an artefact of the model for the membrane stacking disorders.

If indeed each morphological unit of the *Rps viridis* lattice corresponds to a photosynthetic unit consisting of reaction centre, light-harvesting complexes and electron carriers, then determination of the protein and lipid distribution within the unit cell will inform us of the organisation of the photosynthetic apparatus. X-ray diffraction from the membrane lattice has been observed to about 10 Å spacing on the equator (Li, unpublished data). Analysis of the equatorial X-ray intensities may be coordinated with image reconstruction using unstained membranes to yield low- to medium-resolution information about the arrangement of membrane components. This information is a necessary guide for relating the high-resolution structure of the *Rps viridis* reaction centre determined in the crystal to its environment in the functional membrane.

Acetylcholine receptors

Acetylcholine receptors from vertebrate skeletal muscle and electric tissues of electric fish respond to binding by acetylcholine and other agonists by producing a transient increase in the postsynaptic membrane permeability to cations (for review, see Karlin, 1980). It thus acts as a key element in the transmission of electrical signals in many synapses. The permeability increase in the postsynaptic membrane occurs by the opening of a transmembrane channel that accepts cations, including organic cations as large as glucosamine. These properties indicate that, when open, the channel must be at least 6 Å in diameter at its narrowest point. The overall structural organisation of the acetylcholine receptor has been worked out by a combination of physiological, chemical, X-ray and neutron diffraction and electron microscope analyses.

The electric organ of *Torpedo californica* and other electric fishes are far richer sources of acetylcholine receptors than skeletal muscles in which neuromuscular junctions make up only a small fraction of the membrane. For this reason, most of the chemical and structural work has been carried out on preparations from electric organs. All evidence indicates a close homology between receptors from electric organs and from neuromuscular junctions. As isolated from *T. californica* the receptors occur as a mixture of monomers and dimers, the monomer having a molecular weight of 250,000 (Reynolds and Karlin, 1978). The monomer is composed of four types of polypeptide chains with stoichiometry of $\alpha_2\beta\gamma\delta$ (Reynolds and Karlin, 1978; Lindstrom *et al.*, 1980). The subunits have approximate molecular weights of 40,000 (α), 48,000 (β), 58,000 (γ) and 64,000 (δ) (Weill *et al.*, 1974, Raftery *et al.*, 1975). These subunits all have substantial sequence homology, suggesting that they may have evolved from a common ancestral protein through gene duplication (Raftery *et al.*, 1980). The two α chains contain the binding sites for the acetylcholine (Weill *et al.*, 1974, Karlin *et al.*, 1975) and acetylcholine must bind to both sites to induce channel opening. The native dimer is stabilised by a disulphide cross-link between δ chains. Several kinds of evidence indicate that all four types of subunits span the membrane (Strader and Raftery, 1980; Anderson and Blobel, 1981).

Membranes prepared from *T. californica* electroplax containing acetylcholine receptors were studied using X-ray diffraction from disorientated vesicle preparations and partially orientated membrane pellets (Ross *et al.*, 1977; Klymkowski and Stroud, 1979). There was no indication of two-dimensional ordering of the receptors in these preparations. Meridional diffraction was used to derive the electron density profiles shown in Figure 2.30. As the receptor was the predominant protein present in these membranes, the profiles reflect, largely, the

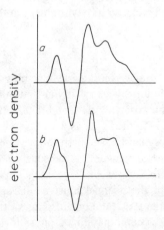

Figure 2.30 Electron density profiles calculated from X-ray scattering: *a*, from a dispersion of acetylcholine receptor vesicles at 22 Å resolution, and *b*, from a partially orientated pellet of membranes at 13 Å resolution. Because the scattering was from non-centrosymmetric membrane preparations, other density profiles corresponding to other phasings of the diffraction data are consistent with the observed intensities (Stroud and Agard, 1980; Makowski, 1981). However, any alternative profiles would share the basic properties of the ones shown here. In particular, the bilayer thickness and total spatial extent will be the same for all possible bilayers (from Klymkowsky and Stroud, 1979)

properties of the receptors. The profiles show that the proteins in these membranes project about 55 Å from one surface of the membrane bilayer and only about 10–20 Å from the other surface. Immunospecific labelling indicates that the 55 Å projection is on the synaptic, extracellular surface (Karlin *et al.*, 1978; Klymkowsky and Stroud, 1979). Wide angle X-ray diffraction indicates that a large proportion of the protein is in an α-helical conformation and that the α helices may be about 80 Å long and orientated approximately perpendicular to the membrane plane (Kistler *et al.*, 1982). In electron micrographs of negatively-stained membranes folded over on the grid, the portion of the receptor extending out from the synaptic side of the membrane bilayer appears to have a funnel shaped structure (Kistler *et al.*, 1982).

The structure of negatively-stained receptor molecules in membrane preparations has been studied, in projection, by using two-dimensional arrays of receptors that form spontaneously when receptor-rich membranes are stored at 4°C for six weeks or more (Ross *et al.*, 1977; Kistler and Stroud, 1981; Kistler *et al.*, 1982), and by using correlation analysis of images of receptors dispersed randomly in receptor-enriched membrane preparations (Zingsheim *et al.*, 1980). Images generated by these two methods are shown in Figures 2.31 and 2.32.

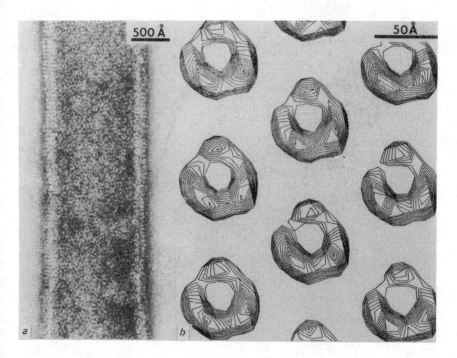

Figure 2.31 Electron micrograph of a negatively-stained membrane tube of acetylcholine receptors (*a*) and a computer generated filtered image (*b*) of the receptor lattice viewed from the cytoplasmic side (from Kistler *et al.*, 1982)

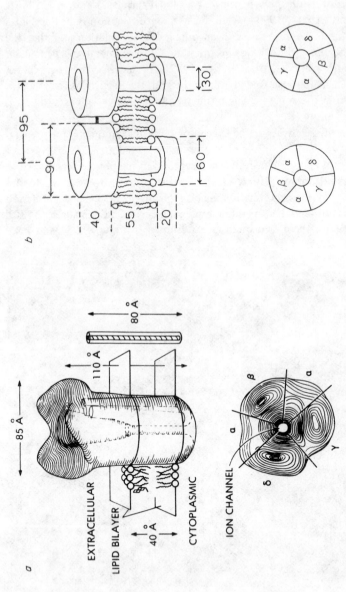

Figure 2.33 *a*, Three-dimensional model for the acetylcholine receptor as deduced by X-ray diffraction and electron microscopy. The protein topography has been inferred from the computer filtered images of receptor tubes assuming that most of the contrast came from the protein on the synaptic side. The assignment of subunits shown is based on crosslinking data. The view shown is from the synaptic side of the postsynaptic membrane (from Kistler *et al.*, 1982). *b*, Three-dimensional model for the receptor based on crosslinking studies and neutron diffraction. The native receptor dimer is shown. The subunit assignments shown are based on studies of receptor-detergent complexes. The direction of the view relative to the two sides of the postsynaptic membrane is unknown (from Wise *et al.*, 1981; Wise *et al.*, 1982)

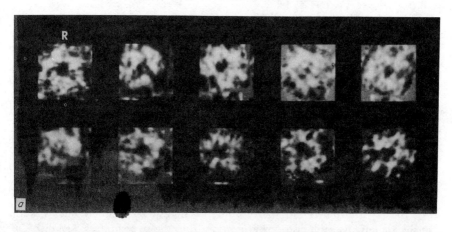

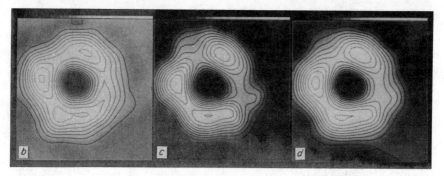

Figure 2.32 *a*, Ten electron micrographs of individual acetylcholine receptors dispersed in the membrane (no lattice is present). *b–d*, Three averaged images generated by computer superposition of 20, 18 and 38 images, respectively. The 38 images that were used to generate the image in *d* were the same as those used for *b* and *c*. Comparison with Figure 2.31 shows that the images obtained from this computer averaging are similar to those generated by the filtering of the receptor lattice. The two sets of images appear to be mirror images of one another, indicating that the particles shown in this figure are being viewed from the synaptic side (from Zingsheim *et al.*, 1980)

These images of the receptor suggest the presence of a toroid-shaped stain-excluding region. The inside diameter of the structure is about 20–30 Å and the outside is about 85 Å in diameter. The stain-excluding region is divided into three principal features connected by regions that exclude less stain. The 20 Å thick wall of the structure visible in these images presumably corresponds to the funnel-shaped structure seen projecting from the bilayer in images of the membrane folded over on the grid and in the electron density profile derived from the X-ray diffraction studies. The combination of these data has led to the proposal of a three-dimensional model (Kistler *et al.*, 1982) shown in Figure 2.33*a*. This model, although based on one- and two-dimensional images of the structure exhibits all the structural features observed by electron microscopy and X-ray diffraction. Its volume is slightly larger than would be expected from the 250,000-MW of the receptor and its radius of gyration is somewhat smaller than that measured by neutron scattering (Wise *et al.*, 1979). A tentative assignment of the positions of subunits is also shown in Figure 2.33*a*. This assignment is consistent with crosslinking data showing prominent α-γ and γ-δ linkages (disuccinimidyl tartrate, 6 Å span).

A similar three-dimensional model for the receptor dimer has been proposed (Wise *et al.*, 1981a, 1981b; Holtzman *et al.*, 1982) based on electron microscopy and neutron diffraction studies of receptor–detergent complexes. Neutron diffraction of complexes of detergent with receptor monomers and dimers were used to determine the radius of gyration of each complex. These measurements suggest that the portion of the receptor spanning the membrane may have a smaller radius than the portions projecting from the two surfaces. Figure 2.33*b* shows one possible model based on these results. Two assignments of the positions of the receptor subunits are consistent with electron microscope studies of complexes of isolated receptor with biotinyl-toxin and avidin and of receptor trimers that are crosslinked by the native disulphide bond between δ chains and by diamide crosslinks between pairs of β chains. These assignments are shown in Figure 2.33*b*.

These structural and biochemical studies indicate that the acetylcholine receptor is a complex of five transmembrane protein subunits, two of which are identical. The cation channel that is induced by acetylcholine binding may be only 7–10 Å in diameter at its narrowest, but appears to have an entrance opening of about 20 Å diameter on the synaptic side. This funnel-shaped opening may enhance the transient rate of cation transmission across the postsynaptic membrane.

Cytochrome oxidase

Cytochrome *c* oxidase is a large enzyme complex associated with the inner mitochondrial membrane that catalyses the transfer of electrons from cytochrome *c* to molecular oxygen. According to Mitchell's chemiosmotic theory, the energy released in this reaction is stored for the synthesis of ATP or other coupled processes by the generation of a proton gradient (Mitchell, 1979; Wikstrom and Krab, 1979). The cytochrome oxidase monomer is composed of at least seven distinct peptide chains (Steffans *et al.*, 1979; Downer *et al.*, 1976). The amino acid sequence of peptides I–VI and of three different low molecular weight polypeptides (VII) have been determined (Buse *et al.*, 1981; Anderson *et al.*, 1981). Assuming a unit stoichiometry of all components, the molecular weight of the monomer is 165,000. In membranes and in non-ionic detergents, the complex is usually present as a dimer (Robinson and Capaldi, 1977; Henderson *et al.*, 1977).

Two different two-dimensional crystal forms of cytochrome oxidase have been produced, membranous vesicle crystals prepared by Triton extraction of mitochondrial membranes (Vanderkooi *et al.*, 1972; Henderson *et al.*, 1977; Deatherage *et al.*, 1980; 1982a, 1982b) and non-membranous sheet crystals prepared by deoxycholate extraction (Seki *et al.*, 1970; Fuller *et al.*, 1979). Analysis of these two crystal forms presented particular problems for the creation of a three-dimensional image of the enzyme complex and motivated the use of electron microscope studies of the lattices embedded in staining media of different electron densities.

The lattices formed by deoxycholate extraction have two-sided plane group symmetry p12, (Fuller *et al.*, 1979). With this symmetry, half the molecules will be orientated 'up' with respect to the surfaces of the sheets and half will be orientated 'down'. Three-dimensional reconstruction of negatively-stained sheets indicated that the crystals do not have a continuous bilayer associated with them. This makes uncertain the relationship of the structure of the complex in the sheets to its structure in the membrane. The monomer in the sheets is about 110 Å long and shaped approximately like a lopsided 'Y'. The arms of the 'Y' are about 55 Å long and have a centre-to-centre separation of about 40 Å. Comparison of this structure with the vesicle crystals derived by Triton extraction (Henderson *et al.*, 1977) indicates that these two domains are buried in the bilayer of the inner mitochondrial membrane. The single large domain making up the stem of the 'Y' projects over 50 Å from the cytoplasmic side of the membrane.

The two-dimensional arrays derived from Triton extraction of the cytochrome oxidase are in the form of vesicle crystals (Henderson *et al.*, 1977). The cytochrome oxidase molecules are all inserted into the vesicles with their cytoplasmic domain projecting from the membrane into the centre of the vesicle. On the electron microscope grid the vesicles are flattened forming a membrane pair. The two membranes in the pair are both asymmetrical, but there are two-fold screw axes in the centre of the vesicle between the two membranes that relate the molecules in one membrane to the molecules in the other. The two-dimensional arrays associated with each membrane of the pair interdigitate, forming a two-layered membrane array with symmetry $p22_12_1$.

A three-dimensional reconstruction of negatively-stained vesicle crystals provided an image of the domains projecting from the membrane (Deatherage *et al.*, 1982a) but could provide no information about the location of the protein domains within the membrane. Antibody binding studies (Frey *et al.*, 1978) have shown that the portion of the complex extending into the centre of the vesicle projects into the cytoplasm *in vivo* and contains the cytochrome *c* binding site. To observe internal details not accessible using negative stains, the vesicle crystals were embedded in glucose. This replaces stain as a means of preserving the specimen for low dose imaging (Unwin and Henderson, 1975). However, as glucose has very nearly the same scattering density as protein, the glucose 'matches out' the protruding protein. That is, protein and glucose cannot be differentiated in the micrographs. Features within the bilayer can, however, be distinguished because the lipid has an electron scattering density substantially less than either protein or glucose.

Figure 2.34 shows the two-dimensional projections of the vesicle crystals of cytochrome oxidase embedded in uranyl acetate and embedded in glucose. The projection of the structure in uranyl acetate should provide a visualisation of the portion of the enzyme complex protruding from the membrane; the projection in glucose, an image of the structure within the membrane. There are, however, four distinct ways, consistent with the lattice symmetry, in which the two maps can be superimposed. Full three-dimensional reconstructions of the structure in these two embedding media cannot resolve the ambiguity. The problem was solved by using gold-thio-glucose and metrizamide as embedding media (Deatherage *et al.*, 1982b). These molecules have scattering densities intermediate between glucose and uranyl acetate. It can be shown that, at low resolution, the scattering amplitudes from any structure are linear functions of the scattering density of the embedding media. The calculated structure factors depend on which point in a unit cell is chosen as the origin. Thus, by calculating the scattering amplitudes for each of the four possible choices of origin, it was possible to distinguish which of the four possible superpositions of the two images was consistent with the expected linear variation of scattering factors with density of embedding media. Only one possible phase origin satisfied this constraint. The result of these calculations is a three-dimensional model of cytochrome *c* oxidase structure where the external features are based on the three-dimensional reconstruction of uranyl acetate embedded material and the internal features on the glucose embedded crystals. Its close similarity to the structure of cytochrome oxidase derive from the cytochrome oxidase sheets confirms this result further.

In the derived three-dimensional model of cytochrome oxidase (Figure 2.35) the complexes are arranged as closely associated dimers. Each monomer consists of a single cytoplasmic domain about 40 Å in diameter and extending about 55 Å into the cytoplasm, and two membrane domains each about 55 Å long. One of the membrane domains is about 20 Å in diameter; the other about 30 Å in diameter. As their centre-to-centre spacing is about 35 Å there may be as much as 10 Å of lipid separating the two domains. X-ray diffraction from a cytochrome oxidase–lipid model membrane with no two-dimensional order in the membrane plane (Blasie *et al.*, 1978) indicates that the complex contains bundles of α-helical polypeptide chain segments with average orientation approximately perpendicular to the membrane plane. Except for the location of the cytochrome *c* binding site on the cytoplasmic domain, the specific functions of the domains have not yet been defined.

Gap junctions

Gap junctions are intercellular connections that mediate the flow of ions and small molecules between the cytoplasms of adjacent cells in many tissues (for

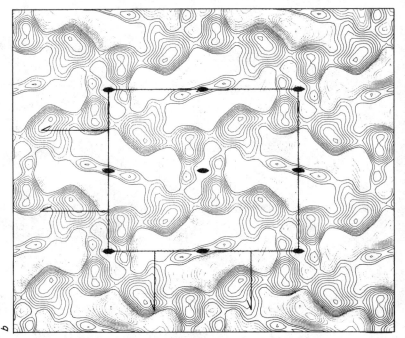

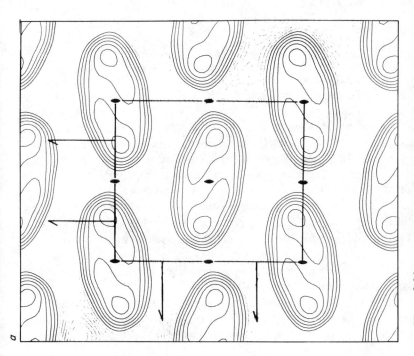

Figure 2.34 Two-dimensional projections of cytochrome *c* oxidase vesicle crystals in *a*, uranyl acetate; and *b*, glucose. Unit cell dimensions are: *a*, 100 Å and *b*, 124 Å. The two projections can be superimposed in any of the four ways in which the two-fold axes of the two projections can be superimposed. Electron microscopy of vesicle crystals in embedding media of different scattering density indicated that the correct superposition of the two projections is the one shown (from Deatheridge *et al.*, 1980)

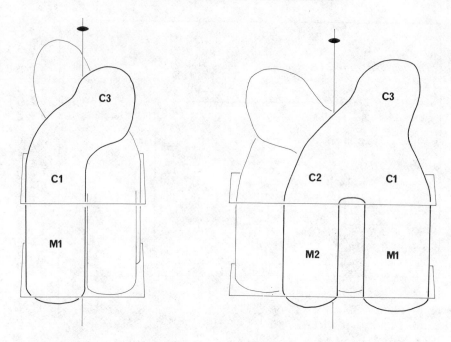

Figure 2.35 Three-dimensional model of the cytochrome *c* oxidase dimer showing the arrangement of the cytoplasmic (C1, C2, C3) domains and the membrane domains (M1, M2) (from Deatheridge, *et al.*, 1982b)

reviews, see Bennett and Goodenough, 1978; Lowenstein, 1981). The junctions are made up of a pair of plasma membranes from adjacent cells separated by an aqueous extracellular gap about 30 Å wide. A polygonal, often hexagonal, lattice of morphological units extends throughout the entire plaque. The morphological units are about 60 Å in diameter with a 20 Å diameter, stain-penetrable core. They are arranged on the lattice with a centre-to-centre separation of 70 to 100 Å. The morphological unit consists of a dimer of hexamers of a 27,000-MW protein (Makowski *et al.*, 1977). A hexamer is associated with each membrane and referred to as a connexon. Two connexons interact in the centre of the gap to form the intact morphological unit. The morphological units extend across both plasma membranes and the intervening gap, apparently connecting the cytoplasms of the two cells (Goodenough and Revel, 1970; Makowski *et al.*, 1977). Junctions from some species are structurally rather different and have significantly larger dimensions.

Many different kinds of tissue contain gap junctions which fulfil different functional roles in the different tissues. For instance, they seem to be responsible for electrotonic coupling of cells in cardiac muscle (Bennett and Goodenough,

1978) and transport of metabolites in lens (Goodenough *et al.*, 1980). They may be responsible for the transmission of developmental signals in embryonic tissue (Lowenstein, 1979) and they may act to promote metabolic cooperation between cells in culture (Subak-Sharpe *et al.*, 1969). Physiological studies indicate that the gap junction channels are gated. Electrical conduction across junctions from different sources has been shown to be sensitive to a variety of environmental factors including pH, Ca^{2+} concentration and transjunctional voltage (Rose and Loewenstein, 1975; Turin and Warner, 1977; 1980; Spray *et al.*, 1981, Harris *et al.*, 1981). There are, however, substantial variations in the structural, chemical and physiological properties of junctions from different tissues and different species. Most of the detailed structural studies have been carried out on mouse or rat liver and for the remainder of this section we limit the discussion to these junctions.

Gap junctions can be isolated from mouse liver (Goodenough and Stoeckenius, 1972, Goodenough, 1974; Henderson *et al.*, 1979; Fallon and Goodenough, 1981) and rat liver (Hertzberg and Gilula, 1979) largely because they remain intact in conditions that solubilise all the other membranes of the liver. Depending on the details of the isolation procedure, the protein-to-lipid ratio in the isolated junctions will vary, the protein usually accounting for more than half the dry weight. The isolated junctions contain a single protein with a molecular weight of 27,000 (Henderson *et al.*, 1979; Hertzberg *et al.*, 1982). X-ray diffraction and electron microscopy have shown that the morphological units in the isolated junctions are made up of twelve copies of this protein, six being associated with each membrane (Makowski *et al.*, 1977). The junction lipids seem to be typical of hepatocyte membranes.

Hexagonal lattices of morphological units are observed by X-ray diffraction of isolated junctions and electron microscopy of negatively-stained, isolated junctions (Goodenough and Stoeckenius, 1972). Hexagonal lattices are also seen in thin sections containing grazing views of the junction lattice (Robertson, 1963; Revel and Karnovsky, 1967). However, replicas of freeze-fractured mouse livers rapidly frozen immediately after removal from the animal show a disordered arrangement of the connexons (Raviola *et al.*, 1980) suggesting that the hexagonal lattice is induced by excision of the liver or by the preparative procedures necessary for electron microscopy and junctional isolation.

Figure 2.9 shows computer filtered images of negatively-stained, isolated gap junctions taken with both normal and low electron doses. The electron micrographs of the isolated plaques on the left were examined to locate regions of the lattice that are particularly well ordered, such as those reproduced at higher magnification in the centre. The diffraction patterns of these highly ordered regions were computed and filtered to produce the images shown on the right. In the filtered images of the micrographs taken at normal electron dose the connexons appear doughnut shaped and relatively featureless. At low doses however, the connexons exhibit hexagonal symmetry with the stain outlining a stain-excluding region shaped like a six-sided star. Stain also accumulates at the six-fold rotation axis as in the micrographs taken at normal doses. In the low dose images, an additional stain-excluding feature appears on the three-fold axis. The low dose images have p6 symmetry, indicating that the junction lattice also has the p6 symmetry. The p6mm symmetry of the normal dose micrographs appears to be induced by the redistribution of stain in response to the electron beam. Although arranged on a lattice with p6 symmetry, the morphological units themselves may have p622 point-group symmetry, the two-fold axes being non-crystallographic. That is, they are local two-fold axes that are not part of the crystal lattice symmetry.

Figure 2.7c shows an X-ray diffraction pattern from a well orientated pellet of isolated gap junctions. In the vertical direction along the meridian there is a series of strong reflections due to the electron density contrast across the width of the junctions. These intensities have been used to calculate the electron density profile shown in Figure 2.36. Perpendicular to the meridian there is a series of sharp reflections along the equator. These have been used to calculate a two-dimensional projection of the electron density onto the plane of the junctions. Both above and below the equator are weak arcs of intensity corresponding to subsidiary maxima on the lattice lines. The arcing of reflections about the centre of the diffraction pattern is due to disorientation of membranes in the X-ray specimens.

Figure 2.36 shows the electron density profile of a gap junction specimen isolated from mouse liver as calculated from the meridional diffraction to 10 Å spacing (Makowski *et al.*, 1977). The pair of junctional membranes is separated by an aqueous gap about 35 Å across. The high electron density in the gap indicates that in this specimen, which had a lattice constant of 86.7 Å, about 40 per cent of the gap region was occupied by protein. The average electron density in the centre of the bilayer is about equal to that of solvent; much higher than would be expected for pure hydrocarbon chains. Assuming that only protein and lipid are present in this part of the structure, this electron density indicates that about 30 per cent of the cross-sectional area in the centre of the membrane bilayer is occupied by protein.

Using the electron density profile, the equatorial projections calculated from the hexagonal lattice reflections in the X-ray diffraction patterns, and the information derived from electron microscopy and chemical analyses, a three-dimensional model, shown in Figure 2.37, was constructed (Makowski *et al.*, 1977). Each morphological unit is made up of a pair of hexamers of the 27,000-MW gap junction protein, one hexamer associated with each bilayer. The two hexamers are joined at the centre of the extracellular gap and the aqueous channel in the centre of the connexon extends most of, if not all, the way through the junction. Observation of strong diffraction at 10 Å on the equator and at 4.7 Å spacing on the meridian indicates that a large proportion of the gap junction protein may be in a β-sheet conformation with the peptide chains running parallel to the membrane plane (Makowski *et al.*, 1982).

This structural model, constructed from the one- and two-dimensional pro-

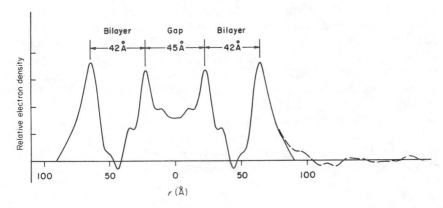

Figure 2.36 Electron density profile of gap junctions calculated from meridional data collected to 10 Å resolution from a specimen with a lattice constant of 87 Å (from Makowski *et al.*, 1977)

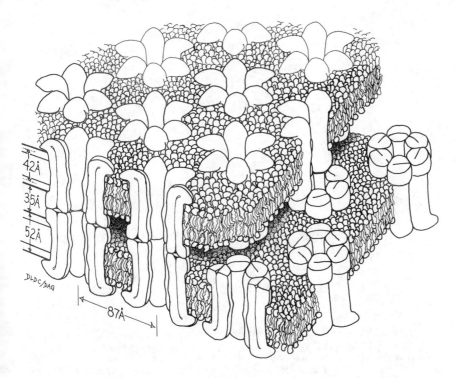

Figure 2.37 Three-dimensional model of gap junction structure. The morphological units are made up of a dimer of hexamer of a 27,000-MW molecule. An aqueous channel extends most or all the way along the connexon axis from one cytoplasm to the other. The centre-to-centre spacing of connexons shown in this drawing is 87 Å but lattice constants in the range of 74–89 Å have been observed (from Makowski *et al.*, 1977)

jections has served as a basis for further structural studies. The gap junction is the first membrane structure for which three-dimensional maps have been calculated from both electron microscopy (Unwin and Zampighi, 1980) and X-ray diffraction (Makowski *et al.*, 1982).

A three-dimensional reconstruction has been calculated from electron micrographs of negatively-stained gap junctions (Unwin and Zampighi, 1980). These micrographs, although taken at electron doses lower than normal, indicated a p622 symmetry for the lattice. Thus, the three-dimensional reconstruction may correspond to either a high-dose image of the junction or an image of the junction in a different structural state from that observed by Baker *et al.* (1983). One section of the three-dimensional reconstruction is shown in Figure 2.38*a*.

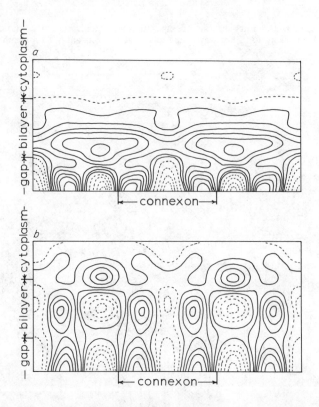

Figure 2.38 *a*, Section through a three-dimensional map of the stain-excluding space of gap junctions isolated from rat liver and stained with uranyl acetate. In this section, the cytoplasm is at the top and the centre of the gap is at the bottom. The connexon channel can be seen in the centre and at the two edges of the drawing (from Unwin and Zampighi, 1980). *b*, Section through a three-dimensional electron density map of gap junctions isolated from mouse liver. Orientation is as in *a*. Most of the features seen in this map can also be seen in the section from the three-dimensional reconstruction (*a*). In the electron density map it is also possible to see the extent of the protein in the lipid bilayer and the low density corresponding to the lipid hydrocarbon chains (from Makowski *et al.*, 1982)

This section is cut perpendicular to the membrane plane and corresponds to the section along the left-hand side of the junction model drawn in Figure 2.37. Only one junction membrane is shown; the bottom of the diagram corresponds to the centre of the gap and the top to the cytoplasmic space. In the three-dimensional reconstruction, the solid contours correspond to stain-excluding regions and the broken contours to stain-filled regions. There are three images of the channel: one in the centre, and two others at the right and left-hand edges. Stain does not appear to penetrate entirely through the junction channel.

Figure 2.37*b* is the corresponding section taken from the three-dimensional electron density map of gap junctions calculated from the X-ray diffraction data (Makowski *et al.*, 1982). X-ray diffraction data indicate that the gap junction lattices in these specimens have two-sided plane group symmetry p622. Peaks of electron density are represented by solid contours and troughs by broken contours. The channel and gap regions of the maps calculated from X-ray diffraction and electron microscopy correspond closely. In addition, contrast between the high density protein and lipid polar head groups and the low density hydrocarbon chains can be seen in the electron density map. The portion of the connexon extending through the bilayer occupies less cross-sectional area than that portion within the gap. As in the three-dimensional reconstruction, the channel in the electron density map appears to extend most, but not necessarily all, of the way through the junction to the cytoplasm. The high electron density on the cytoplasmic surface is probably due to a close association of lipid polar head groups with gap junction protein. Diffraction studies in media of different electron densities suggests that protein takes the place of the water of hydration of the polar groups on the cytoplasmic surface of the gap junction membrane (Makowski, Caspar, Goodenough and Phillips, in preparation).

Analysis of diffraction data from isolated junctions in 50 per cent sucrose shows that the sucrose fills the extracellular gap but fails to enter the channel (Makowski *et al.*, 1982). Some penetration of the cytoplasmic surface region by sucrose is observed and suggests the presence of a funnel-shaped entrance opening on the cytoplasmic surface. It is possible that in the isolated junctions the channel is closed at both cytoplasmic surfaces, excluding sucrose. The electron microscope data that has been interpreted as suggestive of two functional states of the channel (Unwin and Zampighi, 1980) – corresponding to open and closed forms – do not unambiguously show that the aqueous channel extends across the junction in either state.

A variety of structural transitions have been observed in isolated gap junctions. Structural variations have been observed in the gap region (Makowski *et al.*, 1977) and near the cytoplasmic surface (Unwin and Zampighi, 1980; Makowski *et al.*, 1982) and lattice constants of 74 to 88 Å have been recorded. Unfortunately, it is extremely difficult to correlate these structural variations directly with physiologically important gating mechanisms for the control of intercellular communication. Some structural changes have been detected after uncoupling treatments using electron microscopy of replicas of freeze-fractured specimens (Peracchia and Dulhunty, 1976; Peracchia, 1977) but their relevance to physiological control is difficult to assess. Physiological data (Spray *et al.*, 1981; Harris *et al.*, 1981) indicate that some junctions have more than one independent gating mechanism. It is possible that some or all of the structural transitions observed may correspond to these different means for the control of intercellular communication.

Purple membrane

The purple membrane occurs as crystalline patches in the surface membrane of *Halobacterium halobium* (Blaurock and Stoeckenius, 1971). It can be isolated as 0.5 μm diameter sheets, after fragmenting the cell envelope of this halophilic organism by removing salts. Purified purple membrane contains 75 per cent protein and 25 per cent lipid by weight (Oesterhelt and Stoeckenius, 1971). The protein is of a single species of 26,000 MW. This protein, named bacterio-rhodopsin because it contains one molecule of covalently bound retinal, functions as a light-driven proton pump to generate an electrochemical gradient across the cell membrane (Racker and Stoeckenius, 1974).

The crystalline nature of purple membrane was first shown by Blaurock and Stoeckenius (1971). They obtained diffraction patterns from orientated membrane pellets with the incident X rays parallel to the membrane. Sharp reflections were observed on the equator out to 7 Å resolution, and were indexed unambiguously on a planar hexagonal lattice of 63 Å lattice constant. When the incident X rays are normal to the membrane pellet, reflections are observed as rings, due to the cylindrical averaging of lattice lines belonging to membrane lattices in different azimuthal orientations. Henderson (1975) found that the series of rings extends to 3.5 Å spacing. The high resolution and sharpness of the reflections are both evidence of a very high degree of order in the membrane plane. The sharpness shows, in addition, that the membrane lattice is extensive.

The hexagonal lattice constant is 62.7 Å in wet purple membrane and 61.8 Å when dried (Henderson, 1975). The membrane thickness can be assigned an upper limit equal to the minimum meridional repeat distance of 47.6 Å, measured for membranes dried at pH 3, presumably the isoelectric point (Henderson, 1975). The protein:lipid ratio and the protein molecular weight being known, these dimensions are consistent with three or four bacteriorhodopsin molecules per unit cell (Blaurock and Stoeckenius, 1971). The hexagonal lattice rules out four molecules per unit cell. Therefore, the plane group of purple membrane is p3, with one protein molecule and about 10 lipid molecules per asymmetric unit. The p3 lattice requires every bacteriorhodopsin molecule to be orientated with the same polarity.

X-ray diffraction patterns from purple membrane showed that bacterio-rhodopsin contains several α helices orientated predominantly perpendicular to the membrane (Henderson, 1975; Blaurock, 1975). There were three diagnostic features for orientated α helices. First, on the equator, the lattice lines are particularly intense at around 10 Å spacing, which corresponds to the packing distance between adjacent helices. Second, a prominent band at 5.05 ± 0.1 Å spacing corresponding to the pitch of helices in a coiled-coil configuration (Crick, 1953), is seen on the meridian and arcing off it in a manner typical of diffraction from a coiled-coil. Third, a strong reflection at 1.5 Å spacing (1.53 ± 0.05 Å, Henderson, 1975: 1.47 ± 0.4 Å, Blaurock, 1975), is recorded on the meridian. The latter is the most reliable signature for α helix (Perutz, 1951). The spread of orientation among individual helices can be estimated by the spread of the 1.5 Å reflection about the meridian, and from the degree of forward tilt required to record this reflection. This was found to be $12.5°$ about the membrane normal. The widths of the reflections at 5 Å and 1.5 Å spacings are inversely proportional to the length of the α helices. Because the helices are roughly perpendicular to the membrane lattice, the lengths of the lattice lines as they cross the equator are also inversely proportional to the lengths of the helices. From these measurements of the diffraction patterns, the α helices were estimated to be about 30 Å long (Henderson, 1975), probably spanning the membrane thickness.

The number of α helices per bacteriorhodopsin was deduced from the strength of constructive interference at 10 Å spacing on the equator (Henderson, 1975). A model containing between 4 and 7 α helices, 30 Å long and hexagonally close packed was found to account for the ratio of observed intensity around 10 Å relative to that observed elsewhere. These calculations afford a lower estimate of the number of helices, as the actual helices are not all perpendicular to the membrane.

Analysis of the X-ray patterns suggests that the phospholipids and glycolipids of purple membrane (Kates, 1978) are organised in contiguous areas between the protein molecules. Diffuse intensity at 4.6 Å spacing on the equator (Henderson, 1975) has been correlated with the side-to-side spacing of hydrocarbon chains (Stewart, 1928). However, Blaurock (1975) reported a 4.9 Å chain packing for extracted purple membrane lipids. The lipid head groups are not highly ordered in the plane of the membrane lattice, as on binding of uranyl ions to the head groups the intensity difference is confined to lattice lines at spacings greater than 20 Å on the equator (Henderson, 1975). The lipids are probably in a bilayer configuration. When the continuous intensity from purple membrane in dispersion is fitted to membrane profiles, with or without a centrosymmetric approximation (Blaurock and Stoeckenius, 1971; Blaurock, 1975; Blaurock and King, 1977; Stroud and Agard, 1979), all the resultant profiles show a pair of electron density peaks separated by 40 Å. This is the distance between lipid head groups in bilayers formed by extracted purple membrane lipids (Blaurock, 1975).

To determine the three-dimensional structure of the membrane lattice, the Fourier amplitudes and phases must be measured along the lattice lines of its reciprocal lattice. Here, the advantage of electron microscopy over X-ray diffraction is twofold. First, because electrons are more strongly scattered than

X rays, a single membrane sheet can be used as a specimen for electron microscopy. Thus, the amplitudes are observed without the cylindrical averaging due to rotation of the many membrane lattices in the X-ray pellet. Second, by calculating the transform from recorded images, electron microscopy provides the phase information which must be obtained indirectly in X-ray diffraction experiments.

The three-dimensional image reconstruction of purple membrane (Unwin and Henderson, 1975; Henderson and Unwin, 1975) visualised for the first time the arrangement of secondary structures in an integral membrane protein. The amount of structural detail observed is a direct consequence of structural preservation. First, by recording the electron micrographs and electron diffraction patterns from membrane areas with an electron exposure of less than 1 e $Å^{-2}$, the radiation damage which would lead to fragmentation and rearrangement of molecules in the membrane was minimised. The signal-to-noise ratio for detecting Fourier amplitudes along lattice lines is proportional to the square root of the electron dose per unit cell, but also to the square root of the number of coherently scattering unit cells (Unwin and Henderson, 1975). As electron dose is decreased, adequate signal-to-noise ratio can be maintained by diffraction from larger, ordered lattice areas. Therefore, the extensive, highly ordered lattice present in the purple membrane allows reliable amplitudes to be measured in low dose conditions to the resolution limit of structural preservation. Secondly, damage from dehydration *in vacuo* was prevented by embedding the membranes in glucose, a non-volatile substance that mimics the properties of water. This was essential as X-ray diffraction patterns showed that drying causes shrinkage (Henderson, 1975) as well as disordering (Blaurock, 1975) of the purple membrane lattice. Following these precautions, purple membrane diffracts electrons to 3.5 Å spacing, approaching the resolution limit of X-ray diffraction by wet pellets of purple membrane.

Analysis of electron micrographs and electron diffraction patterns from unstained, glucose-embedded purple membrane resulted in a 7 Å resolution, three-dimensional model of bacteriorhodopsin (Unwin and Henderson, 1975; Henderson and Unwin, 1975) (Figure 2.39). It should be explained that image analysis from electron microscopy yields a map of electrical potential in the specimen. At 7 Å resolution, the electrical potential is roughly proportional to the electron density as would be found by X-ray diffraction, and roughly proportional to the atomic number. In this way the map of unstained purple membrane indicates the distribution of chemical groups in the membrane. The map of the asymmetric unit contains seven rods of density which are 35–40 Å long, orientated at 0–20° from the membrane normal, and packed 10–12 Å apart. Based on the evidence from X-ray diffraction, these rods are recognised as the α-helical segments of bacteriorhodopsin. This result shows an integral membrane protein to be globular in shape and exposed at both membrane surfaces. In fact, the peptide chain traverses the membrane seven times. The volume of the rods account for 70–80 per cent of the protein molecular weight. Their relative tilts are consistent with a left-

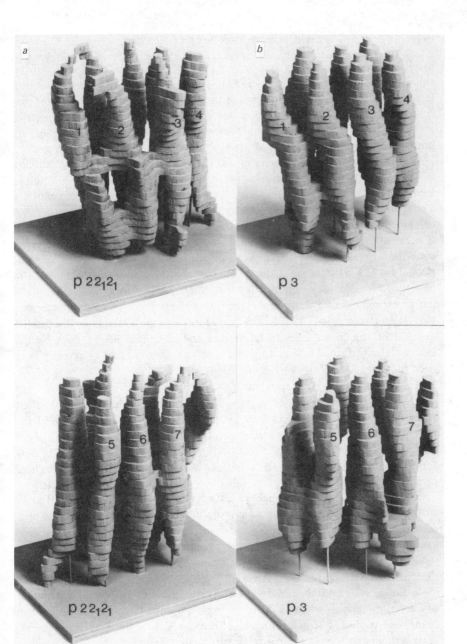

Figure 2.39 Three-dimensional models for the bacteriorhodopsin molecule: a, in the reconstituted orthorhombic $p22_12_1$ lattice; and b, in the native (p3) trigonal lattice. The models represent the protein regions of the 7 Å resolution maps of the membrane lattice which were reconstructed from electron diffraction amplitudes with phases calculated from electron micrographs. The seven rods in the model indicate the seven α-helical segments of the bacteriorhodopsin peptide that span the membrane thickness. Despite the unidirectional insertion of the protein in the native membrane (b, cytoplasmic side up) and the bidirectional insertion in the reconstituted one (a), the 7 Å resolution structures of the protein molecule are very similar. The angles of inclination of the protein in the two lattices differ by less than 3° (from Leifer and Henderson, 1983)

handed supercoiling of the (right-handed) α helices, allowing interlocking of the amino acid side chains (Crick, 1953). This conformation suggests that the tertiary fold of this integral membrane protein is stabilised primarily by strong helix–helix interactions. The notion has been substantiated by experiments in the denaturation, renaturation and reconstitution of bacteriorhodopsin and its proteolytic fragments (Huang *et al.*, 1981).

The polarity of the seven-helix model shown in Figure 2.39 was determined to be cytoplasmic face up (Henderson *et al.*, 1978; Hayward *et al.*, 1978): purple membrane attaches to polylysine coated grids preferentially by the face with the higher negative charge density. This is the extracellular face at *p*H 1.8 to 5.4 (Zingsheim *et al.*, 1978) and the cytoplasmic face at *p*H 7.4 (Fisher *et al.*, 1978). Comparison of the handedness of electron diffraction patterns and the projected structures obtained in each orientation with that reported by Unwin and Henderson (1975) established the polarity of the three-dimensional model. The polarity was also indicated by the handedness of electron diffraction from purple membrane sheets that were labelled on the top face by two biotin derivatives (Henderson *et al.*, 1978). The labelled sites were determined by parallel experiments on intact cells to be lysines and glycolipid head groups on the extracellular surface. These and other indications of membrane asymmetry have been summarised by Zingsheim *et al.* (1978).

Treatments of purple membrane with mixtures of non-ionic and positively charged detergents (Michel *et al.*, 1980), with HCl, or chlorides of trivalent transition metal ions (Henderson *et al.*, 1982), or complete dissolution of the membrane in Triton X-100 and subsequent removal of the detergent by dialysis (Cherry *et al.*, 1978) led to the recrystallisation of bacteriorhodopsin in new forms of membrane lattices. These include two orthorhombic p22$_1$2$_1$ lattices of slightly different unit cell sizes (Michel *et al.*, 1980; Leifer and Henderson, 1983) and a contracted trigonal p3 lattice (Henderson *et al.*, 1982). The *in vitro* crystals all contain one protein molecule per asymmetrical unit, the area of which is between 90 and 100 per cent of that in the native lattice. Judging by their X-ray and electron diffraction patterns, the new lattices are ordered to at least 6 Å spacing. Two-dimensional projections of the native and two recrystallised lattices are shown in Figure 2.40.

In the p22$_1$2$_1$ crystal of Michel *et al.* (1980), despite the bipolar orientation of bacteriorhodopsin which is different from the polar one of the natural membrane, the projected structure of the protein to 6 Å resolution (Figure 2.40*b*) is very similar to that in the native (Figure 2.40*a*). Hence the inclination of the protein to the membrane normal differs by less than 3° in the two lattices. The comparison of these two projections confirmed the previously postulated boundary of bacteriorhodopsin. A three-dimensional map of the other orthorhombic lattice has been calculated (Leifer and Henderson, 1983). Bacteriorhodopsin structure in that lattice is also closely similar to the native structure, as is clear from comparison of the two models in Figure 2.39.

In the contracted p3 lattice, the 10 per cent decrease in membrane area is

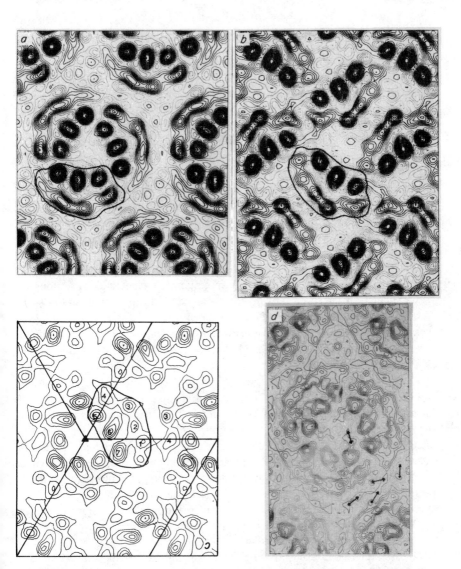

Figure 2.40 Two-dimensional projection of three bacteriorhodopsin membrane lattices. *a*, Projection of purple membrane at 6 Å resolution (Michel *et al.*, 1980). The high density peaks indicate α helices of the protein which are orientated mainly perpendicular to the membrane. Low density contours represent the contiguous membrane lipids which are less well ordered in the membrane plane. *b*, Projection of reconstituted orthorhombic $p22_12_1$ lattice at 6 Å resolution (Michel *et al.*, 1980). The correspondence in projection of the bacteriorhodopsin molecule in this and the native membrane is evident. The protein molecular envelope is drawn on this basis. *c*, Projection of the contracted p3 lattice derived from HCl-treated purple membrane (Henderson *et al.*, 1982). Phases for this projection were obtained by placing the known protein projection from *b* in the new unit cell with optimal translation and rotation. Compared to the native projection in *a* this shows that the bacterio-rhodopsin is rotated by 10° in the plane, which leads to a closer packing and contact between helices 1 and 4. *d*, A projection of purple membrane calculated using weighted data to 3.7 Å spacing. The electron diffraction and image data were recorded at low temperature for improved signal-to-noise ratio. The weighting scheme allowed data from incoherently related areas to be combined objectively and allowed high resolution reflections with large phase error to be included in the reconstruction. Arrows indicate pairs of density features thought to represent lipid hydrocarbon chains spaced 5.6 to 5.8 Å apart (from Hayward and Stroud, 1981)

consistent with the decreased lipid content (Henderson *et al.*, 1982). A considerable rearrangement of the protein in the lattice is indicated by changes in the X-ray intensities. Assuming the projected structure of the protein molecule in the contracted lattice to be the same as in both the native and the orthorhombic lattice of Michel *et al.* (1980), a systematic search was made for the translation and rotation required to place the known molecular projection from the orthorhombic cell into the contracted trigonal cell, that will best account for the observed amplitudes from the contracted cell. The search indicated that, relative to the native lattice, bacteriorhodopsin rotates by $10°$ about the membrane normal to achieve a closer packing. Several new contacts between helices arise from these rearrangements (Figure 2.40c), ruling out the possibility that these interfaces carry like charges.

Recent efforts have been directed at extending the resolution of the three-dimensional model for purple membrane. In the model of Henderson and Unwin (1975), resolution was limited to 7 Å spacing in the plane and 14 Å along the perpendicular. Therefore, retinal, for instance, was not visible in the map. Furthermore, the unobserved membrane transform in a conical region along the meridian causes the map to have artificially low densities near the membrane surfaces: helices are tapered and the linking regions between helices are invisible, as is the lipid bilayer.

Electron diffraction amplitudes from purple membrane have been measured to 3.5 Å spacing. The resolution of the three-dimensional map, however, is limited to 7 Å spacing because of the uncertainty in the phases calculated from the image. This is due to non-ideal conditions for image formation in the electron microscope. Hayward and Stroud (1981) developed a scheme for combining image data from specimen areas that are incoherently related, as for instance due to non-ideal image formation. By down-weighting structure factors in proportion to their probable error of phase and amplitude, these workers were able to obtain a two-dimensional projection of the purple membrane using data to 3.7 Å resolution that were phased from the combined images. This high resolution projection is shown in Figure 2.40d.

An alternative approach proposed by Rossmann and Henderson (1981) is to extend phases beyond the resolution attainable from images, using the molecular replacement method. This method requires the transform of the molecule to be sampled at reciprocal space intervals smaller than the inverse of the molecular size. This requirement is met, to some extent, by all two-dimensional membrane crystals, as their transforms are observable continuously along reciprocal lattice lines. In phase extension, the transform of a low resolution model is evaluated to increased resolution by a step smaller than the inverse molecular size. The calculated phases are combined with the observed amplitudes to give a trial structure at increased resolution, which is refined before the extension is repeated. Rossmann and Henderson (1981) demonstrated the practicality of the procedure on projections. They showed that, given two sets of amplitudes observed from different lattices of bacteriorhodopsin, molecular replacement can determine phases to the same resolution as by image analysis and, given both the amplitudes and the low resolution image phases, molecular replacement can extend phases to the limit of observed amplitudes. Nevertheless, because molecular replacement involves interpolation of the Fourier transform, it cannot bridge large gaps in the data such as the cone unobservable by electron microscopy.

Another alternative is model building. This starts with a model representing the known elements in the structure, and develops the model during refinement by interpreting the difference electron density map corresponding to the difference between the model-predicted and the observed amplitudes. Having collected electron diffraction amplitudes to 3 Å spacing and up to 60° tilts from both the native trigonal and the orthorhombic lattices (Leifer and Henderson, 1983), Henderson and colleagues (Henderson *et al.*, 1982a, 1982b) began model building by replacing the rods of density in the two 7 Å resolution maps with atoms of a polyalanine α-helix, to generate phases for the reflections at spacings between 7 Å and 3 Å. During refinement, the structure of the bacteriorhodopsin molecule was held to be the same in the two lattices. Through cycles of refinement, some bulky residues on the helices have been interpreted based on their shapes, and the positions of more than half of the phospholipid molecules in the unit cell have been determined. However, the amino acid sequence still cannot be recognised in the density features in the map.

Once the amino acid sequence of bacteriorhodopsin became known (Ovchinikov, 1979; Khorana *et al.*, 1979), it was combined with the 7 Å resolution map to formulate a three-dimensional model showing the path of the polypeptide chain (Engelman *et al.*, 1980). As a working model, it has influenced the design and interpretation of further experiments. Because, as shown in Figure 2.41, it predicts the amino acid composition of each α-helical segment and the sequence of connections between the helices, it can be tested and extended by experiments that locate specific amino acids or other chemical groups. For example, a neutron diffraction study was undertaken to determine the distribution of valine and phenylalanine among the helices (Engelman and Zaccai, 1980), and peptide analysis has determined the attachment site of the retinal in the amino acid sequence (Bayley *et al.*, 1981).

It may be anticipated that the combined insights from diffraction and chemical analyses of purple membrane will elevate our understanding of structure–function correlations in membrane proteins to a new level.

CRYSTALS OF MEMBRANE ASSOCIATED PROTEINS

Haemagglutinin

The haemagglutinin membrane glycoprotein of influenza virus is a three domain structure: a large hydrophilic, carbohydrate-containing domain extends from the outer surface of the viral membrane; a small, uncharged, hydrophobic segment of peptide spans the membrane; and a small hydrophilic domain is present on

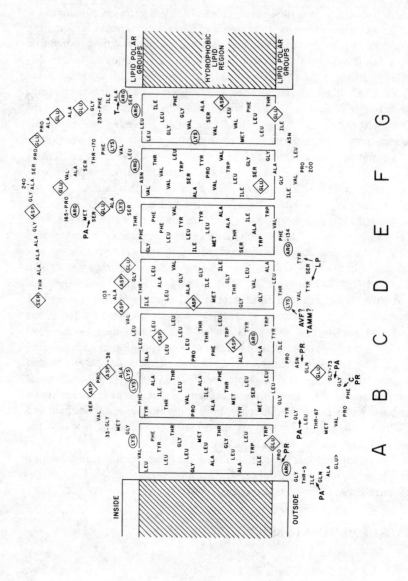

Figure 2.41 Probable arrangement of the amino acid sequence of bacteriorhodopsin along its seven transmembrane helical segments and the non-helical linking segments (from Engelman *et al.*, 1980, revised)

the inside of the membrane. Haemagglutinin trimers form 135 Å long spikes, visible in negative stain, extending out from the viral surface. Haemagglutinin is involved in attaching virus particles to cells (Hirst, 1942), the fusion of cell and viral membranes (Huang *et al.*, 1980) and in the membrane budding processes by which the virus matures. Its large hydrophilic domain can be solubilised by bromelain digestion which removes the small C-terminal hydrophobic and hydrophilic domains from each subunit. The external domain from the haemagglutinin of the A/Hong Kong/1968 virus has been crystallised in three dimensions and its structure solved by X-ray crystallography to 3 Å resolution (Wilson *et al.*, 1981). A similar crystallographic investigation of the external domain of the other influenza glycoprotein, neuraminidase, is underway (Laver *et al.*, 1980).

Haemagglutinin is present in the viral membrane as trimers. The post-translational removal of an arginine divides the monomer into two disulphide-linked peptides, HA1 (328 amino acids) and HA2 (211 amino acids) (Verhoeyen *et al.*, 1980) and activates infectivity (Klenk *et al.*, 1975; Lazarowitz and Choppin, 1975) and membrane fusion (Huang *et al.*, 1980). The 3 Å resolution electron density map has been used to trace the chains of both polypeptides and to identify the position of the carbohydrate attachment sites (Wilson *et al.*, 1981) and antibody binding sites (Wiley *et al.*, 1981).

The haemagglutinin trimer is in the form of a cylinder with triangular cross-section, about 135 Å long and 30-80 Å in diameter. Figure 2.42 shows the general configuration of the trimer and the chain tracing of the monomer. A long fibrous region arranged as a 75 Å long, three-stranded, α-helical coiled-coil extends out from the membrane surface supporting a globular region made up largely of an eight-stranded β-sheet structure. The carbohydrate attachment sites are concentrated into two groups; one is in the globular region and the other is near the membrane end of the fibrous stem. The antibody binding sites are all on the surface of the globular region away from the membrane. A highly conserved pocket of residues on the surface of the globular region at the distal end of the molecule is well located to act as a host cell receptor binding site though, as of yet, there has been no direct demonstration of this.

The activity of haemagglutinin in membrane fusion is still unclear. The 135 Å length of the molecule would seem to act as a barrier to the close approach of the host and viral membranes. The site of the cleavage of HA1 from HA2 that is required for membrane fusion activity is located about 100 Å from the presumed host cell binding site and about 35 Å from the viral membrane. The first 11 amino acids of HA2 directly adjacent to the cleavage site are highly conserved, glycine rich, and in an unusual conformation, forming a contiguous series of sharp bends in the peptide chain. These properties suggest that the amino terminal residues of HA2 might be directly involved in cell fusion. Any function of the protein in fusion is likely to involve gross conformational changes. The globular, β-sheet region of haemagglutinin is connected to the fibrous region by two segments of peptide with extended conformations. It is possible that this

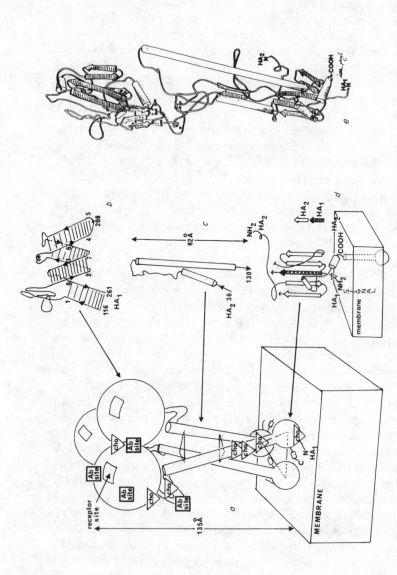

Figure 2.42 Structural organisation of the haemagglutinin trimer (*a–d*) and the chain tracing of the monomer (*e*). *a*, Arrangement of the three haemagglutinin monomers into the trimer that forms the surface spike on the influenza virus membrane. The carbohydrate attachment sites are labelled 'cho'; the antigenic sites, determined by sequence analysis of many influenza haemagglutinins are labelled 'Ab site'. In *b–d* the organisation of the peptides are diagrammed. In *e*, the α helices are represented by solid rods and the regions of peptide in a β-sheet conformation are indicated by flat arrows. Regions of extended peptide are shown as thin, curved rods. In this drawing, the membrane would be at the bottom. The long α helix makes up the stem of the spike and the 8-stranded β-sheet structure makes up the globular domain (from Wilson *et al.*, 1981)

portion of the structure acts as a hinge for the complete reorganisation of the trimer during membrane fusion.

The high resolution image of the soluble, external domain of haemagglutinin shows that the molecule contains patterns of secondary and tertiary structure not unlike soluble proteins, but organised into an extended structure that is unusual and must relate to its membrane bound activities. Although the local patterns of protein folding in haemagglutinin are not unusual, the domain structure is novel.

Melittin

Melittin is a polypeptide consisting of 26 amino acids that is the main toxin of bee venom (Habermann, 1972). The melittin tetramer is soluble in aqueous media. Its relevance here is due to the fact that it interacts very strongly with lipid bilayers and membranes, forming channels (Tosteson and Tosteson, 1981) and causing cell lysis (Sessa *et al.*, 1969; Habermann, 1972). Although not a membrane protein, its strong interaction with membranes suggests that its structure may be informative with regard to the structure of membrane proteins. The structure of the soluble melittin tetramer has been studied at high (2 Å) resolution using X-ray crystallography (Eisenberg *et al.*, 1980; Terwilliger *et al.*, 1982; Terwilliger and Eisenberg, 1982a, 1982b). These studies have clarified, to some extent, its ability to integrate into lipid bilayers.

A single melittin polypeptide chain has, in the soluble tetramer, the conformation of a bent α-helical rod (Terwilliger *et al.*, 1982) (Figure 2.43). Residues 1 to 10 and 13 to 26 form two straight, α-helical segments with residues 11 and 12 forming a bent helical connector lacking the main chain hydrogen bonds of the α-helical conformation. The helical conformation of the peptide almost completely segregates the hydrophobic and hydrophilic residues: the hydrophobic side chains on the side of the molecule on the inside of the bend, and the hydrophilic side chains orientated towards the outside of the bend. The six amino acid residues at the amino-terminal end are entirely hydrophobic and for more than one α-helical turn, the molecule is hydrophobic around its entire circumference.

The soluble melittin tetramer is formed by the juxtaposition of the hydrophobic surfaces of the four monomers. Most of the surface of the tetramer is occupied by polar side chains and the positively charged C-terminal groups are arranged to be relatively far apart. Circular dichroism and NMR studies (Lauterwein *et al.*, 1979; Brown *et al.*, 1980) indicate that the backbone conformation may not change substantially on interaction with a lipid bilayer.

Figure 2.43*b* shows one suggested mode for the interaction of melittin with a lipid bilayer (Terwilliger *et al.*, 1982). The hydrophobic amino acid terminus enters the hydrophobic interior of the bilayer and the remainder of the molecule

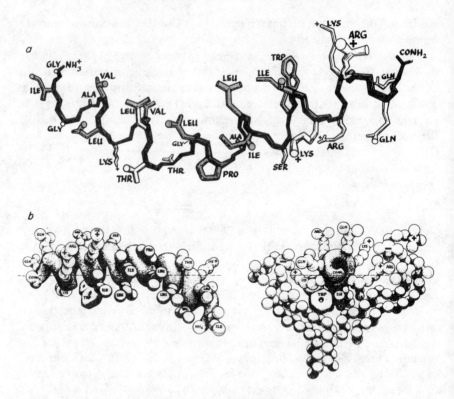

Figure 2.43 *a*, Schematic drawing of a melittin monomer; and *b*, showing how it might interact with a bilayer. In the tetramer, the hydrophobic side chains are arranged so that they are all on one side of the melittin rod. This might allow for easy integration into a lipid bilayer. In *b*, the dashed line represents a possible surface for a lipid bilayer showing the conformation that the melittin monomer might take on during its initial interaction with the bilayer (from Terwilliger *et al.*, 1982)

flattens against the membrane surface, wedging apart the lipid molecules. The effect of a large number of melittin molecules introduced on one side of the membrane may be similar to that of a detergent, destabilising the bilayer and causing an increase in membrane curvature. Its wedged shape is reminiscent of lysolecithin which also disrupts lipid bilayers. This model is based on the interaction of melittin monomers with lipid. Experiments on lecithin bilayer conductance induced by melittin suggests that four melittin monomers may be required to form a transmembrane channel (Tosteson and Tosteson, 1981). This does not necessarily indicate that the tetramer is the active unit in membrane lysis, but it seems clear that, as strong hydrophobic interactions stabilise the tetramer, melittin is likely to remain a tetramer until it interacts with a bilayer. On encountering a bilayer, the hydrophobic interactions among monomers in the melittin tetramer may be replaced by hydrophobic melittin–bilayer interactions. The concerted action of the four melittin monomers might well be more destructive to the bilayer structure than the independent action of each of the four monomers.

The major difference between melittin and proper membrane proteins (Terwilliger *et al.*, 1982) may be that melittin penetrates only part way into one leaflet of a bilayer. This partial penetration may be the cause of membrane destabilisation. It is possible that integral membrane proteins extend either half-way or all the way through the lipid bilayer with fairly uniform cross-section. This might produce the least perturbation of the two halves (leaflets) of the lipid bilayer. The disruptive effect of melittin and its structure as an amphiphilic wedge are consistent with these ideas.

DISCUSSION

It should be clear from the work reviewed in this chapter than X-ray diffraction and electron microscopy have been instrumental in establishing the structural properties of biological membranes. Early work using both techniques suggested that lipids in biological membranes were organised into bilayers. More recent studies have provided images of membranes from many different sources. Application of X-ray diffraction has yielded detailed images of lipid structure and information about the disposition of proteins relative to the bilayer. With the advent of three-dimensional reconstruction, image analysis of electron micrographs has begun to create three-dimensional images of membrane structures.

The bilayer structure of lipids in membranes is, perhaps, the only structural feature that is common to all biological membranes. Electron density profiles of membranes exhibit, in all cases, a pair of high electron density peaks separated by a low density trough. These are features characteristic of a bilayer of lipid molecules. The hydrophobic effect is the principal force stabilising cell membranes, but diffraction studies of lipid crystals and lipid–water liquid crystals have shown that the hydrogen bonding of polar groups and the close packing of hydrocarbon chains have a strong effect on the detailed structure of lipid phases. The interplay between these two forces is demonstrated by the tilting of hydrocarbon chains in some bilayers and in the temperature-dependent phase transition and its response to alterations in bilayer composition.

X-ray diffraction demonstrates that, at physiological temperatures, most lipid hydrocarbon chains are in a fluid, disordered configuration (Wilkins *et al.*, 1970). Two independent sets of data provide evidence for this: first, in electron density profiles, the low density trough is rounded, indicating a broad distribution in the placement of the terminal methyl groups of the hydrocarbons and second, in most diffraction patterns there is a strong broad reflection centered at 4.7 Å spacing. This diffraction maximum is characteristic of liquid paraffin and indicates an organisation of hydrocarbon chains in the bilayer similar to that in liquid paraffin. Hydrocarbon chains that are packed in a regular, two-dimensional hexagonal lattice would give rise to diffraction at

4.2 Å spacing. The maximum at 4.2 Å spacing has been observed in diffraction patterns from many membranes below their phase transition temperature.

The disposition of proteins relative to the bilayer can be determined by interpretation of the electron density profile. This analysis has in several cases, such as purple membrane and gap junctions, demonstrated that proteins span the lipid bilayer. They have also been used to determine the dimensions of proteins projecting from membrane surfaces as in the cases of acetylcholine receptor, sarcoplasmic reticulum and myelin. Protein–lipid interactions can also be illuminated by this kind of study. The polar head groups of lipids in membranes may be hydrogen-bonded to each other, to water, to solutes or to membrane proteins. The close association of myelin basic protein and gap junction protein with the lipid polar groups suggests that proteins may frequently be found to interact with lipids in this way.

One of the most striking patterns of membrane structure that has become evident from X-ray diffraction studies is the common orientation of protein secondary structures relative to the membrane surfaces. All X-ray diffraction and electron microscope evidence for α-helical conformation in membrane proteins has indicated that the α helices are orientated with their axes approximately perpendicular to the membrane plane. In gap junctions, where wide-angle X-ray diffraction suggests a high proportion of β-sheet conformation, the β sheets are also approximately perpendicular to the membrane surfaces. However, the peptide chains in these sheets run approximately parallel to the membrane surface. β Sheets with peptide chains running perpendicular to the membrane plane would be more difficult to demonstrate unambiguously as the 4.7 Å scattering diagnostic of β sheets would then superimpose on the wide-angle scattering from the lipid hydrocarbon chains. As the arrangements that have been observed are topologically distinct, it seems unlikely that specific pathways of membrane assembly are of strong influence (although gap junctions may represent a special case). It is possible that requirements for the stability of lipid bilayers might strongly constrain membrane proteins to be of uniform cross section across the width of the bilayer (or at least half the bilayer width). Arrangement of secondary structures perpendicular to the membrane plane is one way of achieving this. Available evidence is consistent with approximately constant cross-sectional areas of integral membrane proteins across the width of the membrane but the evidence is strong only in the case of bacteriorhodopsin. Analysis of the membrane profile of bacterial photosynthetic reaction centres suggests that the protein has a constant cross section in each of the two halves of the bilayer, but that it is different in the two halves (Pachence *et al.*, 1979; 1981). This arrangement may also be consistent with lipid bilayer stability. Alternatively, variation in the average tilt of hydrocarbon chains as a function of distance from the bilayer surface may provide a means of maintaining close packing within the membrane interior when the cross-sectional area of proteins is variable. In some cases, variation of protein cross section may have functional importance, for instance in inducing membrane curvature.

Computer processing of electron micrographs to create three-dimensional reconstructions has been used to produce accurate, low-resolution images of membrane structures. These images demonstrate the structural diversity among membrane components. The method can be used to obtain images of the structures both projecting from the membrane surfaces and within the membrane bilayer. The necessity of a well ordered, two-dimensional lattice has, to date, limited the number of structures which have been solved by this technique. However, as the methods for isolation and reconstitution of membrane components improve, the preparation of more two-dimensional crystals seems very likely.

In the absence of three-dimensional crystals, the use of electron microscopy to produce three-dimensional images has several advantages over X-ray diffraction. As electron microscopy can image single membranes, it is possible to obtain both the intensities and phases directly from a micrograph. X-ray diffraction requires many membranes in a specimen to obtain observable diffraction. It is necessary to orientate these membranes so their planes are parallel to one another in the specimen. Furthermore, as each membrane may be rotated about its normal relative to others in the specimen, lattice lines at the same reciprocal spacings will be averaged. Thus, in an X-ray diffraction pattern from these specimens it is necessary not only to recover phases but also to separate out intensities due to different lattice lines that have been averaged in the diffraction pattern.

Combination of X-ray, electron microscopy and other data, such as physiological measurements has also led to the identification of structural patterns. For instance, several unrelated transmembrane channels appear to have funnel-shaped entrance openings. Physiological measurements have been used to estimate the diameter of the narrowest part of the channels in acetylcholine receptor, gap junctions and matrix porin. In the cases of porin and receptor, electron microscope evidence is consistent with much larger openings than indicated by the physiological evidence in the cases of porin and receptors. Furthermore, electron micrographs of negatively-stained receptor membrane folded over on the grid are suggestive of a funnel shape in the portion of the receptor projecting from the membrane into the synaptic space. X-ray diffraction measurements suggest a funnel shape for the gap junction channel. The possibility that all three of these structures have funnel-shaped entrance openings is remarkable because of their very different structural organisations and functions. Although not affecting any equilibria, a funnel-shaped opening may enhance the rate of transport in response to a change in the concentration of the molecules being transported. The kinetic advantage of a large entrance opening combined with the specificity intrinsic to a much narrower passage may combine to give funnel-shaped openings substantial selective advantage for many membrane channels.

Membrane–membrane interactions have been studied by a combination of X-ray diffraction and electron microscopy. Transient contacts such as those that occur during membrane fusion can only be studied by electron microscopy, but the structures involved in fusion, such as the influenza haemagglutinin molecule, can be studied by both techniques. Stable membrane–membrane interactions involve either direct contacts or long-range forces. Direct contacts found, for example, in gap junctions and nuclear envelope pores, are generally maintained by specific protein–protein interactions (although some exceptions are possible; see Kachar and Reese, 1982). Long-range forces maintain equilibrium separations of membranes in the membrane stacks of myelin and rod outer segments. The distance between membranes interacting through long-range forces is a function of the properties of both the membranes and the aqueous phase in between the membranes. Alterations in the lipids or in the water activity will affect the distance between membranes. Because the long-range forces are relatively weak there is often substantial variability in the separation of membranes that are not directly linked.

The interaction of membranes with functional molecules (for example, ligands, effectors) in the aqueous phase around the membranes can be studied by both X-ray diffraction and electron microscopy. For instance, X-ray diffraction has been used to study the effect of anaesthetics on lipid bilayers (Franks and Lieb, 1978; 1979). X-ray crystallography has visualised the role of melittin structure in the lysis of cell membranes by bee venom (Terwilliger *et al.*, 1982) and the interaction of gramicidin with lipids to form ion channels (Kimball and Wallace, 1981). Electron microscopy of acetylcholine receptors with and without bound α-bungarotoxin has located the two toxin binding sites on the receptor (Zingsheim *et al.*, 1982).

It is not always sufficient to take apart a complex structure like a membrane and study the pieces. The workings of a membrane may only become clear once all the pieces are reassembled into an intact structure. X-ray diffraction and image processing techniques in electron microscopy are both averaging methods and their application to a complex membrane structure does not necessarily result in data interpretable in terms of membrane function. Just as in most techniques of solution chemistry or spectroscopy, the study of a simple system results in more easily interpretable data. Some membrane systems have a relatively simple protein composition, and some of these, such as purple membrane and gap junctions, consist of differentiated portions of a larger membrane in which natural crystalline order may occur. In most cases, however, it is necessary to dissect a membrane into its component parts and study each one separately. Once each component is characterised it may be possible to develop an overall picture of the membrane. For this to be done, it is necessary to know the relative positions of the components *in vivo*. Electron microscopy of thin-sectioned or freeze-fractured material can be used for determining this.

Ultimately, the coordinated use of all available techniques of structural analysis has the greatest promise for producing detailed images of biological membranes. The very different ways in which X rays and electrons interact with matter make X-ray diffraction and electron microscopy remarkably complementary sources of structural information. For instance, to obtain an electron micrograph of a structure, it is necessary to place the structure in a vacuum and, usually, to stain or shadow it with a heavy metal. These operations may cause some structural alterations. However, an image derived from electron microscopy can be tested for consistency with X-ray diffraction patterns taken using hydrated specimens at controlled temperature in an essentially physiological state. This allows evaluation of the integrity of the structure as seen by electron microscopy. Although the overall dimensions of repeating units can be measured very accurately with X-ray diffraction, phase information cannot be obtained directly. Electron microscopy cannot provide dimensions with the accuracy of X-ray diffraction. However, electron micrographs provide direct phase information and can be used to produce three-dimensional images of structures using two-dimensional crystals. This is much more difficult using X-ray diffraction.

Micrographs of negatively-stained specimens provide information about the shape of the stain-excluding portion of the structure. Wide-angle X-ray diffraction provides information about the secondary structure of the proteins and the ordering in the packing of lipid hydrocarbon chains. A three-dimensional reconstruction from electron microscopy usually suffers because the Fourier transform of the specimen along the meridional direction cannot be measured. In the analysis of X-ray diffraction, the meridian is usually the simplest part of the diffraction pattern to analyse. X-ray crystallography provides the potential for visualising the molecular structure of membrane components at atomic resolution. But only electron microscopy can provide detailed information about the distribution of components on the disordered surface of a membrane.

An understanding of the detailed mechanism of action of any macromolecule is greatly enhanced by the determination of its molecular structure at high resolution. Two-dimensional crystals can potentially yield high resolution information. A high resolution three-dimensional map of bacteriorhodopsin will soon be produced using data from electron micrographs and electron diffraction. The limitations on the use of this technique derive from the difficulty in producing extensive, highly ordered two-dimensional crystals and the problems in phasing electron diffraction patterns at resolutions beyond about 7 Å. X-ray crystallographic analysis of three-dimensional crystals is an alternative method for producing high resolution images of macromolecules. Although only two integral membrane proteins have been induced to form crystals suitable for high resolution X-ray crystallography, these first successes hold promise for the production of two- and three-dimensional crystals of other membrane proteins in the near future. The application of electron microscopy and X-ray diffraction to these crystals should result in high resolution images of a variety of membrane proteins. When this has been accomplished, our understanding of membrane function will have entered a new era.

ACKNOWLEDGEMENTS

We thank our many colleagues who provided us with figures, reprints and manuscripts before publication. This review would not have been possible without their help. Research in our laboratory, some of which has been described here, is supported by NSF grant PCM-81-04323 and NIH grant GM 29829. L.M. is an Alfred P. Sloan Foundation fellow and an Irma T. Hirschl Career scientist.

REFERENCES

Abrahamsson, S. and Pascher, I. (1966). *Acta crystallogr.*, **21**, 79–87.
Acheson, N. H. and Tamm, I. (1970). *Virology*, **41**, 306–320.
Agard, D. A. and Stroud, R. M. (1982). *Biophys. J.*, **37**, 589–602.
Aidley, D. J. (1971). *The Physiology of Excitable Cells*, Cambridge University Press, London.
Anderson, D. J. and Blöbel, G. (1981). *Proc. natn. Acad. Sci. U.S.A.*, **78**, 5598–5602.
Anderson, J. M. (1975). *Biochim. biophys. Acta*, **416**, 191–235.
Anderson, J. M. and Boardman, N. K. (1966). *Biochim. biophys. Acta*, **112**, 403–421.
Anderson, J. M. and Levine, R. P. (1974). *Biochim. biophys. Acta*, **357**, 118–126.
Anderson, R. G. W., Brown, M. S. and Goldstein, J. L. (1977). *Cell*, **10**, 351–364.
Anderson, S. *et al.* (1981). *Nature*, **290**, 457–465.
Armond, P. A., Arntzen, C. J., Briantais, J.-M. and Vernotte, C. (1976). Differentiation of chloroplast and grana development. *Arch. biochem. biophys.*, **175**, 54–63.
Arntzen, C. J., Armond, P. A., Briantais, J.-M., Burke, J. J. and Novitsky, W. P. (1976). *Brookhaven Symp. Biol.*, **28**, 316–337.
Baker, T. S., Caspar, D. L. D., Hollingshead, C. J. and Goodenough, D. A. (1983). *J. Cell Biol.*, **96**, 204–216.
Bear, R. S., Palmer, K. J. and Schmitt, F. O. (1941). *J. Cell comp. Physiol.*, **17**, 355–367.
Becker, D. P., Young, H. F., Nulsen, F. E. and Jane, J. A. (1969). *Expl Neur.*, **24**, 272–276.
Bennett, H. S. and Porter, K. R. (1953). *Am. J. Anat.*, **93**, 61–105.
Bennett, M. V. L. and Goodenough, D. A. (1978). *Neurosci. Res. Prog. Bull.*, **16**, 373–486.
Bennett, V. and Stenbuck, P. J. (1979). *Nature*, **280**, 468–473.
Berg, S., Dodge, S., Krogmann, D. W. and Dilley, R. A. (1974). *Pl. Physiol.*, **53**, 619–627.
Björkman, O. (1972). *Photosynthetic adaption to contrasting light climates, A. Rep. Director, Dept Pl. Biol.*, Carnegie Institution of Washington, Stanford, California, 82–135.
Blasie, J. K. and Stamatoff, J. (1980). *A. Rev. Biophys. Bioengng*, **10**, 451–458.
Blasie, J. K., Erecinska, M., Samuels, S. and Leigh, J. S. (1978). *Biochim. biophys. Acta*, **501**, 33–52.
Blasie, J. K. *et al.* (1982). *Biochim. biophys. Acta*, **679**, 188–197.
Blasie, J. K., Worthington, C. R. and Dewey, M. M. (1969). *J. molec. Biol.*, **39**, 407–416.
Blaurock, A. E. (1967). PhD thesis, University of Michigan, Ann Arbor.
Blaurock, A. E. (1971). *J. molec. Biol.*, **56**, 35–52.
Blaurock, A. E. (1975). *J. molec. Biol.*, **93**, 139–157.
Blaurock, A. E. (1976). *Biophys. J.*, **16**, 491–501.
Blaurock, A. E. (1981a). *Biochim. biophys. Acta*, **650**, 1–57.
Blaurock, A. E. (1981b). *Brain Res.*, **210**, 383–387.
Blaurock, A. E. and King, G. I. (1977). *Science*, **196**, 1101–1104.
Blaurock, A. E. and Nelander, J. C. (1976). *J. molec. Biol.*, **103**, 421–431.
Blaurock, A. E. and Nelander, J. C. (1979). *J. Neurochem.*, **32**, 1753–1760.
Blaurock, A. E. and Stoeckenius, W. (1971). *Nature new Biol.*, **233**, 152–154.
Blaurock, A. E. and Wilkins, M. H. F. (1969). *Nature*, **233**, 906–909.
Blaurock, A. E. and Wilkins, M. H. F. (1972). *Nature*, **236**, 313–314.
Blow, D. M. and Crick, F. H. C. (1959). *Acta crystallogr.*, **12**, 794–802.
Blundell, T. L. and Johnson, L. N. (1976). *Protein Crystallogr.*, Academic Press, New York.

Bownds, D., Gordon-Walker, A., Gaide-Huguenin, A.-C. and Robinson, W. (1971). *J. gen. Physiol.*, **58**, 225–237.

Brady, G. W., Fein, D. B., Harder, M. E. and Meissner, G. (1982). *Biophys. J.*, **37**, 637–646.

Brady, G. W., Fein, D. B., Wood, D. D. and Moscarello, M. A. (1981a). *FEBS Lett*, **125**, 159–160.

Brady, G. W., Fein, D. B., Harder, M. E., Spehr, R. and Meissner, G. (1981b). *Biophys. J.*, **34**, 13–34.

Bragg, W. L. and Perutz, M. F. (1952). *Proc. R. Soc.*, **A213**, 425–435.

Branton, D., Cohen, C. M. and Tyler, J. (1981). *Cell*, **24**, 24–32.

Bretscher, M. S. (1973). *Science*, **181**, 622–629.

Brown, L. R., Lauterwein, J. and Wüthrich, K. (1980). *Biochim. biophys. Acta*, **622**, 231–244.

Brunisholtz, R. A., Cuendet, R. A., Theiler, R. and Zuber, H. (1981). *FEBS Lett.*, **129**, 150–154.

Burke, J. J., Ditto, C. L. and Arntzen, C. J. (1978). *Arch. biochem. Biophys.*, **187**, 252–263.

Buse, G., Steffans, G. J., Steffans, G. C. M., Sacher, R. and Erdeg, M. (1981). In *Interactions between Iron and Proteins in Electron Transport*, (ed. C. Ho) Elsevier, New York.

Caron, F., Mateu, L., Rigny, P. and Azerad, R. (1974). *J. molec. Biol.*, **85**, 279–300.

Caspar, D. L. D. and Klug, A. (1962). *Cold Spring Harb. Symp. quant. Biol.*, **27**, 1–24.

Caspar, D. L. D. and Kirschner, D. A. (1971). *Nature new Biol.*, **231**, 46–52.

Caspar, D. L. D., Goodenough, D. A., Makowski, L. and Phillips, W. C. (1977). *J. Cell Biol.*, **74**, 605–628.

Caspar, D. L. D., Melchior, V., Hollingshead, C. J. and Kirschner, D. A. (1980). *Membrane-membrane Interactions* (ed. N. B. Gilula) Raven Press, New York, 195–211.

Cartaud, J., Benedetti, E. L., Sobel, A. and Changeux, J.-P. (1978). *J. Cell Sci.*, **29**, 313–337.

Cartaud, J., Benedetti, E. L., Cohen, J. B., Meunier, J.-C. and Changeux, J.-P. (1973). *FEBS Lett.*, **33**, 109–113.

Chabre, M. and Cavaggioni, A. (1973). *Nature new Biol.*, **244**, 118–120.

Chabre, M. (1975). *Biochim. biophys. Acta*, **382**, 322–325.

Chabre, M. and Cavaggioni, A. (1975). *Biochim. biophys. Acta*, **382**, 336–343.

Chapman, D. (1965). In *The Structure of Lipids*, Methuen and Co., London.

Clayton, R. K. and Haselkorn, R. (1972). *J. molec. Biol.*, **68**, 97–105.

Clayton, R. K. and Wang, R. T. (1971). *Meth. Enzym.*, **23**, 696–704.

Cohen, L. K. and Kaplan, S. (1981a). *J. biol. Chem.*, **256**, 5901–5908.

Cohen, L. K. and Kaplan, S. (1981b). *J. biol. Chem.*, **256**, 5909–5915.

Cohen, C. M., Tyler, J. M. and Branton, D. (1980). *Cell*, **21**, 875–883.

Compton, A. H. and Allison, S. K. (1935). *X-rays in Theory and Experiment*, Van Nostrand Co. Inc., New York.

Corless, J. M. (1972). *Nature*, **237**, 229–231.

Corless, J. M., Cobbs III, W. H., Costello, M. J. and Robertson, J. D. (1976). *Expl Eye Res.*, **23**, 295–324.

Corless, J. M., McCaslin, D. R. and Scott, B. L. (1982). *Proc. natn. Acad. Sci. U.S.A.*, **75**, 1116–1120.

Cowley, A. C., Fuller, N. L., Rand, R. P. and Parsegian, V. A. (1978). *Biochemistry*, **17**, 3163–3168.

Craven, B. M. (1976). *Nature*, **260**, 727–729.

Crick, F. H. C. (1953). *Acta crystallogr.*, **6**, 689–697.

Crowther, R. A., Finch, J. T. and Pearse, B. M. F. (1976). *J. molec. Biol.*, **103**, 785–798.

Crowther, R. A. and Pearse, B. M. F. (1981). *J. Cell Biol.*, **91**, 790–797.

Cuendet, P. A. and Zuber, H. (1977). *FEBS Lett.*, **79**, 96–100.

Cuendet, P. A., Zürrer, H., Snozzi, M. and Zuber, H. (1978). *FEBS Lett.*, **88**, 309–312.

Cuillel, M., Tripper, F., Braunwald, J. and Jacrot, B. (1979). *Virology*, **99**, 277–285.

Davis, H. L., Davis, N. L., Clemens, A. L. (1967). *Ann. N.Y. Acad. Sci.*, **141**, 310–325.

Deatherage, J. F., Henderson, R. and Capaldi, R. A. (1980). In *Electron Microscopy at Molecular Dimensions* (eds W. Baumeister and W. Vogell) Springer-Verlag, New York, 91–100.

Deatherage, J. F., Henderson, R. and Capaldi, R. A. (1982a). *J. molec. Biol.*, **158**, 487–499.

Deatherage, J. F., Henderson, R. and Capaldi, R. A. (1982b). *J. molec. Biol.*, **158**, 501–514.

DeRosier, D. J. and Klug, A. (1968). *Nature*, 217, 130–134.
DiRienzo, J. M., Nakamura, K. and Inouye, M. (1978). *A. Rev. Biochem.*, 47, 481–532.
Dratz, E. A., Miljanich, G. P., Nemes, P. P., Gaw, J. E. and Schwartz, S. (1979). *Photochem. Photobiol.*, 29, 661–670.
Drews, G. (1978). *Curr. Topics Bioengng*, 8, 161–207.
Dumont, M. E., Wiggins, J. W. and Hayward, S. B. (1981). *Proc. natl. Acad. Sci. U.S.A.*, 78, 2947–2951.
Dunbar, J. C. and Ralston, G. B. (1978). *Biochim. biophys. Acta*, 510, 283–291.
Dupont, Y., Harrison, S. C. and Hasselbach, W. (1973). *Nature*, 244, 555–558.
Eisenberg, D. and Crothers, D. (1979). *Physical Chemistry with Applications in the Life Sciences*, Benjamin/Cummings, Menlo Park, Ch. 16, 749–797.
Eisenberg, D., Terwilliger, T. C. and Tsui, F. (1980). *Biophys. J.*, 32, 252–254.
Elder, M., Hitchcock, P., Mason, R. and Shipley, G. G. (1977). *Proc. R. Soc.*, A354, 157–170.
Elgsaeter, A. and Branton, D. (1974). *J. Cell Biol.*, 63, 1018–1030.
Engelman, D. M. (1971). *J. molec. Biol.*, 58, 153–165.
Engelman, D. M. and Zaccai, G. (1980). *Proc. natn. Acad. Sci. U.S.A.*, 77, 5894–5898.
Engelman, D. M., Henderson, R., McLachlan, A. D. and Wallace, B. A. (1980). *Proc. natn. Acad. Sci. U.S.A.*, 77, 2023–2027.
Erikson, H. P. and Klug, A. (1971). *Phil. Trans. R. Soc.*, B261, 105–118.
Fallon, R. F. and Goodenough, D. A. (1981). *J. Cell Biol.*, 90, 521–526.
Finean, J. B. and Burge, R. E. (1963). *J. molec. Biol.*, 7, 672–687.
Fisher, K. A., Yanagimoto, K. and Stoeckenius, W. (1978). *J. Cell Biol.*, 77, 611–621.
Fowler, V. and Bennett, V. (1978). *J. Supramolec. Res.*, 8, 215–221.
Fowler, V. and Branton, D. (1977). *Nature*, 268, 23–26.
Frank, J., Goldfarb, W., Eisenberg, D. and Baker, T. S. (1978). *Ultramicroscopy*, 3, 283–290.
Franks, N. P. (1976). *J. molec. Biol.*, 100, 345–358.
Franks, N. P., Arunachalam, T. and Caspi, E. (1978). *Nature*, 276, 530–532.
Franks, N. P. and Levine, Y. K. (1981). *Membrane Spectroscopy* (ed. E. Grell) Springer-Verlag, Berlin, 437–487.
Franks, N. P. and Lieb, W. R. (1978). *Nature*, 274, 339–342.
Franks, N. P. and Lieb, W. R. (1979). *J. molec. Biol.*, 133, 469–500.
Franks, N. P., Melchior, V., Kirschner, D. A. and Caspar, D. L. D. (1982). *J. molec. Biol.*, 155, 133–154.
Frey, T. G., Chan, S. H. P. and Schatz, G. (1978). *J. biol. Chem.*, 253, 4389–4395.
Friend, D. S. and Farquar, M. G. (1967). *J. Cell Biol.*, 35, 357–376.
Fuller, S. D., Capaldi, R. A. and Henderson, R. (1979). *J. molec. Biol.*, 134, 305–327.
Fung, B. K. K. and Hubbell, W. L. (1978). *Biochemistry*, 17, 4403–4410.
Funk, J., Welte, W., Hodapp, N., Wutschel, I. and Kreutz, W. (1981). *Biochim. biophys. Acta*, 640, 142–158.
Ganser, A. L. and Kirschner, D. A. (1980). In *Neurological Mutations Affecting Myelination* (ed. N. Baumann) Elsevier-North Holland Biomedical Press, INSERM Symp., 14, 171–176.
Garavito, R. M. and Rosenbusch, J. P. (1980). *J. Cell Biol.*, 86, 327–329.
Garoff, H. and Simons, K. (1974). *Proc. natn. Acad. Sci. U.S.A.*, 71, 3988–3992.
Garoff, H. and Sonderlund, H. (1978). *J. molec. Biol.*, 124, 535–549.
Geren, B. B. (1954). *Expl Cell Res.*, 7, 558–562.
Giesbrecht, P. and Drews, G. (1966). *Arch. Microbiol.*, 54, 297–330.
Goldstein, J. L., Anderson, R. G. W. and Brown, M. W. (1979). *Nature*, 279, 679–685.
Goodenough, D. A. (1974). *J. Cell Biol.*, 61, 557–563.
Goodenough, D. A. and Revel, J.-P. (1970). *J. Cell Biol.*, 45, 272–290.
Goodenough, D. A. and Stoeckenius, W. (1972). *J. Cell Biol.*, 54, 646–656.
Goodenough, D. A., Dick II, J. S. B. and Lyons, J. E. (1980). *J. Cell Biol.*, 86, 576–589.
Goodenough, U. W. and Staehlin, L. A. (1971). *J. Cell Biol.*, 48, 594–619.
Gorter, E. and Grendel, F. (1928). *Biochem. Z.*, 192, 431–456.
Govindjee (1975). *Bioenergetics of Photosynthesis*, Academic Press, Yew York.
Gras, W. J. and Worthington, C. R. (1969). *Proc. natn. Acad. Sci. U.S.A.*, 63, 233–237.
Guinier, A. (1963). *X-ray Diffraction Analysis in Crystals, Imperfect Crystals and Amorphous Bodies*. W. H. Freeman and Co., London.

Gruner, S. M., Barry, D. and Reynolds, G. T. (1978). *Biophys. J.*, 21, 134a.
Gulik-Krzywicki, T. (1975). *Biochim. biophys. Acta*, 415, 1–28.
Gulik-Krzywicki, T., Shechter, E., Luzzati, V. and Faure, M. (1969). *Nature*, 233, 1116–1121.
Gulik-Krzywicki, T., Tardieu, A. and Luzzati, V. (1969). *Molec. Crystals Liquid Crystals*, 8, 285–291.
Habermann, E. (1972). *Science*, 177, 314–322.
Hagins, W. A. (1972). *A. Rev. Biophys. Bioengng*, 1, 131–158.
Hainfield, J. F. and Steck, T. L. (1977). *J. Supramolec. Structure*, 6, 301–311.
Hargrave, P. A. *et al.* (1980). *Neurochem. Int.*, 1, 231–244.
Harris, A. L., Spray, D. C. and Bennett, M. V. L. (1981). *J. gen. Physiol.*, 77, 95–117.
Harrison, S. C. (1968). *J. appl. Crystallogr.*, 1, 84–90.
Harrison, S. C., Caspar, D. L. D., Camerini-Otero, R. D. and Franklin, R. M. (1971a). *Nature new Biol.*, 229, 197–201.
Harrison, S. C., David, A., Jumblatt, J. and Darnell, J. E. (1971b). *J. molec. Biol.*, 60, 523–528.
Harrison, S. C. and Jack, A. (1975). *J. molec. Biol.*, 97, 173–191.
Harrison, S. C., Jack, A., Goodenough, D. A. and Sefton, B. M. (1974). *J. supramolec. Struct.*, 2, 486–495.
Hartley, G. S. (1936). *Aqueous Solutions of Paraffin Chain Salts*, Hermann, Paris.
Hasselbach, W. and Makinose, M. (1961). *Biochem. Z.*, 333, 518–528.
Hauser, H., Guyer, W., Spiess, M., Pascher, I. and Sundell, S. (1980). *J. molec. Biol.*, 137, 265–282.
Hauser, H., Pascher, I. and Sundell, S. (1980). *J. molec. Biol.*, 137, 249–264.
Hauser, H., Pascher, I., Pearson, R. H. and Sundell, S. (1981). *Biochim. biophys. Acta*, 650, 21–51.
Hayward, S. B., Grano, D. A., Glaeser, R. M. and Fisher, K. A. (1978). *Proc. natn. Acad. Sci. U.S.A.*, 75, 4320–4324.
Hayward, S. B. and Glaeser, R. M. (1980). In *Electron Microscopy at Molecular Dimensions* (eds E. Baumeister and W. Vogell), Springer-Verlag, Berlin, 226–233.
Hayward, S. B. and Stroud, R. M. (1981). *J. molec. Biol.*, 151, 491–517.
Henderson, D., Eibl, H. and Weber, K. (1979). *J. molec. Biol.*, 132, 193–318.
Henderson, R. (1975). *J. molec. Biol.*, 93, 123–138.
Henderson, R., Capaldi, R. A. and Leigh, J. S. (1977). *J. molec. Biol.*, 112, 631–648.
Henderson, R., Jubb, J. S. and Rossmann, M. G. (1982). *J. molec. Biol.*, 154, 501–514.
Henderson, R., Jubb, J. S. and Whytock, S. (1978). *J. molec. Biol.*, 123, 259–274.
Henderson, R. and Unwin, P. N. T. (1975). *Nature*, 257, 28–32.
Herbette, L., Marquardt, J., Scarpa, A. and Blasie, J. K. (1977). *Biophys. J.*, 20, 245–272.
Herbette, L. *et al.* (1981a). *Biophys. J.*, 36, 27–46.
Herbette, L. *et al.* (1981b). *Biophys. J.*, 36, 47–72.
Hertzberg, E. L. and Gilula, N. B. (1979). *J. biol. Chem.*, 245, 2138–2147.
Hertzberg, E. L., Anderson, D. J., Friedlander, M. and Gilula, N. B. (1982). *J. Cell Biol.*, 92, 53–59.
Heuser, J. (1980). *J. Cell Biol.*, 84, 560–583.
Heuser, J. E. and Reese, T. S. (1973). *J. Cell Biol.*, 57, 315–344.
Hirst, G. K. (1942). *J. exp. Med.*, 75, 49–64.
Hitchcock, P. B., Mason, R., Thomas, K. M. and Shipley, G. G. (1974). *Proc. natn. Acad. Sci. U.S.A.*, 71, 3036–3040.
Hodapp, N. and Kreutz, W. (1980). *Biophys. Struct. Mech.*, 7, 65–95.
Hollingshead, C. J., Caspar, D. L. D., Melchior, V. and Kirschner, D. A. (1981). *J. Cell Biol.*, 89, 631–644.
Holmes, K. C. and Blow, D. M. (1965). *Meth. Biochem. Analysis*, 13, 113–239.
Holser, W. T. (1958). *Z. Kristallogr.*, 110, 266–281.
Holtzman, E., Wise, D., Wall, J. and Karlin, A. (1982). *Proc. natn. Acad. Sci. U.S.A.*, 79, 310–314.
Hosemann, R. and Bagchi, S. N. (1962). *Direct Analysis of Diffraction by Matter*. North-Holland, Amsterdam.
Huang, K.-S., Bayley, H., Liao, M. J., London, E. and Khorana, H. G. (1981). *J. biol. Chem.*, 256, 3802–3809.

Huang, R. T. C., Wahn, K., Klenk, H.-D. and Rott, R. (1980). *Virology*, **104**, 294–302.
Hubbard, R. (1954). *J. gen. Physiol.*, **37**, 381–399.
Hui, S. W. (1977). *Biochim. biophys. Acta*, **472**, 345–371.
Hui, S. W., Parsons, D. F. and Cowden, M. (1974). *Proc. natn. Acad. Sci. U.S.A.*, **71**, 5068–5072.
Hui, S. W., Cowden, M., Papahadjopoulos, D. and Parsons, D. F. (1975). *Biochim. biophys. Acta*, **382**, 265–275.
Huxley, H. E. and Brown, W. (1967). *J. molec. Biol.*, **30**, 383–434.
Huxley, H. E. and Zubay, G. (1960). *J. molec. Biol.*, **2**, 10–18.
Ikemoto, N., Sreter, F. A., Nakamura, A. and Gergeley, J. (1968). *J. Ulstrastruct. Res.*, **23**, 216–222.
Inesi, G. and Scales, D. (1974). *Biochemistry*, **13**, 3298–3306.
International Tables for X-ray Crystallography (1969) (eds N. F. M. Henry and K. Lonsdale) Kynoch Press, Birmingham, Vol. 1.
Israelachvili, J. N. and Mitchell, D. J. (1975). *Biochim. biophys. Acta*, **389**, 13–19.
Izawa, S. and Good, N. E. (1966). *Pl. Physiol.*, **41**, 544–552.
Jack, A., Harrison, S. C. and Crowther, R. A. (1975). *J. molec. Biol.*, **97**, 163–172.
Jacob, J. and Miller, K. R. (1982). *The structure of a bacterial photosynthetic membrane. II. Isolation of pure photosynthetic membranes and their polypeptide composition.*
James, R. W. (1958). *The Optical Principles of the Diffraction of X-rays*, G. Bell and Sons, London.
Kachar, B. and Reese, T. S. (1982). *Nature*, **296**, 464–466.
Kanaseki, T. and Kadota, K. (1969). *J. Cell Biol.*, **42**, 202–220.
Karlin, A. (1980). In *The Cell Surface and Neuronal Function* (eds C. W. Cotman, G. Poste and G. L. Nicolson), Elsevier Biomedical Press, 191–260.
Karlin, A., McNamee, M. G., Weill, C. L. and Valderrama, R. (1975). *Cold Spring Harb. Symp. quant. Biol.*, **40**, 203–213.
Karlin, A. *et al.* (1978). *J. Cell Biol.*, **76**, 577–592.
Kates, M. (1970). *Adv. Lipid Res.*, **8**, 225–267.
Kates, M. (1978). *Prog. Chem. Fats other Lipids*, **15**, 301–342.
Khorana, H. G. *et al.* (1979). *Proc. natn. Acad. Sci. U.S.A.*, **76**, 5046–5050.
Kimball, M. R. and Wallace, B. A. (1981). XIIth *Int. Congr. Crystallogr. Proc.* C-50.
Kirschner, D. A. and Caspar, D. L. D. (1975). *Proc. natn. Acad. Sci. U.S.A.*, **72**, 3513–3517.
Kirschner, D. A. and Caspar, D. L. D. (1977). In *Myelin* (ed. P. Morell), Plenum, New York, 51–89.
Kirschner, D. A., Caspar, D. L. D. and Ganser, A. L. (1983). In *Myelin* (ed. P. Morell), Plenum, New York (in the press).
Kirschner, D. A. and Ganser, A. L. (1980). *Nature*, **283**, 207–210.
Kirschner, D. A. and Ganser, A. L. (1982). *J. molec. Biol.*, **157**, 635–658.
Kirschner, D. A., Hollingshead, C. J., Thaxton, C., Caspar, D. L. D. and Goodenough, D. A. (1979). *J. Cell Biol.*, **82**, 140–149.
Kirschner, D. A. and Sidman, R. L. (1976). *Biochim. biophys. Acta*, **448**, 73–87.
Kirchhausen, T. and Harrison, S. C. (1981). *Cell*, **23**, 755–761.
Kistler, J. and Stroud, R. M. (1981). *Proc. natn. Acad. Sci. U.S.A.*, **78**, 3678–3682.
Kistler, J., Stroud, R. M., Klymkowsky, M. W., Lalancette, R. and Fairclough, R. H. (1982). *Biophys. J.*, **37**, 371–383.
Klenk, H.-D., Rott, R., Orlich, M. and Blodorn, J. (1975). *Virology*, **68**, 426–439.
Klug, A. and DeRosier, D. J. (1966). *Nature*, **212**, 29–32.
Klymkowsky, M. W. and Stroud, R. M. (1979). *J. molec. Biol.*, **128**, 319–334.
Kreutz, W. (1970). *Adv. Bot. Res.*, **3**, 53–169.
Kühn, H., Bennett, N., Michel-Villaz, M. and Chabre, M. (1981). *Proc. natn. Acad. Sci. U.S.A.*, **78**, 6873–6877.
Laine, R., Soderlund, H. and Renkonen, O. (1973). *Intervirology*, **1**, 110–121.
Lauterwein, J., Bösch, C., Brown, C. R. and Wüthrich, K. (1979). *Biochim. Biophys. Acta*, **556**, 244–264.
Laver, W. G. *et al.* (1980). In *Structure and Variation in Influenza Virus* (eds W. G. Laver and G. M. Air), 295–306.
Lazarowitz, S. G. and Choppin, P. W. (1975). *Virology*, **68**, 440–454.

Leifer, D. and Henderson, R. (1983). *J. molec. Biol.*, 163, 451-466.
LeNeveu, D. M., Rand, R. P., Parsegian, V. A. and Gingell, D. (1977). *Biophys. J.*, 18, 209-230.
Levine, Y. K. and Wilkins, M. F. (1971). *Nature new Biol.*, 230, 69-72.
Li, J. (1978). PhD thesis, Harvard University.
Li, J. (1979). *Biophys. J.*, 28, 190a.
Li, J. and Hollingshead, C. (1982). *Biophys. J.*, 37, 363-370.
Lindstrom, J., Merlie, J. and Yogeeswaran, G. (1980). *Biochemistry*, 18, 4465-4470.
Lipson, H. and Cochran, W. (1953). *The Determination of Crystal Structures.* G. Bell and Sons, London.
Loach, P. A. (1978). *Meth. Enzym.*, 69c, 155-172.
Lodish, H. F., Wirth, D. and Porter, M. (1980). *Ann. N.Y. Acad. Sci.*, 343, 319-334.
Loewenstein, W. R. (1979). *Biochim. biophys. Acta*, 560, 1-65.
Loewenstein, W. R. (1981). *Physiol. Rev.*, 61, 829-913.
Lux, S. E. (1979). *Nature*, 281, 426-429.
Luzzati, V. (1968). In *X-ray diffraction studies of lipid-water systems.* (ed D. Chapman), Academic, New York, 71-123.
Makowski, L. (1981). *J. appl. Crystallogr.*, 14, 160-168.
Makowski, L., Caspar, D. L. D., Phillips, W. C. and Goodenough, D. A. (1977). *J. Cell Biol.*, 74, 629-645.
Makowski, L., Caspar, D. L. D., Goodenough, D. A. and Phillips, W. C. (1982). *Biophys. J.*, 37, 189-191.
Markham, R., Hitchborn, J. H., Hills, G. J. and Frey, S. (1964). *Virology*, 22, 342-374.
Mateu, L. *et al.* (1973). *J. molec. Biol.*, 75, 697-709.
McCaslin, D. R. and Tanford, C. (1981a). *Biochemistry*, 20, 5207-5212.
McCaslin, D. R. and Tanford, C. (1981b). *Biochemistry*, 20, 5212-5221.
McCaughan, L. and Krimm, S. (1980). *Science*, 207, 1481-1483.
McDonnel, A. and Staehelin, L. A. (1980). *J. Cell Biol.*, 84, 40-56.
McIntosh, T. J. (1978). *Biochim. biophys. Acta*, 513, 43-58.
McIntosh, T. J. (1980). *Biophys. J.*, 29, 237-246.
McIntosh, T. J. and Worthington, C. R. (1974). *Biophys. J.*, 14, 363-386.
Meek, G. A. (1973). *Practical Electron Microscopy for Biologists* (2nd edn) Wiley-Intersci. Inc., Chichester, New York.
Meissner, G. and Fleischer, S. (1974). *J. biol. Chem.*, 249, 302-309.
Mellema, J. E. *et al.* (1981). *J. molec. Biol.*, 151, 329-336.
Michel, H. (1982). *J. molec. Biol.*, 158, 567-572.
Michel, H., Oesterhelt, D. and Henderson, R. (1980). *Proc. natn. Acad. Sci. U.S.A.*, 77, 338-342.
Miller, K. R. (1976). *J. Ultrastruct. Res.*, 54, 159-167.
Miller, K. R. (1979). *Proc. natn. Acad. Sci. U.S.A.*, 76, 6415-6419.
Miller, K. R. (1982). *Nature* (in the press).
Miller, K. R., Miller, G. J. and McIntyre, K. R. (1976). *J. Cell Biol.*, 71, 624-638.
Mitchell, P. (1979). *Science*, 206, 1148-1159.
Moody, M. F. (1963). *Science*, 142, 1173-1174.
Mullet, J. E. and Arntzen, C. J. (1980). *Biochim. biophys. Acta*, 589, 100-117.
Nagle, J. F. (1976). *J. membrane Biol.*, 27, 233-250.
Nelander, J. C. and Blaurock, A. E. (1978). *J. molec. Biol.*, 118, 497-532.
Neugebauer, D.-Ch. and Zingsheim, H. P. (1978). *J. molec. Biol.*, 123, 235-246.
Norton, W. T. (1977). In *Myelin* (ed. P. Morell), Plenum, New York, 161-200.
Oelze, J. and Drews, G. (1972). *Biochim. biophys. Acta*, 265, 209-239.
Oesterhelt, D. and Stoeckenius, W. (1971). *Nature new Biol.*, 233, 149-152.
Okamura, M. Y., Steiner, L. A. and Feher, G. (1974). *Biochemistry*, 13, 1394-1403.
Op den Kamp, J. A. F. (1979). *A. Rev. Biochem.*, 48, 47-71.
Ovchinkov, Yu. A., Abdulaev, N. G., Feigina, M. Yu., Kiselev, A. V. and Lobanov, N. A. (1979). *FEBS Lett.*, 100, 219-224.
Pachence, J. M., Dutton, P. L. and Blasie, J. K. (1979). *Biochim. biophys. Acta*, 548, 348-373.
Pachence, J. M., Dutton, P. L. and Blasie, J. K. (1981). *Biochim. biophys. Acta*, 635, 267-283.

Padron, R., and Mateu, L. (1980). *J. Neurosci. Res.*, **5**, 611–620.
Palmer, K. J., Schmitt, F. O. and Chargaff, E. (1941). *J. Cell comp. Physiol.*, **18**, 43–48.
Pape, E. H., Klott, K. and Kreutz, W. (1977). *Biophys. J.*, **19**, 141–161.
Parsegian, V. A. (1973). *A. Rev. Biophys. Bioengng*, **2**, 221–255.
Parsegian, V. A., Fuller, N. and Rand, R. P. (1979). *Proc. natn. Acad. Sci. U.S.A.*, **76**, 2750–2754.
Pascher, I. and Sundell, S. (1977). *Chem. Phys. Lipids*, **20**, 175–191.
Pascher, I., Sundell, S. and Hauser, H. (1981a). *J. molec. Biol.*, **153**, 791–806.
Pascher, I., Sundell, S. and Hauser, H. (1981b). *J. molec. Biol.*, **153**, 807–824.
Pearse, B. M. F. (1975). *J. molec. Biol.*, **97**, 93–98.
Pearse, B. M. F. (1976). *Proc. natn. Acad. Sci. U.S.A.*, **73**, 1255–1259.
Pearse, B. M. F. (1978). *J. molec. Biol.*, **126**, 803–812.
Pearson, R. H. and Pascher, I. (1979). *Nature*, **281**, 499–501.
Penn, R. D. and Hagins, W. A. (1969). *Nature*, **233**, 201–205.
Peracchia, C. (1977). *J. Cell Biol.*, **72**, 628–641.
Peracchia, C. and Dulhunty, A. F. (1976). *J. Cell Biol.*, **70**, 419–439.
Peterson, R. G. and Gruener, R. W. (1978). *Brain Res.*, **152**, 17–29.
Pinto da Silva, P. and Miller, R. G. (1975). *Proc. natn. Acad. Sci. U.S.A.*, **72**, 4046–4050.
Racker, E. and Stoeckenius, W. (1974). *J. biol. Chem.*, **249**, 662–663.
Raftery, M. A., Hunkapiller, M. W., Strader, C. D. and Hood, L. E. (1980). *Science*, **208**, 1454–1456.
Raftery, M. A., Vandlen, R. L., Reed, K. L. and Lee, T. (1975). *Cold Spring Harb. Symp. quant. Biol.*, **40**, 193–202.
Ranck, J. L. *et al.* (1974). *J. molec. Biol.*, **85**, 249–277.
Rand, R. P. (1981). *A. Rev. Biophys. Bioengng*, **10**, 277–314.
Rand, R. P. and Luzzati, V. (1968). *Biophys. J.*, **8**, 125–137.
Raviola, E., Goodenough, D. A. and Raviola, G. (1980). *J. Cell biol.*, **87**, 273–279.
Reisse-Husson, F. and Luzzati, V. (1964). *J. Phys. Chem.*, **68**, 3504–3511.
Revel, J. P. and Karnovsky, J. J. (1967). *J. Cell Biol.*, **33**, C7–C12.
Reynolds, J. and Karlin, A. (1978). *Biochemistry*, **17**, 2035–2038.
Rivas, E. and Luzzati, V. (1969). *J. molec. Biol.*, **41**, 261–275.
Rizzolo, L. J., LeMaire, M., Reynolds, J. A. and Tanford, C. (1976). *Biochemistry*, **15**, 3433–3437.
Robertson, J. D. (1963). *J. Cell Biol.*, **19**, 201–221.
Robinson, N. C. and Capaldi, R. A. (1977). *Biochemistry*, **16**, 375–381.
Rogan, P. K. and Zaccai, ?. (1981). *J. molec. Biol.*, **145**, 281–284.
Rose, B. and Loewenstein, W. R. (1975). *Nature*, **254**, 250–252.
Rose, J. K., Welsh, W. J., Seftom, B. M., Esch, F. S. and Ling, N. C. (1980). *Proc. natn. Acad. Sci. U.S.A.*, **77**, 3884–3888.
Rosenbusch, J. P. (1974). *J. biol. Chem.*, **249**, 8019–8029.
Rosenbusch, J. P., Steven, A. C., Alkan, M. and Regenass, M. (1980). In *Electron Microscopy at Molecular Dimensions* (eds W. Baumeister and W. Vogell), Springer-Verlag, Berlin, 1–10.
Ross, M. J., Klymkowsky, M. W., Agard, D. A. and Stround, R. M. (1977). *J. molec. Biol.*, **116**, 635–659.
Rossmann, M. J. and Henderson, R. (1982). *Acta crystallogr.* **A38**, 13–20.
Roth, T. F. and Porter, K. R. (1964). *J. Cell Biol.*, **20**, 313–332.
Rothman, J. E. and Engelman, D. M. (1972). *Nature new Biol.*, **237**, 42–44.
Rothman, J. E. and Fine, R. E. (1980). *Proc. natn. Acad. Sci. U.S.A.*, **77**, 780–784.
Rothman, J. E. and Leonard, J. (1977). *Science*, **195**, 743–753.
Sadler, D. M. (1976). *FEBS Lett.*, **67**, 289–293.
Sadler, D. M., Lefort-Tran, M. and Pouphile, M. (1973). *Biochim. biophys. Acta*, **298**, 620–629.
Saibil, H., Chabre, M. and Worcester, D. L. (1976). *Nature*, **262**, 266–270.
Saito, A., Wang, C.-T. and Fleischer, S. (1978). *J. Cell Biol.*, **79**, 601–616.
Sams, W. M. Jr (1967). *Ann. N.Y. Acad. Sci.*, **141**, 242–247.
Sane, P. V., Goodchild, D. J. and Park, R. B. (1970). *Biochim. biophys. Acta*, **216**, 162–178.
Santillan, G. (1975). PhD thesis, University of Pennsylvania.

Schindler, H. and Rosenbusch, J. P. (1978). *Proc. natn. Acad. Sci. U.S.A.*, **75**, 3751–3755.
Schlesinger, M. J., Schlesinger, S. and Burge, B. W. (1972). *Virology*, **47**, 539–541.
Schmitt, F. O., Bear, R. S. and Clark, G. L. (1935). *Radiology*, **25**, 131–151.
Schmitt, F. O., Bear, R. S. and Palmer, K. J. (1941). *J. Cell Comp. Physiol.*, **18**, 31–42.
Schwartz, S., Cain, J. E., Dratz, E. A. and Blasie, J. K. (1975). *Biophys. J.*, **15**, 1201–1233.
Seki, S., Hayashi, H. and Oda, T. (1970). *Arch. Biochem. Biophys.*, **138**, 110–121.
Sessa, G., Freer, J. H., Colacicco, G. and Weissmann, G. (1969). *J. biol. Chem.*, **244**, 3575–3582.
Sheetz, M. P. (1979). *Biochim. biophys. Acta*, **557**, 122–134.
Sheetz, M. P. and Sawyer, D. (1978). *J. supramolec. Struct.*, **8**, 399–412.
Shichi, H. and Shelton, E. (1974). *J. supramolec. Struct.*, **2**, 7–16.
Shieh, H. S., Hoard, L. G. and Nordman, C. E. (1977). *Nature*, **267**, 287–289.
Shipley, G. G. (1973). In *Biological Membranes* (eds D. Chapman and D. F. H. Wallach), **2**, Academic, London, 1–89.
Shipley, G. G., Green, J. P. and Nichols, B. W. (1973). *Biochim. biophys. Acta*, **311**, 531–544.
Shipley, G. G., Leslie, R. B. and Chapman, D. (1969a). *Nature*, **222**, 561–562.
Shipley, G. G., Leslie, R. B. and Chapman, D. (1969b). *Biochim. Biophys. Acta*, **173**, 1–10.
Shotton, D., Thompson, K., Wofsy, L. and Branton, D. (1978). *J. Cell Biol.*, **76**, 512–531.
Shotton, D. M., Burke, B. E. and Branton, D. (1979). *J. molec. Biol.*, **131**, 303–329.
Singer, S. J. (1971). In *Structure and Function of Biological Membranes* (ed. L. I. Rothfield), Academic, New York, 145–222.
Singer, S. J. and Nicholson, G. L. (1972). *Science*, **175**, 720–731.
Slayter, H. S. (1976). *Ultramicroscopy*, **1**, 341–357.
Spray, D. C., Harris, A. L. and Bennett, M. V. L. (1981). *J. gen. Physiol.*, **77**, 77–93.
Staehelin, L. A. (1976). *J. Cell Biol.*, **71**, 136–158.
Staehelin, L. A., Armond, P. A. and Miller, K. R. (1976). *Brookhaven Symp. Biol.*, **28**, 278–315.
Stamatoff, J. B. and Krimm, S. (1973). *Biophys. J.*, **16**, 503–516.
Stamatoff, J. B., Krimm, S. and Harvie, N. R. (1975). *Proc. natn. Acad. Sci. U.S.A.*, **72**, 531–534.
Steck, T. L. (1974). *J. Cell Biol.*, **62**, 1–19.
Steffans, G. C. M., Steffans, G. J. and Buse, G. (1979). *Physiol. Chem.*, **360**, 1641–1650.
Steinback, K. E., Burke, J. J., Mullet, J. E. and Arntzen, C. J. (1978). In *Chloroplast Development* (ed. G. Akoyunoglu), Elsevier, Amsterdam, 389–400.
Steven, A. C. and Navia, M. A. (1980). *Proc. natn. Acad. Sci. U.S.A.*, **77**, 4721–4725.
Steven, A. C., ten Heggler, B., Muller, R., Kisterl, J. and Rosenbusch, J. P. (1977). *J. Cell Biol.*, **72**, 292–301.
Stewart, P. S. and MacLennon, D. H. (1974). *J. biol. Chem.*, **249**, 985–993.
Strader, C. D. and Raftery, M. A. (1980). *Proc. natn. Acad. Sci. U.S.A.*, **77**, 5807–5811.
Strauss, J. H., Burge, B. W., Pfefferkork, E. R. and Darnell, J. E. (1968). *Proc. natn. Acad. Sci.*, **59**, 533–537.
Stroud, R. M. and Agard, D. A. (1979). *Biophys. J.*, **25**, 495–512.
Stubbs, G. W., Smith, H. G. and Litman, B. J. (1976). *Biochim. biophys. Acta*, **426**, 46–56.
Subak-Sharpe, H., Burk, R. R. and Pitts, J. D. (1966). *Heredity*, **21**, 342–343.
Tanford, C. (1980). *The Hydrophobic Effect: Formation of Micelles and Biological Membranes*, John Wiley, New York.
Tardieu, A., Luzzati, V. and Reman, F. C. (1973). *J. molec. Biol.*, **75**, 711–733.
Taylor, K. A. and Glaeser, R. M. (1976). *J. Ultrastruct. Res.*, **55**, 448–456.
Terwilliger, T. C., Weissman, L. and Eisenberg, D. (1982). *Biophys. J.*, **37**, 353–361.
Terwilliger, T. C. and Eisenberg, D. (1982a). *The structure of melittin. I. Structure determination and partial refinement* (in the press).
Terwilliger, T. C. and Eisenberg, D. (1982b). *The structure of melittin. II. Interpretation of the structure* (in the press).
Thornber, J. P. (1975). *A. Rev. Pl. Physiol.*, **26**, 127–158.
Thornber, J. P. (1979). *Photochem. Photobiol.*, **29**, 1205–1216.
Thornber, J. P. and Thornber, J. M. (1980). *Meth. Enzym.*, **69**, 172–178.
Thornber, J. P., Cogdell, R. J., Seftor, R. E. B. and Webster, G. D. (1980). *Biochim. biophys. Acta*, **593**, 60–75.

Tilney, L. G. and Detmers, P. (1975). *J. Cell Biol.*, **66**, 508–520.

Tomita, T. (1970). *Q. Rev. Biophys.*, **3**, 179–222.

Tonn, S. J., Gogel, G. E. and Loach, P. A. (1977). *Biochemistry*, **16**, 877–885.

Torbet, J. and Wilkins, M. H. F. (1976). *J. theoret. Biol.*, **62**, 447–458.

Tosteson, M. T. and Tosteson, D. C. (1981). *Biophys. J.*, **36**, 109–116.

Turin, L. and Warner, A. E. (1977). *Nature*, **270**, 56–57.

Turin, L. and Warner, A. E. (1980). *J. Physiol., Lond.*, **300**, 489–504.

Ueki, T., Kataoka, M. and Mitsui, T. (1976). *Nature*, **262**, 809–810.

Unanue, E. R., Ungewickell, E. and Branton, D. (1981). *Cell*, **26**, 439–446.

Ungewickell, E., Bennett, P. M., Calvert, R., Ohanian, V. and Gratzer, W. B. (1979). *Nature*, **280**, 811–814.

Ungewickell, E. and Branton, D. (1981). *Nature*, **289**, 420–422.

Unwin, P. N. T. and Henderson, R. (1975). *J. molec. Biol.*, **94**, 425–440.

Unwin, P. N. T. and Zampighi, G. (1982). *Nature*, **283**, 545–549.

Utermann, G. and Simons, K. (1974). *J. molec. Biol.*, **85**, 569–587.

Vanderkooi, G., Senior, A. E., Capaldi, R. A. and Hayashi, H. (1972). *Biochim. biophys. Acta*, **274**, 38–48.

Verhoeyen, M. *et al.* (1980). *Nature*, **286**, 771–776.

Wang, J. K., McDowell, J. H. and Hargrave, P. A. (1980). *Biochemistry*, **19**, 5111–5117.

Webb, N. G. (1972). *Nature*, **235**, 44–46.

Webb, N. G. (1977). *Vision Res.*, **17**, 625–631.

Wehrli, E., Kubler, O. and Koller, Th. (1979). *Experientia*, **35**, 984.

Weill, C. L., McNamee, M. G. and Karlin, A. (1974). *Biochem. Biophys. Res. Commun.*, **61**, 997–1003.

Welte, W., Hodapp, N., Aehnelt, C. and Kreutz, W. (1981). *Biophys. Struct. Mech.*, **7**, 209–212.

Wikstrom, M. K. F. and Krab, K. (1979). *Biochim. biophys. Acta*, **253**, 177–222.

Wiley, D. C., Wilson, I. A. and Skehel, J. J. (1981). *Nature*, **289**, 373–378.

Wilkins, M. H. F. (1972). *Ann. N.Y. Acad. Sci.*, **195**, 291–292.

Wilkins, M. H. F., Blaurock, A. E. and Engelman, D. M. (1971). *Nature new Biol.*, **230**, 72–76.

Williams, R. C. and Fisher, H. W. (1970). *J. molec. Biol.*, **52**, 121–123.

Wilson, I. A., Skehel, J. J. and Wiley, D. C. (1981). *Nature*, **289**, 366–373.

Wise, D. S., Karlin, A. and Schoenborn, B. P. (1979). *Biophys. J.*, **28**, 473–496.

Wise, D. S., Schoenborn, B. P. and Karlin, A. (1981a). *J. biol. Chem.*, **256**, 4124–4126.

Wise, D. S., Wall, J. and Karlin, A. (1981b). *J. biol. Chem.*, **256**, 12624–12627.

Witz, J. (1969). *Acta crystallogr.*, A**25**, 30–42.

Worcester, D. L. and Franks, N. P. (1976). *J. molec. Biol.*, **100**, 359–378.

Worthington, C. R. and Liu, S. C. (1973). *Arch. Biochem. Biophys.*, **157**, 573–579.

Worthington, C. R. and McIntosh, T. J. (1974). *Biophys. J.*, **14**, 703–729.

Yeager, M., Schoenborn, B. P., Engelman, D., Moore, P. and Stryer, L. (1980). *J. molec. Biol.*, **137**, 315–348.

Yu, J., Fischman, D. A. and Steck, T. L. (1973). *J. supramolec. Struct.*, **1**, 233–248.

Zingsheim, H. P. and Bachmann, L. (1971). *Kolloid-Z. Z. Polym.*, **246**, 561–570.

Zingsheim, H. P., Barrantes, F. J., Frank, J., Hanicke, W. and Neugebauer, D.-Ch. (1982). *Nature*, **299**, 81–84.

Zingsheim, H. P., Neugebauer, D.-Ch., Barranges, F. J. and Frank, J. (1980). *Proc. natn. Acad. Sci. U.S.A.*, **77**, 952–956.

Zingsheim, H. P., Neugebauer, D.-Ch. and Henderson, R. (1978). *J. molec. Biol.*, **123**, 275–278.

3

Raman spectroscopy of lipids and biomembranes

Surendra P. Verma and Donald F. H. Wallach
Tufts-New England Medical Center, Therapeutic Radiology Department,
Radiobiology Division, 171 Harrison Avenue, Boston, MA 02111, USA

INTRODUCTION

The application of laser Raman spectroscopy to membrane structure analysis was initiated at the beginning of the nineteen seventies. Since then this approach has expanded into a diversity of areas, including studies on the organisation of lipids at different low temperatures, thermal transitions in biomembranes and lipid-sterol interactions.

General introductions to Raman spectroscopy are found in Tobin (1971); Anderson (1971) and Colthup *et al.* (1975). Most of the literature up to 1978 has been reviewed by Wallach *et al.* (1979).

TECHNICAL

Sample handling

Samples are usually sealed in melting point capillaries and held in a vibration-free, temperature controlled device, such as a Harney-Miller cell or a metal block cooled by circulating fluid. We generally obtain Raman spectra on plasma membrane suspensions containing $\sim$10 mg protein ml^{-1}. These yield 10^3–10^6 CH-stretching counts per sec after $\sim$15 min of exposure to 500 mW laser power. Higher counts indicate fluorescence.

Conventional scanning

In simple scanning Raman spectroscopy, the scattered light is collected at right angles to the capillary and analysed, usually at 1 cm^{-1} intervals (channels), using a double monochromator equipped with either plane or holographic gratings. The signal, detected by a thermoelectrically cooled photomultiplier, is amplified and recorded, usually in the order of photons sec^{-1}.

In computer-assisted recording systems, data acquisition is more speedy and the quality of the spectra improved. The computer moves the spectrometer from channel to channel and allows it to rest at each channel for the time interval required to accumulate a significant number of photon counts. Photon counts are stored in the computer memory during scanning (1-4 scans) and the stored spectra, averaged and smoothed by a least-squares procedure (when appropriate), are stored in the computer memory during scanning (1-4 scans) and the stored spectra, average and smoothed by a least-squares procedure (when appropriate), are ultimately plotted on a recorder. Spectra stored in the computer memory and collection of difference spectra with great precision. Here, the photon counter, spectrometer drive and the analyser are under computer control. Our own general procedure for biological membranes is as follows (Wallach *et al.*, 1979): *a*, maximum and minimum time per data point – 1.5 sec and 0.5 sec, respectively; *b*, photon counts – 10^4-10^5 sec^{-1} maximum and 10^2 minimum. For liposomes, which can be studied at higher concentrations, recording time can be reduced.

Optical multichannel analysers

Even with computer-assisted single-channel scanning, acquisition of good Raman spectra from biological samples is time consuming. This limits the number of experiments that can be performed on biological membranes. For example, to monitor the CH-stretching region between $-20°$ to $+45°C$ during membrane phase changes takes six to seven hours. It also requires replacement of the sample at least twice because laser light may induce membrane modifications, and necessitates controls to check on possible time-dependent changes.

Many of these difficulties are avoided by vidicon detectors coupled to an optical multichannel analyser (OMA). Here a 300–600 cm^{-1} section of the Raman spectrum, projected onto the detector, is rapidly recorded in a computer memory without mechanical scanning. The vidicons used in Raman spectroscopy have cooled silicon intensified targets (SIT) which allow a desired spectral segment to be sampled within 1 sec. Several multichannel detector Raman systems have been described (Bridoux and Delhaye, 1976; Sturm *et al.*, 1978; Woodruff and Farquharson, 1978; Terner *et al.*, 1977; Mathies and Yu, 1978).

To convert our scanning instrument, we replaced the 1,200 g mm^{-1} gratings of the SPEX 1401 double monochromator with 600 g mm^{-1} gratings, the variable centre slit with a 12.7 x 6.00 mm fixed slit (plus baffles) and the 0.85 m mirror of the second monochromator by a 1 m focal length mirror. We use an additional filter in front of the entrance slit to reduce Rayleigh scattered light when studying the CH-stretching region. Our detector, a Princeton Applied Research (PAR) 1205D SIT, housed in a PAR 1212 cooled chamber, is rigidly attached to the exit part of the monochromator so that the Raman-scattered light is focused onto the face of the SIT tube. The detector is precisely orientated in the optical axis. The output of the SIT is processed by a PAR 1205A optical multichannel analyser. Stabilisation of the SIT (cooled by dry ice to $\sim -40°C$) takes about 2 h.

MEMBRANE PREPARATION

Model membranes

Raman studies on model membranes generally involve unilamellar or multi lamellar liposomes composed of phospholipids alone or associated with other lipids or polypeptides or proteins (Wallach *et al.*, 1979). However, Lis *et al.* (1977) have proposed that phospholipid multilayers deposited using the Langmuir-Blodgett technique (Waldbillig *et al.*, 1976) might provide reference Raman spectra suitable for the quantitative analysis of lipid packing in membranes.

Aurengo *et al.* (1979) have devised an apparatus which obtains Raman spectra from very thin phospholipid films. A high refractive index prism is coated with a 40 nm silver layer and 7.5–42.5 nm phospholipid layers are deposited on top of the silver. The silver layer enhances the electric field of the laser beam in the sample and also attenuates the scattered light from the prism by absorption (≈ 97 per cent) and reflection. The Raman-scattered light origi-nating in the phospholipid film above the metallic surface is evaluated by a MOLE Raman microprobe. The approach of Aurengo *et al.* (1979) is particularly exciting since spectra are obtained from phospholipid films the thickness of the lipid bilayer in biomembranes (near 7.5 nm).

Biological membranes

Except for resonance spectra, Raman spectra can be obtained only from membranes lacking intrinsic chromophores, such as cytochromes or flavoproteins. Moreover, in preparing biological membranes for Raman spectroscopy one must rigidly avoid contamination with extrinsic chromophores and fluorophores. Impure samples fluoresce in the laser beam and this interferes with spectral analysis. Light absorption also produces sample heating which complicates evaluation of thermal transitions and may cause sample denaturation. Details have been reported for the necessary purification of membranes from erythrocytes (Wallach and Verma, 1975), rabbit thymocytes (Verma *et al.*, 1975), as well as normal and neoplastic lymphocytes (Verma *et al.*, 1977).

USEFUL SPECTRAL REGIONS

Characteristic bands in the CH-stretching region (2,800–3,000 cm^{-1})

The CH_2 and CH_3 residues of lipids and proteins in biological and model membranes yield prominent CH-stretching bands. Membrane lipids with saturated acyl chains in crystalline array give sharp bands near 2,850 cm^{-1} and 2,880 cm^{-1}. These features are attributed to symmetric and asymmetric methylenic CH_2 stretching of polymethylenic segments, respectively (Spiker and Levin, 1975; Verma and Wallach, 1977a). Raman features due to methyl groups occur at 2,932, 2,952 and 2,964 cm^{-1} (Verma and Wallach, 1977a). The 2,930±2 cm^{-1} feature is seen also with 18,18,18-trideuterated stearic acid, although at lesser intensity than in non-deuterated material, indicating that this band contains a contribution from asymmetric CH_2 stretching. Deuteration of stearic acid at specific positions reveals that CH_2-stretching vibrations of long methylenic segments are not representative of CH_2 residues adjacent to the CH_3 terminus or such residues adjacent to the carboxyl residues (Verma and Wallach, 1977a) (Figure 3.1). The latter gives rise to a feature at 2,920 cm^{-1}.

Raman spectra of unsaturated fatty hydrocarbon chains (Figure 3.2) yield complex banding in the CH-stretching region (Verma and Wallach, 1977a), depending on the number and configuration of the unsaturated residues. The non-equivalence of CH_2 residues, that is, CH_2 group adjacent to one or two HC=CH bonds, or a HC=CH bond and a CH_3 terminus, contribute to the band complexity. Interactions between CH-stretching fundamentals and HCH-deformation overtones are also involved.

Snyder *et al.* (1978) interpret the complexity of the CH-stretching region of hydrocarbon chains by Fermi resonance interactions involving binary combinations between methylene bending modes (fundamentals, 1,443–1,467 cm^{-1}) and the symmetric methylene CH-stretching mode. The asymmetric mode, near 2,890 cm^{-1}, is forbidden by symmetry from participating in Fermi resonance interactions and is thus not sensitive to changes in chain environment. However, the strong Fermi resonance interactions between symmetric CH-stretching fundamentals and appropriate binary combinations involving methylene bending modes produce 'broad, often strong secondary maxima', including the band underlying the sharp features at ~2,880 cm^{-1}. The breadth of the secondary maxima is attributed to the existence of a 'virtual continuum' of binary combination states and not just a few zone centres. Fermi interactions can be both intramolecular and intermolecular, the latter being dependent on chain packing and/or environment. Environmentally-induced shifts in the 2,880–2,890 cm^{-1} region are thus ascribed to altered Fermi resonance interactions, between symmetric CH-deformation and CH-stretching modes.

Verma and Wallach (1977a) explain thermally-induced changes in the 2,843–2,850 cm^{-1} bands of fatty acids (Figure 3.1) as reflecting reduced Fermi interaction with an overtone of a symmetric methylene bending component

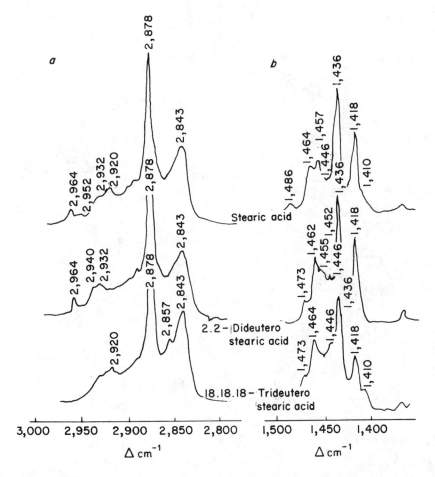

Figure 3.1 Raman spectra of solid stearic acid, 2,2-dideuterostearic acid, and 18,18,18-tri-deuterostearic acid in *a*, the CH-stretching region 2,800–3000 cm⁻¹); and *b*, the HCH-deformation range (1,400–1,500 cm⁻¹). Recorded at 22°C. From Verma and Wallach, 1977a, with permission

contributing to the 1,418 cm⁻¹ feature (Gall *et al.*, 1972) of solid stearic acid. The broadening and the shift of the 2,880–2890 cm⁻¹ band are attributed to the diffuseness of the CH-deformation band and its greater relative intensity at approximately 1,450 cm⁻¹. The processes responsible for such changes in the deformation region would reflect in the overtones lying in the CH-stretching region. This would account for the diffuse, frequency-shifted pattern observed between 2,880 and 3,000 cm⁻¹, which is in the main similar to the pattern observed with liquid-crystalline phases (Figure 3.3).

The emergence, in the liquid-crystalline state, of the prominent feature near 2,926 cm⁻¹ cannot be attributed exclusively to CH_3 stretching, or CH stretching

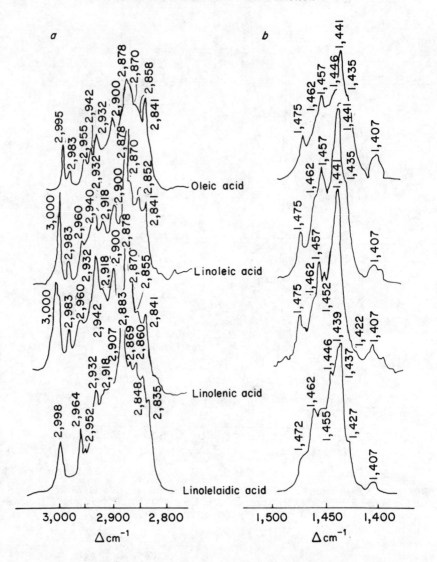

Figure 3.2 Raman spectra of solid oleic, linoleic, linolenic and linolelaidic acid in *a*, the CH-stretching region (2,800–3,100 cm^{-1}); and *b*, the HCH-deformation region (1,400–1500 cm^{-1}). Recorded at −40°C. From Verma and Wallach, 1977a, with permission

of CH$_2$ residues adjacent to carboxyls (Verma and Wallach, 1977a), but enhancement in this region might be expected from the broadening and intensity shifts in the CH-deformation region.

The CH-deformation differences between solid, saturated and unsaturated C-18 acids, as well as the distinctions between the various unsaturated acids, demonstrate the sensitivity of CH-deformation modes to lipid chain interactions.

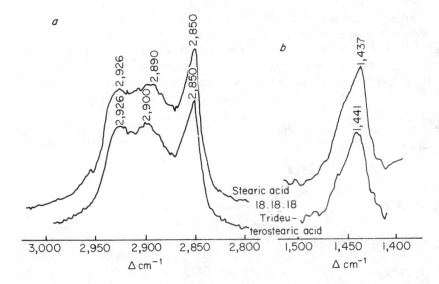

Figure 3.3   Raman spectra of liquid stearic acid and 18,18,18-trideuterostearic acid in *a*, the CH-stretching region (2,800–3,100 cm^{-1}); and *b*, the HCH-deformation region (1,400–1500 cm^{-1}). Recorded at 75–80°C. From Verma and Wallach, 1977a, with permission

This sensitivity, and the non-equivalence of CH$_2$ residues in unsaturated chains together contribute to the great complexity of the CH-stretching regions of solid unsaturated fatty acids, as well as to the different scattering patterns found with increasing unsaturation and *trans* versus *cis* unsaturation (Verma and Wallach, 1977a).

Thermally-induced variations in the CH-stretching region

The intensities and widths of CH$_2$-stretching bands depend on chain packing. When lipids melt (compare Figures 3.1 and 3.3) the 2,880 cm^{-1} feature reduces in intensity, broadens in width and shifts to 2,890 cm^{-1}. The intensity ratio, r, $[I_{\sim 2880}/I_{\sim 2850}]$ has proved useful in evaluating such changes. The intensity of the 2,850 cm^{-1} band serves as an internal standard (Gaber and Peticolas, 1977), but it is not constant for all chain packing situations (Wallach *et al.*, 1979). The value r for solid phospholipids ranges from 2.8 (distearoylphosphatidylcholine) to 1.6 (dimyristoylphosphatidylcholine) and reduces to 0.7 in solution. The theoretical basis for the changes in the CH-stretching region has not been fully established. Gaber and Peticolas (1977) explain both the decrease in r and the shift of the 2,880 cm^{-1} feature to 2,890 cm^{-1} by assuming that the lipid chains constitute one all-*trans* species in the solid form but, in the liquid condition, exist as multiple rotameric forms, each with one line. These multiple species produce 'rotamer broadening'. However, it is known now that the condition of a single all-*trans* species holds only for very low temperatures and that some all-*trans* isomers exist even in the liquid state. Verma and Wallach (1977a) and Snyder *et al.* (1978) attribute the observed changes in the CH-stretching region to alterations in Fermi resonance. They argue that the shape of CH-stretching bands depend strongly on the bending-mode fundamental, that this depends on chain-packing and that Fermi resonance interactions are greater in the case of packed chains.

Gaber and Peticolas (1977) have proposed a 'lateral order parameter', S_{lat}, defined in terms of the ratio r:

$$S_{lat} = \frac{r-0.7}{1.5}$$

$S_{lat} = 1$ for a chain in the crystalline state ($r = 2.2$) and 0 for chains in solution ($r = 0.7$). (Only the ratio of peak heights, not integrated intensities, are environmentally sensitive (Snyder *et al.*, 1978).) Because the intensities at both 2,890 and $\sim$ 2,850 cm^{-1} originate from multiple vibrational modes (as is obvious with unsaturated acyl chains (Verma and Wallach, 1977a),) r is a hybrid quantity. Furthermore, the intensities of the 2,850 cm^{-1} and 2,880 cm^{-1} features depend on chain packing and chain mobility (Snyder *et al.*, 1980). S_{lat} may therefore be most useful in monitoring the effects of specific variables on given membrane systems. For example, S_{lat} has been shown to change linearly with the rate of rotational diffusion of fatty acid spin probe in dipalmitoyl phosphatidylcholine liposomes (Horvath *et al.*, 1980).

Mendelsohn *et al.* (1976a) have used variations in the width of the C^{2}H-stretching band of phosphatidylcholine liposomes containing deuterated stearate as an alternative to monitoring peak height changes. Verma *et al.* (1977) have applied this approach to the 2,880–2,890 cm^{-1} stretching band of biomembranes.

Bunow and Levin (1977a) have critically examined the temperature sensitivity of the 2,935–2,910 cm^{-1} region of phospholipids. They find that the 2,920 cm^{-1} infrared feature, assigned to methylene asymmetric stretching (Wallach *et al.*, 1979), shifts to higher frequency and gains intensity as the temperature increases, becoming superimposed on the weak 2,932–2,935 plateau assigned to methyl symmetric CH-stretching (Verma and Wallach, 1977a). Bunow and Levin (1977a) argue that the 2,935 cm^{-1} methyl symmetric stretching band is thermally insensitive and that thermally-induced changes in the 2,930$\pm$5 cm^{-1} contour reflect alterations in methylene asymmetric stretching (secondary to changes in chain packing). Bunow and Levin (1977a) find that the value of [I_{2935}/I_{2880}] depends on the phospholipid. Moreover, according to this ratio, dimyristoyl-phosphatidylcholine ($T_c = 23°C$) is more disordered at 5°C than dipalmitoyl-phosphatidylcholine ($T_c = 41°C$) at 25°C (0.45 against 0.38). Dioleoylphosphat-idylcholine ($T_c = -20°C$) is more disordered at $-58°C$ than dipalmitoylphos-phatidylcholine ($T_c = 40°C$) at 0°C.

Methyl stretching

As noted earlier, the methyl-stretching modes (near 2,935 and 2,954 cm^{-1}) of lipids appears insensitive to chain packing as well as environment. However, proteins yield a strong broad band at 2,935±5 cm^{-1} which has been shown to reflect protein state changes. Thus, thermally-induced unfolding of ribonuclease at low pH (say, 2.72) produces a large increase of Raman scattering intensity of the 2,930 cm^{-1} CH_3-stretching band relative to the intensity of a thermally stable internal standard (Verma and Wallach, 1977b). A plot of the intensity at 2,930 cm^{-1} against temperature reveals a broad transition between 24 and 44°C which corresponds in position and width to the transition detected at this pH by differential thermal calorimetry (Brandts and Hunt, 1967). Larson and Rand (1973) reported that the intensity of methyl CH-stretching varies with solvent polarity and Wallach *et al.* (1979) have used plots of $[I_{2935}/I_{2850}]$ against temperature to monitor protein state transition in plasma membranes from various cells.

Skeletal optical region (C–C stretching 1,050–1150 cm^{-1})

Long chain hydrocarbons yield three intense bands in this region. The sharp features at 1,064 and 1,130 cm^{-1} are assigned to all-*trans* chain segments and the broader third band, at $\sim 1,090$ cm^{-1}, is attributed to chains containing *gauche* configurations (Figure 3.4) (Lippert and Peticolas, 1971; Gaber *et al.*, 1978a; Pink *et al.*, 1980). In phospholipids the $\sim 1,090$ cm^{-1} feature is superimposed upon the symmetric O-P-O stretching mode. Above the T_c, the 1,064 and 1,130 cm^{-1} features reduce in intensity and the 1,090 cm^{-1} band intensifies. The intensity ratios $[I_{1064}/I_{\sim 1090}]$ or $[I_{1130}/I_{\sim 1090}]$, and frequency differences, (1,095–1,064 cm^{-1}) or (1,129–1,064 cm^{-1}), have been used a, to minotor acyl chain 'fluidity' and order disorder transitions (Lippert and Peticolas, 1971; Spiker and Levin, 1976a, Gaber and Peticolas, 1977; Yellin and Levin, 1977a, b; Gaber *et al.*, 1978a); b, to determine the size of cooperative units undergoing a chain melting (Yellin and Levin, 1977a); and c, to evaluate the number of *trans* and *gauche* bonds per molecule (Gaber and Peticolas, 1977; Yellin and Levin, 1977b; Pink *et al.*, 1980). Gaber and Peticolas (1977) have proposed the use of a *trans* order parameter, 'S_{trans}' to monitor chain order. S_{trans} is defined as:

$$S_{trans} = \frac{(I_{1133}/I_{ref}) \text{ observed}}{(I_{1133}/I_{ref}) \text{ solid phospholipid}}$$

where I_{ref} is I_{1090} or I_{722} (choline CH stretching).

In using the C–C stretching region to evaluate lipid chain order, one has generally assumed that scattering from individual *trans* bonds is independent of other such bonds (incoherent) and that the intensity at 1,130 cm^{-1} therefore varies linearly with the number of *trans* segments in the laser beam. However,

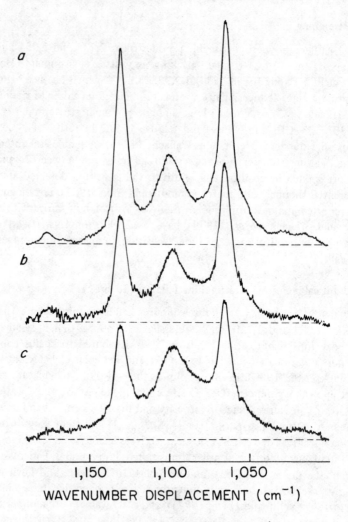

Figure 3.4   Raman spectra of 1,2-dipalmitoylphosphatidylcholine in the *a*, polycrystalline; *b*, multilayer; and *c*, vesicle forms in the 1,020–1,170 cm⁻¹ region utilising 5,145 Å excitation. From Spiker and Levin, 1976a, with permission

Pink *et al.*, (1980) show that the 1,130 cm⁻¹ band represents the vibration of the entire chain, rather than summed contributions of *trans* bonds. I_{1130} is thus *not* linearly proportional to the number of *trans* bonds in a chain. Calculations (Yellin and Levin 1977b) for average number of *gauche* bonds and use of 'S_{trans}' (Gaber and Peticolas, 1977) must, therefore, be reassessed. Moreover, Karvaly and Loshchilova (1977) find a 'S_{trans}' value greater than 1 for dipalmitoylphosphatidylcholine liposomes in the presence of certain monovalent and divalent cations. This may mean that the reference bands (at 772 cm^{-1} and 1,096 cm^{-1}) are not as constant as assumed and that the contributions of choline CN and O-P-O stretching may vary with head group environment.

The C—C stretching spectra of unsaturated lipids have been little studied. This is unfortunate since biological membranes contain substantial proportions of unsaturated lipids and also because some membrane proteins, such as myelin proteolipid apoproteins, associate unsaturated fatty acids (Verma *et al.*, 1980a).

C=C stretching and =C—H twisting

Cis double bonds of unsaturated acyl chains give a peak at 1,660±2 cm^{-1} and *trans* double bonds at 1,670 cm^{-1} (Davies *et al.*, 1975). In some circumstances the C=C stretching bands can be used to give a measure of unsaturation, but this is not possible in biological membranes where amide I vibrations of the proteins dominate this region (Milanovitch *et al.*, 1976a).

Butler *et al.* (1979) have monitored unsaturation by use of the bands at 1,303 cm^{-1} and 1,267 cm^{-1}, features which are assigned to in-phase methylene twisting and =C—H in-plane deformation, respectively. Plots of $[I_{1303}/I_{1267}]$ versus the ratio $[CH_2/=C-H]$ yield a straight line for fatty acids with varying unsaturation, and chain length. The unsaturation values for brain white matter, as derived by use of this plot, correspond to results obtained by gas chromatography.

Acoustic and lattice vibrations (10-400 cm^{-1})

This region contains bands arising from collective, coherent motions of molecules in lattice arrays, for example of water (Eisenberg and Kauzman, 1969), or the headgroups of phospholipid bilayers in crystalline or liquid-crystalline states. Other bands arise from accordion-like longitudinal vibrations of extended acyl chains. For example, solid lauric acid at −160°C, gives an acoustic mode at 205 cm^{-1} and torsional or lattice modes at 119 and 171 cm^{-1} (Mendelsohn *et al.*, 1975), while dilauroylphosphatidylethanolamine displays broader, weaker features at 224 and 138 cm^{-1} with shoulders at 218 and 148 cm^{-1}. The differences in band positions are related to chain packing. All of these components disappear when the acyl chains become thermally disordered. The bulk motions of ordered polypeptide segments can also give rise to bands in this region 925 cm^{-1} − 160 cm^{-1} (Brown *et al.*, 1972). In the case of biomembranes one might expect contributions from all of the vibrational elements listed.

Verma and Wallach (1976b) have used the acoustic region to monitor thermotropic order ⇌ disorder transition of liposomes composed of egg phosphatidylcholine ± cholesterol. Spectra obtained above the T_c (− 6°C) of the phospholipid show a band at 365 cm^{-1}, a shoulder near 350 cm^{-1}, and a band at 290 cm^{-1} (phosphate deformation). These shift to 370, 350 and 310 cm^{-1}, respectively, below the T_c and are thought to represent head group order. A strong band at 245 cm^{-1}, attributed to ordered oleate chains in the crystalline state, becomes diffuse above the T_c. Recent technical advances will allow more detailed studies of the acoustic region and such should enhance the understanding of membrane structure.

Deuterated probes

It is often difficult to distinguish between the CH stretching contributions of methyl and methylene groups in mixtures of lipids or of lipids and protein. To circumvent this problem, Mendelsohn and Maisano (1978) and Bansil *et al.* (1980) have used specifically deuterated fatty acids and deuterated phospholipids as Raman probes.

The C^{2}H-stretching bands occur in the 2,100 cm^{-1} region and signals of specifically deuterated acyl chains are free from interfering bands. However, such probes are only useful when the deuterated molecules themselves are the components being investigated (Bansil *et al.*, 1980). Moreover, the use of fatty acids as probes creates some ambiguities as they need to be used at high proportions to yield satisfactory signals (Mendelsohn *et al.*, 1976a) and perturb the thermal transition of phospholipids at such levels (Verma *et al.*, 1980a).

MODEL MEMBRANES

Pure phospholipids

Raman spectroscopy has helped to define the changes occurring in phospholipid bilayers as acyl chains are thermally shifted between the solid and the liquid state.

Analysis of the C–C stretching region by difference Raman spectroscopy, using lipids in known crystal states as reference materials (Chrisman *et al.*, 1976; Gaber *et al.*, 1978a,b) indicates that the acyl chains of dipalmitoylphosphatidyl-choline exist in a triclinic array below the pretransition temperature (34±2°C). Between 34 and 40°C the acyl chains are packed in a hexagonal array. Raising the temperature above T_c causes a cooperative breakdown in chain order. This is evident in a sharp increase in the ~1,080 cm^{-1} difference band, indicating the appearance of closely coupled *gauche* bonds and a reduction in the proportion of *trans* segments.

It appears that phospholipid acyl chains undergo changes of structure and organisation over a wider temperature range than previously realised (Bunow and Levin, 1977a; Pink *et al.*, 1980). Measuring the area under the 1,130 cm^{-1} (C–C stretching) band of coarse suspensions of dipalmitoyl- and dimyristoylphosphatidylcholine, Pink *et al.* (1980) find that the proportion of all-*trans* conformers reaches unity only at very low temperatures, such as −200°C. Bunow and Levin (1977a) have reached a similar conclusion from evaluations of the 2,930 cm^{-1} CH-stretching band.

The complete all-*trans* condition appears to be the state of lowest internal energy for the bilayer. As the temperature is raised to about $-100°C$, one *gauche* bond appears per chain, probably near the methyl end. This represents the initial deviation from the pure bilayer state, that is the first excited state of the system. (The probability of its occurrence rises to about 0.1 by T_c.)

As temperature rises further, single "kinks" appear (two *gauche* bonds separated by a *trans* bond). Such kinks pack well with adjacent chains and single kinks represent the most probable state of disorder above $-100°C$. Further disordering proceeds between -50 and $+15°C$, but a drastic increase in *gauche* conformers, that is, the cooperative phase transition, occurs at T_c.

Because their radii of curvatures are rather large, coarse phospholipid suspensions and multilamellar liposomes appear more suitable models for biomembranes than sonicated unilamellar liposomes (radii 12–15 nm). Indeed, there is Raman spectral evidence that the array of acyl chains in small unilamellar vesicles deviates from that in essentially flat bilayers. Most workers (but see Mendelsohn *et al.*, 1976b) find that sonicated liposomes of dimyristoyl- and dipalmitoylphosphatidylcholine exhibit much broader crystal ⇌ liquid-crystal transitions than multilamellar liposomes, as well as a greater proportion of *gauche* conformers and lesser interactions between chains (Spiker and Levin, 1976b; Gaber and Peticolas, 1977).

Phospholipid–cholesterol systems

Many physical techniques indicate that inclusion of cholesterol in phospholipid bilayers tends to reduce the fluidity of acyl chains above the T_c of the phospholipid and increase it below T_c, thereby broadening the phase transition. These effects have been studied by direct Raman spectroscopy (Lippert and Peticolas, 1971; Spiker and Levin, 1975; Verma and Wallach, 1976b; Bunow and Levin, 1977b; Pink *et al.*, 1980), as well as by evaluation of the resonance Raman spectra of β-carotene (Verma and Wallach, 1975) and of amphotericin B (Bunow and Levin, 1977b).

Studies of the C–C stretching region (Lippert and Peticolas, 1971; Spiker and Levin, 1975) indicate that cholesterol inhibits the formation of *gauche* isomers above T_c and reduces the proportion of all-*trans* conformers below T_c. However, Umemura *et al.* (1980), examining cholesterol/dipalmitoylphosphatidylcholine systems at 40–60 mol % cholesterol by Fourier transform infrared spectroscopy, discovered additional details: *a*, some all-*trans* conformers are present in the liquid-crystalline state; *b*, at all temperatures below $30°C$, cholesterol causes segregation of at least two phases, one of phospholipid alone, one of cholesterol/ phospholipid and presumably one of cholesterol alone; and *c*, the two acyl ester linkages of a phospholipid molecule are made non-equivalent by the presence of cholesterol. Bush *et al.* (1980a,b) confirm the last and argue that the positions, intensities and half-widths of the C=O frequencies at 1,671, 1,720 and 1,738 cm^{-1} of dipalmitoylphosphatidylcholine/cholesterol preclude hydrogen bonding at either of the two carbonyl sites. The splitting and broadening of the C=O band upon the addition of cholesterol (Brown and Brown, 1980) also indicates that cholesterol modifies the configuration of at least one of the ester linkages of dipalmitoylphosphatidylcholine.

Studies of the low frequency Raman region of egg phosphatidylcholine liposomes ± cholesterol (Verma and Wallach, 1976b) suggest that cholesterol perturbs the lattice structure of phosphatidylcholine head groups above the phospholipid T_c. Below T_c the sterol impedes the ordering of acyl chains. The last is evident from the loss of the 245 cm^{-1} band characteristic of ordered oleate chains.

β-Carotene, a native component of some biomembranes, has been used as a Raman active probe of phospholipid/cholesterol bilayers (Verma and Wallach, 1975). β-Carotene has resonance-enhanced −C=C− and =C−C= stretching vibrations at 1,527 cm^{-1} and 1,158 cm^{-1}, respectively. The relative intensity of the 1,527 cm^{-1} band (using the non-enhanced 1,440 cm^{-1} band as reference) decreases precipitously with increasing cholesterol/phospholipid ratio, reaching a minimum value at a cholesterol/phospholipid ratio near 0.9. It appears that β-carotene does not fit easily into phosphatidylcholine liposomes containing cholesterol and almost not at all so at a cholesterol/phospholipid molar ratio near 1. The data suggest extrusion of the β-carotene chain from cholesterol-containing regions.

Combinations of phospholipids and unsaturated fatty acids

Depending on the number, position and conformation of their C=C bonds, the inclusion of unsaturated fatty acids (alcohols) can perturb the organisation of phospholipids in a bilayer (Barton and Gunstone, 1975; Pringle and Miller, 1979).

Verma *et al.* (1980a) have used Raman spectroscopy to study some details of interactions in several combinations of fatty acids and phosphatidylcholines. Plots of $[I_{2880}/I_{2850}]$ versus temperature or ln $[I_{2880}/I_{2850}]$ versus $1/T$ revealed multiple thermal transitions, each representing a separate phase with distinctive phosphatidylcholine/fatty acid proportions. Similar behaviour has been detected by calorimetry (Mabrey and Sturtevant, 1976; 1977). The Raman data further suggest, in the case of dipalmitoylphosphatidylcholine/linoleic acid, that the low-temperature transition (∼ −5 to ∼ −1°C) represents a phase rich in linoleic acid, while the higher temperature transition (∼ 27°C) represents a phase rich in saturated phospholipid. Among the fatty acids used (oleic acid, linoleic acid, linolenic acid and linolelaidic acid), linoleic acid interfered most with cooperative interactions between phospholipid acyl chains. Linolelaidic acid increased the T_c when combined with dimyristoylphosphatidylcholine (23 to 28°C). The last finding is consistent with the spin probe data of Pringle and Miller (1979) on mixtures of phospholipids and long-chain unsaturated alcohols.

Effects of ions

Raman spectroscopy has been used to evaluate the effects of divalent (Hark and Ho, 1979; 1980) and polyvalent (Loshchilova and Karvaly, 1977) ions on the thermal transitions and *trans-gauche* ratios of phospholipid bilayers. Mg^{2+} added to phosphatidylserine, shifts the break in the plot of $[I_{1063}/I_{1086}]$ against temperature from $10°C$, the T_c, to $20°C$, without change in the numerical value of the ratio. Ca^{2+}, in contrast, abolished the thermal transition and increased the proportion of *trans* conformers at temperatures below the T_c of the pure lipid (Hark and Ho, 1979). In the case vesicles composed of phosphatidylserine and ^{2}H-dimyristoylphosphatidylcholine (deuterated at C54), analysis of the C^2H-stretching band width ($2,103$ cm^{-1}) suggests immiscibility at a phosphatidylserine/phosphatidylcholine molar ratio of $1/2$. However, Ca^{2+} (50 mM) induced fusion when the two phospholipids were in the ratio of $2/1$ (phospholipid concentration 50 mM). The C–C and CH-stretching data further indicate that in fused vesicles both phospholipids contain higher proportions of *trans* conformers than expected at or below T_c for either pure phospholipid alone.

I_2 (which increases the electrical conductivity of black lipid membranes), increase the proportion of *gauche* conformers of dipalmitoylphosphatidylcholine according to C–C stretching analyses (Loshchilova and Karvaly, 1977). This disordering effect manifests itself by increases of $[I_{1092}/I_{1066}]$, $[I_{1092}/I_{1128}]$ and $[I_{2850}/I_{2882}]$ from 0.51, 0.67 and 0.80 to 0.67, 0.85 and 0.86, respectively, upon the addition of I_2 to dipalmitoylphosphatidylcholine. The results suggest that I_2, not I^- or I_3^- is responsible for the increase in the electrical conductivity of black lipid membranes.

Phospholipid–polypeptide/protein systems

Phospholipid–polypeptide systems

Raman spectroscopy has been used to characterise the phospholipid interactions with melittin (Verma and Wallach, 1976a; Lavialle *et al.*,, 1980), poly-L-lysine (Susi *et al.*, 1979) gramicidin (Weidekamm *et al.*, 1977; Susi *et al.*, 1979) and valinomycin (Lis *et al.*, 1976; Susi *et al.*, 1979).

Melittin is a 3,000 molecular weight polypeptide from bee venom containing positively-charged or polar residues at the N terminus, attached to a block of apolar amino acids. Because of its amphipathic nature, melittin inserts readily into phospholipid bilayers and may disrupt these by a detergent-like action. At a $1/28$ (mole/mole) ratio of melittin to dimyristoylphosphatidylcholine (about 0.035 mole l^{-1}), the polypeptide shifts the native T_c of the phospholipid ($23°C$) to $34°C$ (Verma and Wallach, 1976a). Higher proportions of mellitin have been reported to produce two thermal transitions, one at $17°C$ and one at $29°C$ (Lavialle *et al.*, 1980). All the data indicate that the interactions of melittin with phospholipids change the thermal transitions of acyl chains and that melittin imposes constraints extending over boundary layers of lipid surrounding the polypeptide. The origin of the 17°C transition described by Lavialle *et al.* (1980) is not clear.

Thermal transitions and *trans/gauche* ratios have been evaluated for phospholipids in the presence of valinomycin (Lis *et al.*, 1976; Susi *et al.*, 1979) gramicidin A and S (Weidekamm *et al.*, 1977; Susi *et al.*, 1979) by analyses of the CH and C–C stretching regions.

Gramicidin A broadens the crystal ⇌ liquid-crystal transition of dipalmitoyl-phosphatidylcholine (T_c=41°C) at very low molar ratios (1/650). The thermal transition, as reported by plots of $[I_{2880}/I_{2850}]$ against temperature, disappear at a molar ratio of 1:150, while the transition reported by plots of $[I_{2930}/I_{2850}]$ versus temperature shift upward by 2-3°C (Weidekamm *et al.*, 1977). Plots of I_R versus temperature, where $I_R = [I_{1062}/I_{715}]/[I_{1062}I_{715}]_{(\text{liquid } N_2)}$, give concordant results with gramicidin A (Susi *et al.*, 1979). The I_R values increase/decrease by about 20 per cent above or below the T_c of dimyristoylphosphatidyl-choline in the presence of gramicidin A (3 per cent w/w). This study suggests that gramicidin A increases the fluidity of phospholipids below T_c and decreases it above. Gramicidin S, in contrast, lowers the T_c of dimyristoylphosphatidyl-choline (23°C) to ~12°C. It is proposed that this behaviour indicates that gramicidin S molecules are not embedded in lipid domains in an ordered way (Susi *et al.*, 1979).

Phospholipid-protein systems

The lipid–protein recombinants studied to date by laser Raman spectroscopy include cytochrome oxidase and cytochrome *c* (Lis *et al.*, 1976), myelin proteo-lipid apoprotein (Curatolo *et al.*, 1978; Verma *et al.*, 1980a), the B-protein of fd phage (Dunker *et al.*, 1979), and lysozyme (Lippert *et al.*, 1980).

Proteolipid apoprotein (PLA) is the most abundant protein of myelin sheath membranes and is the delipidated form of white matter proteolipid. We examined the CH stretching and C–C stretching regions of PLA–phosphatidylcholine liposomes, containing 1 mol PLA per 700 mol phospholipid, that is, about 1/20 w/w (Curatolo *et al.*, 1978), and equivalent systems containing phospholipids and unsaturated fatty acids (Verma *et al.*, 1980a). Below the T_c of dimyristoyl-phosphatidylcholine the CH stretching region appears the same with or without PLA. As the temperature is raised the 2,880 cm^{-1} band does not shift to 2,890 cm^{-1} immediately above 23°C (T_c), as with pure dimyristoylphosphatidylcholine, but only at or above 40°C. Plots of $[I_{2880}/I_{2850}]$ against temperature for the recombinants show an asymmetric broadening of the main lipid transition; the chain-melting process does not seem complete until 40°C. This is consistent with calorimetric data (Curatolo *et al.*, 1977). PLA markedly broadens the main transition of egg phosphatidylcholine (~ −6°C) and also creates a new transition, centred at about +12°C, which is also detectable by differential thermal calorimetry.

The C–C stretching regions of phosphatidylcholines and their PLA recombinants were analysed using a modification of the S_{trans} order parameter of Gaber and Peticolas (1977), where the maximum value, 1.0, defines acyl chains in the all-*trans* state. Below the crystal⇌liquid-crystal transition of dimyristoylphosphatidylcholine, $[I_{1064}/I_{1095}]$ reaches a maximum of 2.45 and its value above 35°C is 0.28. The PLA recombinant with dimyristoylphosphatidylcholine gives a value of 1.80 below T_c and 0.48 at 35°C, that is, 12° above T_c. The data suggest that PLA inhibits acyl chains in assuming the all-*trans* form below T_c, while favouring *trans* conformers above T_c. A theoretical basis for these result can be found in a study of Owicki and McConnell (1979).

The action of PLA on egg phosphatidylcholine is more complex because of the unsaturated and somewhat heterogeneous acyl chains of this phospholipid. The transition (T_c normally about $-6°C$) extends from -26 to $-4°C$ and a biphasic transition appears at about $+12°C$. Curatolo *et al.* (1978) explain these findings by a preferential binding of PLA for acyl chains of a particular length or unsaturation. This suggestion was substantiated by Verma *et al.* (1980a) who studied combinations of PLA with phosphatidylcholines of differing acyl chain lengths and mixtures thereof with fatty acids of varied chain lengths and unsaturation.

The effect of PLA on the thermal behaviour of dipalmitoylphosphatidylcholine/linoleic acid, is to shift the transition temperature ($\sim -2°C$; midpoint) of the phase rich in linoleic acid to about 14°C (midpoint), without affecting its width, and to sharpen the broad main transition (midpoint $\sim 27°C$). The data suggest that: a, PLA causes unsaturated fatty acids to partition into its boundary gradient; and b, the protein raises the T_cs of phases rich in unsaturated acyl chains more than phases enriched in saturated acyl chains. The following possibilities exist: a, *cis* double bonds create domains more accommodating for PLA than other configurations; b, the unpaired electrons in double bonds provide regions of lowered hydrophobicity that do not exist in a single bond environment and PLA molecules prefer such regions.

The interaction of the major coat protein, B-protein, from the filamentous phage fd with dipalmitoylphosphatidylcholine has been studied by conventional and differential Raman spectroscopy (Dunker *et al.*, 1979). The melting curves constructed from the relative intensities in the C–C stretching region $[I_{1062}/I_{1002}]$ (I_{1002} is the intensity of protein Phe peak) indicate that the B-protein broadens and lowers (by 15-20°) the order⇌disorder transition of dipalmitoylphosphatidylcholine. The S_{trans} values (Gaber and Peticolas, 1977) for B-protein-associated phospholipids at 15°C (0.63) are comparable to that of pure lipid at 26°C for sonicated vesicles and at 35°C for dispersions. Similarly the value of S_{lat} (0.25) at 15°C for the lipid–protein complex lies between that of pure dipalmitoylphosphatidylcholine vesicles and dispersons at 30°C.

The secondary structure of B-protein (c-state) contains an appreciable amount of β-pleated sheet (Nozaki *et al.*, 1976; Williams and Dunker, 1977). This is in contrast to PLA which is rich in α helix when associated with lipids (Cockle *et al.*, 1978). It is, possible, therefore, that α helix stabilises boundary lipid (Curatolo *et al.*, 1977, 1978) while hydrophobic beta structures act in an opposite fashion (Dunker *et al.*, 1979). However, the proportions of B-protein used by Dunker *et al.* (1979) were high in comparison to that used in the studies of PLA recombinants (1/1 w/w, against 1/20, w/w). It is possible, therefore, that protein–protein interactions might be the dominant factors in the studies of B-protein-lipid interactions. In view of the behaviour shown by PLA (Verma *et al.*, 1980a), it would be interesting to investigate the effect of B-protein on the thermotropism of unsaturated lipids.

A relationship between the α helix–β sheet transition and lipid acyl chain stability has been demonstrated by Lippert *et al.* (1980) using lysozyme and mixtures of dipalmitoylphosphatidic acid and dimyristoylphosphatidylcholine. The intensity of the amide III band at $1,257 \text{ cm}^{-1}$ (assigned to β sheet; Frushour and Koenig, 1975) decreases and the intensity of the $1,322 \text{ cm}^{-1}$ feature (assigned to α helix; Frushour and Koenig, 1975) of lysozyme increases as the latter interacts with dimyristoylphosphatidylcholine/dipalmitoylphosphatidic acid liposomes below their crystal $\rightleftharpoons$ liquid crystal T_c (23°C). The beta content of the combination increases above 30°C, indicating a possible relationship between the onset of beta-structure formation and disorientation of lipid acyl chains. On the other hand, the C–C stretching band analysis (S_{trans}) of the protein–lipid mixtures suggests that lysozyme has a minor effect on the *trans/gauche* transition of dimyristoylphosphatidylcholine (T_c lowered by 3°). In contrast, the T_c (58°C) of the dipalmitoylphosphatidic component of the mixed lipids is lowered by about 12°. Interestingly, lysozyme preserves the all-*trans* content of dipalmitoyl-phosphatidic acid above its T_c. This behaviour is similar to that observed in the interaction of PLA with dimyristoylphosphatidylcholine (Curatolo *et al.*, 1978).

APPLICATION TO BIOLOGICAL MEMBRANES

Plasma membranes isolated as small, sealed vesicles have proved very suitable for Raman analyses, as have sarcoplasmic reticulum vesicles. Good Raman spectra have also been obtained with intact erythrocyte ghosts. Qualitatively, the spectra obtained are on the whole what one would expect from protein–lipid composites. Quantitative analyses, however, have provided important insights into the structural dynamics of proteins and lipids in biomembranes.

Erythrocyte ghosts

Wallach and Verma (1975) and Lippert *et al.* (1975) reported the well-resolved Raman spectra of erythrocyte ghosts. From amide I and amide III analyses, Lippert *et al.* (1975) arrived at an estimate of "40–55 per cent α helix with little β configuration" for the membrane proteins, a value supported qualitatively by Wallach and Verma (1975). Milanovitch *et al.* (1976a), working with membranes from Dutch belt rabbit erythrocytes, also estimated "considerable α helix" on the basis of the amide I and III intensities.

The extraction of peripheral proteins is thought to change the environment of peptide bonds, as well as of phenylalanine and tryptophan rings of integral membrane proteins, according to modifications in the amide I and 950 cm^{-1} region (Goheen *et al.*, 1977). However, the CH stretching region did not shown any deviation upon extraction of peripheral proteins by these workers and the C–C stretching data (1,100 cm^{-1} region) appear contradictory. Specifically, $[I_{1130}/I_{1085}]$ increased while $[I_{1065}/I_{1085}]$ remained unchanged. Goheen *et al.*, (1977) argue that membrane proteins may contribute to the 1,100 cm^{-1} region, accounting for an unexpected increase in $[I_{1130}/I_{1080}]$. It is possible also that the strong β-carotene band at 1,159 cm^{-1} (which quenches upon irradiation) interferes with intensity measurements at 1,130 cm^{-1}.

In their initial Raman study of erythrocyte ghosts, Wallach and Verma (1975) observed two prominent resonance-enhanced bands at 1,530 cm^{-1} and 1,165 cm^{-1}. These bands were assigned to –C=C– and =C–C= stretching vibrations, respectively, of membrane associated β-carotene. Several membrane perturbations, for example, trypsinisation, lysophosphatidylcholine, and reduction of pH, increased the relative intensity of the β-carotene bands, whereas heating (50°C, 15 min) or addition of ~ 0.1 per cent sodium dodecylsulphate decreased their intensity (Verma and Wallach, 1975). The data suggest that membrane-associated β-carotene is neither fully extended nor fully folded. Since the electronic spectra of carotenoids are sensitive to configuration, membrane structure changes leading to either extension or folding would explain the resonance Raman spectra.

Lipid state transitions

The CH stretching region of erythrocyte membranes resembles those of pure liposomes in band positions (Wallach and Verma, 1975). A band of 1,655 cm^{-1} (in the amide I region) does not shift upon deuteration, suggesting stretching of *cis* C=C bonds in unsaturated phospholipids (Verma and Wallach, 1976b). A poorly resolved band at 1,659 cm^{-1} in the erythrocyte membranes of Dutch belt rabbits in ^{2}H$_2$O (Milanovitch *et al.*, 1976a) may have the same origin.

Verma and Wallach (1976b) examined the C–H stretching region (2,700-3,000 cm^{-1}) and low frequencies due to acoustic vibrations, of erythrocyte membranes, as well as the –C=C– and =C–C= stretching of membrane-associated β-carotene, in the temperature range of –30 to +40°C. They found that the plot $[I_{2880}/I_{2850}]$ against temperature reports discontinuities at –8°C and at ~18°C. The authors ascribe 18° discontinuity to a ~ crystal⇌liquid-crystal transition in a region of low cholesterol content (~ 6 mol %). The fact that this transition corresponds to the abrupt decrement of $[I_{1527}/I_{1158}]$ of membrane-bound β-carotene would fit the suggestion that a low cholesterol region is involved, since β-carotene appears excluded from cholesterol-rich domains (Verma and Wallach, 1975).

Brandts *et al.* (1978), using calorimetry, have reported lipid–protein phase transitions in erythrocyte membranes at a very high temperature. These have not yet been confirmed by other techniques. On the other hand, Zimmer and associates (1974; 1975) describe a thermotropic viscosity change, discontinuous at 18-20°C, in erythrocyte membranes, as well as in cholesterol-depleted membrane lipids and correlate this with the discontinuity at 19°C in the Arrhenius plot for glucose transport (Lack *et al.*, 1973). Recent ESR studies of normal erythrocyte ghosts labelled with nitroxide fatty acids demonstrate a thermal transition at 13-16°C and a *p*H-sensitive transition at 37.5-40.5°C (Sato *et al.*, 1978). Hui and Strozewski (1979), using electron diffraction studies of erythrocyte membranes, noted a thermal transition at −3°C in both fresh membranes and in its total lipid extracts, and at ∼ 18°C in the stored ghosts.

Protein state transition
Membrane proteins generally yield a strong broad band at 2,935±5 cm^{-1} (Wallach *et al.*, 1979). This feature includes contributions from methyl and methylene groups of both lipids and proteins. In protein-rich membranes, the variation in the intensity of 2,935 cm^{-1} band with *p*H and temperature, can be assigned to folding/unfolding of membrane proteins (Wallach *et al.*, 1979).

Verma and Wallach (1976c) have examined the CH stretching region of erythrocyte ghosts as a function of temperature and *p*H and detected a transition at ∼ 39°C at *p*H 7.4 which can be brought to lower temperatures by a small change of [H$^+$]. An increase of about 0.6 × 10^{-7} M, (*p*H 7.0 to 6.5) corresponds to a 16° lowering of transition temperature. The authors propose that the large response in the *p*H range 7.0-6.0 might derive from the low dielectric constant of the membrane core: small changes in charge might influence the structure of proteins in membranes much more than that of proteins dissolved in aqueous solvents.

Membrane potential
Addition of either impermeant or lipophilic anions, respectively decreases or increases the membrane potential (negative inside) and produces a corresponding decrease or intensification of [I_{2930}/I_{2850}] (Mikkelsen *et al.*, 1978). The imposition of cation gradients across erythrocyte membrane vesicles also modifies the amide I and amide III frequencies in the direction of increased α-helicity of membrane proteins (Figure 3.5). However, spectrin-free vesicles, with or without cation gradient, do not show an appreciable difference in the intensity of these frequencies. It is proposed that a transmembrane potential (negative inside) and/or cation gradient can energise membranes. In this the apolar region would be compressed and some protein residues transfer into more polar regions.

Thymocyte plasma membranes

Raman spectra of highly purified rabbit thymocyte plasma membrane vesicles yield an amide I band at 1,660 cm^{-1} and amide III bands at 1,228 cm^{-1} and

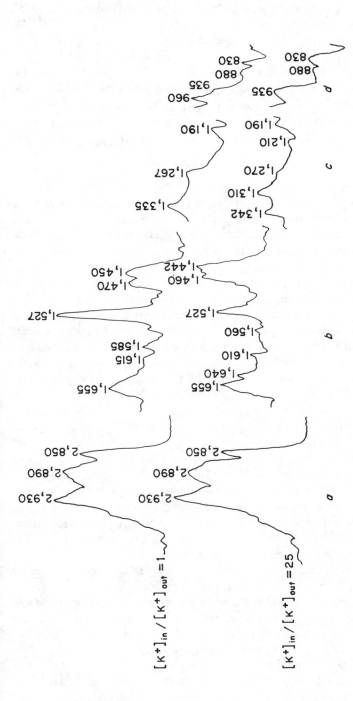

Figure 3.5 Raman spectra of erythrocyte membrane vesicles without and with transmembrane $[K^+]$ gradients. Intravesicular ionic composition: 10 mM Hepes/65 NaCl/75 mM Kc 1/0.25 mM MgCl$_2$ (pH 7.5). With cation gradients, the extracellular ionic composition is 140 mM NaCl/10 mM Hepes/0.25 mM MgCl$_2$ (pH 7.5). a, 2,800–3,100 cm^{-1} in H$_2$O; b, 1,400–1,700 cm^{-1} in ^{2}H$_2$O; c, 1,170–1,360 cm^{-1} in H$_2$O; d, 750–1,000 cm^{-1} in ^{2}H$_2$O. From Mikkelsen *et al.*, 1978, with permission

1,240 cm^{-1}, suggesting appreciable β-structured peptide (Verma *et al.*, 1975). Infrared studies support this conclusion.

Plots of $[I_{2880}/I_{2850}]$ versus temperature (Verma *et al.*, 1980b) show two transitions: an asymmetrical one with a midpoint at $-6°$C (onset $\sim -20°$C, completion $\sim 5°$C); and a symmetrical one centred at $\sim 25°$C. Plots of the position and width of the 2,880 cm^{-1} feature against temperature also reveal the middle transition. The plot of $[I_{2932}/I_{2850}]$ versus temperature shows a transition extending from $+ 35°$C to above $50°$C with a major increase in the ratio $[I_{2932}/I_{2850}]$. There is a minor increase in the $[I_{2930}/I_{2880}]$ in $25°$C region.

Effect of concanavalin A

Concanavalin A (Con A), a plant lectin, binds cooperatively to plasma membrane receptors of many cells (Wallach, 1975, Schmidt-Ullrich and Wallach, 1976). The Con A receptor of thymocyte membranes is a 55,000-molecular weight glyco-protein which traverses the plasma membrane.

Raman spectroscopy has revealed that stimulation of thymocytes with Con A enhances membrane protein amidation (Schmidt-Ullrich *et al.*, 1976b). This is evident from a series of sharp bands on the low frequency side (1,660 cm^{-1}) of the broad amide I/water peak, in plasma membranes isolated from Con A-stimulated cells. In membranes from resting cells these bands are absent or weak. Taking the band positions of simple amides as references, these new bands were assigned to amide I and amide II modes of side chain asparagine and glutamine. Enhanced amidation has also been confirmed by isoelectric focusing (Schmidt-Ullrich *et al.*, 1976a).

Verma *et al.* (1980b) have evaluated the changes in thymocyte membrane structure that follow immediately upon Con A binding. They reacted isolated pure thymocyte vesicles with Con A (Con A/plasma membrane protein ratios 10μg/2mg, 2μg/2mg, and 0.4μg/2mg). Plots of $[I_{2880}/I_{2850}]$ and $[I_{2930}/I_{2850}]$ against temperature between $-20°$C and $+50°$C, show that Con A binding lowers the temperature of the normal $\sim 25°$C transition to the range $0-21°$C depending on the Con A level and broadens it asymmetrically towards higher temperatures. Con A further broadens the transition reported by plots of $[I_{2930}/I_{2850}]$ against temperature, and shifts its range of $\sim 35-50°$C to the range of $\sim 17-50°$C. $[I_{2880}/I_{2850}]$ is stable from $\sim21°$C to at least $50°$C.

Although one cannot assign the high-temperature transition quite unambiguously, it must be due in large part to proteins (Verma *et al.*, 1980b). Proteins contribute at least 65 per cent of the membrane mass and therewith numerous methyl groups scattering at 2,932 cm^{-1}. That membrane proteins are known to undergo state changes at or above $40°$C (Verma and Wallach, 1976c; 1977; Mikkelsen *et al.*, 1978) favours this interpretation.

The perturbation by mitogenic doses of Con A of both the proteins and lipid state transitions is interpreted to indicate an important structure change in the 55,000-molecular weight Con A receptor (Schmidt-Ullrich *et al.*, 1978).

Plasma membranes from normal hamster lymphocytes and lymphoid cells neoplastically converted by Simian 40 virus (SV40)

The thermal transitions of highly purified plasma membranes from SV40-transformed GD248 lymphocytes and from normal splenocytes have been compared by Verma *et al.* (1977), analysing the CH stretching and acoustic region. The plasma membranes from the normal cells revealed thermal transitions at about 7°C, (approximately 5° wide) and at 37–43°C, as shown by plots of $[I_{2880}/I_{2850}]$ against temperature and $[I_{2930}/I_{2850}]$ against temperature, respectively. The plots of $[I_{\sim 2880}/I_{\sim 2850}]$ versus temperature for membranes of neoplastic lymphocytes, in contrast yield a transition centering around $-5°$C, about 12° to 20° wide. These transition ranges are also supported by analyses of the acoustic region. It is clear that the lipid transition of plasma membranes of neoplastic cells is shifted by at least 12° and that it is less cooperative. This difference in thermal transition might represent the composite contributions of cholesterol and lipid unsaturation. Domains rich in unsaturated lipids show a transition below zero (Verma *et al.*, 1980a).

The plot of $[I_{2930}/I_{2850}]$ versus temperature for membranes of normal cells remains stable to a temperature of 37°C and then increases abruptly up to 43°C. In the tumour cells, this ratio is stable to a temperature of 23°C, increases slowly until about 28°C and then increases quickly at higher temperatures, reaching a limit of 34°C. Verma *et al.* (1977) propose a protein origin for these transitions (as discussed before for erythrocyte and thymocyte plasma membranes). The plasma membranes of the neoplastic cells, at a sample temperature of $\sim 37°$C, are in a state achieved by normal membranes at $\sim 47°$C. It is conceivable that abnormal proteins in tumour cell plasma membranes might account for this anomalous thermotropic behaviour.

SARCOPLASMIC RETICULUM MEMBRANES

Milanovitch *et al.* (1976b) have described the Raman spectrum of sarcoplasmic reticulum membranes of lobster muscle in the 600 cm^{-1} to 3,000 cm^{-1} regions. They observe a strong 1,658 cm^{-1} band, unaltered in the presence of ^2H_2O, assigned to C=C stretching in acyl chains exhibiting *cis* conformation and resonance-enhanced membrane-associated carotene bands at 1,160 cm^{-1} and at 1,527 cm^{-1}.

The presence of the amide III band at 1,246 cm^{-1} possibly indicates a β- or unordered structure of membrane proteins. However, the amide I and amide I′ region could not be analysed due to the strong *cis* C=C band at 1,658 cm^{-1}. Comparisons of the C–C stretching bands of sarcoplasmic reticulum membranes with human erythrocyte ghosts led Milanovitch *et al.* (1976b) to suggest that the latter membranes are more rigid. This is consistent with the strong band at 1,658 cm^{-1} due to highly unsaturated lipids.

REFERENCES

Anderson, A. (1971). *The Raman effect,* Vol. 1 Marcel Dekker N.Y., pp. 1–402.
Aurengo, A. *et al.* (1979). *Biochem. Biophys. Res. Commun.*, **89**, 559.
Bansil, R., Day, J., Meadows, M., Rice, D. and Oldfield, E. (1980). *Biochemistry*, **19**, 1938.
Barton, P. G. and Gunstone, F. D. (1975). *J. biol. Chem.*, **250**, 4470.
Brandts, J. F. and Hunt, L. (1967). *J. Am. Chem. Soc.*, **89**, 4826.
Brandts, J. F., Taverna, R. D., Sadasivan, E. and Lysko, K. A. (1978). *Biochim. biophys. Acta*, **512**, 566.
Bridoux, M. and Delhaye, M. (1976). In *Advances in infrared and Raman spectroscopy*, Vol 2 (eds R. J. H. Clark and R. E. Hester) Heyden, London, pp. 140–165.
Brown, K. G., Erfurth, S. L., Small, W. W. and Peticolas, W. L. (1972). *Proc. natn. Acad. Sci. U.S.A.*, **69**, 1467.
Brown, K. G., Peticolas, W. L. and Brown, E. (1973). *Biochem. Biophys. Res. Commun.*, **94**, 358.
Brown, A. and Brown, K. G. (1980). *Biochem. Biophys. Res. Commun.*, **94**, 638.
Bunow, M. R. and Levin, I. W. (1977a). *Biochim. biophys. Acta.*, **487**, 388.
Bunow, M. R. and Levin, I. W. (1977b). *Biochim biophys. Acta.*, **464**, 202.
Bush, S. F., Adams, R. G. and Levin, I. W. (1980a). *Biochemistry*, **19**, 4429.
Bush, S. F., Levin, H. and Levin, I. W. (1980b). *Chem. Phys. Lipids*, **27**, 101.
Butler, M., Salem, N. Jr, Hoss, W. and Spoonhower, J. (1979). *Chem. Phys. Lipids*, **29**, 99.
Chrisman, R., English, J. C. and Tobias, R. S. (1976). *Appl. Spectrosc.*, **30**, 168.
Colthup, N. B., Daly, L. H. and Wiberly, S. E. (1975). *Introduction to Infrared and Raman Spectroscopy*, Academic Press, New York, pp. 324–325.
Cockle, S. A., Epand, R. M., Boggs, J. M. and Moscarello, M. A. (1978). *Biochemistry*, **17**, 624.
Curatolo, W., Sakura, J. D., Small, D. M. and Shipley, G. G. (1977). *Biochemistry*, **16**, 2313.
Curatolo, W. *et al.* (1978). *Biochemistry*, **17**, 1802.
Davies, J. E. D., Hodge, P., Gunstone, F. C. and Leikenjie, M. S. F. (1975). *Chem. Phys. Lipids*, **15**, 48.
Dunker, A. K., Williams, R. W., Gaber, B. P. and Peticolas, W. L. (1979). *Biochim. biophys. Acta*, **553**, 351.
Eisenberg, D. and Kauzmann, W. (1969). *The Structure and Properties of Water*, Oxford University Press, pp. 121–135.
Frushour, B. G. and Koenig, J. L. (1975). In *Advances in infrared and Raman spectroscopy*, Vol. 1 (eds R. J. H. Clark and R. G. Hester) Heyden, New York, pp. 35–94.
Gaber, B. P. and Peticolas, W. L. (1977). *Biochim. biophys. Acta*, **465**, 260.
Gaber, B. P., Yager, P. and Peticolas, W. L. (1978a). *Biophys. J.*, **21**, 161.
Gaber, B. P., Yager, P. and Peticolas, W. L. (1978b). *Biophys. J.*, **24**, 677.
Gall, M. H., Hendra, P. J., Peacock, G. J., Cudby, M. E. A. and Willis, H. A. (1972). *Spectrochim. Acta*, **28A**, 1485.
Goheen, G. C., Gilman, T. H., Kauffman, J. W. and Garvin, J. E. (1971). *Biochem. Biophys. Res. Commun.*, **79**, 805.
Hark, S. K. and Ho, J. T. (1979). *Biochem. Biophys. Res. Commun.*, **91**, 655.
Hark, S. K. and Ho, J. T. (1980). *Biochim. biophys. Acta*, **601**, 54.
Horvath, L. I., Cirak, J. and Vigh, L. (1980). *Chem. Phys. Lipids*, **27**, 237.
Hui, S. W. and Strozewski, C. M. (1970). *Biochim. biophys. Acta*, **555**, 417.
Karvaly, B. and Loshchilova, E. (1977). *Biochim. biophys. Acta*, **470**, 492.
King, S., Elsken, R. H. and Scherer, J. R. (1976). *Appl. Spectrosc.*, **30**, 281.
Lacko, L., Wittke, B. and Geck, P. (1973). *J. cell Physiol., Lond.*, **82**, 213.
Larson, K. and Rand, R. P. (1973). *Biochim. biophys. Acta*, **326**, 245.
Lavialle, F., Levin, I. W. and Mollay, C. (1980). *Biochim. biophys. Acta*, **600**, 62.
Lippert, J. L. and Peticolas, W. L. (1971). *Proc. natn. Acad. Sci. U.S.A.*, **68**, 1572.
Lippert, J. L., Govezyca, L. E. and Meiklejohn, G. (1975). *Biochim. biophys. Acta*, **382**, 51.
Lippert, J. L., Lindsay, R. M. and Schultz, R. (1980). *Biochim. biophys. Acta*, **599**, 32.
Lis, L. J., Kauffman, J. W. and Shriver, D. R. (1976). *Biochim. biophys. Acta*, **436**, 513.
Lis, L. J., Goheen, S. C. and Kauffman, J. W. (1977). *Biochem. Biophys. Res. Commun.*, **78**, 492.

Loshchilova, E. and Karvaly, B. (1977). *Chem. phys. Lipids*, 19, 159.
Mabrey, S. and Sturtevant, J. (1976). *Proc. natn. Acad. Sci. U.S.A.*, 73, 3862.
Mabrey, S. and Sturtevant, J. (1977). *Biochim. biophys. Acta*, 486, 444.
Mathies, R. and Yu, N. T. (1978). *J. Raman Spectrosc.*, 7, 349.
Mendelsohn, R., Sunder, S. and Bernstein, H. J. (1975). *Biochim. biophys. Acta*, 413, 329.
Mendelsohn, R., Sunder, S. and Bernstein, H. J. (1976a). *Biochim. biophys. Acta*, 443, 613.
Mendelsohn, R., Sunder, S. and Bernstein, H. J. (1976b). *Biochim. biophys. Acta*, 419, 563.
Mendelsohn, R. and Maisano, J. (1978). *Biochim. biophys. Acta*, 506, 192.
Mikkelsen, R. B., Verma, S. P. and Wallach, D. F. H. (1978). *Proc. natn. Acad. Sci. U.S.A.*, 75, 5478.
Milanovich, F. P., Shore, B., Harney, R. C. and Tu, A. T. (1976a). *Chem. Phys. Lipids*, 17, 79.
Milanovich, F. P., Yeh, Y., Baskin, R. J. and Harney, R. C. (1976b). *Biochim. biophys. Acta*, 491, 243.
Nozaki, Y., Chamberlain, B. K., Webster, R. E. and Tanford, C. (1976). *Nature*, 259, 335.
Owicki, J. C. and McConnell, H. M. (1979). *Proc. natn. Acad. Sci. U.S.A.*, 76, 4750.
Pink, D. A., Green, T. J. and Chapman, D. (1980). *Biochemistry*, 19, 349.
Pringle, M. J. and Miller, K. W. (1979). *Biochemistry*, 18, 3314.
Sato, B., Nishikida, K., Samuels, L. T. and Tyler, F. H. (1978). *J. Clin. Invest.*, 61, 251.
Schmidt-Ullrich, R. and Wallach, D. F. H. (1976). *Biochem. Biophys. Res. Commun.*, 69, 1011.
Schmidt-Ullrich, R., Verma, S. P. and Wallach, D. F. H. (1976a). *Biochem. Biophys. Res. Commun.*, 67, 1062.
Schmidt-Ullrich, R., Verma, S. P. and Wallach, D. F. H. (1976b). *Biochim. biophys. Acta*, 426, 477.
Schmidt-Ullrich, R., Mikkelsen, R. B. and Wallach, D. F. H. (1978). *J. biol. Chem.*, 253, 6973.
Snyder, R. G., Hsu, F. L. and Krimm (1978). *Spectrochim. Acta, Part A*, 34, 395.
Snyder, R. G., Scherer, J. R. and Gaber, B. P. (1980). *Biochim. biophys. Acta*, 601, 47.
Spiker, R. C. and Levin, I. W. (1975). *Biochim. biophys. Acta*, 388, 361.
Spiker, R. C. and Levin, I. W. (1976a). *Biochim. biophys. Acta*, 433, 457.
Spiker, R. C. and Levin, I. W. (1976b). *Biochim. biophys. Acta*, 455, 560.
Strum, J., Savoie, R., Edelson, M. and Peticolas, W. L. (1978). *Indian J. pure appl. Phys.*, 16, 327.
Susi, H., Sampugna, J., Hampson, J. W. and Ard, S. (1979). *Biochemistry*, 18, 297.
Terner, J., Campion, A. and El-Sayed, M. A. (1977). *Proc. natn. Acad. Sci. U.S.A.*, 74, 5212.
Tobin, M. C. (1971). *Laser Raman Spectroscopy*, Wiley-Interscience, New York, pp. 1–126.
Umemura, J., Cameron, D. G. and Mautsch, H. H. (1980). *Biochim. biophys. Acta*, 602, 32.
Verma, S. P., Wallach, D. F. H. and Schmidt-Ullrich, R. (1975). *Biochim. biophys. Acta*, 394, 633.
Verma, S. P. and Wallach, D. F. H. (1975). *Biochim. biophys. Acta*, 401, 168.
Verma, S. P. and Wallach, D. F. H. (1976a). *Biochim. biophys. Acta*, 416, 616.
Verma, S. P. and Wallach, D. F. H. (1976b). *Biochim. biophys. Acta*, 436, 307.
Verma, S. P. and Wallach, D. F. H. (1976c). *Proc. natn. Acad. Sci. U.S.A.*, 73, 3558.
Verma, S. P. and Wallach, D. F. H. (1977a). *Biochem. biophys. Acta*, 486, 217.
Verma, S. P. and Wallach, D. F. H. (1977b). *Biochem. Biophys. Res. Commun.*, 74, 473.
Verma, S. P., Schmidt-Ullrich, R., Thompson, W. S. and Wallach, D. F. H. (1977). *Cancer Res.*, 37, 3490.
Verma, S. P., Wallach, D. F. H. and Sakura, J. D. (1980a). *Biochemistry*, 19, 574.
Verma, S. P., Schmidt-Ullrich, R. and Wallach, D. F. H. (1980b). *J. Receptor Res.*, 1, 1.
Waldbilig, R. C., Robertson, J. D. and McIntosh, T. J. (1976). *Biochim. biophys. Acta*, 448, 1.
Wallach, D. F. H. (1975). *Membrane Molecular Biology of Neoplastic Cells*, Elsevier, Amsterdam, pp. 435–481.
Wallach, D. F. H. and Verma, S. P. (1975). *Biochim. biophys. Acta*, 382, 542.
Wallach, D. F. H., Verma, S. P. and Fookson, J. (1979). *Biochim. biophys. Acta*, 559, 153.
Weidekamm, E. *et al.* (1977). *Biochim. biophys. Acta*, 464, 442.

Williams, G. W. and Dunker, A. K. (1977). *J. biol. Chem.*, **252**, 6253.
Woodruff, W. and Farquharson, S. (1978). *Analyt. Chem.*, **50**, 1389.
Yellin, N. and Levin, I. W. (1977a). *Biochim. biophys. Acta*, **468**, 490.
Yellin, N. and Levin, I. W. (1977b). *Biochemistry*, **16**, 642.
Zimmer, A. and Schirmer, H. (1974). *Biochim. biophys. Acta*, **345**, 314.
Zimmer, G., Schirmer, H. and Bastian, P. (1975). *Biochim. biophys. Acta*, **401**, 244.

Table 1 Membrane characterisation by Raman spectroscopy

System	Parameters	Spectral region (cm^{-1})	Comments	Reference
1. *Phospholipids*				
DMPC (M/U)	T_c	2,800–3,000 1,064–1,130	$23\pm1°C$	Spiker and Levin (1976a)
DMPC (U)	T_c	2,800–3,000 1,064–1,300	Transition broadened	Spiker and Levin (1976a)
DMPC (M)	Trans/gauche ratio	1,064–1,300	More gauche below T_c	Spiker and Levin (1976a)
DMPC–H$_2$O (gel)	Trans/gauche ratio	1,064–1,300	Two gauche bonds/lipid molecule below T_c and seven above	Yellin and Levin (1977b)
DMPC (M)	Cooperative units	2,800–3,000	400	Verma et al. (1980a) Pink et al. (1980); Bunow and Levin (1977a)
DMPC (M)	gauche conformers	1,130; 2,930	gauche bonds start to appear at −100°C	Gaber et al. (1978a)
DPPC (M)	T_c	2,800–3,000	41°C	Spiker and Levin (1976a)
DPPC (U)	T_c	1,064–1,130	T_c broadened	Gaber et al. (1980a)
DPPC (suspension)	Chain order	Diff. spectr. (2,880–3,000; 1,064–1,130)	Triclinic below 30°C loose hexagonal 30–40°C	
DPPC (M)	Cooperative units	1,064–1,130	31	Yellin and Levin (1977a)
DPPC–H$_2$O (gel)	trans/gauche ratio	1,064–1,130	Two gauche bonds below T_c; 8–9 gauche bonds above	Yellin and Levin (1977b)
DSPC (M)	T_c	2,800–3,000 1,064–1,130	54°C	Verma et al. (1980)
DSPC (M)	Cooperative units	2,800–3,000	200	Verma et al. (1980a)
DSPC–H$_2$O (gel)	trans/gauche ratio	1,064–1,130	Six gauche bonds/molecule below T_c and 13–14 above	Yellin and Levin (1977b)
Egg PC	T_c	2,800–3,000 1,064–1,130	−6°C	Verma and Wallach (1976b)

System	Parameter	Frequency (cm^{-1})	Observation	Reference
Sphingomyelin (dry)	T_c	2,800–3,000 1,064–1,130	85–87°C	Mendelsohn et al. (1975)
Sphingomyelin (dry)	trans/gauche ratio	1,064–1,130	gauche isomers below T_c	Mendelsohn et al. (1975)
PE (79 per cent in water)	T_c	2,800–3,000	71°C	Brown et al. (1973)
PS (water dispersion)	T_c	2,800–3,000	10°C	Hark and Ho (1979)
DPPA + DMPC	T_c	1,064–1,130	20–24°C (DMPC) and 57–59°C (DPPA)	Lippert et al. (1980)
2. Phospholipids/ions				
PS + Mg^{2+}	T_c	2,800–3,000 1,063–1,130	Mg^{2+} shifts T_c from 10 to 20°C	Hark and Ho (1979)
PS + Ca^{2+}	T_c	1,063–1,130	Ca^{2+} abolishes T_c	Hark and Ho (1980)
PS + DMPC + Ca^{2+}	trans/gauche ratio	1,063–1,130	More trans at/below T_c	Loshchilova and Karvaly (1977)
DPPC + I$_2$	trans/gauche ratio	1,063–1,130	I$_2$ raises gauche fraction	
3. Phospholipid/cholesterol				
DMPC/cholesterol (50 mol %)	T_c	2,800–3,000 1,064–1,130	Transition broadened	Spiker and Levin (1975)
DPPC or egg PC (50 mole %)	T_c	2,800–3,000 1,064–1,130	Transition widened by 160°C	Spiker and Levin (1976a)
DMPC OR DPPC/cholesterol (30 mole %)	1,100–1,600 cm^{-1} β-carotene as resonance Raman probe	Intensity of 1,527 cm^{-1}	β-Carotene band reduces to a minimum (at 21°C).	Verma and Wallach (1976b)
DMPC/cholesterol or DPPC/cholesterol	trans/gauche ratio	1,064–1,130	Cholesterol induces gauche conformation below and prevents gauche conformation above T_c	Lippert and Peticolas (1971) Spiker and Levin (1975)
DPPC/cholesterol frequencies	C=O stretching	1,720–1,740	Cholesterol does not form H bonds with C=O groups; induces non-equivalence of two ester linkages	Bush et al. (1980a,b) Umemura et al. (1980)

Table 1 *cont.*

System	Parameters	Spectral region (cm^{-1})	Comments	Reference
Egg PC/cholesterol	Chain conformation	Acoustic; lattice vibrations $1,400{-}1,600\ \text{cm}^{-1}$	Cholesterol impedes ordering of acyl chains	Verma and Wallach (1976)
Egg PC/cholesterol/	β-Carotene state; $1,527\ \text{cm}^{-1}$ resonance band	$1,400{-}1,600\ \text{cm}^{-1}$	$[I_{1527}/I_{1440}]$ reaches minimum at cholesterol/lipid ratio of 0.9, indicating oxidation of carotene	Verma and Wallach (1975)
DPPC/cholesterol/ amphotericin B	Interaction of amphotericin B	$1,400{-}1,600\ \text{cm}^{-1}$ resonance band at $1556\ \text{cm}^{-1}$	Amphoteracin B reacts specifically with cholesterol	Bunow and Levin (1977b)
4. Phospholipid/fatty acid DMPC, DPPC, DSPC, Egg PC/oleic acid, linoleic acid, linolenic acid, linolelaidic acid	T_c	2,800–3,000	*cis*-unsaturated fatty acids split the transition. Main T_c broadens and shifts to lower temperatures. Linoleic acid most effective	Verma *et al.* (1980a)
5. Phospholipid/peptide; phospholipid/protein DMPC/melittin (28:1 M/M)	T_c	2,800–3,000	T_c shifts from 23 to 34°C. Long-range lipid perturbation	Verma and Wallach (1975)
DMPC/melittin (14:1 M/M)	T_c	2,800–3,000	T_c at 17°C and 29°C	Lavialle *et al.* (1980)
DMPC/valinomycin	*trans/gauche* ratio	1,064–1,130	Increased *gauche* fraction	Susi *et al.* (1979)
DPPC/valinomycin	*trans/gauche* ratio	1,064–1,130	No change	
DMPC (DPPC)/gramicidin A	T_c	2,800–3,000	Broadening of T_c at low molar ratio. Higher concentration abolishes the T_c	Weidekamm *et al.* (1977)
DMPC/gramicidin S	T_c	2,800–3,000	T_c shifts to 12°C	Susi *et al.* (1979)

Sample	Parameter	Wavenumber (cm⁻¹)	Observations	Reference
DMPC/PLA (20:1 w/w)	T_c	2,800–3,000	Asymmetrical broadening of T_c; melting completes at 41°C	Curatolo et al. (1978)
DMPC/PLA (20:1 w/w)	trans/gauche ratio	1,064–1,130	PLA prevents the formation of trans segments below T_c and preserves the trans configuration above T_c	Curatolo et al. (1978)
Egg PC/PLA	T_c	2,880–3,000	Broader main T_c (−6°C) and new transition at 12°C	Curatolo et al. (1978)
DPPC/B-protein (from phage fd)	T_c	1,064–1,130	21°C	Dunker et al. (1979)
DPPC/B-protein	trans/gauche ratio	1,064–1,130	0.63 at 15°C	Dunker et al. (1979)
DPPC/B-protein	S_{lat}	2,800–3,000	0.25 at 15°C	Dunker et al. (1979)
DPPC/DMPC/lysozyme	S_{trans}	1,064–1,130	No change	Lippert et al. (1980)
DPPC/DMPC/lysozyme	T_c	1,064–1,130	17°C (DMPC) and 45°C (DPPC)	Lippert et al. (1980)
DPPC/DMPC/lysozyme	trans/gauche ratio	1,064–1,130	all-trans increases above 60°C	Lippert et al. (1980)

6. *Phospholipid/PLA/fatty acid*

Sample	Parameter	Wavenumber (cm⁻¹)	Observations	Reference
DMPC/oleic acid	T_c	2,800–3,000	−2 to +8°C 18 to 29°C	Verma et al. (1980a)
DMPC/oleic acid/PLA	T_c	2,800–3,000	−10 to 12°C 20 to 25°C 25 to 38°C	Verma et al. (1980a)
DMPC/linoleic acid	T_c	2,800–3,000	−28 to −15°C −8 to 2°C 11 to 20°C	Verma et al. (1980a)
DMPC/linoleic acid/PLA	T_c	2,800–3,000	5 to 15°C 19 to 30°C	Verma et al. (1980a)
DOPC/PLA	T_c	2,800–3,000	−16 to −26°C −9 to +5°C	Verma et al. (1980a)
DPPC/linoleic acid	T_c	2,800–3,000	−1 to 5°C 18 to 40°C	Verma et al. (1980a)
DPPC/linoleic acid/PLA	T_c	2,800–3,000	12 to 15°C	Verma et al. (1980a)

Table 1 cont.

7. Biomembranes

System	Parameters	Spectral region (cm^{-1})	Comments	Reference
Erythrocyte ghosts (pH 7.4)	Protein secondary structure	Amide I, Amide III	40–55 percent α-helix	Lippert et al. (1975); Wallach and Verma (1975)
Erythrocyte ghosts (pH 7.4)	Protein state transitions	2,930 cm^{-1}	~41°C	Verma and Wallach (1976c)
Erythrocyte ghosts (pH 6.5)	Protein state transition	2,930 cm^{-1}	~31°C	Verma and Wallach (1976c)
Erythrocyte ghosts (pH 6.0)	Protein state transition	2,930 cm^{-1}	0 to 7°C	Verma and Wallach (1976c)
Erythrocyte ghosts (pH 7.4)	Lipid state T_c	2,800–3,000	~ −3 and ~ 18°C	Verma and Wallach (1976b)
Erythrocyte ghosts—K$^+$ gradient	Protein structure	2,800–3,000 and amide I and III	The intensity of 2,930 cm^{-1} feature increases; more α helices are formed	Mikkelsen et al. (1978)
Erythrocyte ghosts (human and rabbit)	Resonance Raman	1,530 and 1,160	Presence of β-carotene	Wallach and Verma (1975); Milanovich et al. (1976a); Verma et al. (1977)
Plasma membranes from normal hamster lymphocytes	Lipid transitions	2,800–3,000	7°C	
Plasma membranes from SV40 transformed lymphocytes	Protein transitions	2,800–3,000	37 to 43°C	Verma et al. (1977)
	Lipid transitions	2,800–3,000	0 to +5°C (−5°C midpoint)	
Sarcoplasmic reticulum membranes (lobster)	Protein transitions	2,800–3,000	22 to 40°C (broad)	Milanovich (1976b)
	Lipid composition	1,600–1,700	Highly unsaturated lipids	
	Resonance Raman	1,527–1,160	Presence of β-carotene or disordered coil	
Thymocyte plasma membranes	Protein structure	Amide I and III		Verma et al. (1975)
	Protein structure	Amide I, Amide III	Appreciable β-structure	

+Con A (5 µg/mg protein)	Protein transitions	2,800–3,000	35 to ~50°C	Verma et al. (1980b)
	Lipid transitions	2,800–3,000	22–25°C and (symmetric) +5 to −20°C	
	Lipid transitions	2,800–3,000	0 to 21°C (asymmetric broadening)	Verma et al. (1980b)
	Protein transitions	2,800–3,000	17 to 50°C	

8. *Other*

Isolated plasma membranes from Con A stimulated rabbit thymocytes	Protein amidation	1,600–1,700	Enhanced amidation (asparagine and glutamine)	Schmidt-Ullrich et al. (1976b)
DPPA + DMPC + lysozyme	Protein structure	Amide I Amide III	Marked increase in β-sheet parallels the trans to gauche transition of DPA and vice versa	Lippert et al. (1980)

Abbreviations: DMPC, DOPC, DPPC, DSPC, dimyristoyl-, dioleoyl-, dipalmitoyl-, distearoylphosphatidylcholine; DPPA, dipalmitoylphosphatidic acid; PE, phosphatidylethanolamine; PS, phosphatidylserine; (U) and (M), unilamellar and multilamellar liposomes; T_c, temperature of crystal $\rightleftharpoons$ liquid–crystal transition; Con A, concanavalin A; PLA, myelin proteolipid apopprotein; Diff. spectr. – difference spectroscopy.

4

Infrared spectroscopic studies of model and natural biomembranes

Ralph L. Amey and Dennis Chapman, Department of Biochemistry and Chemistry, Royal Free Hospital School of Medicine, University of London, Rowland Hill Street, London NW3 2PF, UK

INTRODUCTION

Infrared spectroscopy is a method of analysis, whose roots, in commercial instrumentation, go well back into the first half of this century. The percentage of papers cited in chemical abstracts which indicate use of infrared spectroscopy seems to be holding steady at a respectable 1 per cent (McDonald, 1980). Thus, it remains a vigorous field of activity.

One particular quality in its favour is its nondestructive — and equally important nonperturbing — applicability to all phases of virtually any substance. Spectra can be obtained relatively rapidly, frequently with little or no sample preparation, and both qualitative and quantitative results can be obtained. Both sensitive and specific, it requires little sample material (milligram to microgram quantities) and can respond to subtle changes in molecular environment.

The continued interest and use of infrared methods has been aided by the increased use of a complementary technique, Raman spectroscopy (see chapter 3). Also of import is the rapidly growing use of Fourier transform infrared (FT-IR) spectroscopy. Despite its high initial cost, FT-IR spectrometers are being used to solve problems which would have been intractable or impractical using the infrared methods of ten years ago. The remarkable developments in computer hard- and software have led to the possibility of "massaging" data digitally, and revealing fine details of information which previously were buried hopelessly under broad solvent peaks, or lay undetected at the far infrared end of the spectrum.

Although infrared spectroscopy has been used routinely for many years by biologists, chemists and their interdisciplinary colleagues, an ever increasing number now use it in far more creative and productive ways. Several earlier reviews have included biological applications (Chapman, 1965; Wallach, 1979; Fringeli, 1981). Our review includes coverage of FT-IR spectroscopy for the investigation of biomembrane systems. Recent texts covering the general topic of infrared spectroscopy include Bellamy's (1975) and Nakamishi's (1977) new editions. Continuing series include those edited by Clark (1982), Ferraro (1979) and Barrow (1979). Two texts devoted to interferometry and transform techniques in chemistry are by Chamberlain (1979) and Griffiths (1978).

TECHNICAL

Types of instrumentation

The two common types of commercial infrared spectrometers currently available are of the dispersive and interferometric types. By far the most frequently used is the dispersive type, where a source of infrared radiation passes through a sample, is dispersed into its frequencies by a monochrometer, and the relative intensities of individual frequencies measured by a detector are displayed on a stripchart recorder. Typical infrared sources are electrically heated proprietary solids made from sintered mixtures of rare earth oxides (Nernst glowers), silicon carbide (Globars), and selected refractory ceramics. A variable slit placed in front of the source is programmed to compensate for changes in source intensity throughout the scanning range (Kemp, 1975).

Although prism monochromators were once common dispersing devices in the infrared region, the superior high-frequency resolution of gratings, along with the lack of need for a constantly heated compartment to eliminate moisture condensation, has led to the virtual replacement of prisms by gratings. The signal is detected by a thermopile: the induced electrical current, proportional to the transmitted radiation intensity is displayed on the abscissa of a chart recorder, usually as a function of wavenumber (less frequently as a function of wavelength in microns).

The first microprocessor-controlled commercial dispersion infrared spectrometer was the Perkin-Elmer 283, introduced in 1975. Subsequent developments have led to the PE 680 series of double beam, ratio recording instruments with dual microprocessor electronics and single beam facility (Perkin-Elmer, 1980). Maximum abscissa range is $4,000 \text{ cm}^{-1}$ to 200 cm^{-1} with ± 0.4 to 0.2 cm^{-1} repeatability. The monochromator (containing two gratings, one of 100 and the other of 25 lines per millimetre) is synchronised with the recorder drive by the abscissa microprocessor for accurate reproduction of wavenumber settings. The source radiation is split in two, one beam passing through the sample, whilst the other serves as a reference. A rotating sector mirror in the photometer section converts the pair into a single pulsed beam as it enters the monochromator.

The eventual detector signal is applied via a preamplifier to an A/D converter. The resultant digital signal is applied to the ordinate microprocessor, converted back to an analogue form and applied to the recorder servo system. A uniform signal-to-noise response is maintained by programming the monochromator slit widths to vary in a manner which holds the detector output approximately constant. McDonald has noted (McDonald, 1980) that practically all functions of the spectrometer benefit by the use of a microprocessor, including maintenance troubleshooting.

Furthermore, the microprocessor-controlled spectrometer should be recognised as separate in function from the computer data processing unit, which is increasingly being offered as an integral part of a spectrometer "system". By means of such a system the digital data can be stored, retrieved and "massaged" without suffering loss of quality. One of the most valuable operations such a system can do is the selective and controlled subtraction of two or more spectra. This will be discussed in a following section.

As is evidenced by the number of published papers which have its name in their title, Fourier Transform Infrared (FT-IR) spectroscopy is becoming an increasingly popular method of analysis. Briefly stated (Green, 1978), an FT-IR spectrometer consists of two parts: (1) an interferometer-based optical system; and (2) a dedicated computer which controls the optical system and all aspects of data collection and analysis. Most currently available commercial FT-IR spectrometers use some form of the Michelson interferometer (Griffiths, 1980). Basically it consists of two plane mirrors at right angles to each other. One mirror is stationary, while the other can travel along a path perpendicular to its plane. A beamsplitter, consisting of a semi-reflecting film (germanium in mid-infrared, Mylar in far infrared), is situated between the two mirrors. A collimated beam of infrared radiation from a source passes to the beamsplitter where the beam is divided, part being transmitted to the movable mirror and part being reflected to the stationary mirror. Interference occurs when the return beams recombine at the beamsplitter. From there a portion of the beam passes through the sample and on to the detector. The travelling mirror yields a sinusoidal signal at the detector which is digitised by an A/D converter and computer-stored. The interferogram of this scan, or the sum of many such scans, is then converted, by means of a fast Fourier transform (FFT), into a conventional absorbance (or percent transmission) versus wavenumber spectrum.

Two of the three most popular commercial FT-IR spectrometers (Nicolet Instrument Corp and Digilab Inc.) have their fixed and moving mirrors mutually perpendicular. Bruker Instruments Inc., however, places both mirrors and the beamsplitter coplanarly along the path of the source beam. The two beams from the beamsplitter are collected, collimated and passed to each side of the moving mirror. In addition to doubling the potential travel distance over that of the conventional design, the Bruker interferometer reduces the number of moving parts somewhat and reduces the beamsplitter size considerably. Thus several beamsplitters can be fitted on a carousel wheel permitting one to scan several spectral regions without breaking purge or vacuum.

Perkin-Elmer recently entered the low-cost FT-IR market with the model 1500 FTIR spectrophotometer. Using a refractively scanned interferometer, Perkin-Elmer claims an order of magnitude less sensitivity to changes in mirror position and 3,000 times less sensitivity to angular deviations of the scanning mechanism than with a conventional interferometer. Pathlength scanning is accomplished by uniformly moving one of two matched wedges so that it effectively changes the thickness of a uniform layer of optically transparent material in one arm. For data processing, Perkin-Elmer uses its proven Model 3600 IR Data Station with an upgraded softward package. Although of lower resolution (2 cm^{-1}), more limited far infrared range ($4,400-450 \text{ cm}^{-1}$ at present), and less spectacular data processing capability than is offered by Bruker, Digilab or Nicolet, its specifications are quite adequate for most biological applications. Its lower price (approximately \$50,000) and promise of high reliability should make it an attractive choice for those laboratories on limited budgets.

The question of which is better, a dispersive spectrometer with microprocessor-coupled data station or a FT-IR spectrometer, is becoming increasingly difficult to answer in simple terms. However, some observations concerning their relative merits have been made and are valid to repeat here.

FT-IR spectrometry provides a higher S/N ratio for spectra obtained in conditions of equal measuring time or, alternatively, measurements of equal S/N ratio and resolution taken on instruments with equal optical throughput and efficiency with identical sources, will take less time on an FT-IR spectrometer. This is the multiplex or Fellgett's advantage and is the result of concurrent measurement of detector signals for all resolution elements of the spectrum (Green, 1978). McDonald notes that standard survey runs, including plotting, can require about the same length of time with both types of spectrometers (1980). However, for potentially long data acquisition times, FT-IR spectroscopy can offer a considerable advantage, as the S/N ratio increases only with the square root of the time.

FT-IR spectrometers offer higher frequency (abscissa) accuracy for spectra taken over a wide range of frequencies. This is a consequence of the use of laser referencing of measurements made by interferometry. Obviously, abscissa accuracy is essential when spectral subtractions are being performed but what accuracy demands are needed will vary with the nature of the bands in the subtracted spectra. Extremely sharp absorption bands will require greater abscissa accuracy.

The double-beam dispersive spectrometer usually demonstrates superior ordinate stability over that of the single beam FT-IR spectrometer. Although most biochemical applications at present are of a qualitative nature, it is not unreasonable to anticipate that quantitative measurements will be made in the near future. A dedicated computer is an obvious necessity with FT-IR spectroscopy, whereas the dispersion instrument user will find a mini-computer data processing system of tremendous help in data acquisition, processing and enhancement and spectral storage, retrieval and interpretation (McDonald, 1980).

Indeed, the serious investigator of aqueous systems will find the ancillary computer system a virtual necessity.

The computer acquisition of data gives the great advantage of obtaining and storing data digitally at the highest undegraded level of sensitivity. This obviates the need to rescan when some peaks are off scale or too small. It is also a simple matter to retrieve and display some portion of the spectrum in expanded form.

Computer enhancement provides a means of subtracting (or adding or dividing) one absorbance spectrum from another digitally. Such a technique allows the investigator to subtract a water or buffer spectrum from that of an aqueous membrane system, followed by ordinate expansion of 100× to observe small differences due to the nonaqueous membrane components. Both dispersive and FT-IR systems have been used to report analysis of biological systems in this manner (see application section).

A final comment should be made concerning prices. An FT-IR system currently costs approximately $50,000 to $100,000. Some companies are beginning to offer basic low-cost FT-IR spectrometers which compete in price with top-of-the-line dispersive spectrometers equipped with computer data systems.

Sampling techniques and cells

For those samples which permit it, the formation of a thin film on a suitably transparent and rigid substrate provides adequate concentration of sample components to give a satisfactory spectrum. Among the problems to anticipate are:

1. *Removal of "all" the solvent dispersant (usually water)*. Although freeze drying (in a dry atmosphere at $-20\,^\circ$C) has been recommended to dry the film (Wallach, 1979), considerable trial and error may be necessary before the desired level of dryness is achieved.

2. *Effect of drying on sample "structure"*. As all biological systems *in vivo* involve water to some degree, its total removal may result in conformational changes or other unanticipated modifications. Although of considerable interest themselves (see applications section), failure to account for such effects may lead to erroneous interpretations of the film spectrum.

3. *The extent of rehydration structure reversibility*. The rehydration of the sample film to any desired vapour pressure level is achieved easily through use of saturated salt solutions (Washburn, 1926). What is not so easily established is whether rehydration to the original water value of the sample also re-establishes the original micro/macro component structure within the sample. The fact that one or some of the sample's original properties are restored does not ensure that all of them will be.

The primary criterion for selection of a substrate for the film is that it be transparent in the optical region to be scanned. Silver chloride, silver bromide and calcium fluoride plates are all used in the mid-infrared region.

For randomly orientated samples, KBr discs can provide excellent spectra of solid dried and hydrated samples. If difference spectra are desired, however, compensating for the amount of water present may be difficult. Samples containing polymorphic materials may undergo phase transformations while grinding with KBr due to excessive pressure and localised heating. Thus, care should be taken during sample preparation (Kemp, 1975). Fuller and Griffiths have reported (1978) spectra obtained with a FT-IR spectrometer equipped with a HgCdTe detector and have applied the technique to several types of sample, including powders. This technique is reported to have extremely high sensitivity for measuring spectra of materials deposited from solution on KCl powder. Sample preparation is very fast, but data acquisition time is longer than for transmission spectra.

For measurements below 200 cm^{-1}, one can make satisfactory discs with petroleum wax (42 °C melting point) pellets. Approximately $1\frac{1}{2}$ pellets are combined with the sample in an agate mortar which has been preheated to about 60 °C (this would have to be adjusted for more heat-sensitive samples). A small spatula is used to blend the sample into the wax and form a round pellet. This is placed in the pellet press as usual and formed into a rather flexible disc, which can be mounted. It has been found useful to prepare a new die for the press having a slight bevel to its face. This tends to minimise "fringe effects" in the far infrared spectra.

Liquids and solutions can be measured using commercially available cells with appropriate windows (Table 4.1). In the mid-infrared region there is no clear-cut best choice for window material: CaF_2 has the least reflection loss but is expensive; KBr is the cheapest, has almost as low a reflection loss as CaF_2 but,

Table 4.1 Properties of infrared window materials

Material	Useful range (cm^{-1})	Reflection loss at 1,000 cm^{-1} (per cent)	Solubility (g per 100 ml H$_2$O at 20°C)	Relative cost
Sodium chloride (NaCl)	>4,000–625	7.5	40	1.0
Potassium bromide (KBr)	>4,000–400	8.5	70	1.3
Calcium fluoride (CaF$_2$)	>4,000–1,000	5.5	Almost insoluble	3.6
Irtran – 2 (polycrystalline ZnS)	>4,000–700	12	Insoluble	10
Silver chloride (AgCl)	>4,000–450	19.5	Insoluble	7
Silver bromide (AgBr)	>4,000–280	25	Almost insoluble	7
KRS – 5 (TlBr/TlI)	>4,000–250	28	0.1	10
High density PE	625–10	N/A	Insoluble	0.6

as with NaCl, it is soluble in water; AgCl and AgBr both have low water solubility but suffer from high cost and high reflection losses. High density polyethylene is the choice below 300 cm^{-1}.

Polarised infrared spectroscopy

The intensity of a band, that is, the energy absorbed by the oscillating group, is proportional to the square of the dipole moment change with respect to the normal coordinate of the vibration. It is also proportional to the cosine of the angle between the electric vector of the light wave and the direction of the dipole moment change. Thus, when linearly polarised light is used, the absorption is maximal when the plane of polarisation coincides with the direction of dipole moment change. In molecules of known structure, knowledge of the direction of the dipole moment change of the vibrations belonging to the different species has been used to confirm previously uncertain band assignments, for example in polyethylene and hydrocarbon work and with fatty acids and esters (for review see Fischmeister, 1975). In simple cases the dipole moment change can coincide with the bond direction, but often it does not. Studies have been made of model and natural biomembranes, for example purple membrane, using polarised infrared spectroscopy (see Application section).

Multiple attenuated total reflection (MATR)

Not all samples provide good transmission spectra. Some absorb strongly in the region of interest and are essentially opaque at all but impractically short pathlengths. Some pose the opposite problem of absorbing too little when they are cast as thin films. Finally, there are those samples for which molecular orientation is desired and the latter cannot be achieved conveniently in solution without the application of an orientating field.

For all of these problems, multiple attenuated total reflection (MATR) (alternatively known as multiple internal reflection (MIR)) can often provide a partial solution. With this method, a sample is placed in intimate contact with at least one of the parallel faces of a thin, optically transparent crystal of high refractive index (see Figure 4.1). The spectrometer source beam is focused and

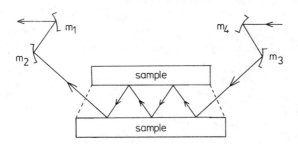

Figure 4.1   Optical diagram for Multiple Attenuated Total Reflection (MATR)

directed by suitable mirrors into one end of the crystal where it strikes the sample-crystal interface. As the refractive index of the sample is less than that of the crystal, total internal reflection occurs.

In fact, the light beam travels a few μm into the sample before returning to the crystal. If the sample absorbs energy at that wavelength, the beam will be attenuated rather than be totally reflected. Depending on the incident angle and the length of the crystal, anywhere from 6 to 35 reflections can be achieved before the beam reemerges from the crystal and is directed back into the spectrometer for detection. If the ratio of the two refractive indices changes, as will be the case in the region of a sample absorption band, then a change in the amount of energy reflected will occur and the resulting MATR spectrum will approximate a normal transmission spectrum. Because of the small amount of energy absorbed during any single reflection, many reflections are needed to produce a usable spectrum (Harrick, 1967).

Successful spectra require a crystal which is IR transparent and has a high refractive index (2.5-4.0). Commonly used materials are germanium (water insoluble, RI = 4.01, 3,300-400 cm^{-1}, very brittle), silver chloride (soluble in acids/NH_4Cl, sensitive to mechanical shock and cold forms, corrosive to metals, RI = 2.0, > 400 cm^{-1}), KRS-5 (soluble in bases, acid insoluble, not hygroscopic, RI = 2.38, > 260 cm^{-1}), zinc selenide (insoluble in water, organic solvents, dilute acid/base, RI = 2.4, > 500 cm^{-1}, higher transmission than KRS-5, non toxic).

Because the MATR unit increases the sample optical pathlength, it is advisable to place a blank MATR unit in the reference beam when using a double beam spectrometer to eliminate interference from atmospheric CO_2 and water vapour absorption. A variable attenuator in the reference beam will assist in obtaining a better energy balance but will not compensate for atmospheric CO_2/H_2O.

MATR has proven to be of considerable utility in the IR analysis of opaque slurries, pastes and films, as well as highly absorbing solutions and thin films. Measurement of the optical properties of thin layers can be made by the application of single and/or multilayers directly onto the MATR crystal. With the deposition of orientated layers (or bilayers), MATR provides a simple method for making IR polarisation measurements.

Most units permit the crystal to be mounted in several positions, with a different incident angle and number of internal reflections occurring in each position. This allows one to choose a position which optimises the resulting spectrum. Thus if an initial scan proves to be to weak, adjustment to a lower incident angle will increase the number of internal reflections and the extent of sample penetration, resulting in a stronger spectrum.

Isotopic substitution

According to equation 1 a change in mass by isotopic substitution will change the frequency of absorption of a given group. The force constants are not affected. The largest shifts are attained with deuterium, which has the greatest mass ratio between the two isotopes. The expected frequency change can be described by the ratio:

$$\frac{\upsilon}{\upsilon^i} = \sqrt{\frac{\mu^i}{\mu}} \cong \sqrt{2} = 1.41$$

where υ is the frequency of the hydrogen compound and υ^i that of the deuterium analogue; μ are the reduced masses. Band shifts on selective deuteration reveal vibrations where hydrogen is involved.

The medium to weak rocking–twisting progression bands, which are present in the spectra of methyl esters in the solid state, are also decoupled by the CD_2 group, as their positions coincide with those in the homologous hydrocarbon spectra. But these two-progression distributions react differently when the terminal methyl group is deuterated. The wagging band positions remain unchanged, while the rocking band positions are shifted as if the hydrocarbon chain had been shortened by one carbon atom. Thus the rocking–twisting of the chain involves the terminal methyl group, while the wagging mode does not. Schachtschneider and Snyder (1963) showed from a normal coordinate analysis of hydrocarbon spectra that the strong coupling of the CH_3 out-of-plane rocking mode with the rocking–twisting motions of the CH_2 groups makes it appropriate to consider the terminal CH_3 group as a continuation of the methylene chain with regard to rocking–twisting.

Perdeuteration of long-chain acids and esters has a strong effect on the spectra. The wagging progression bands disappear from their normal position at 1,380–1,170 cm^{-1}, leaving only the strong C–O stretching band at 1,285 cm^{-1}. No band progression is found in the region around 900 cm^{-1} where CD_2 wagging would be expected.

CHARACTERISTIC ABSORPTION FREQUENCIES AND SPECTRAL COMPILATIONS

Those infrared absorption frequencies which are characteristic of biological systems are tabulated in several references cited earlier (Chapman, 1965; Wallach, 1979; Fringeli, 1981). Table 4.2 lists some of the more frequently encountered absorption bands. Table 4.3 lists the so called amide group vibrations which are characteristic of polypeptides.

Although there is no compilation of spectra of biological materials at present, several general collections are available and may be of interest. The latest edition of the Hummel/Scholl *Atlas of Infrared Spectra of Polymers* (Hummel, 1978) contains about 1,900 high quality spectra of various polymers. *The Coblentz Society Desk Book of Infrared Spectra* (Craver, 1977) contains 860 high quality spectra selected from their collection of 11,000 spectra. It also contains information on sample preparation, spectrometer operation, spectral interpretation and a bibliography of other sources of spectra. *The Sadtler Handbook of Infrared Spectra* (Simons, 1978) contains 3,000 high quality grating spectra from their

Table 4.2 Group vibrations useful for biomembrane studies

Functional group	Description of vibration	Symbol	Wavenumber (cm^{-1}) (intensity)
C–CH$_3$	Antisym. stretching	ν_{as} (CH$_3$)	2,962 ± 10 (s)
	Sym. stretching	ν_s (CH$_3$)	2,872 ± 10 (s)
	Antisym. bending	δ_{as} (CH$_3$)	1,450 ± 20 (m)
	Sym. bending	δ_s (CH$_3$)	1,375 ± 5 (s)
(–CH$_2$–)$_n$	Antisym. stretching	ν_{as} (CH$_2$)	2,926 ± 10 (s)
	Sym. stretching	ν_s (CH$_2$)	2,853 ± 10 (s)
	CH$_2$-bending	δ (CH$_2$)	1,465 ± 20 (m)
			> 1,470
	CH$_2$-wagging and	γ_w (CH$_2$)	1,180–1,345
	CH$_2$-twisting	γ_t (CH$_2$)	
	CH$_2$-rocking	γ_r (CH$_2$)	720–~1,000 (m)
	C–C stretching	ν (C–C)	1,150 ± 50
			1,080 ± 50
$\overset{R}{\underset{H}{}}C=C\overset{R'}{\underset{H}{}}$	C=C-stretching	ν (C=C)	1,600–1,680 (v)
	CH antisym. stretching	ν_{as} (CH=CH)	~3,010 (m)
–CH$_2$–$\overset{\overset{O}{\parallel}}{C}$–O–R	CH$_2$-bending of α-methylene group	δ (α–CH$_2$)	~1,420 (w)
	C–O single bond stretching	ν (C–O)	1,160–1,190 (m)
	C=O double bond stretching	ν (C=O)	1,720–1,745 (s)
R–$\overset{\overset{O}{\parallel}}{C}$–OH	OH-stretching	ν (OH)	3,500–3,560 (m)
			2,500–2,700 (w)
	C=O double bond stretching	ν (C=O)	1,700–1,725 (s)
	OH-bending	δ (OH)	1,210–1,320 (s)

Structure	Assignment	Symbol	Frequency (cm⁻¹)
O=C−O R−C−O	Antisym. and sym. C=O double stretching	$v_{as}(COO^-)$	1,550–1,610 (s)
		$v_s(COO^-)$	1,300–1,420 (m)
R−OH	OH-stretching	$v(OH)$	3,590–3,650 (v)
			3,200–3,400 (v.s)
			3,450–3,570 (v)
	OH-bending	$\delta(OH)$	1,200–1,400 (m)
	CO-stretching	$v(CO)$	~1,050 (m, s)
			~1,100 (m, s)
			~1,150 (m, s)
R−NH₂	NH₂-stretching	$v_{as}(NH_2)$ and	3,000–3,500 (m)
	NH₂-bending	$v_s(NH_2)$	1,590–1,650 (m)
		$\delta(NH_2)$	
	C−N-stretching	$v(C-N)$	1,020–1,220 (m, w)
R−NH₃⁺	Antisym. NH₃⁺-stretching	$v_{as}(NH_3^+)$	~3,200 (m)
	Sym. NH₃⁺-stretching	$v_s(NH_3^+)$	~3,020 (m)
	Antisym. NH₃⁺-bending	$\delta_{as}(NH_3^+)$	1,570–1,620 (w, m)
	Sym. NH₃⁺-bending	$\delta_s(NH_3^+)$	~1,520 (s)
	C−N-stretching	$(C-N)$	~1,090 (w)
	Combination of sym. NH₃⁺-bending and CCN-bending	$\delta_s(NH_3^+) + \delta(CCN)$	~2,050 (w)
R \ NH / R	NH-stretching	$v(NH)$	3,300–3,500 (m)
	NH-bending	$\delta(NH)$	1,520–1,650 (w)
	Antisym. (N)−CH₃-bending	$\delta_{as}(CH_3)$	1,470–1,510 (m)
	Antisym. CNC-stretching	$v_{as}(CNC)$	1,020–1,040 (m)
	Sym. CNC-stretching	$v_s(CNC)$	920–990 (m)
R' − N with R, R''	Antisym. (N)−CH₃-bending	$\delta_{as}(CH_3)$	1,470–1,510 (m)
	Antisym. CN-stretching	$v_{as}(CN)$	940–1,040 (m)
	Sym. CN-stretching	$v_s(CN)$	800–900

Table 4.2 cont.

Functional group	Description of vibration	Symbol	Wavenumber (cm^{-1}) (intensity)
Amino acids	C–C–N band or COO$^-$ rock		500–560
$-N(CH_3)_3^+$	Antisym. CH$_3$-stretching	ν_{as} (CH$_3$)	3,020–3,030 (w, m)
	Antisym. CH$_3$-bending	$\delta_{as}^{A_1}$	1,480–1,490 (m)
	Antisym. CH$_3$-bending	δ_{as}^{E}	1,470–1,480 (m)
	Sym. CD$_3$-bending	$\delta_{s}^{A_1}$	965–980 (w, m)
	Sym. CH$_3$-bending	$\delta_{s}^{A_1}$	1,395–1,405 (m)
	Antisym. N–(CH$_3$)$_3^+$-stretching	δ_{as} (N–CH$_3$)	950–970 (m)
	Sym. C–N–(CH$_3$)$_3^+$-stretching	ν_s (N–CH$_3$)	920–930 (w, m)
			875–895 (w, m)
Totally sym. C–N-stretching	trans d$_o$-isotope		750–770 (vw)
	trans d$_q$-isotope		695–715 (vw)
	gauche d$_o$-isotope		710–720 (vw)
	gauche d$_q$-isotope		665–685 (vw)
$\begin{array}{c}O\\\parallel\\R-O-P-O-R\\\mid\\O-\end{array}$	Antisym. PO$_2^-$-double bond stretching	ν_{as} (PO$_2^-$)	1,220–1,260 (s)
(R–O)$_3$–P	Sym. PO$_2^-$-double bond stretching	ν_s (PO$_2^-$)	1,085–1,110 (m)
	Antisym. PO single bond stretching	ν_{as} (P(OR)$_2$)	815–825 (m, s)
			510–580
			300–400
			550–560
(R–O)$_2$–P=O, H			500–560
(R–O)$_2$–P=O, R			500–550
			465–480

		v_s (P(OR)$_2$) v (C–O)
		465–495
	Sym. PO single bond stretching	755–765 (m, s)
	C–O stretching	1,040–1,090 (m, s)

O
‖
—C–CH–NH—
  |
  R
	N–C=O band	570–635

	C–C=O band	430–480
	Amide group vibrations	*see table 4.3*
Inorganic	SO$_4^{2-}$	580–670
Skeletal	Epoxy ring derived from internal R–C=C–R (*trans*)	893
	Epoxy ring derived from internal R–C=C–R (*cis*)	833
	Hydroperoxide	833
	Ethyl	725
	CH$_3$ rocking on long carbon chain	772
	R–C≡C–H	770
	C–C–H band, out of plane	335–355
	R–CH$_2$–C≡N band	965–972
	–NO$_2$ band, sym.	350–390
		600–650
Unsaturated	1-alkyne≡C–H band	685–575
	Normal R–CH=CH$_2$ twist	635
	(C$_4$–C$_{16}$)	525
	Normal *cis* R–CH=CH–CH$_3$	570–587
		465–490
	Normal *trans* R–CH=CH–CH$_3$	385–420

	Branched R–CH–CH$_2$–CH=CH$_2$
	        |
	        R
		290–325

		615–625

	Branched R–C=CH$_2$
	        |
	        R
		530–555

Table 4.3   Amide group vibrations (Fraser and MacRae, 1973)

Designation	Approximate frequency (cm^{-1})	Description
Amide A B	3,300 3,100	Result of Fermi resonance between the first excited state of the N–H stretching mode and the second excited state of the amide II vibration.
Amide I II III IV	1,650 1,550 1,300 625	In-plane modes; the potential energy distributions are such that none is capable of simple description although amide I approximates a C=O stretching mode.
Amide V VI VII	650 550 200	Out-of-plane modes; amide V involves an N–H bending motion, amide VI a C=O bending motion, and amide VII a torsional motion about the C–N bond.
	4,600 4,860 4,970	Combination of amide A and amide III. Combination of amide A and amide II. Combination of amide A and amide I.

collection of 59,000 spectra with sections on spectral interpretation and a name index. *The Infrared Handbook* (Wolfe, 1978) thoroughly covers topics such as detectors, sources, optical materials and scattering. A somewhat older but massive collection is the *Atlas of Spectral Data and Physical Constants for Organic Compounds* (Grasselli, 1975). The second edition of the *Aldrich Library of Infrared Spectra* (Pouchent, 1975) is an excellent collection of 11,000 spectra organised conveniently according to chemical class and includes 150 polymers. Reference spectra are essential to the serious infrared user. Seldom is one able to assign a structure exclusively from its infrared spectrum without use of the spectrum of some reference material. IUPAC has published their *Tables of Wavenumbers for the Calibration of Infrared Spectrometers* (Cole, 1977). *Chemical Abstracts Services* offers through its CA Selects (CAS) two abstract journals related to infrared spectroscopy. These are based on computer searches of the *Chemical Abstracts Services* Information Base and contain the complete abstracts. Note also that the subject indices of *Chemical Abstracts* contain a heading, "infrared spectra", which lists compounds and classes of compounds whose spectra are found in published papers.

Finally, one might well ask when libraries of digitised spectra will become available for direct visual comparison with laboratory-run spectra. This complex problem has not yet been solved satisfactorily and several aspects of it have been discussed by McDonald (1980; 1978; 1976).

Liquid water and its absorption bands

Liquid water has very strong and broad absorption bands which overlap a considerable part of the infrared spectral range (see Table 4.4). The low transmittance of even thin water layers is the principal reason why most infrared investigations of biological materials have been performed with dry samples.

Table 4.4 Infrared vibrational spectra of H_2O and D_2O*

Vibration	H_2O	D_2O
O–X stretching (v_s)	Very broad band with two main maxima and a shoulder (sh) at 25°C	
	$v = 3,920$ sh	$v = 2,900$ sh
	$\epsilon = 0.83$	$\epsilon = 0.60$
	$v = 3,490$	$v = 2,540$
	$\epsilon = 62.7$	$\epsilon = 59.8$
	$v = 3,280$	$v = 2,450$
	$\epsilon = 54.5$	$\epsilon = 55.2$
Association (v_A)	$v = 2,125$	$v = 1,555$
	$\epsilon = 3.23$	$\epsilon = 1.74$
X–O–X' bending (v_2)	$v = 1,645$	$v = 1,215$
	$\epsilon = 20.8$	$\epsilon = 16.1$
Libration (v_L)	Broad band between 300 cm^{-1} and 900 cm^{-1}	
Hindered translation (v_T)	Prominent shoulder on v_L band at 190 cm^{-1}; 30°C	

*Wallach and Winzler, 1974
v, frequency of band maximum in cm^{-1}; ϵ, extinction coefficient $\times 10^{-3}$ cm^2 mol^{-1} at absorption maximum.

INFRARED ABSORPTION OF NORMAL LONG-CHAIN COMPOUNDS

Vibrations of methylene groups

The vibrations of a methylene group in the chain are shown in Figure 4.2. The asymmetrical and symmetrical stretching and the deformation vibration are the three modes due to the isolated methylene groups. (In a group containing n atoms, there are $3n - 6$ vibrations.) When the methylene group forms part of a chain, rotational motions, called wagging, twisting and rocking, occur in relation to the chain. Some of these vibrations absorb at the same frequency for all methylene groups in the chain, while others have different frequencies for each methylene according to the phase differences of neighbouring oscillators. A measurable phase difference of neighbouring oscillators occurs when the vibration of one methylene group disturbs the vibration of the next methylene group.

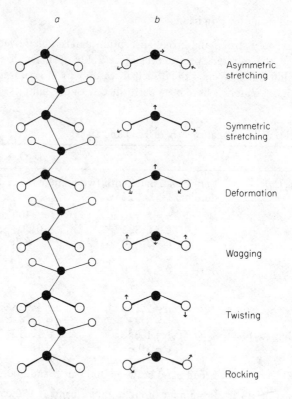

Figure 4.2 *a*, Section of a polymethylene chain; *b*, vibrations of the methylene groups, in the chain (Fischmeister, 1975)

The characteristic frequency of a vibrator (assuming linear elastic interaction according to Hooke's law) is given by:

$$v = \frac{1}{2\pi c}\sqrt{k\left(\frac{1}{m_1} + \frac{1}{m_2}\right)} = \frac{1}{2\pi c}\sqrt{\frac{k}{\mu}} \tag{1}$$

It is proportional to the strength of the spring (force constant k of the bond in dynes per centimetre) and reciprocally proportional to both masses in grams (v is the wavenumber of frequency $1/\lambda$ in cm^{-1}, c is the velocity of light and μ is the reduced mass).

Coupling effects appear when two vibrators are joined by a common atom or a common bond, provided their individual frequencies are not too dissimilar and the vibrations belong to the same symmetry species. For example, the C–H stretching mode at 3,000 cm^{-1} and the C–C stretching mode at 1,000 cm^{-1} do not influence each other, but the two C–H bonds in the methylene group do. Their asymmetric stretching mode absorbs at 2,920 cm^{-1}; their symmetric mode at 2,850 cm^{-1}.

Bending modes behave similarly. Strong coupling between equivalent modes occurs when both motions have one bond in common. If no common bond is involved, only weak coupling occurs and neighbouring groups absorb at similar frequencies. This is the case for the CH_2 deformation mode where the two C–H bonds bend against each other without the need for a compensating motion by the carbon atom. In this case (Figure 4.3) the next CH_2 group is hardly affected.

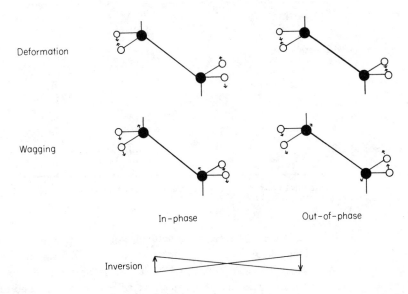

Figure 4.3 In-phase and out-of-phase methylene deformation and wagging modes in the chain (Snyder, 1960)

If, however, the C–H bending has to be compensated by a deformation of the C–C bond angle, the next CH_2 group is "disturbed" by the first one and strong coupling results. This is the case for the wagging, twisting and rocking vibrations. Coupled vibrations can be "in-phase" or "out-of-phase". Snyder (1960) discusses this in terms of the symmetry property of the motion of two oscillators with respect to an inversion through the midpoint of the C–C bond. Out-of-phase implies that they can be brought to coincide by inversion.

An example where in-phase and out-of-phase vibrations of the methylene groups determine the spectrum is polyethylene. In the crystalline state the chains assume a planar conformation with the chain planes perpendicular to each other. The unit cell contains two chains each with two methylene groups. In the crystal only unit cells moving in phase can absorb in the infrared and Raman spectrum. The normal modes of polyethylene have been derived (Tobin, 1955) regarding the molecule as a one-dimensional crystal. Table 4.5 gives the normal modes, phase conventions, frequencies and symmetry species for an isolated molecule.

Table 4.5 Description of normal modes of polyethylene, their phase conventions, frequencies and symmetry species between 1,500 and 700 cm^{-1}

Description of modes	Polyethylene		
	Phase difference ϕ (rad)	v (cm^{-1})	Symmetry species*
Methylene rocking-twisting	0	722	B_{2u}
	π	1,063	A_u
Methylene twisting-rocking	0	1,295	B_{3g}
	π	1,174	B_{1g}
Methylene wagging	0	1,170	B_{1u}
	π	1,415	B_{2g}
C–C stretching	0	1,133	A_g
	π	1,065	B_{2g}
Methylene bending	0	1,440	A_g
	π	1,475	B_{3u}

*Species A_u and B_u are infrared active; species A_g and B_g are Raman active.

When intermolecular effects between the two chains in the crystal are taken into account, each single-chain mode is found to split into two components. This "crystal field splitting" is about 10 cm^{-1}. It can be observed at room temperature for the rocking band at 730 and 720 cm^{-1} and for the band of the deformation mode at 1,473 and 1,463 cm^{-1}. Raman studies at low temperature (Boerio and Koenig, 1970) show that both components of all Raman-active fundamentals are resolved at −160°C (for polyethylene and hydrocarbons).

Ranges of 340, 120 and 200 cm^{-1} are covered by rocking-twisting, twisting-rocking and wagging, respectively. There is a mixing of rocking and twisting so that the in-phase mode at 720 cm^{-1} is pure rocking, whereas the out-of-phase mode at 1,063 cm^{-1} is twisting. The in-phase mode at 1,295 cm^{-1} is pure twisting, whereas the out-of-phase mode at 1,174 cm^{-1} is rocking. C–C stretching absorbs with its in- and out-of-phase modes at 1,133 and 1,065 cm^{-1}, extending to about 880 cm^{-1} in the hydrocarbon spectra. This frequency-phase curve has a minimum, whereas the others are monotonic functions.

These limiting frequencies for in-phase and out-of-phase vibrations have been established not only by investigations on polyethylene, but also of solid homologous hydrocarbons.

Vibrational spectra of hydrocarbons

A number of investigations have contributed to the understanding of the vibrational spectra of hydrocarbon-type chain molecules (see Fischmeister, 1975). The distributions of the methylene wagging, twisting, rocking and C–C stretch-

ing frequencies in the spectra of the homologous hydrocarbons were first established by the systematic analysis based on the symmetry properties and selection
rules of the crystalline compounds by Brown *et al.* (1950, 1954) and by
Tschamler (1954). In Figure 4.4 a schematic representation of the vibrational
spectra of the homologous *n*-paraffins is shown, divided into regions characteristic of the various CH_2 and skeletal vibrations.

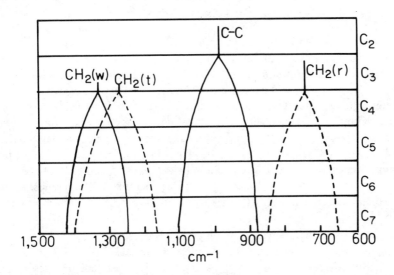

Figure 4.4 A schematic representation of the vibrational spectra of the *n*-paraffins divided
into regions characteristic for the various CH_2 and skeletal vibrations. CH_2 (t) = CH_2 twisting; CH_2 (w) = CH_2 wagging; CH_2 (r) = = CH_2 rocking; C–C = skeletal stretching. (From
Fischmeister, 1975)

In the spectra of the homologous hydrocarbons the various distributions
branch out from the frequency values in the propane spectrum and diverge to
the limiting frequencies in the polyethylene spectrum. In the analyses carried
out, good agreement was found between expected and observed distributions.

The intensities of the vibrational spectra of chain molecules were investigated
by Primas and Gunthard (1955) who derived a theory for their calculation, and
by Theimer (1957) who calculated the Raman and infrared intensities in the
spectra of hydrocarbons.

By normal coordinate calculations the frequencies for the permissible vibrations in homologous hydrocarbons have been estimated, together with the
potential energy distribution among the various types of modes. An extended
normal coordinate analysis of the homologous hydrocarbon spectra was performed by Schachtschneider and Snyder (1963) in which the hybrid character
of twisting and rocking vibrations was shown.

Vibrational spectra of long-chain compounds with polar end groups (Fischmeister, 1975)

Band progression

The distributions of the vibrational frequencies of the methylene chain were established in detail for the hydrocarbon spectra, after they were initially observed and described for spectra of long-chain fatty acids and esters and dicarboxylic esters and keto esters. The band progression is especially prominent because the methylene wagging absorption is found to be enhanced in the presence of polar end groups. As early as 1952, Jones demonstrated the dependence of the progression bands on the chain length, end groups and substituents in the chain (Primas and Gunthard, 1953). The frequencies of the progression have been calculated by a normal coordinate analysis.

Metal salts of saturated and unsaturated long-chain fatty acids have been studied (Kirby *et al.*, 1965) with the aim of determining the chain length from the band progressions. For the saturated salts, both wagging and rocking progressions indicated the length of the whole chain. In unsaturated compounds, the wagging progression revealed the position of the double bond both for *cis* and *trans* unsaturation, and so did the rocking progression in *cis* compounds. In the *trans* compounds, remarkably, the rocking progression indicated the whole chain length.

The progression bands were not only found valuable for identification of homologues, but also for distinguishing different crystal forms of fatty acids. The intensity of the wagging progression bands is dependent on the crystal structure. Nujol spectra of the A′, B′ and C′ forms of two odd-numbered acids (chain length C_{15}, C_{17}), and of the A, B and C forms of one even-numbered acid (C_{16}) have been published (Von Sydow, 1955). The spectral features of the different crystal forms were studied using polarised spectra and variable temperature techniques (Susi, 1959; Susi and Smith, 1960; Chapman, 1962).

Chapman (1955–1958) settled by solid state infrared spectroscopy the controversy concerning the correlation of melting points of the polymorphous mono-, di-, and triglycerides with structural models derived from X-ray powder data. The intensity of wagging bands and the single or double appearance of the 720 cm^{-1} rocking band were found to be valuable criteria for the crystal forms. Meiklejohn's rule of band counting was used for chain length determination.

A systematic infrared spectroscopic study of the mono-acid triglycerides of the homologous fatty acids C_2–C_{22} in solid state at $-180°C$ (and as liquids) for the different polymorphic forms was performed (De Ruig, 1971). The wagging, rocking-twisting, and C–C stretching chain absorptions were coordinated with the well-established distributions of vibrational modes in hydrocarbon spectra.

Polymorphism. Among the long-chain molecules, polymorphism occurs quite frequently. Different crystal forms of one solid compound are usually stable in different temperature ranges, but there are also cases where two forms crystallise simultaneously from a solution. Each crystal form usually has its own spectrum, which means that a polymorphic substance can have as many spectra as it has crystal forms. When such substances are investigated it is necessary to state the crystal form of the sample, or otherwise describe thoroughly the solvent and temperature of crystallisation.

The structural differences can concern the chain packing. The different packing modes are quite well known from X-ray crystallographic work and their correlation with spectral features is so well established that it is frequently used to indicate chain packing for substances of unknown structure. Structural differences can also concern the polar group, which can be arranged in several orientations to give good packing. Such structural differences seem to be quite widespread, but too few structural details are available for correlation with the absorption spectra.

In hydrocarbon crystals the methylene chains are arranged either with their planes parallel (as in the hexagonal and triclinic crystal forms), or alternatively rotated by about 90°, as in the orthrhombic form designated $O \perp$ (Figure 4.5). There also exists a less common orthorhombic unit cell with parallel chain planes $O \parallel$. Crystals with all chain planes parallel show single rocking (720 cm^{-1}) and bending bands. The perpendicular chain plane arrangement produces splitting of these bands into two components. At room temperature, splitting of these two bands only is observed, whereas at $-180°C$ all bands of the rocking progression are split, as shown by low-temperature investigation of hydrocarbons. With the perpendicular arrangement of chains, the nearest contacts between methylene hydrogen atoms are 2.7–2.9 Å. Other contacts are all greater than 3.7 Å. This doubling is thus indicative of the alternative chain plane arrangement in the common orthorhombic chain packing of crystals.

In studies of the polymorphic forms of glycerides Chapman and coworkers (1955–1958) used the single or double appearance of the band at 720 cm^{-1} to infer the chain packing.

The polymorphism of long chain alcohols has been related to the rotational isomerism of the alcoholic hydroxyl group (Tasumi *et al.*, 1964). In both crystal forms, β and γ, the chain packing is orthorhombic, but in β (Figure 4.6*a*), alternation of molecules occurs with the hydroxyl group in an in-plane *trans* conformation and with an out-of-plane *gauche* conformation giving a certain type of hydrogen bond connection. In the γ form only *trans* hydroxyl orientation occurs, leading to a different hydrogen bond system (Figure 4.7*a*).

The spectra of the γ crystals show a regular, simple band progression between 1,380 and 1,150 cm^{-1}, and weak bands in the region 950–850 cm^{-1} (Figure 4.7*b*). The spectrum of the β-form crystals (Figure 4.6*b*) however, has a complex absorption between 1,380 and 1,150 cm^{-1} and strong bands between 950 and 850 cm^{-1}.

These features can be associated with the different orientations of the hydroxyl group. The C–OH stretching mode vibrates within the skeletal plane in the

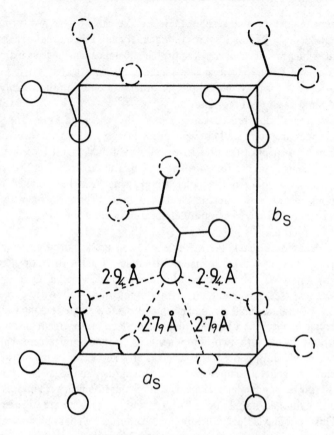

Figure 4.5 Schematic representation of the orthorhombic subcell O ⊥ of paraffins. Solid circles represent hydrogens in the *i*th plane, dashed circles hydrogens in the (*i* + 1)th plane (Fischmeister, 1975)

trans form, and out of it in the *gauche* form. The in-plane stretching mode is assumed to couple with the in-plane methylene wagging modes, intensifying these bands to make them appear as a regular progression in the γ-form crystals. In the *gauche* or out-of-plane orientation, the C—OH stretching is likely to couple with the out-of-plane twisting-rocking-progression between 1,295 and 1,174 cm^{-1}, enhancing the intensity of these bands. Their superposition with the wagging progression of the *trans* molecules results in the complex absorption between 1,380 and 1,150 cm^{-1} in the β-form. Also the rocking-twisting bands between 950 and 850 cm^{-1} are able to couple in the *gauche* molecules and are found to be intense in the β-form spectra. Thus the spectral differences can be understood on the basis of the symmetry properties of the C—OH bond in the two rotational isomeric conformations *trans* and *gauche* with respect to the skeletal plane.

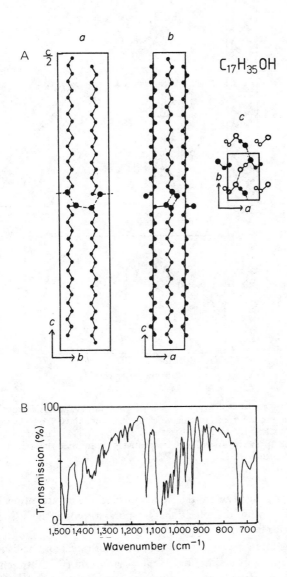

Figure 4.6 *A*, Molecular arrangement in the β-form crystal ($C_{17}H_{35}OH$) as viewed along the *a* axis (*a*), along the *b* axis (*b*) and along the molecular axis (*c*). Large circle represents the O atom. Filled and hollow circles in *c* represent the atoms belonging to the upper and lower layers, respectively. *B*, Infrared spectrum for the β-form of $C_{17}H_{35}OH$ (solid film). (Adapted from Fischmeister, 1975)

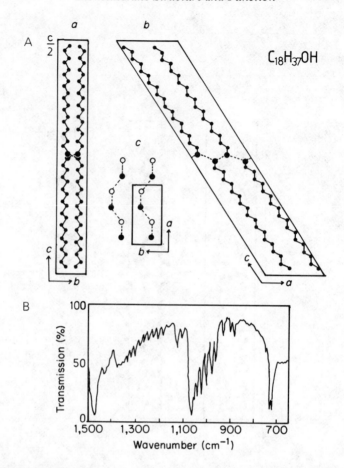

Figure 4.7 *A*, Molecular arrangement in the γ-form crystal ($C_{18}H_{37}OH$) as viewed along the *a* axis (*a*) and along the *b* axis (*b*). Large circle represents the O atom. In *c* the O atoms are projected perpendicularly to the *a–b* plane. Filled and hollow circles represent the atoms belonging to the upper and lower layers, respectively. *B*, Infrared spectrum for the γ-form of $C_{18}H_{37}OH$ (solid film) (Fischmeister, 1975)

It should be mentioned that polymorphic forms are often stabilised by impurities. To avoid complications by polymorphism the use of extremely pure compounds is recommended.

The strong intensity of the wagging bands in esters and acids is assumed to be due to coupling of a vibration of the polar group (C—O stretching) with the wagging motions, since both vibrations are symmetrical to the chain plane. In methyl stearate (Figure 4.8) very strong intensity of the wagging bands occurs, implying strong coupling despite a deviation of the ester group from the chain plane by 27°. In this case the deviation is gradual, taking the form of a successive twist over the first few bonds adjacent to the ester group. When the polar

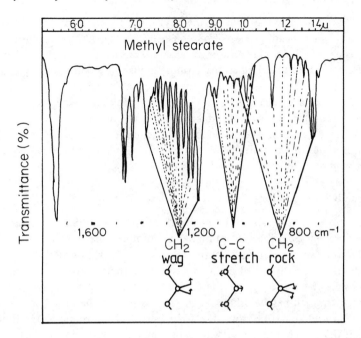

Figure 4.8 Spectrum of methyl stearate from 1,800 to 600 cm^{-1}. Bands are assigned to the different progressions (Fischmeister, 1975)

group deviates strongly from the chain the coupling is diminished, resulting in a weak progression with a strong C−O band. This occurs, for instance, in the 2- and 3-methyl substituted acids where the substituent continues the straight chain, while the carboxyl group sticks out sideways.

For the methylene bending (1,470 cm^{-1}) and rocking-twisting at 720 cm^{-1}, crystal field splitting is observed, in agreement with the orthorhombic packing (O⊥) of the chains.

PHASE TRANSITIONS OF LONG CHAIN MOLECULES USING INFRARED SPECTROSCOPY

Frequency shifts

The more commonly used IR parameters are the frequency ($\bar{v}$) and the half-bandwidths ($\Delta v_{1/2}$) of the individual vibrational modes. These parameters have the advantage of relating to specific phenomena at the molecular level and can be used to discriminate between different motions of the absorbing groups.

The frequency of a vibrational absorption is determined by the nature of both the vibrational mode and the vibrating group. The C−H and C−D stretching vibrations in acyl chains are decoupled from other vibrations occurring within the molecule; the bulk of the acyl groups are electronically decoupled from the polar head groups. Consequently, in the all-*trans* conformational state, each of these absorptions is observed at its characteristic frequency, regardless of the terminal functional groups, and is shifted only slightly as a result of interactions with molecules of a different class (for example, proteins). However, the effects of changes in conformation, specifically the introduction of *gauche* conformers, are large, producing shifts to higher frequencies. One can use these shifts to determine the introduction of *gauche* conformers or chain melting, the magnitudes of the shifts being related to the number of *gauche* bonds, (see Cameron *et al.*, 1980; Snyder *et al.*, 1982).

Half-bandwidth variations

In principle, a considerable amount of information regarding molecular motion can be obtained from the absorption band contour by means of moment analysis and the study of correlation functions (Bailey, 1974). This is difficult in the case of systems such as hydrated membranes because the spectrum of the particular species must be isolated from the curved background of the water absorption. However, the half-bandwidth is much less susceptible than the above methods to the introduction of errors due to imperfect background correction. The width of the band contour results from rotational, translational and/or collisional effects. Thus, the half-bandwidth monitors the freedom of motion of the absorbing group, that is, the amplitudes and rates of motion within its immediate environment. The half-bandwidths will, therefore, reflect the main thermal transition where a considerable change in this environment occurs. It is also sensitive to other changes which do not introduce *gauche* conformers, such as a decreased freedom of librational or torsional motion of the chains.

APPLICATIONS

Micelle formation with surfactants

Umemura *et al.* (1980) have used infrared spectroscopy (FT-IR) for the study of aqueous surfactant solutions to give useful information concerning micelle formation. They were able to show that with aqueous sodium *n*-hexanoate, spectral changes occurred consistent with progressive aggregation and sodium ion binding commencing at a concentration of 0.75 M. A second inflection point is observed at ~ 1.75 M and was interpreted as marking the transition to a homogeneous micellar solution. For example, marked changes occur in the gradient of the plots of the methyl and methylene frequencies and band widths with concentration.

Polypeptides and conformational changes

Numerical values of amide frequencies are summarised in review articles by Susi (1969), Fraser and MacRae (1973) and by Wallach and Winzler (1974). An example is that of poly-L-lysine.

pH-Induced conformation changes of poly-L-lysine

Poly-L-lysine assumes random coil conformation in aqueous solution of pH 9. Increase of pH to 11.9 induces a time-dependent conformational change to antiparallel β structure where the α-helical form appears as transient (Susi *et al.*, 1967). The corresponding time-dependent spectra measured in D₂O solutions are shown in Figure 4.9. This example demonstrates that, in favourable conditions, a clear distinction between β structure and α helix or random coil is

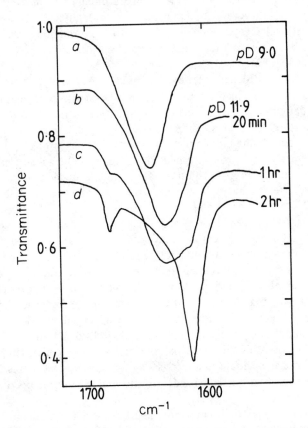

Figure 4.9 Rearrangement of poly-L-lysin in D₂O solution as reflected in the infrared transmission spectrum. Path length, 0.1 mm; concentration, 0.4 wt %; pure D₂O as reference; consecutive spectra displaced by 0.1 scale units (upper curve is on scale). *a*, Random conformation, pD 9.0; *b*, α helix, pD 11.9, 20 min; *c*, transition between α helix and antiparallel-chain β-conformation, pD 11.9, 1 hr; *d*, antiparallel-chain β-conformation, pD 11.9, 2 hr (Susi *et al.*, 1967)

possible. A distinction between corresponding amide I bands of α helix and random coil, respectively, becomes difficult. In the case of orientated fibrous proteins and polypeptides, however, a distinction appears possible by means of the applications of both polarised light and band shape analysis.

Further extensive use of line shape analysis has been made by Rüegg *et al.* (1975) in the infrared study of the amide I, II and III band regions of ribonuclease, lysozyme, chymotrypsin, myoglobin, α-casein, α-lacto-albumin, β-lactoglobulin A and β-lactoglobulin. The fraction of β structure determined in these proteins was found to be in good agreement with X-ray data.

Proteins

Detailed structure of protein conformation are obtained from X-ray diffraction of single crystals; however, globular proteins occur naturally in aqueous environment. Vibrational spectroscopy is sensitive to conformational changes in biopolymers and can be used to obtain structural information in both the solid and solution states. Infrared and Raman spectroscopy have been applied to the study of protein structure. Raman spectroscopy has been used to study globular proteins in the solid state and aqueous state, whilst infrared spectroscopy has been fundamental in determining the secondary conformation of fibrous proteins in their native solid state. Infrared spectrscopic studies of proteins in aqueous solutions have been severely limited in scope due to the overlapping strong H_2O absorption.

Most studies have been concerned with studies of the amide I and amide II bands with proteins in D_2O solution. The amide frequencies observed in D_2O solution are affected by hydrogen–deuterium exchange in D_2O solution with the peptide groups. Koenig and Tabb (1980) have studied the infrared absorption spectra of a number of globular proteins in H_2O solution in the frequency range from 2,000 to $800\,cm^{-1}$. The spectra were obtained with a Fourier transform infrared spectrophotometer and the contribution from the water absorption was digitally subtracted from the solution spectra.

The spectra of solid and solutions of haemoglobin, bovine serum albumin, ribonuclease, β-lactoglobulin and α-casein were also examined. The effect on the secondary structures of these globular proteins was studied.

Koenig and Tabb observed that for each individual protein the amide I frequency is essentially the same in solid and aqueous phases. In Figure 4.10 the spectra of haemoglobin in aqueous solution and as a cast film is shown. Susi *et al.* (1969) observed the same result with the amide I frequencies of myoglobin and β-lactoglobulin.

The amide I bands of haemoglobin and bovine serum albumin, both highly α-helical, occur at $1,656 \pm 1\ cm^{-1}$. The amide I frequency of α-helical myoglobin has previously been observed at $1,652\ cm^{-1}$ (Susi *et al.*, 1967). For β-lactoglobulin the amide I frequency is at $1,632\ cm^{-1}$, as was found by Susi *et al.* From polypeptide and fibrous protein studies (Susi, 1969; Krimm, 1962), this particular amide I frequency is indicative of the anti-parallel β-sheet con-

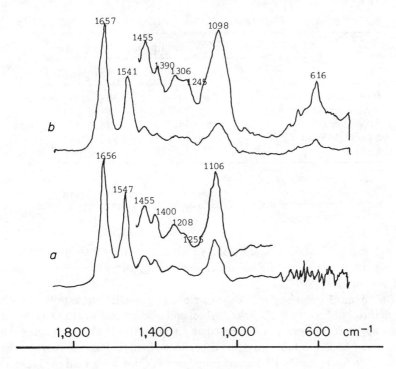

Figure 4.10 Infrared absorbance spectra of haemoglobin: a; Aqueous solution (pH = 4.8) cast films (Koenig and Tabb, 1980)

formation. The amide I band of β-lactoglobulin is highly asymmetrical. The skewness of this band towards higher frequencies is indicative of the high disordered content present in the protein. Ribonuclease in both solution and solid phases shows two amide I frequencies: 1,653 and 1,647 cm^{-1} in the solid and 1,656 and 1,646 cm^{-1} in solution. The stronger band is at 1,646 cm^{-1}, but this amide I value does not indicate a well-formed anti-parallel β-sheet structure in ribonuclease. Even though there is extensive extended chain structure present, X-ray diffraction results indicate that the β-structure is somewhat irregular. The 1,646 cm^{-1} band seems to indicate the presence of irregularly formed β sheet together with a disordered structure in ribonuclease (see Table 4.8).

It was noted that, whilst the amide I frequency does not essentially change upon dissolution for any of the globular proteins, there are changes in the amide I band contour upon dissolution. The bandwidths at half-height for the amide I bands for the five globular proteins are given in Table 4.6. The amide I band is sharper for the more ordered haemoglobin and bovine serum albumin. Even though the amide I frequencies do not change upon dissolution, the distribution of frequencies shifts to lower values. Such a shift for the amide I mode they observed is indicative of an increase in hydrogen bonding upon dissolution.

Table 4.6   Amide I bandwidths*

| Protein | Amide I bandwidth[†] at half-height (cm^{-1}) | |
	Film	Solution
Haemoglobin	45 (24/21)	38 (17/21)
Bovine serum albumin	50 (27/23)	41 (17/24)
Ribonuclease	66 (44/22)	58 (36/22)
β-Lactoglobulin	54 (44/10)	53 (39/14)
α-Casein	59 (31/28)	58 (27/31)

*Koenig and Tabb, 1980.
[†] For each protein the total bandwidth is given first. The values in parentheses are the contribution of the bandwidth from the high and low frequency sides of the bands, respectively.

Koenig and Tabb (1980) noted a sharpening in the amide I frequency for the proteins that have some α-helical structure (haemoglobin, bovine serum albumin and ribonuclease).

The amide II frequency of these five globular proteins does not permit a distinction to be made among α-helix, β-sheet and random-coil structure. However, frequency shifts of the amide II band upon dissolution in H_2O suggest changes in hydrogen bonding which may be dependent upon protein structure/order. Absorption in the amide III region, although weak, has been used to determine globular protein secondary structure (Belloco *et al.*, 1972; Koenig, 1972; Yu, 1972).

Koenig and Tabb (1980) concluded that the secondary structure of globular proteins can be distinguished by infrared spectroscopy by utilisation of a combination of amide I frequency and the comparative intensity in the amide III region (see Tables 4.7 and 4.8).

The amide I region of aqueous solutions of concanavalin A and human immunoglobulin G (IgG) have been investigated (Painter and Koenig, 1975). These workers demonstrated that the structure of immunoglobulins are predominantly β-sheet by the strong correlation of the amide I region of IgG and concanavalin A. The amide I regions of these proteins are shown in Figure 4.11.

Table 4.7   Determination of secondary structure in globular proteins by infrared spectroscopy*

| | Secondary structure | | |
	α helix	β sheet	Disordered
Amide I frequency (cm^{-1})	1652–56	1632	1655
Amide III intensity	weak	strong	strong

*Koenig and Tabb 1980.

Table 4.8 Infrared bands of globular proteins*

Haemoglobin Film	Haemoglobin Solution	Bovine serum albumin Film	Bovine serum albumin Solution	Ribonuclease Film	Ribonuclease Solution	β-Lactoglobulin Film	β-Lactoglobulin Solution	α-Casein Film	α-Casein Solution	Assignments
1,657 vs	1,656 vs	1,656 vs	1,655 vs	1,653 vs	1,656 vs	1,633 vs	1,632 vs	1,656 vs	1,655 vs	Amide I
				1,647 vs	1,646 vs					Amide I
1,541 s	1,547 s	1,540 s	1,548 s	1,538 s	1,548 s	1,538 s	1,551 s	1,538 s	1,551 s	Amide II
			1,517 sh	1,518 sh	1,520 sh	1,517 sh				
1,467 w	1,469 w									$\delta\,(CH_2)$, $\delta\,(CH_3)$
1,455 m	1,455 m	1,452 m	1,452 m	1,450 m	1,453 m	1,451 m	1,450 m	1,448 m	1,453 m	
1,390 m	1,400 m	1,390 m	1,401 m	1,394 m	1,405 m	1,398 m	1,401 m	1,399 m	1,402 m	$\nu_s\,(COO^-)$
1,367 w	1,367 w									
1,306 m	1,308 m	1,305 m	1,305 m	1,309 vw		1,313 w	1,315 w	1,312 w	1,319 w	$\nu_t\,(CH_2)$, $\nu_w\,(CH_2)$
			1,282 sh	1,260 sh	1,260 sh					Amide III
1,245 w	1,255 w	1,248 w	1,247 w	1,237 m	1,240 m	1,238 m	1,247 m	1,242 m	1,245	Amide III
1,170 w	1,170 w	1,172 w	1,173 w			1,168 w	1,165 w	1,158 w	1,162 w	
1,124 sh	1,130 sh									$\nu_t\,(NH_2)$, $\nu_t\,(NH_3^+)$, $\nu\,(C-N)$
1,098 ms	1,106 ms			1,089 ms	1,101 ms			1,101 m	1,098 m	
1,050 sh										
970 w								980 m	979 m	

* Frequencies in cm^{-1}.
s, strong; m, medium; w, weak; v, very; sh, shoulder.

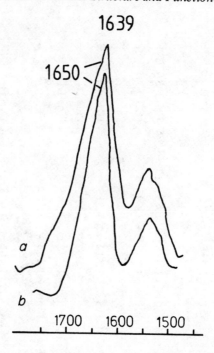

Figure 4.11 Amide I region of *a*, concanavalin A; and *b*, human IgG in aqueous solution after digital subtraction of water contribution (Painter and Koenig, 1975)

For both these spectra the absorbance contribution of water has been removed by digital subtraction.

Bare *et al.* (1975) made use of the sensitivity and increased signal-to-noise ratio obtainable with FT-IR in their study of the weakly absorbing sulphydryl groups of cysteine residues in the haemoglobins of various species. To attain maximum sensitivity in detecting these weak absorptions a liquid nitrogen cooled InSb detector was used. Infrared absorbance spectra of aqueous solutions of the carboxyhaemoglobins of man, pig and horse are shown in Figure 4.12. In each case the absorbance contribution due to water has been eliminated by digital subtraction. Assignments to specific cysteine residues was based on a comparison of human and animal carboxyhaemoglobins. In each case cow carboxyhaemoglobin, which possesses only the β-93 cysteines, was used as a reference for all three spectra so that no contribution from this S—H group would be observed. To eliminate these absorptions, the spectrum of cow haemoglobin was subtracted from each of the spectra. Horse and pig haemoglobins contain in addition α-104 cysteine, and their spectra in the S—H stretching region consisted of a single symmetrical absorption band of similar intensity and frequency to the lower frequency, higher intensity absorption band of human carboxyhaemoglobin. The band at $2,552 \text{ cm}^{-1}$ from human HbCO

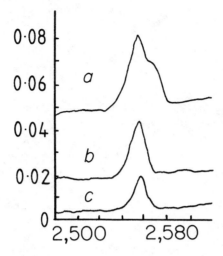

Figure 4.12 Infrared absorbance difference spectra of *a*, human (17 mM heme); *b*, pig (16 mM); and *c*, horse (11 mM) carboxyhaemoglobins (HbCO), each against cow carboxy-haemoglobin as reference. Absorbance spectrum of water was subtracted from each sample spectrum. The spectrum of cow haemoglobin was treated similarly and, after normalisation to the appropriate haemoglobin concentration, was subtracted from each of the human, pig and horse absorbance spectra. This produced absorbance spectra containing only the haemoglobin SH absorptions of interest (Bare *et al.*, 1975)

was assigned to α-104 (G11) cysteine. The shoulder at 2,556 cm^{-1} was assigned to the β-112 cysteine residue of human Hb. They suggest that these assignments provide a new molecular probe into a region of haemoglobin, that is, the α_1-β_1 interface, which previously has been relatively inaccessible.

In a study of the carbon monoxide binding site of haemocyanins (Alben and Fager, 1972), infrared spectra were recorded on the haemocyanin–carbon monoxide complexes of limulus squid, limpet, crab and crayfish and are shown in Figure 4.13. The results are summarised in Table 4.9. In this stuay the functional group of interest, CO, has an absorption at approximately 2,100 cm^{-1}, a region in which water also has a weak absorption. As these binding studies were undertaken in aqueous solution, it was imperative to compensate for this absorption to be able to discern the slight variations in the carbon monoxide stretching vibrations upon binding to the haemocyanins.

For each species only a single absorption band was observed due to v (CO), suggesting that only a single type of carbon monoxide molecular environment could be present in carboxyhaemocyanin for each of these species. The differences in v (CO) for the various carbon monoxide complexes with haemocyanin indicated different local molecular environments of the haemocyanin copper carbonyls. These shifts are apparently due to different sets of ligands coordinated to copper. The frequencies of the absorption maxima v (CO) for carboxy-haemocyanin showed good correlation with species type. It was surmised that

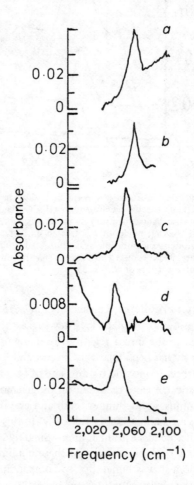

Figure 4.13 Infrared spectra of carbon monoxide ($^{12}C^{15}O$) coordinated to haemocyanins from several invertebrate species. Difference spectra were obtained by use of digitally stored single-beam spectra for reference, which were chosen to yield relatively flat base lines. Single-beam spectra were obtained by coherent coaddition of repetitively scanned interferograms, followed by a computed fast Fourier transform, as follows: a, squid (3,330 scans) vs water as reference; b, limpet (1,995 scans) vs water; c, limulus (4,000 scans) vs oxyhaemocyanin; d, crab (2,000 scans) vs methaemoglobin A; e, crayfish (3,315 scans) vs methaemoglobin A. All spectra were obtained at 2 cm^{-1} resolution. The proteins absorb very little here and only serve to decrease the effective concentration of water, which has strong, broad absorption bands. Mismatch in the amount of water in sample and reference cells is the major contributor to sloping base lines (Alben and Fager, 1972)

Table 4.9 Comparison in eight proteins of the position of IR absorption maximum in the amide I band and conformation contents by X-ray structural analysis*

Protein numeral	Protein	Position of absorption maximum† (cm^{-1})	Percentages of major conformations		
			α	β	ρ
1	Ribonuclease	1,639	12	36	52
2	Lysozyme	1,646	35	10	55
3	Methaemoglobin	1,650	71	0	29
4	Insulin	1,647	49	24	27
5	Concanavalin A	1,636	2	38	60
6	Cytochrome *c*	1,650	39	0	61
7	α-Chymotrypsin	1,637	8	22	70
8	Papain	1,645	21	5	74

*Proteins 1–6 were used as reference proteins for the calculation of IR basis spectra.
†Within experimental error the positions shown for proteins 1–3 and 7 were the same as those found by Timasheff *et al.* (1967), only for insulin they reported a somewhat different position $(1,654 \ cm^{-1})$

the electronic environment of CO bound to the haemocyanins of the two molluscs, squids and limpet must be different from that of limulus haemocyanin. The larger difference in $\upsilon(CO)$ for the two crustaceans, crab and crayfish, reflect an even larger difference in their CO environment compared to the other two species.

Eckert *et al.* (1977) have carried out calculations and examined the infrared spectra of various proteins (Figure 4.14). To derive estimates of their secondary structure, the absorption spectra between 1,720 and 1,594 cm^{-1} of proteins dissolved in D_2O were analysed. The spectra of the deuterated reference proteins partially reflect their different conformation composition. Table 4.9 shows that there are essentially two groups characterised: on the one hand, by absorption maxima between 1,650 and 1,646 cm^{-1} and relatively high contents of α helix (methaemoglobin, insulin, lysozyme and cytochrome) and, on the other hand, by absorption maxima between 1,639 and 1,636 cm^{-1} and relatively high contents of β-conformation (concanavalin A, ribonuclease). However, the absorption spectra of the proteins with relatively high contents of the ρ-conformation (cytochrome *c*, concanavalin A, lysozyme and ribonuclease) give no hint as to the position of their absorption maxima.

Table 4.10 shows the β-conformation percentages of the proteins as derived from X-ray structural analysis or calculated from IR spectra by the elaborated curve-fitting analysis. They concluded that the curve-fitting analysis of IR spectra

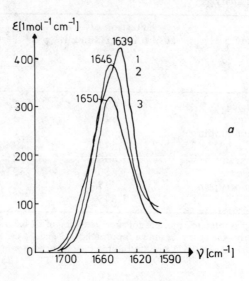

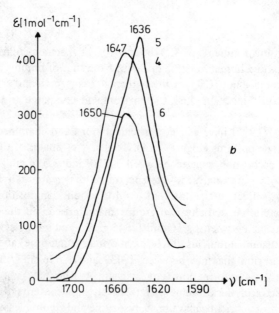

Figure 4.14 *a* and *b*, Infrared spectra of the deuterated reference proteins used for the calculation of the IR basis spectra. The numerals, identical with those used in Table 4.9, refer to (1) ribonuclease, (2) lysozyme, (3) methaemoglobin, (4) insulin, (5) concanavalin A, (6) cytochrome *c* (Eckert *et al.*, 1977)

Table 4.10 Comparison of β-conformation percentages of eight
proteins derived from X-ray structural analysis or
calculated from IR spectra by curve-fitting analysis

	Percentage of β-conformation			
Protein	From X-ray structural analysis			Calculated from IR spectra
Ribonuclease	38	44	36	26
Lysozyme	16	16	10	8
Methaemoglobin	0	0	0	0
Insulin	12	24	NA	35
Concanavalin A	NA	38	NA	38
Cytochrome *c*	0	0	NA	1
α-Chymotrypsin	NA	34	22	28
Papain	14	14	NA	17

NA, not available

may be suitable for the rough estimate of the β-conformation percentage of proteins. For a given protein, the results of this procedure were reproducible, the standard deviations on the average being ± 5.4.

Phospholipids

Chapman and coworkers (1966; 1967) studied the spectra of films of pure phospholipids, including phosphatidylcholine and phosphatidylethanolamine. This allowed identification of the primary CH-stretching and bending modes, the carbonyl absorption, the OH-stretching and bending bands in hydrated samples and the complex phosphate vibrations. These results showed that the phospholipid spectra, particularly below $1,400 \text{ cm}^{-1}$, were extremely variable, changing markedly with temperature and method of sample preparation. Spectra of cold or anhydrous films exhibited considerable fine structure which vanished on reaching a certain transition temperature. This was good evidence to show the nature of the main endothermic phase transition that occurs with phospholipid molecules. The melting of the chains of the lipid molecules (many tens of degrees below the capillary melting point) causes the resultant vibrational bands to be smeared out and devoid of fine structure (see Figure 4.15).

Wallach and coworkers (1978) studied multibilayer films of phosphatidylcholine, phosphatidylethanolamine and mixed films of phosphatidylcholine/phosphatidylethanolamine (1 : 1, mol/mol) as a function of fatty acid composition, temperature and hydration in order to clarify band assignments and examine the head group interactions among the different phosphatides. They compared spectra in the range $700–850 \text{ cm}^{-1}$ and $1,200–3,600 \text{ cm}^{-1}$ of dipalmitoyl phosphatidylcholine (anhydrous and monohydrate) and anhydrous

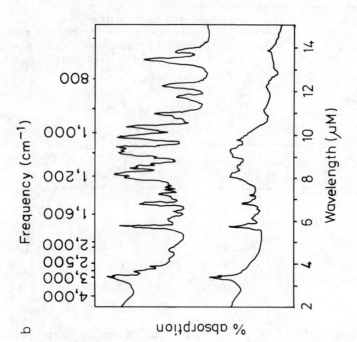

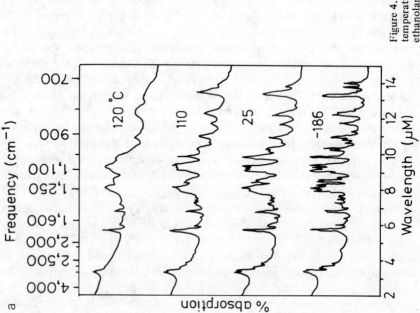

Figure 4.15 *a*, Infrared spectra of 2,3-dilauroyl-DL-phosphatidylethanolamine at different temperatures. *b*, Infrared spectra of (top) dielaidoyl- and (bottom) dioleoylphosphatidyl-ethanolamine at room temperature (Chapman *et al.*, 1966)

dipalmitoyl phosphatidylethanolamine (evaporated from both chloroform and chloroform/methanol, $2:1$, v/v) to show the principal difference between the various systems. Table 4.11 lists the corresponding band frequencies.

Infrared dichroic measurements on dipalmitoyl phosphatidylethanolamine multilayers

More specific conformational details of phosphatide multibilayers have been deduced by Akutsu et al. (1975), who used polarisation techniques to obtain the direction for selected transition moments in built-up films of dipalmitoyl phosphatidylethanolamine. These workers evaluated dichroic ratios for six vibrational modes: CH_2 symmetric and asymmetric stretching, CH_2 scissoring, $C=O$ stretching, PO_2^- asymmetric stretching and $C-C-N^+$ asymmetric stretching. In all cases, no dichroism in the x–y plane could be observed for incident radiation in the z-direction, normal to the multilayer plane. This indicates that the molecules distribute randomly about the z axis. When the film plane was rotated about the x axis by $\alpha_0 = 30°$ (independent measurements were made at $\alpha_0 = 45°$ to check for consistency of the method) dichroism in the x'-y' plane appeared. From the measured dichroic ratios, the authors calculated the transition vector orientations. They found that the moments of $C=O$ stretching, and the PO_2^- and $C-C-N^+$ asymmetric stretching modes orientate nearly parallel to each other and deviate by less than $20°$ from the film plane. They also found that the hydrocarbon chain axes are tilted at about $75°$ to the film plane. These results demonstrate that the phosphatidylethanolamine film is very tightly packed with the hydrogen-bonded polar moiety aligned along the film surface.

Fringeli and Gunthard (1981) have discussed the infrared vibrations and bands associated with the structure of polar head groups and phospholipids. The infrared spectra of simple model compounds were compared with phospholipid or polypeptide spectra. Edsall (1937) reported Raman spectra of $N(CH_3)_4^+$ ions in aqueous solution: a single Raman line was observed at 955 cm^{-1}, which was assigned to threefold degenerate (F_2-type) $C-N$ stretching vibrations due to the tetrahedral symmetry (T_d) of the ion in aqueous solution. This band should split into three absorption bands when the symmetry is decreased to C_s or lower.

Three bands are observed in the case of crystalline $N(CH_3)_4Cl$. The space-group D_{4h}^7, as determined by Wyckoff (1966), results in a site symmetry of C_2 or C_s, leading to the threefold splitting of the F_2-type vibration of the unperturbed $N(CH_3)_4^+$ group. The bands are observed at 915 cm^{-1}, 945 cm^{-1} and 955 cm^{-1}. Corresponding triplets exist in the spectra of $CH_3-(CH_2)_{14}-N(CH_3)_3Cl$, choline, acetylcholine, phosphoryl choline and lecithin, respectively. However, the band situated at $\sim 920 \text{ cm}^{-1}$ is in some cases shifted to $\sim 870 \text{ cm}^{-1}$, depending on the conformation of $O-C-C-N$ in the choline part. This 920 cm^{-1} band is of importance for structural studies of the polar head group of lecithin. The doublet in the 960 cm^{-1} region has been assigned to the symmetric and anti-symmetric $C-N$ stretching vibration of the $N(CH_3)_3$ group. The correspond-

Table 4.11 Infrared-active bands (in cm^{-1}) of various phosphatidylcholines (PC) and phosphatidylethanolamine (PE)*

Band	DPPC (dry)	DPPC (monohydrate)	DLPC (dry)	Egg PC (dry)	DPPE (dry)	DPPE (monohydrate)	Egg PE (dry)
$\nu_s CH_2$	2,848	2,849	2,848	2,853	2,848	2,848	2,848
$\nu_{as} CH_2$	2,915	2,918	2,915	2,920	2,918	2,915	2,918
$\nu_{as} CH_3$	2,957	2,958	2,953	2,959	2,958	2,956	2,958
δCH_2	1,461	1,466	1,467	1,469	1,462 / 1,471	1,469	1,462
$\nu(C=O)$	1,724 / 1,734	1,733	1,734	1,740	1,739	1,720 / 1,730	1,740
$\nu(P=O)$	1,254	1,248	1,252	1,260	1,222 / 1,241s	1,215	1,224
terminal CH$_2$ rock	722	721	720	720	715 / 725	720	720
$\nu(CH_2)$ of N$^+$CH$_3$	3,028	3,028	3,028	3,013			
$\nu(NH_3^+)$					2,128, 2,328, 2,558, 2,646, 2,688, 2,728	2,108, 2,328, 2,548, 2,728	2,558, 2,638, 2,708
$\delta(NH_3^+)$					1,550, 1,625	1,580, 1,620	1,559, 1,638
$\nu(OH)$		3,373					
$\delta(OH)$		1,645					

*Wallach *et al.*, 1979.

All films were prepared from solutions in chloroform/methanol (2 : 1, v/v), except for dipalmitoyl phosphatidylethanolamine films which were prepared from a chloroform solution.

DPPC, dipalmitoyl phosphatidylcholine; DLPC, dilauroyl phosphatidylcholine; DPPE, dipalmitoyl phosphatidylethanolamine; s, shoulder.

ing oscillating dipole moments are expected to be in the plane and perpendicular to the plane of symmetry, respectively.

Normal coordinate analysis of dimethyl- and diethyl-phosphate has been carried out by Shimanouchi *et al.* (1964) for three assumed conformations of the C–O–P–O–C frame, the extended all-*trans* conformation (C_{2v} symmetry) the *gauche-gauche* conformation (C_2 symmetry), and the unsymmetric *trans/gauche* conformation. It was found that the $g^{\pm}/g^{\pm}$ conformation results in the best coincidence between calculated and measured vibrational frequencies. Several group vibrations in the 700–1,300 cm^{-1} region are of diagnostic value, especially the four P–O stretching modes v_{as} (PO$_2^-$) ($\sim$1,230 cm^{-1}), v_s (PO$_2^-$) ($\sim$1,090 cm^{-1}), v_{as} (P(OC)$_2$) ($\sim$820 cm^{-1}), and v_s (P(OC)$_2$) ($\sim$760 cm^{-1}). From IR polarisation measurements with oriented layers of a series of phospholipids it has been concluded that C–O single bond stretching is significantly involved in both P(OC)$_2$ modes (Fringeli, 1977). The most important results with respect to the structure of the polar head group of DPPC may be summarised as follows (Fringeli and Gunthard, 1981).

The symmetric N–(CH$_3$)$_3$ stretching (v_s(N–(CH$_3$)$_3$)) in choline depends strongly on the torsional angle of the C–C bond. For the *trans* conformation the absorption band is calculated to be near 920 cm^{-1}, whereas the *gauche* conformation results in two bands, one near 900 cm^{-1} and the other near 860 cm^{-1}. The calculated potential energy distribution is >90 per cent for *trans* (C_s symmetry; however, strong coupling with other vibrations occurs in *gauche* conformation. The corresponding potential energy distributions are v_s (N–(CH$_3$)$_3$) (21 per cent), v (C–O) (33 per cent), γ_r (α–CH$_2$) (20 per cent), γ_w (β–CH$_2$) (14 per cent) for the 895 cm^{-1} band of choline and v_s (N–(CH$_3$)$_3$) (67 per cent), v_s (NC$_4$) (13 per cent) for the 866 cm^{-1} band.

Lathanide ions are often used as shift reagents in NMR spectroscopy (Hauser, 1976; Hauser *et al.*, 1976). As these ions bind to the phosphate group a question which arises is whether induced conformational changes occur, that is, whether the structure of the polar head group derived from such NMR experiments corresponds to the natural structure or to a structure which is altered due to lanthanide ion complexation.

IR-ATR measurements with dry oriented layers of lysolecithin (Fringeli and Gunthard, 1981) have been shown to give drastic spectral change of typical phosphate group, hydroxyl group, and hydrocarbon chain absorption bands. Hydration in an atmosphere of 60 per cent relative humidity restores the original conformation to a small extent. La (III) cations are obviously chelated by lysolecithin with the > PO$_2^-$ and OH groups acting as ligands. No infrared data with the same experimental conditions of Hauser (1976) and Hauser *et al.* (1976) are available at this time. Structural changes induced by La (III) cation binding may occur under the conditions used by these authors.

The main endothermic phase transition of the phospholipid–water systems results in an abrupt change in the band parameters of both methylene bands (Asher and Levin, 1977; Cameron *et al.*, 1980; Cortijo and Chapman, 1981).

This parameter (that is, the frequency of the band maximum) has been used to monitor changes in the lipid conformation. The temperature profiles of the band-maximum frequencies for the methylene asymmetric stretching vibrations of L-DPPC and L-DMPC are shown in Figure 4.16. As has been observed by the use of other different physical techniques such as calorimetry (Alonso *et al.*, 1981), slight impurities in the samples make the main transition less sharp (T_c for pure L-DPPC is 41°C and for L-DMPC is 23°C). Studies of the symmetric

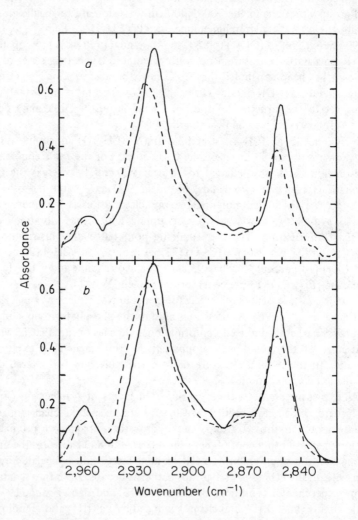

Figure 4.16 Difference infrared spectra of *a*, L-DPPC; and *b*, L-DPPC-gramicidin A with a 2.5:1 (lipid/gramicidin) molar ratio dispersed in the H_2O buffer minus the buffer at 10°C (—) and 51°C (---). A flat subroutine was applied to the spectra to adjust the absorbances at 2,970, 2,890 and 2,805 cm^{-1} to a parabola. Abex 10. (Cortijo *et al.*, 1982)

stretching vibrations around $2,850 \ cm^{-1}$ are not shown although they give practically the same results. Due to the greater relative influence of the experimental error in the band position ($\sim 0.5 \ cm^{-1}$ in our conditions) the minor overall change of the band maximum frequencies for the symmetric vibration (only $3-4 \ cm^{-1}$) during the lipid chain melting transition make it less suitable for these types of studies.

The results obtained with the pure lipid–water systems are in accord with those of various workers, using a variety of physical techniques, including calorimetry and NMR spectroscopy. The way in which the abrupt endothermic lipid phase transition (Chapman *et al.*, 1967) is indicated by the shift of the asymmetric methylene band as the appropriate T_c temperature (see Figure 4.17) is reassuring for the application of this technique.

The effect observed by incorporation of cholesterol into the lipid bilayers provides results which are in general accord with those obtained by the use of a

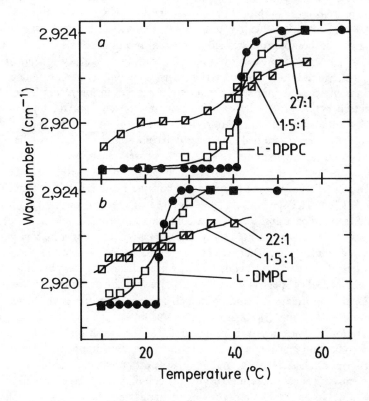

Figure 4.17 Temperature dependence of the maximum wave number of the CH_2 asymmetric stretching vibrations in *a*, L-DPPC-cholesterol; and *b*, L-DMPC-cholesterol at the molar ratios indicated. The temperature dependence for the pure lipids (•) is also given (Cortijo *et al.*, 1982)

range of physical techniques (Ladbrooke *et al.*, 1968; Oldfield and Chapman, 1972), that is, there is an increase in the number of *gauche* conformers below T_c (less order) and a decrease in this number above T_c (more order). This effect increases with greater amounts of cholesterol in the bilayer. At very high cholesterol concentrations (see Figure 4.17) almost no change occurs with temperature in the relative population of *gauche* and *trans* conformers of the lipid chains (the abrupt lipid phase transition is essentially smeared out and removed).

Cameron *et al.* (1980) have also used IR spectroscopy to study the pretransition observed in calorimetric studies of saturated lecithins. They used Fourier transform infrared spectroscopy to study the infrared-active acyl chain vibrational modes of fully hydrated multibilayers of 1,2-dipalmitoyl-sn-glycero-3-phosphocholine (L-DPPC) over the temperature range 0 to 55°C. Frequencies, bandwidths and other spectral parameters were measured as a function of temperature for the methylene scissoring, rocking and wagging modes as well as for the C–H stretching modes, and these were used to monitor the packing of the acyl chains. Particular emphasis was placed on determining the nature of the pretransition event. They showed that between 36°C and 38°C the spectral changes are indicative of a phase change in the acyl chain packing from an orthorhombic to a hexagonal subcell. It was concluded that in the gel phase, at all temperatures below the main transition, the acyl chains are predominantly in all-*trans* conformations and that the temperature-dependent variations of spectral parameters result from changes in interchain interactions.

Mantsch *et al.* (1981) have shown that phase transitions of phospholipids related to the lamellar → hexagonal transitions can be studied using infrared spectroscopy. They studied the egg yolk phosphatidylethanolamine (PE) - water system which exhibits this type of phase transition. Two phase transitions were monitored in this system, a bilayer to bilayer phase transition centred at 12°C (T_m), and a bilayer to nonbilayer phase (H_{II}) transition centred at 28°C (T_h). The spectral changes observed in the acyl chains bands at T_m are indicative of a transition from a conformationally and motionally ordered gel phase to a disordered liquid–crystalline phase containing a high population of *gauche* conformers. There were also considerable changes in the relative intensities of the carbonyl bands at T_m, whilst changes in the phosphate bands were minimal. The spectral changes at T_h are indicative of the introduction of additional conformational and motional disorder into the acyl chains. While the transition to the H_{II} phase is promoted by an increase in the degree of unsaturation, it is not observed in sonicated PE. The transition T_m is not affected by the sonication and is less sensitive to the fatty acid composition. On the basis of the spectral changes at T_m and T_h, it was proposed that the bilayer to nonbilayer phase transition results from the fact that the bilayer structure is no longer able to accommodate the simultaneous requirements of a continous head-group surface and the volume required by the highly disordered acyl chains, the driving force being the introduction of additional conformational disorder into the already disordered liquid–crystalline bilayer phase.

The bands resulting from the phosphate and ethanolamine groups are rather insensitive to both phase changes, whereas those resulting from the ester linkages show large changes both at T_m and T_h. The temperature profiles derived from the ester group $C=O$ and $C-O$ absorption bands show the same general form: therefore, we restrict the discussion to the $C=O$ stretching band which does not suffer from overlap with other bands. The temperature profiles derived from this band are given in Figure 4.18. The $\Delta A/\Delta T$ plot identifies the two temperature

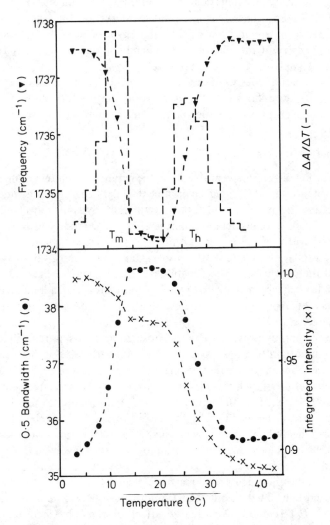

Figure 4.18 Temperature-induced changes in the IR spectral parameters of the $C = O$ stretching vibration of the egg yolk phosphatidylethanolamine–water system (Mantsch *et al.*, 1981)

intervals within which there is an increased overall rate of change and which define T_m and T_h. Again, the symmetric shape of T_h contrasts with the ramp-like shape of the acyl chain melting transition T_m. Neither of these two transitions is very sharp: T_m occurs over a temperature range of about $10°$, while T_h covers a range of about $13°$.

The bandwidth and intensity of the C=O stretching band also exhibit large changes with temperature. As in the case of the frequencies, the bandwidths are nearly identical in the gel-phase bilayer and in the inverted hexagonal phase, while a substantially different value is observed for the bilayer in the liquid-crystalline phase. Both phase changes result in a decrease in integrated intensity (a total decrease of about 12 per cent), the larger decrease being observed at T_h. The complexity of the changes in this band contour results partly from the fact that it is comprised of two components.

The frequencies of the two deconvoluted C=O bands in PE are almost invariant with temperature; however, the relative peak heights vary substantially and thus result in the changes in the spectral parameters shown in Figure 4.18.

Protein–lipid interactions

The organisation of membrane proteins and the nature of the interaction between intrinsic proteins and their lipid environment in both natural and model biomembranes and the degree to which each perturbs the dynamic movement of the other are subjects of considerable interest at present. Studies of protein–lipid interactions have been made using a variety of probe techniques (for example, fluorescent probes, ESR and NMR probes), but considerable controversy has surrounded the conclusions. The debate has centred upon the possible ordering effect of lipid chains by neighbouring intrinsic proteins within a lipid bilayer and the residence or exchange time of these lipids with the bulk lipid (for review see Chapman *et al.*, 1979).

It is clear that to provide definite information about protein–lipid interactions it is important to use, as far as possible, non-perturbing probe techniques. The probe methods involving fluorescent probes or ESR spin probes have been shown to be useful but such techniques are always subject to the question of how far they are able to mimic the lipid chains and, furthermore, conclusions from such studies need to be qualified by the extent to which the probes themselves may perturb the lipid–protein environment. Techniques involving deuterium or phosphorus NMR probes are superior in so far as they involve non-perturbing probes.

Recent results using deuterium magnetic resonance indicate that the effect of intrinsic proteins on the lipid chain conformation (above its main transition temperature, T_c) is different from the effect observed by incorporation of cholesterol. The inclusion of cholesterol into the lipid bilayer always induces an increased (static) order of the lipid chain above its T_c temperature, as indicated by the deuterium quadrupole splitting measurements. On the other hand, proteins (for example cytochrome oxidase, sarcoplasmic reticulum ATPase, myelin proteolipid apoprotein (PLA) and lipophilin), when incorporated into fluid bilayers, give deuterium quadrupole splitting values, Δv_Q, associated with the end methyl group of the hydrocarbon chains, which appear to decrease as the protein concentration increases (Kang *et al.*, 1979; Rice *et al.*, 1979).

The deuterium quadrupole data for the polypeptide gramicidin A (an intrinsic polypeptide) included in lipid bilayers shows a more complicated behaviour and interpretation of the data is not unequivocal (Rice and Oldfield, 1979). There are limitations of the NMR technique associated with line-narrowing effects dependent upon the size of the membrane fragments or vesicles which are being examined.

Vibrational spectroscopy (Raman and infrared spectroscopy) is yet another powerful non-perturbing technique for determining the conformation of lipids and proteins and protein–lipid interactions (Wallach and Winzler, 1974; Wallach *et al.*, 1979). Indeed, Raman spectroscopy has been used to study the relative population of the *gauche* and *trans* conformers and, therefore, the order of the lipid chain within lipid bilayer systems (Chapman *et al.*, 1977; Wallach *et al.*, 1979). The high fluorescence levels obtained at high protein concentration of model and natural biomembranes makes for difficulties, however, in the general application of this approach. Fourier transform infrared spectroscopy has been used for the study of the influence of cholesterol on lipid structure (Cameron *et al.*, 1980; Umemura *et al.*, 1980) and conventional IR spectroscopy has also been applied to very simple model biomembrane systems (Asher and Levin, 1977; Chapman *et al.*, 1980; Cortijo and Chapman, 1981).

Cortijo *et al.* (1982) recently reported studies of protein–lipid interactions and membrane protein organisation using infrared spectroscopy with an intrinsic polypeptide (gramicidin A) and various intrinsic proteins including Ca^{2+}-ATPase and bacteriorhodopsin.

The absorption bands arising from water and buffer solutions were eliminated by means of an infrared spectrometer data station. Spectra were examined using H_2O and D_2O aqueous buffer systems. Pure lecithin–water systems, and various model biomembranes containing cholesterol, gramicidin A, bacteriorhodopsin or Ca^{2+}-ATPase were examined. The IR spectra of the reconstituted biomembranes were compared with those of the corresponding natural biomembranes, that is, the purple membrane of *Halobacterium halobium* and also sarcoplasmic reticulum membranes, respectively.

Changes in lipid chain conformation caused by the various intrinsic molecules incorporated within the model lipid bilayer structures were monitored by studying the shifts in frequency (cm^{-1}) of the CH_2 symmetric and asymmetric absorption bands arising from the lipid chains. The effect of gramicidin A and also the intrinsic proteins, as indicated by the shift of band frequencies, are quite different from that of cholesterol at temperatures above the main lipid T_c transition temperature. Cholesterol causes a reduction in *gauche* isomers which increases with concentration of cholesterol within the lipid bilayer.

The effects observed on the band frequency by incorporation of gramicidin A into the lipid bilayer are more complex than those which occur due to the influence of cholesterol. It can be seen in Figure 4.19 that gramicidin A at L/G higher than 10 (~20 per cent weight) show frequency–temperature profiles similiar to those obtained by addition of cholesterol, and it can be deduced that the presence of the intrinsic polypeptide causes an increase in *gauche* isomers below T_c and a decrease in *gauche* isomers above T_c (see ratio of 20 : 1 in Figure 4.19). However, when higher polypeptide concentrations are included

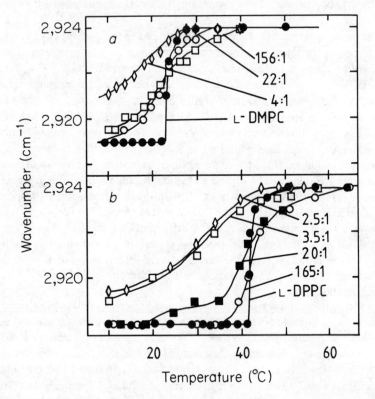

Figure 4.19 Temperature dependence of the maximum wave number of the CH₂ asymmetric stretching vibrations in *a*, L-DMPC-gramicidin A; and *b*, L-DPPC-gramicidin A at the molar ratios indicated. The temperature dependence for the pure lipids (●) is also given. (Cortijo *et al.*, 1982)

within the lipid bilayer the band maximum frequencies, above T_c, now increase and can reach the same frequency as that of the pure lipid, that is the presence of the polypeptide does not cause a decrease in *gauche* isomers above T_c. The overall effect of cholesterol and low proportion of gramicidin A can be described as affecting the cooperativity of the transition decrease whilst T_c remains practically constant. However, the samples with high content of gramicidin A appear to show lower T_c than the pure lipid in addition to the observed decrease of phase cooperativity.

The effects observed by incorporation of the intrinsic proteins of bacteriorhodopsin or Ca^{2+}-ATPase into the lipid bilayer (Figure 4.20) are more similar

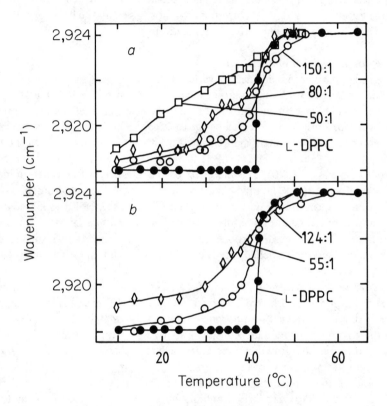

Figure 4.20 Temperature dependence of the maximum wave number of the CH_2 asymmetric stretching vibrations in *a*, L-DPPC-Ca^{2+}-ATPase; and *b*, L-DPPC-bacteriorhodopsin at the molar ratios indicated. The temperature dependence for the pure lipids (●) is also given (Cortijo *et al.*, 1982)

to those observed with gramicidin A than those observed with cholesterol; that is, there is little evidence from the observed shifts of band frequency to indicate that a marked increase of *gauche* isomers occurs at temperatures above T_c due to the presence of high concentrations of intrinsic protein (see Figure 4.20). There is, however, some indication of such an effect when lower concentrations of intrinsic protein are present ∼100 : 1 lipid-protein ratio.

Below the lipid T_c temperature the band frequencies are indicative of an increase in *gauche* isomers; the presence of the intrinsic protein disturbs the *trans* packed crystalline lipid chains. Both proteins smear out the abrupt change of band frequency associated with the lipid phase transition (see Figure 4.20). However, there is evidence at a lipid to Ca^{2+}-ATPase ratio of $80:1$ that at least two transitions occur: one near $30°C$ and the other centred around $41°C$. A similar clear-cut second transition is not so obvious with the BR–lipid systems.

The frequencies of the methylene bands in the purified SR and purple membrane between $10°C$ and $50°C$ correspond to those given by the lipids of L-DPPC and L-DMPC above their respective T_c temperatures.

Acholeplasma laidlawii biomembranes

Many studies have been made using a variety of techniques of the microorganism *Acholeplasma laidlawii*. This microorganism is capable of accepting particular fatty acids in its growth medium and studies have shown that the membranes of the microorganism can be enriched up to 95 per cent with a given fatty acid. The microorganism exhibits a marked phase transition and this has been shown by calorimetric (Steim *et al.*, 1969; Chapman and Urbina, 1971) and X-ray methods (Engelman, 1970). The sharpness of the phase transition is determined by the heterogeneity of the lipid chains present in the membrane. Fourier transform infrared spectroscopy has been applied (Casal *et al.*, 1980) to a study of intact and deproteinated plasma membrane of *Acholeplasma laidlawii* enriched biosynthetically with perdeuteropalmitoyl chains. (The microorganism readily incorporates deuterium-labelled fatty acids into the membranes: Oldfield *et al.*, 1972; Stockton *et al.*, 1977.)

The temperature-dependent behaviour was monitored via the CD stretching modes and compared with that observed with a model biomembrane 1,2 diperdeuteropalmitoyl-sn-glycero-3-phosphocholine. A broad transition is observed with the natural biomembrane consisting of two overlapping stages. Over a 5° range, centred at the growth temperature, a larger change in the *gauche trans* conformer ratio of the acyl chains occurs.

A plot of the temperature dependence of the frequency (cm^{-1}) of the maximum of the CD_2 symmetric stretching vibration of the perdeuteropalmitoyl chains in intact plasma membranes, deproteinated membranes and a DPPC–D_2O model membrane is shown in Figure 4.21.

Sarcoplasmic reticulum membranes

An examination of the IR spectra of the sarcoplasmic reticulum membrane when in H_2O and D_2O buffers (see Figure 4.22) suggests that the intrinsic proteins of this membrane show a proportion of unordered polypeptide structure in the protein as well as an appreciable proportion of the α-helix structure. A similar conclusion can be deduced from the circular dichroism measurements reported by Dean and Tanford (1978). The maximum for the amide I band appears in the expected frequency for both α helix and unordered conformations (see Table 4.12). This result contrasts with that of the purple membrane indicating that, as occurs with water-soluble proteins, different intrinsic membrane proteins adopt very different conformations in the membrane.

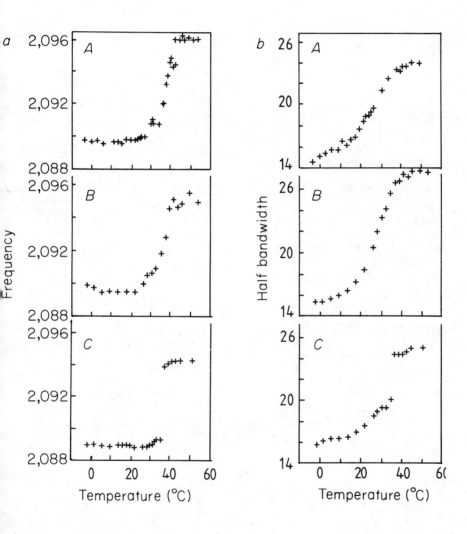

Figure 4.21 *a*, Temperature dependence of the frequency (in cm^{-1}) of the maximum of the CD_2 symmetric stretching vibration of the perdeuteriopalmitoyl chains in *A*, intact plasma membranes; *B*, deproteinated plasma membranes; and *C*, DPPC-d$_{62}$ model membranes. *b*, Temperature dependence of the half-bandwidths (in cm^{-1}) of the symmetric CD_2 stretching vibration of the perdeuteriopalmitoyl chains in *A*, intact plasma membranes; *B*, deproteinated plasma membranes; and *C*, DPPC-d$_{62}$ model membranes (Casal *et al.*, 1980)

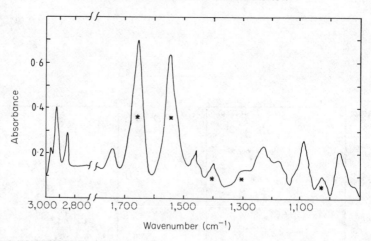

Figure 4.22 Difference infrared spectrum of sarcoplasmic reticulum suspended in the H_2O buffer minus the buffer multiplied by a calculated factor of 0.75. Abex 15; temperature 30°C. The frequencies and assignments of the principal bands of the spectrum of sarcoplasmic reticulum are given in Table 4.12. Five of the bands are attributed to the protein moiety. These are marked with an asterisk here and in Table 4.12. The remainder of the spectrum is similar to that of hydrated pellets of lecithins

Table 4.12   Infrared frequencies of the main bands for the purified sarcoplasmic reticulum in the standard buffer at 30°C

Frequencies (cm^{-1})	Tentative assignments
2,956	CH$_3$ asymmetric stretching
2,924	CH$_2$ asymmetric stretching
2,872	CH$_3$ symmetric stretching
2,853	CH$_2$ symmetric stretching
1,738	C=O stretching
1,655*	Amide I
1,550*	Amide II
1,460–80	CH$_2$ scissoring
1,400*	$\begin{cases} CO_2^- \text{ symmetric stretching} \\ \text{tyrosine OH bending} \end{cases}$
1,300*	Amide III
1,230	Phosphate asymmetric stretching
1,180	C–O–C asymmetric stretching
1,090	Phosphate symmetric stretching
1,030*	C–O stretching (in hydroxyl groups)
970	(CH$_3$)$_3$N$^+$ stretching

*These bands are mainly due to vibrations of the protein moiety.

The purple membrane and bacteriorhodopsin

The IR spectra of the purple membrane in H_2O and D_2O buffers confirm that the polypeptide structure within the protein is mainly helicoidal in character, although the abnormal frequency for the amide I maximum may be due to a distortion of the helix (see also Rothschild and Clark, 1979). The purple membrane in the D_2O buffer shows two clear shoulders at 1,640 and 1,690 cm^{-1}. The presence of these shoulders could mean that there is a contribution of the anti-parallel β-sheet structure which is small but not negligible. The electron diffraction results and the present models of purple membrane seem to agree in that they predict that only a very small proportion of non-helical structure will be present (Henderson and Unwin, 1975; Ovchinnikov *et al.*, 1979; Engelman *et al.*, 1980). The surprisingly low helical content predicted by ultraviolet circular dichroism (Becher and Cassium, 1976) may, therefore, be due to the optical artefacts described by Holzwarth (1972). A possible explanation for the wider band observed in the reconstituted system is the existence of more conformational and motional freedom of the protein in the model biomembrane structure compared with the native membrane.

Information about the polypeptide structure within gramicidin A, the reconstituted proteins and also the proteins in the natural biomembranes were obtained by examining the region of the IR spectrum between 1,600 and 1,700 cm^{-1}, associated with the amide I and amide II bands. An examination of the IR band frequencies of the different systems in this region leads to the conclusions: (1) that gramicidin A within a phospholipid bilayer structure probably has a single helix rather than a double helix structure; (2) that there are differences in band widths of the reconstituted Ca^{2+}-ATPase and bacteriorhodopsin compared with the spectra of the corresponding sarcoplasmic reticulum and purple membrane; (3) different membrane proteins can adopt different conformations as evidenced by a comparison of the spectra of the sarcoplasmic reticulum and purple membrane; (4) the polypeptide arrangment in the purple membrane is mainly helical but the abnormal frequency of the amide I band suggests that some distortion of the helix occurs; and (5) the sarcoplasmic reticulum membrane contains unordered as well as α-helix polypeptide arrangements.

Rothschild and Clark (1979) have used polarised infrared spectroscopy to determine the average α-helix tilt of bacteriorhodopsin in dried purple membrane. From samples deposited on Irtran-4 plates they calculated an upper value of 26° which is consistent with the electron microscope model of Henderson and Unwin (1975).

The anomalously high amide I and amide II bands have been attributed to a distorted conformation of the α helices of the membrane protein. This has been recently examined (Krimm and Dwivedi, 1982) and attributed to α_{II} helices on the basis of normal mode calculations. These types of α_{II} helices have been observed with some proteins and postulated for poly-L-alanine in hexafluoro isopropanol. The α_I and α_{II} structures differ in that the plane of the peptide group in α_I is essentially parallel to the helix axis, whereas in α_{II} it is tilted with the N—H bond pointing inward towards the axis.

Michel-Villaz *et al.* (1979) have measured the infrared polarisation spectra of rod outer segments suspended in D_2O Ringer's solution and orientated in a magnetic field in the presence of gluteraldehyde. They estimated the α-helix orientation in rhodopsin as $38°$ based on dichroism of the amide I band. The amide II band yielded as a similar value. They reasoned that as the latter band is due to unexchanged N—H groups probably contained within the protein, one could conclude that the orientated α helices are hydrophobic. The exchanged amide II band displayed no dichroism, suggesting to them a less orientated structure for the hydrophilic regions of rhodopsin. Rothschild *et al.* (1980a,b) have also measured the infrared dichroism of orentated photoreceptor membrane films. They report for the orientated films an unusually high amide II/amide I absorption ratio, nearly twice that observed for disordered preparations. They interpret this as being due to the preferential orientation of rhodopsin α helices perpendicular to the membrane. Their estimates of α-helix tilt $(29\text{-}41°)$ are higher than the previously published value $(17°)$ based on visible dichroism of the α band.

FT infrared difference spectra of purple membrane films deposited on AgCl plates and measured at 77K have been reported by Rothschild *et al.* (1981; 1982). Illumination of the samples before and/or during the scan permitted their subtraction from film spectra recorded in the dark. Analysis of changes in the amide I and II bands has been used by them to suggest evidence for the carbohydrate group protonation which occurs during the formation of the M_{412} intermediate of bacteriorhodopsin. Their low temperature measurement on the photoconversion from BR_{570} to the first intermediate, K, are consistent with an alteration in the local environment of the Schiff base proton (see Figure 4.23).

FUTURE DEVELOPMENTS

It seems clear that the application of modern infrared spectroscopy, particularly with the use of data stations and Fourier transform spectrometers, will be of immense value for the study of biomembrane systems. The rapidity of obtaining information, the elimination of the difficult water absorption and the potential for obtaining sensitive difference spectra will make for many future applications. The present study of systems such as bacteriorhodopsin, the Ca^{2+}-ATPase protein and many other simple biomembranes shows the feasibility of obtaining information about the subtle changes involved in these membranes as a function of light, calcium, pH changes or other trigger events.

Until recently, the use of the weaker amide (III-VII) bands, as well as cooperative absorption modes active in the far infrared region, have been ignored in the interpretation of membrane and protein structure. The higher sensitivity and greater signal-to-noise ratios now possible should encourage more extensive and constructive use of these regions.

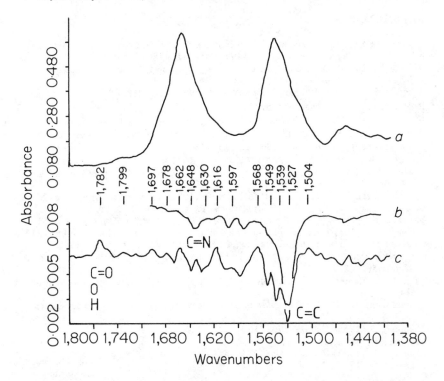

Figure 4.23 *a*, Infrared absorption spectrum of a purple membrane film deposited on AgCl. The Nicolet MX-1 spectrometer was scanned 32 times (1 minute total) and the Fourier transform performed using triangular apodisation. The major peaks at 1,660 and 1,547 cm^{-1} correspond to the amide I and II bands. *b*, The resonance Raman spectrum of purple membrane suspension measured with 5,145 A excitation and a power of 30 mW. The sample was placed in a spinning cell rotating at 30 Hz which eliminated contributions from intermediates after L550. The Raman intensity has been displayed on an arbitrary negative scale for comparison to the FTIR difference spectrum. Only the protonated C=N appears. *c*, The difference spectrum of *a* and a spectrum recorded immediately afterwards for 1 minute (32 scans) during illumination. The frequencies of some of the major peaks are shown. The spectrum was smoothed by a 17 point fit which resulted in 8 cm^{-1} resolution. However, the frequency of the peaks measured in different experiments was repeatable to less than 1 cm^{-1} (Rothschild *et al.*, 1981, 1982)

ACKNOWLEDGEMENTS

We wish to acknowledge support for our research studies from the Wellcome Trust and the Humane Society. One author (RLA) expresses his appreciation to the Royal Free Hospital School of Medicine for hospitality during the preparation of this chapter, and to Occidental College, Department of Chemistry, for sabbatical leave.

REFERENCES

Akutsu, H., Kyogoku Nakahara, H. and Fukuda, K. (1975). *Chem. Phys. Lipids*, 15, 222.
Alben, J. O. and Fager, L. T. (1972). *Biochemistry*, 11, 4786.
Alonso, A., Restall, C. J., Clark, A. D., Turner, M., Gomez-Gernandez, J. C. and Chapman, D. (1982). *Biochim. biophys. Acta*, 689, 283.
Asher, I. M. and Levin, I. W. (1977). *Biochim. biophys. Acta*, 468, 63.
Bailey, R. T. (1974). *Molec. Spectrosc.*, 2, 173.
Bare, G. H., Alben, J. O. and Bromberg, P. A. (1975). *Biochemistry*, 14, 1578.
Barrow, R. F., Long, D. A. and Sheridan, J. (1979). Specialist Periodical Reports: *Molecular Spectroscopy*, Vol. 6, (Chem. Soc. Lond.), 328 pp.
Becher, B. and Cassium, J. Y. (1976). *Biophys. J.*, 16, 1183.
Bellamy, L. J. (1975). *Advances in Infrared Group Frequencies*, Chapman and Hall, London, 304 pp.
Belloco, A. M., Lord, R. C. and Mendelsohn, R. (1972). *Biochim. biophys. Acta*, 257, 280.
Boerio, F. J. and Koenig, J. L. (1970). *J. Chem. Phys.*, 52, 3425.
Brown, J. K., Sheppard, N. and Simpson, D. M. (1950). *Discussion Faraday Soc.*, 261.
Brown, J. K., Sheppard, N. and Simpson, D. M. (1954). *Phil. Trans R. Soc., Lond.*, 247, 35.
Cameron, D. G., Casal, H. L. and Mantsch, H. H. (1980). *Biochemistry*, 19, 3665.
Casal, H. L., Smith, I. C. P., Cameron, D. G. and Mantsch, H. H. (1979). *Biochim. biophys. Acta*, 550, 145.
Casal, H. L., Cameron, D. G., Smith, I. C. P. and Mantsch, H. H. (1980). *Biochemistry*, 19, 444.
Chamberlain, J. (1979). *Principles of Interferometric Spectroscopy*, Wiley-Interscience, New York.
Chapman, D. (1955). *Nature*, 176, 216.
Chapman, D. (1956). *J. Chem. Soc.*, 55; 2522
Chapman, D. (1957). *J. Chem. Soc.*, 2715; 4489.
Chapman, D. (1958). *J. Chem. Soc.*, 784.
Chapman, D. (1962). *Chem. Rev.*, 62, 433.
Chapman, D. (1965). *The Structure of Lipids*, Methuen and Co., London, 323 pp.
Chapman, D., Byrne, P. and Shipley, G. G. (1966). *Proc. R. Soc., Lond.*, 290, 115.
Chapman, D., Cornell, B. A., Eliasz, A. W. and Perry, A. (1977). *J. molec. Biol.*, 113, 517.
Chapman, D., Gomez-Fernandez, J. C. and Goni, F. M. (1979). *FEBS Lett.*, 98, 211.
Chapman, D. and Urbina, J. (1971). *FEBS Lett.*, 12, 169.
Chapman, D., Williams, R. M. and Ladbrooke, B. D. (1967). *Chem. Phys. Lipids*, 1, 445.
Clark, R. J. H. and Hester, R. E. (1982). *Adv. in IR and Raman Spectrosc.*, 9, 360pp.
Cole, A. R. H. (1977). IUPAC Commission on Molecular Structure and Spectroscopy. *Table of Wavenumbers for the Calibration of IR Spectrometers*, (2nd edn), Pergamon, Oxford, 219 pp.
Cortijo, M., Alonso, A., Gomez-Fernandez, J. C. and Chapman, D. (1982). *J. molec. Biol.*, 157, 597.
Cortijo, M. and Chapman, D. (1981). *FEBS Lett.*, 131, 245.
Craver, C. D. (1977). *The Coblentz Society Desk Book of IR Spectra*, Coblentz Soc. Inc., Kirkwood, Mo., 498 pp.
C. A. Selects. *IR Spectrometry* (Physiochemical Aspects).
C. A. Selects. *IR Spectrometry* (Organic Aspects).
Chemical Abstracts Service, Box 3012, Columbus, Ohio 43210, USA.
Dean, W. L. and Tanford, C. (1978). *Biochemistry*, 17, 1683.
De Ruig, W. G. (1971). *Infrared spectra of Monoacid Triglycerides*, Wageningen.
Eckert, K., Grosse, R., Malur, J. and Repke, K. R. H. (1977). *Bipolymers*, 16, 2549.
Edsall, J. T. (1937). *J. Chem. Phys.*, 5, 225.
Engelman, D. M. (1970). *J. molec. biol.*, 47, 115.
Engelman, D. M., Henderson, R., McLachlan, A. D. and Wallace, B. A. (1980). *Proc. natn. Acad. Sci. U.S.A.*, 77, 2023.
Ferraro, J. R. and Basile, L. J. (1978). *Fourier Transform IR - Applications to Chemical Systems*, Vols 1 and 2, Academic Press, New York.

Fischmeister, I. (1975). *Prog. Chem. Fats and Other Lipids*, XIV, 91.

Fookson, J. E. and Wallach, D. F. H. (1978). *Archs. Biochim. Biophys.*, 189, 195.

Fraser, R. D. B. and MacRae, T. P. (1973). *Conformations in Fibrous Proteins and Related Synthetic Polypeptides*, Ch. 5, Academic Press, New York.

Fringeli, U. P. (1977). *Z. Naturforsch.*, 32, 20.

Fringeli, U. P. and Gunthard, Hs. H. (1981). In *Membrane Spectroscopy*, (ed. Ernst Grell) *Molec. Biol., Biochem. and Biophys.*, 31, Springer-Verlag, Berlin, p. 270.

Fuller, M. P. and Griffiths, P. R. (1978). *Analyt. Chem.*, 50, 1906.

Grasselli, J. G. and Ritchey, W. M. (eds) (1975). *Atlas of Spectral Data and Physical Constants for Organic Compounds*, (2nd edn), CRC Press, Cleveland Ohio, 4, 527 pp.

Green, D. W. and Reedy, T. (1978). *FT-IR Spectroscopy*, 1, 1.

Griffiths, P. R. (1980). In *Analytical Application of FT-IR to molecular and biological Systems* (ed. J. R. Durig) Reidel, Holland.

Griffiths, P. R. (ed.) (1978). *Transform Techniques in Chemistry*, Plenum, New York.

Harrick, N. J. (1967). *Internal Reflection Spectroscopy*, Wiley, New York.

Hauser, H. (1976). *J. Colloid. Interface Sci.*, 55, 85.

Hauser, H., Phillips, M. C., Levine, B. A. and Williams, R. J. P. (1976). *Nature*, 261, 390.

Henderson, R. and Unwin, R. N. T. (1975). *Nature*, 257, 28.

Holzwarth, G. (1972). *Membrane Molecular Biology* (eds C. F. Fox and A. D. Keith), Sinaul Ass. 228.

Hummel, D. O. and Scholl, F. (1978). *Atlas of Polymer and Plastics Analysis*, Vol. 1, Verlag Chemie, Weinheim, Germany, 708 pp.

Jones, R. N., McKay, A. F. and Sinclair, R. G. (1952). *J. Am. Chem. Soc.*, 74, 2575.

Kang, S. Y., Gutowsky, H. R. S., Hsung, J. C., Jacobs, R., King, T. E., Rice, D. and Oldfield, E. (1979). *Biochemistry*, 18, 3257.

Kemp, W. (1975). *Organic Spectroscopy*, Macmillan, London.

Kirby, E. M., Evans Vader, M. J. and Brown, M. A. (1965). *J. Am. Oil Chem. Soc.*, 42, 437.

Koenig, J. L. and Frushour, B. G. (1972). *Biopolymers*, 11, 1871.

Koenig, J. L. and Tabb, D. L. (1980). In *Analytical Application of FT-IR to molecular and biological Systems*. (ed. J. R. Durig) Reidel, Holland, pp. 241–255.

Krimm, S. (1962). *J. molec. Biol.*, 4, 528.

Krimm, S. and Dwivedi, A. M. (1982). *Science*, 216, 407.

Ladbrooke, B. D., Williams, R. M. and Chapman, D. (1968). *Biochim. biophys. Acta*, 150, 333.

McDonald, R. S. (1976). *Analyt. Chem.*, 48, 196R; (1978). *Analyt. Chem.*, 50, 282R; (1980). *Analyt. Chem.*, 52, 361R.

Mantsch, H. H., Martin, A. and Cameron, D. G. (1981). *Biochemistry*, 20, 3138.

Michel-Villaz, M., Saibil, H. R. and Chabre, M. (1979). *Proc. natn. Acad. Sci. U.S.A.*, 76, 4405.

Nakamishi, Koji and Solomon, P. H. (1977). *Infrared Absorption Spectroscopy* (2nd edn), Holden-Day, San Francisco, 287 pp.

Oldfield, E. and Chapman, D. (1972). *FEBS Rev. Lett.*, 23, 285.

Oldfield, E., Chapman, D. and Derbyshire, W. (1972). *Chem. Phys. Lipids*, 9, 69.

Ovchinnikov, Y., Abdulaev, N., Feigiri, M., Kiselev, A. and Lobanov, N. (1979). *FEBS Lett.*, 100, 219.

Painter, P. C. and Koenig, J. L. (1975). *Biopolymers*, 14, 457.

Perkin-Elmer Ltd (1980). *680 Series IR Spectrophotometers Operator's Manual*, Beaconsfield, England.

Pouchert, C. J. (1975). *The Aldrich Library of Infrared Spectra* (2nd edn), Aldrich, Milwaukee, Wis., 1600 pp.

Primas, H. and Gunthard, Hs. H. (1953). *Helv. Chem. Acta*, 36, 1791.

Primas, H. and Gunthard, Hs. H. (1955). *Helv. Chem. Acta*, 38, 1254.

Rice, D. M., Meadows, M. D., Scheinman, A. O., Goni, F. M., Gomez, J. F., Mascarello, M.A., Chapman, D. and Oldfield, E. (1979). *Biochemistry*, 18, 5893.

Rice, D. M. and Oldfield, E. (1979). *Biochemistry*, 18, 3272.

Rothschild, K. J. and Clark, N. A. (1979). *Biophys. J.*, 25, 473.

Rothschild, K. J., Clark, N. A., Rosen, K. M., Sancher, R. and Hsiao, T. L. (1980). *Biochem. Biophys. Res. Commun.*, 92, 1266.

Rothschild, K. J., Sanches, R., Hsiao, T. L. and Clark, N. A. (1980). *Biophys. J.*, **31**, 53.
Rothschild, K. J. and Massero, H. (1982). *Proc. natn. Acad. Sci. U.S.A.*, **79**, 4045.
Rothschild, K. J., Zagaeski, M. and Cantore, W. A. (1981). *Biochem. Biophys. Res. Commun.*, **103**, 483.
Rüegg, M., Metzger, V. and Susi, H. (1975). *Biopolymers*, **14**, 1465.
Schachtschneider, J. H. and Snyder, R. G. (1963). *Spectrochim. Acta*, **19**, 117.
Simons, W. W. (1978). *The Sadtler Handbook of IR Spectra*, Sadtler, Philadelphia, 1089pp.
Shimanovchi, T., Tsuboi, M. and Kyogoku (1964). *Adv. Chem. Phys.*, **VII**, p 435.
Snyder, R. G. (1960). *J. molec. Spectrosc.*, **4**, 411.
Snyder, R. G., Strauss, H. L. and Elliger, C. A. (1982). *J. Phys. Chem.*, **86**, 5145.
Steim, J. M., Tourtellote, M. E., Reinert, J. C., McElhaney, R. N. and Radar, R. L. (1969). *Proc. natn. Acad. Sci. U.S.A.*, **63**, 104.
Stockton, G. W., Johnson, K. G., Butler, K. W., Tulloch, A. P., Boulanger, Y., Smith, I. C. P., Davis, J. H. and Bloom, M. (1977). *Nature*, **269**, 267.
Susi, H., Timasheff, S. N. and Stevens, L. (1967). *J. biol. Chem.*, **242**, 5460.
Susi, H. (1969). In *Structure and stability of Biological Macromolecules* (eds S. N. Timasheff and G. D. Fasman) 575.
Tasumi, M., Schimanouchi, T., Watanabe, A. and Goto, R. (1964). *Spectrosc. chim. Acta*, **20**, 629.
Theimer, O. (1957). *J. Chem. Phys.*, **27**, 1041.
Timasheff, S. N., Susi, H. and Stevens, L. (1967). *J. biol. Chem.*, **242**, 5467.
Tobin, M. C. (1955). *J. Chem. Phys.*, **23**, 891.
Tschamler, H. (1954). *J. Chem. Phys.*, **22**, 1845.
Umemura, J., Cameron, D. G. and Mantsch, H. H. (1980). *J. Phys. Chem.*, **84**, 2272.
Von Sydow, E. (1955). *Act. Chem. Scand.*, **9**, 1119.
Wallach, D. F. H., Verma, S. P. and Fookson, J. (1979). *Biochim. biophys. Acta*, **559**, 153.
Wallach, D. F. H. and Winzler, R. J. (1974). *Evolving strategies and tactics in membrane research*, Springer, New York.
Washburn, E. W. (1926). *International Critical Tables*, 1st edn, Vol. 1, McGraw-Hill, New York, 67.
Wolfe, W. L. and Zissis, G. I. (1978). *The Infrared Handbook*, Erim, Ann Arbor, 1700 pp.
Wyckoff, R. W. G. (1966). *Crystal Struct.*, **5**, 254.
Yu, N. T. and Liu, C. S. (1972). *J. Am. Chem. Soc.*, **94**, 5127.

5

Rotational and lateral diffusion of membrane proteins as determined by laser techniques

Winfried Hoffmann§ and Colin J. Restall†
§NUKEM GmbH, Postfach 11 00 80, D-6450 Hanau 11,
Federal Republic of Germany
†Department of Biochemistry, Royal Free Hospital Medical School,
8 Hunter Street, London WC1N 1 BP, UK

INTRODUCTION

Diffusion processes within cell membranes have attracted much interest in the past decade. The simple fact that specialised structures, such as junctions or pits, exist on the cell surface implicates either the occurrence of immobilised membrane components and rigid cell areas, or both. On the other hand, other cells or cell areas have to be in a fluid state to allow diffusion of membrane components; this in order to serve signal transduction and distribution and redistribution of matter within the cell and between the cell and its environment. Studies of rotational and lateral diffusion of membrane components have become powerful tools to help elucidate some of these aspects.

The rotational diffusion of macromolecules in aqueous solution has long been studied by the fluorescence depolarisation method (for reviews see Weber, 1953; 1973; Yguerabide, 1972; Badea and Brand, 1979). This method of study is possible because the diffusion times to be measured are comparable to the lifetime of the fluorescent probes; that is, in the nanosecond time domain. However, rotational relaxation times of either more extended molecular assemblies (for example, DNA, virus particles) or proteins within viscous environments (for example membranes) take place in times of the order of microseconds or longer. Consequently, other methods have been developed based upon electromagnetic absorption, resonance scattering, saturation transfer electron spin resonance, and polarised flash photolysis methods (for reviews see Johansson and Lindblom, 1980; Hyde, 1978; Thomas, 1978; Cherry, 1978). The latter method, using absorption depolarisation (Cherry, 1978) and also delayed luminescence depolarisation (Moore *et al.*, 1979; Greinert *et al.*, 1979; Jovin *et al.*, 1981) exploit long-lived photoproducts or triplet probes having lifetimes of the order of milliseconds. The development of more sophisticated apparatus and data evaluation has made it feasible to have available data on a whole variety of different proteins.

Lateral diffusion of proteins in biological membranes was first inferred from cell fusion (Frye and Edidin, 1970), patching and capping phenomena (Taylor *et al.*, 1971), and electron microscopic observations (Pinto da Silva, 1972). After these indirect methods the first quantitative data using microphotolysis measurements were reported by Poo and Cone (1974) and Peters *et al.* (1974). Since these initial studies were performed a wealth of information has been accumulated on a great variety of different membrane systems.

In this review we aim firstly to give a comprehensive description of the different methods using laser techniques to study rotational and lateral diffusion of membrane proteins and, secondly, to summarise some of the experimental findings together with their implications. Finally, a comparison is made between rotational and lateral diffusion data for systems where both values are available.

PHOTOPHYSICAL PRINCIPLES

The absorption of light by organic molecules creates a variety of excited singlet S_n and triplet T_n states ($n = 1, 2, \ldots$). By internal conversion the first excited singlet S_1 and triplet T_1 states, respectively, are formed rapidly in the subpicosecond timescale.

Two possibilities then exist: (1) the molecule returns to the ground state S_0 via one of various deactivation pathways (Figure 5.1); or (2) either the excited molecule undergoes conformeric changes leading in a cyclic pathway back to the original ground state or other stable species are formed irreversibly after excitation. Examples of the latter possibility are bacteriorhodopsin (cyclic photoreaction) and rhodopsin (irreversible photoreaction).

The luminescence of excited molecules originates in general from the first excited singlet S_1 and triplet T_1 states, respectively. The various electronic transitions involved after excitation are summarised in Figure 5.1. For the sake of simplicity other deactivation pathways (for example resonance energy transfer, solvent relaxation, collisional or binding interactions with other excited or ground state species) have been omitted. More detailed discussion can be found in McGlynn *et al.* (1969), Parker *et al.* (1980), Lower and El-Sayed (1966), Birks (1976) and Turro *et al.* (1978).

The transition from the S_1 state to the less energetic T_1 state — called inter-

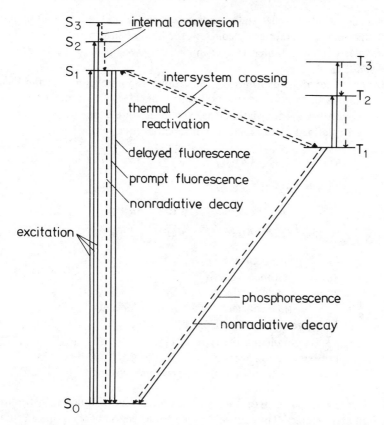

Figure 5.1 Electronic energy scheme. Solid arrows indicate radiative transitions, dashed arrows nonradiative transitions (vibrational states are omitted)

system crossing (isc) — involves a change in spin multiplicity. Without spin-orbital coupling, such a transition could not occur. Introduction of internal or external heavy atoms, however, can greatly enhance this spin-orbital coupling. Hence, the usual effect of substituting a fluorescent aromatic compound with halogens of increasing atomic weight is to increase intersystem crossing. At the expense of ϕ_f (quantum yield for prompt fluorescence) the quantum yield for phosphorescence ϕ_p is increased and the lifetime of the radiative transition from the triplet to the ground state (phosphorescence) is shortened (Cox and Kemp, 1971; Kasha, 1960; McClure, 1949; Zander, 1968). Other transitions from the triplet state back to the ground state include non-radiative deactivation and delayed fluorescence. The first includes collision with solvent or paramagnetic molecules, such as ground state oxygen (which is why systems making use of triplet states have to be purged free of air). Delayed fluorescence is caused by intersystem crossing from the triplet back to the excited singlet state, followed by a radiative transition from S_1 to the ground state. The lifetimes for phosphorescence, delayed fluorescence, and the triplet state are almost identical and in the order of about 1 msec at room temperature. By contrast, the lifetime of prompt fluorescence is in the order of about 1 nsec (for example, 0.9 nsec for eosin, as reported by Porter *et al.*, 1974).

In order to describe quantitatively the various reactions summarised in Figure 5.1 we adopt a description given by Jovin *et al.* (1981). Assuming a gaussian light pulse with standard deviation σ as excitation source, the decay processes in Figure 5.1 are defined by the following differential equations:

$$dS_1/dt + a_{11}S_1 + a_{12}T_1 = [\sigma\sqrt{2\pi}]^{-1} \exp(-t^2/(2\sigma^2))$$

$$dT_1/dt + a_{21}S_1 + a_{22}T_1 = 0$$

$$a_{11} = k_d^S + k_{isc} \qquad a_{12} = -k_{tr}$$

$$a_{21} = -k_{isc} \qquad a_{22} = k_d^T + k_{tr}$$

(1)

where $k_d^S = k_f + k_{nr}^S$ time constant for decay from S_1 and
$\qquad\qquad k_f$ is fluorescence from S_1;
$\qquad\qquad k_{nr}^S$ is nonradiative decay from S_1
$\quad k_d^T = k_p + k_{nr}^T$ time constant for decay from T_1 and
$\qquad\qquad k_p$ is phosphorescence from T_1;
$\qquad\qquad k_{nr}^T$ is nonradiative decay from T_1;
$\quad k_{isc}$ is intersystem crossing;
$\quad k_{tr}$ is thermal reactivation and intersystem crossing from T_1 to S_1.

S_1 and T_1 are given in terms of fractional quantities representing the distribution of excited state species. Time t is referenced to the centre of the gaussian excitation light pulse.

At all times:

$$\text{fluorescence} \propto k_f S_1(t)$$

$$\text{phosphorescence} \propto k_p T_1(t)$$

(2)

where the proportionality factor includes the chemical concentration (ground state), extinction coefficient, and instrumental parameters (spectral sensitivity, bandwidth, optical collection, electronic amplification) that determine the absolute and relative signal intensities. It is assumed that the latter are proportional to excitation intensity, that is, the system is operating well below saturation.

The eigenvalues ($\lambda_1 \gg \lambda_2$) of equation (1) yield the two lifetimes for prompt (τ_1) and delayed (τ_2) emission:

$$\lambda_1 = k_d^S + k_{isc} = \tau_1^{-1}$$

$$\lambda_2 = k_{nr}^T + k_p + k_{tr}(1 - \phi_{isc}) = \tau_2^{-1}$$

(3)

For times much longer than prompt emission ($t \gg \tau_1$), the time course for delayed emission can be approximated by a mono-exponential function:

$$S_1(t) = S_d \exp(-\lambda_2 t)$$

$$T_1(t) = T_d \exp(-\lambda_2 t)$$

(4)

where S_d and T_d are that fraction of molecules taking the pathway for delayed rather than prompt emission from the singlet S_1 and triplet T_1 states, respectively.

EXPERIMENTAL METHODS AND DATA EVALUATION

Particles suspended in a liquid are exposed to forces originating in the interaction between the particles and the surrounding medium. The theory of brownian motion can be applied if these particles are considerably larger than the liquid molecules — still small, however, on a macroscopic scale.

Rotational diffusion

Principles of the method
Consider an idealised experimental situation where at zero time a light pulse of infinitely short duration, polarised in the z direction of the laboratory coordinate system, excites identical light-sensitive particles. These particles may all have one chromophore firmly attached to them at the same site. The chromophores should be characterised by one transition dipole moment; its direction for ground state absorption is designated by μ_a. The excited particles may be characterised either by absorbance changes with two measuring light beams, one polarised parallel and the other perpendicular with respect to the exciting light pulse, or, if the particles are luminescent, the emitted light is analysed in the z and y directions. The intensity components in both cases are denoted $I_{\parallel}$ (parallel with respect to the flash, z direction) and $I_{\perp}$ (perpendicular with respect to the flash, y direction).

Let the distribution of the particles be completely isotropic before the flash. When the light pulse hits the sample, those chromophores with their transition moment in a favourable direction with respect to the polarisation of the incoming light will have a greater probability of being excited than others. This probability is proportional to $(\mu_a e_z)^2$, where e_z is the unity vector along the z axis. Hence, photon absorption will occur with greatest probability in those molecules having their transition moments parallel to the polarisation plane of light flash. The sub-ensemble of excited species will thus have a directional anisotropy immediately after excitation. Signals arising from such excited molecules reflect this anisotropic distribution and emission signals will be polarised and absorption signals will be dichroic. This anisotropy will remain constant if the sample is immobilised. However, if brownian motion takes place, the sub-ensemble will become completely randomised again and the anisotropy vanishes.

With regard to the above, it should be borne in mind that the term immobile is relative; if the lifetime of the excited chromophore is short compared to motion occurring within the sample, one is tempted to postulate a rigid system. This was indeed the case about 10 years ago when Wahl *et al.* (1971) conducted depolar- isation experiments on fluorescent-labelled proteins from the electric organ of the eel. No depolarisation was observed within the lifetime of the fluorescent label (around 10 nsec); nor would it have been seen in any other membrane system. Based upon this result the authors concluded that proteins are strongly immobilised within a membrane. In an elegant experiment, Cone (1972) showed one year later that particular proteins may rotate quite rapidly in the μsec time domain. He chose a molecule, rhodopsin, the photoproducts of which have life- times long enough for this rotation to be followed.

The measured intensity changes $I_{\parallel}$ and $I_{\perp}$ have, in the case of absorption measurements, first to be converted into absorbance changes according to:

$$A_{\parallel} = -\log\left(1 + I_{\parallel}/I_0\right)$$
$$A_{\perp} = -\log\left(1 + I_{\perp}/I_0\right) \tag{5}$$

where I_0 is the light intensity before the flash. A measure of the flash-induced dichroism, or polarised emission signal, is defined as the anisotropy parameter (Jablonski, 1961):

$$r(t) = (A_{\parallel} - A_{\perp})/(A_{\parallel} + 2A_{\perp}) \quad \text{(absorption)}$$
$$r(t) = (I_{\parallel} - I_{\perp})/(I_{\parallel} + 2I_{\perp}) \quad \text{(emission)} \tag{6}$$

The value of r_0 (anisotropy parameter immediately after the flash) depends on the angle, β, between the transition moment of excitation, μ_a, and absorption, μ_a^*, or emission, μ_e, and on experimental factors. Provided this angle is zero, the theoretical value of r_0 is 0.4. This value can only be predicted for an allowed transition not contaminated by other differently polarised transitions. In general, for a two-step photoselection reaction, this value can range from anywhere between -0.33 and 0.4, depending on the molecule (Albrecht, 1961; 1970). Hence, for rotational diffusion measurements one should always choose a chromophore with the highest possible value of r_0. The decrease in r_0 due to experimental factors will be discussed later.

The time dependence of the anisotropy parameter for an irregular body diffusing in an isotropic medium has been shown to consist of the sum of five exponential terms (Rigler and Ehrenberg, 1973; Belford *et al.*, 1972; Chuang and Eisenthal, 1972):

$$r(t) = \sum_{i=1}^{5} a_i \exp\left(-t/\Gamma_i\right) \tag{7}$$

where the a_i functions of the absorption and emission transition moments and the Γ_i functions of the three principal diffusion constants describe the three independent rotations around the three coordinate axes.

Effects of inhomogeneous sites on the anisotropy In equation 7 the time dependence of the anisotropy parameter is only a function of the transition moments and diffusion constants. A prerequisite for this result was the firm attachment of the chromophore at the same site of the rotating particles. In labelling experiments, however, there is good reason to believe that the chromophores occupy a variety of different sites. Hence the directions of the dipole moments and the decay constants for the excited states may all be different for different sites. Extending the results for two different sites given by Rigler and Ehrenberg (1973) to n sites we have:

$$r(t) = \left[\sum_{i=1}^{n} b_i \exp\left(-k_i t\right) r_i(t) \right] / \left[\sum_{i=1}^{n} b_i \exp\left(-k_i t\right) \right] \tag{8}$$

where b_i is weighting factors, k_i is the decay constant, and $r_i(t)$ the anisotropy parameter, given by equation 7, for the site i.

If the excited state lifetimes are all equal (k_i = constant for all i values) then the anisotropy parameter is still lifetime-independent (for example eosin and erythrosin bound to albumin (Garland and Moore, 1979):

$$r(t) = (1/n) \sum_{i=1}^{n} b_i r_i(t) \tag{9}$$

If the lifetimes are different, but the directions of the transition moments equal, then all r_i are the same and equation 8 reduces to equation 7 (for example bacteriorhodopsin, rhodium (III) protoporphyrin IX in cytochrome b_5). However, if both parameters — excited state lifetimes and angular dependent parts — in equation 8 are different ($k_i \neq k_j$, $r_i \neq r_j$; $1 \leq i, j \leq n$), then the anisotropy parameter is dependent on the excited state lifetimes.

Evaluation methods for protein rotation

There are two major classes of proteins the rotational diffusion of which have been studied: firstly, intrinsic proteins which span the lipid bilayer (for example, rhodopsin, bacteriorhodopsin, band 3 protein); and secondly, proteins that are only anchored in the membrane by a small hydrophobic segment (for example, cytochrome b_5). The first class of proteins may be approximated by a model based upon rotation of the protein around the membrane normal and given by Cherry *et al.* (1976). The second class may be described by the wobbling within a cone model, developed by Kawato and Kinosita (1981).

Rotation around membrane normal Following an approach given by Cherry *et al.* (1976) we may characterise the rotational diffusion of proteins in membranes by two diffusion constants, $D_{\parallel}$, for rotation about an axis normal to the membrane, and $D_{\perp}$, for rotation about either of the two perpendicular axes. Then the problem becomes formally equivalent to the case where rotation of a body with one symmetry axis (protein) occurs within an isotropic medium. For the angle $\beta = 0$ the time dependence of the anisotropy parameter then becomes:

$$r(t) = \sum_{i=1}^{3} A_i \exp(-E_i t) \tag{10}$$

with $A_1 = (6/5) \sin^2\gamma \cos^2\gamma$

$A_2 = (3/10) \sin^4\gamma$

$A_3 = (1/10)(3\cos^2\gamma - 1)^2$

$E_1 = 5D_\perp + D_\parallel$

$E_2 = 2D_\perp + 4D_\parallel$

$E_3 = 6D_\perp$

where γ is the angle between μ_a and the axis of symmetry.

There is good evidence for a variety of integral membrane proteins that rotation around an axis within the plane of the membrane does not occur. Thus, with the assumption $D_\perp \approx 0$ equation 10 simplifies to:

$$r(t) = A_1 \exp(-D_\parallel t) + A_2 \exp(-4D_\parallel t) + A_3 \tag{11}$$

with A_i having the same meaning as in equation 10. Equation 11 predicts that for a single rotating species the anisotropy parameter decays by two exponential functions to a time-independent value, called residual anisotropy r_∞ and determined by A_3.

The theoretical expression for $r(t)$ in equation 11 may be further simplified for most practical cases. Depolarisation due to light scattering in turbid membrane suspensions, use of laser excitation intensities so high as to excite only a negligible fraction of chromophores, and experimental factors, all combine to decrease $r(t)$ by a constant factor. This is one reason why, in most cases, the flash-induced anisotropy r_0 is lower than theoretically expected.

Two examples have been reported which show that in certain circumstances this theoretical value r_0 is attained (Heyn et al., 1981; Greinert et al., 1979).

Even with signal averaging it is in most cases observed that the data are not sufficiently accurate to discriminate between the two exponential decaying functions given in equation 11. The experimental data are in most cases best described by the simplified expression:

$$r(t) = (r_0 - r_\infty) \exp(-t/\varphi) + r_\infty \tag{12}$$

where φ is obtained through the time-dependent part of equation 12 and called hereafter rotational motion parameter. It should be noted that if temperature dependencies are studied for rotational diffusion, the value of interest (for example, activation energy in an Arrhenius plot) is the same whether calculated in an Arrhenius plot using the proper rotational diffusion constant $D_\parallel$ or the reciprocal of φ.

From the residual anisotropy together with r_0 it is possible to calculate the angle γ between the transition moment and membrane normal, provided that there is only a unique and firm binding site of the chromophore on the protein and all proteins are rotating within the timescale of observation. In this case we obtain:

$$\gamma = \arccos\ [1 \pm 2(r_\infty/r_0)^{1/2}/3]^{1/2} \tag{13}$$

The dependence of γ on r_∞/r_0 is illustrated in Figure 5.2.

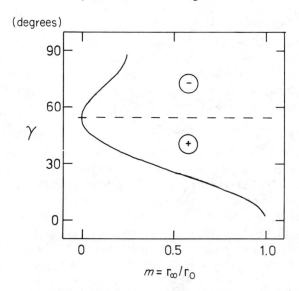

Figure 5.2 Dependent of the angle γ between transition moment and rotational diffusion axis on the ratio $m = r_\infty/r_0$. In the region $+$ and $-$, the values of γ are calculated taking the $+$ and $-$ sign, respectively, in front of the square root in $\gamma = \arccos\ [(1 \pm 2m^{1/2})/3]^{1/2}$

"Immobile" and mobile protein fractions A population of proteins is called immobile if their rotational relaxation time $\overline{D_\parallel}$ is about 10 times larger than the time interval used for the experiment. This time is limited in the case of triplet probes to five times at most of the lifetime of the excited state, that is, 5 to 10 msec, depending on the probe. With bacteriorhodopsin, some cytochromes and, particularly, rhodopsin this time is extended, because one can use photoproducts with longer lifetimes.

If a fraction f of molecules is immobile within a mobile population of proteins, the measured $r(t)$ curve is no longer given by equation 11. In this case we have:

$$r(t) = r^{\mathrm{mob}}\ (1-f) + r^{\mathrm{imm}}\ f \tag{14}$$

where r^{mob} is given by equation 12 and the fraction f of immobile proteins can be calculated according to:

$$f = [(r_\infty/r_0)_{\mathrm{exper}} - (r_\infty/r_0)_{\mathrm{th}}]/[1 - (r_\infty/r_0)_{\mathrm{th}}] \tag{15}$$

where $(r_\infty/r_0)_{exper}$ is the ratio of residual and flash-induced anisotropy from an experiment where an immobile population of proteins is expected and $(r_\infty/r_0)_{th}$ has to be determined independently. The latter value can be obtained either by first determining the angle γ by optical or electron spin resonance techniques and then calculating $(r_\infty/r_0)_{th}$ using equation 13, or by choosing the experimental conditions such that for the same membrane system immobile proteins can be excluded and then measuring the residual and flash-induced anisotropy directly. It should be remembered that these considerations are only valid if the direction of the transition moments (or the mean value for this direction in the case of heterogeneous binding sites) is the same for mobile and immobile proteins. An example of the determination of the fraction of immobile proteins will be given later for the system $(Ca^{2+} + Mg^{2+})$ATPase reconstituted with dipalmitoylphosphatidylcholine (Hoffmann *et al.*, 1980a).

Wobbling diffusion The idea of the tumbling of a molecule with its symmetry axis within the confines of a cone (wobbling diffusion) has been introduced only recently. Israelachvili *et al.* (1975) proposed a method to analyse line shapes of electron spin resonance spectra assuming both wobbling diffusion and restricted rotations about the long axis of a probe molecule. Kawato *et al.* (1977) described the motion of a fluorescence probe, diphenylhexatriene, incorporated into dipalmitoylphosphatidylcholine liposomes by a similar model and extended it recently to independent wobbling of hydrophilic parts of rotating membrane proteins (segmental motion) and independent probe motion (Kawato and Kinosita, 1981). Proteins anchored in the membrane by only a small hydrophobic group may also be described by this model.

The wobbling diffusion model can be described as follows. Suppose the direction of the transition moment of the chromophore is allowed to move within a cone of half angle θ_c. For the following it does not matter whether this movement is connected with independent probe motion (centre of the cone would be the reactive group of the probe), independent segmental motion of parts of the protein (centre of the cone would be the site of attachment of the respective moving part), or movement of almost all of the protein, if it is only attached to the membrane via a small hydrophobic group. The half angle θ_c in all cases may be given by steric hindrance of the respective surrounding structure. In the simplest case we may assume that the diffusion constant within the cone is constant. This corresponds to the case where the barrier against wobbling motion is supposed to be a rigid wall (square well potential). As shown by Kawato and Kinosita (1981), this model is already a good approximation when compared to more realistic potentials. The time dependence of the anisotropy parameter for wobbling diffusion is given by (Kawato and Kinosita, 1981):

$$r(t) = \sum_{i=1}^{\infty} c_i \exp\left(-D_w t/\sigma_i\right) \qquad (16)$$

where c_i and σ_i depend only on θ_c and D_w is the wobbling diffusion constant. The half angle θ_c is related to the ratio between residual and flash-induced anisotropy by:

$$r_\infty/r_0 = [(1/2) \cos \theta_c (1 + \cos \theta_c)]^2 \tag{17}$$

In actual experiments the time dependence of r is closely approximated by:

$$r(t) = (r_0 - r_\infty) \exp (-D_w t/\langle \sigma \rangle) + r_\infty \tag{18}$$

where D_w/σ is given by the measured rotational relaxation time.

Rotational diffusion around membrane normal and additional wobbling diffusion
In general, rotational diffusion around the membrane normal and wobbling diffusion can be superimposed. An approximate expression for the time-dependent anisotropy parameter in these conditions was provided by Lipari and Szabo (1980). For a single species we may write:

$$r(t) = \sum_{i=1}^{3} a_i \exp (-b_i^r t/\Gamma^r) S^2 + (1 - S^2) \exp (-b_i^w t/\Gamma^w) \tag{19}$$

$S = (3\cos^2 \delta - 1)/2$ where δ is the instantaneous angle between molecular symmetry axis and membrane normal

The superscripts r and w refer to the contributions from rotation and wobbling, respectively. The constants a_i, b_i^r, and b_i^w are given as follows:

i	a_i	b_i^r	b_i^w	
1	$(3/10) \sin^2 \gamma_a \sin^2 \gamma_e \cos^2 \gamma_d$	4	2	
2	$(3/10) \sin^2 \gamma_a \sin^2 \gamma_e \cos \gamma_d$	1	5	(20)
3	$(1/10) (3\cos^2 \gamma_a - 1) (3\cos^2 \gamma_e - 1)$	0	6	

γ_a and γ_e are the angles between the membrane normal and the direction of the transition moment for absorption and emission, respectively, and γ_d is the difference angle between the projections of the two transition moments into the plane of the membrane.

Additional comments regarding equations 19 and 20 have been given by Jovin *et al.* (1981).

Absorption depolarisation
The first successful measurement on rotational diffusion of membrane proteins was performed by Cone (1972) on the rhodopsin system. As this molecule is not luminescent, but does possess a variety of spectrally-defined intermediates with suitable lifetimes, rotational diffusion was followed using the time dependence of flash-induced dichroism. Until recently, triplet probes were also characterised by absorption measurements of ground state depletion or triplet–triplet absorption (Razi-Naqvi *et al.*, 1973; Cherry, 1978; Hoffmann *et al.*, 1979).

Flash photolysis apparatus The basic components of a flash photolysis apparatus for measuring rotational diffusion of proteins by absorption depolarisation are as follows. The exciting source is conveniently given by a laser with an output energy of 10 to 150 mJ per flash which is vertically polarised. This may be either a dye laser or a frequency doubled neodymium laser. The advantage of the former is that it allows easy alteration of the excitation wavelength (fixed excitation wavelength of 530 nm for the neodymium laser), while the advantage of the latter is its short pulse width of about 20 nsec (compared with a few μsec pulse width for the dye laser).

If triplet probes are to be used, the sample in a fluorimeter cuvette should be degassed by pure nitrogen or argon in order to remove oxygen, thus effectively quenching the triplet states. Furthermore, removal of oxygen prevents photo-oxidation of, for example, $(Ca^{2+} + Mg^{2+})$ATPase (Bürkli and Cherry, 1981).

Absorption changes in the sample initiated by laser flash excitation are followed with a continuous measuring white light beam (50–100 W light intensity). After passing through the sample, the light is focused at the entrance slit of a monochromater. The light emerging from the exit slit is divided into parallel and perpendicular components with respect to the polarisation of the exciting flash with the aid of a polarising beam splitter. Each of the two components pass though a polarising filter orientated with its polarising axis according to its relation to the beam splitter. Light detection for the two components is measured simultaneously with two photomultipliers. The photomultiplier gains are most easily matched by adjustment of their separate high-voltage supplies. The two signals from the photomultiplier tubes can then be recorded and stored in a transient recorder with suitable time resolution. To increase the signal to noise ratio of the signals it is advantageous to use signal averaging.

With these averaged signals data analysis can then be performed by computer fitting of the experimental results. For more details of the apparatus the reader is referred to Cherry (1978), Garland and Moore (1979), and Hoffman *et al.* (1979).

Probe molecules Let ϵ^g_{max} and ϵ^*_{max} be the maximal extinction coefficients of the molecule in the ground state and excited state (or for the flash-induced photoproduct), respectively. If the absorption spectrum of the excited state (or photoproduct) does not interfere with the absorption spectrum of the ground state and has only a small ϵ^*_{max} (for example, triplet probes), one may use the ground state depletion and the signal is proportional to ϵ^g_{max}. Alternatively, one may use the absorption evoked from the excited state or photoproduct. An example of the latter is lumirhodopsin within the reaction cascade of rhodopsin.

Special features Light-sensitive probe molecules which show almost exclusively absorbance changes after excitation (for example retinal in rhodopsin and bacteriorhodopsin) are required for this method. However, kinetic absorbance measurements are inherently insensitive because one has to measure a small difference between two much larger signals, each of which carries light-source noise and photomultiplier shot noise.

Because of signal-to-noise considerations the samples have to have a chromophore concentration in the range of 1 to 10 μM (Austin *et al.*, 1979; Cherry, 1978). Attempts to improve the sensitivity of the method by use of higher concentrations of labelled proteins or by use of cuvettes with longer light paths do not help because particle scattering causes depolarisation of the signal of interest (anisotropy parameter) to occur (Junge and DeVault, 1975).

These effects restrict the applicability of absorption depolarisation to relatively few *in vivo* or *in vitro* membrane systems.

Fluorescence and phosphorescence depolarisation

The advantage of using delayed fluorescence (also called E(osin)-type delayed fluorescence) in probing rotational diffusion of membrane proteins was first pointed out by Razi-Naqvi and Wild (1975). However, it was 1979 before Greinert *et al.* (1979) published a paper describing the application of the method.

Phosphorescence depolarisation, extending the sensitivity for depolarisation methods about 100-fold with respect to absorption depolarisation, was introduced almost at the same time by Garland and Moore (1979) and Austin *et al.* (1979).

Flash photolysis apparatus The apparatus for these measurements is very similar to that already described for absorbance measurements. The main alterations are as follows. The laser energy can be made much lower (in the order 20-200 μJ per flash) and hence nitrogen pumped dye laser with short pulse widths (about 5 nsec) become available. It is no longer necessary to use a monochromator behind the sample as the whole phosphorescence spectrum can be used for measurement and only a filter allowing the passage of the red phosphorescence and blocking the prompt and delayed fluorescence is necessary for phosphorescence measurements.

In the case of delayed fluorescence measurements it becomes more complicated as the very intense prompt fluorescence, having an identical emission spectrum to delayed fluorescence, must not reach the photomultipliers. This is achieved by a fast rotating mechanical chopper. The dead-time of such an apparatus was 76 μsec and said to have the potential to be shortened to a few μsec (Greinert *et al.*, 1979).

From the above it can be appreciated that phosphorescence depolarisation measurements are easier to perform than delayed fluorescence measurements.

Special features For delayed fluorescence measurements the direction of the transition moment for absorption and emission is the same. The time dependence for the anisotropy parameter is therefore given by equation 11 for rotation about the membrane normal. In the case of phosphorescence depolarisation it is unlikely that the dipole moments for absorption and triplet emission are parallel. As shown by Rigler and Ehrenberg (1973) and stated by Moore *et al.* (1979), the three constants A_i in equation 11 are now given by:

$$A_1 = (6/5)\sin\gamma_a\sin\gamma_e\cos\gamma_a\cos\gamma_e\cos\gamma_d$$
$$A_2 = (3/10)\sin^2\gamma_a\sin^2\gamma_e(\cos^2\gamma_d - \sin^2\gamma_d) \qquad (21)$$
$$A_3 = (1/10)(3\cos^2\gamma_a - 1)(3\cos^2\gamma_e - 1)$$

where γ_a and γ_e are the angles between the axis of rotation and the transition moments for excitation and emission, respectively and γ_d is the angle difference between the projections of these two transition moments into the plane of the membrane.

Fluorescence depletion depolarisation

Very recently, Johnson and Garland (1981) have developed a new method for measuring the rotational diffusion of membrane proteins within single cells. Following absorption of light by a triplet probe there is ground state depletion due to triplet formation. In the absorption measurements it was this ground state depletion which was measured spectroscopically. As most triplet probes are also fluorescent, it is possible to measure the small fluorescence depletion due to triplet formation following the exciting flash by using an attenuated measuring light source. This fluorescence depletion is polarised when induced with a polarised laser flash, and becomes depolarised by rotational diffusion of the probe or the protein, to which it is attached. This method combines therefore the high sensitivity of prompt fluorescence measurements with the long lifetime of triplet probes.

Flash photolysis apparatus The apparatus is based on a laser–microscope combination originally used for translational diffusion measurements by fluorescence microphotolysis. For these latter measurements it has already been suggested by Garland (1981) that laser intensities are best controlled by an acousto-optic modulator. A pockels cell is used which serves to rotate the polarisation plane of the laser by 90° within less than 1 μsec.

The sample is mounted in a temperature-regulated stage of a microscope. The laser used for measuring fluorescence (attenuated) and causing ground state depletion (unattenuated) is a continuous ion laser (for example, 1 W continuous argon ion laser). The fluorescence is measured by photon counting and the counts are accumulated in a multichannel analyser. A typical experiment for measuring the parallel and perpendicular signal is performed in the following way.

Assume one sweep with the multichannel analyser to consist of 1,024 addresses with an address time of, say, 10 μsec. Initially, the laser beam is attenuated about 10^3-fold from its unattenuated level to a measuring intensity of a few μW and the undepleted fluorescence signal is recorded for about 0.5 msec. The attenuation of the laser beam is then briefly released for a bleach period of 2-80 μsec. This causes about 20-30 per cent ground state depletion due to triplet formation. The photomultiplier is gated out electronically during this bleach period. The intensity then returns to the original measuring level for several msec. during which time the measured fluorescence increases again towards its level before the bleach period due to repopulation from the triplet state. Next, the measuring intensity is further attenuated to a maximal level in order to allow full recovery of the ground state. These events occur during the first half of the sweep (with the above chosen address time, in 5.12 msec). The same events occur over the second half with one difference: the pockels cell rotates the polarisation plane of the laser at the beginning of the bleach period in about 200 nsec by 90° and back again at the end of the bleach period. Hence the signal measured during the first half of the sweep is the parallel signal that during the second half is the perpendicular one. The sweeps are repeated until a sufficient number of counts per address has been collected. A typical example of such an experiment is shown in Figure 5.3.

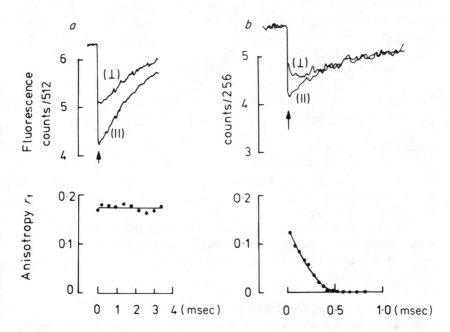

Figure 5.3 Fluorescence depletion depolarisation measurements on: *a*, eosin in solid solution; and *b*, eosin attached to albumin in viscous solution. The upper traces are fluorescence photon counts per address, the lower ones are the anisotropy curves. The data, taken from Johnson and Garland (1981), should indicate the sensitivity of this method (data shown are for 10^5 eosin molecules; the same data quality could be obtained for only 10^3 tetramethylrhodamine molecules)

Probe molecules The probe molecules should exhibit photochemical stability to improve the signal-to-noise ratio by signal averaging (in the example shown in Figure 5.3*b* a total of 8,192 sweeps were collected, in an application to band 3 protein in erythrocyte ghosts even 32,768 sweeps were necessary to obtain reasonable signals (Johnson and Garland, 1981)). Furthermore, the choice of the probe for this technique has to be a compromise between two extremes. First, if probe molecules have a quantum yield near one for triplet formation (for example, erythrosin), then there is rapid and sufficient ground state depletion; however, the fluorescence yield is low and consequently the fluorescence measured is weak. An increase of the measuring intensity to increase the fluorescence is of limited appeal because there should be no significant ground state depletion during the measuring period. Second, at the other extreme, ϕ_T may be small, whereas ϕ_F can approach unity. In this case ground state depletion during the bleach period is only significant with higher laser powers and longer bleach periods. This should not cause thermal artefacts because, as Axelrod (1977) calculated, even with higher laser powers (20–30 mW at 514 nm), smaller spot diameters for observation (2.5 μm), and longer bleach periods (up to 50 μsec) the local temperature of the cell containing 5×10^3 μm rhodamine molecules should not rise by more than 0.1°C. In addition, the measuring intensity in this case can be made high, because there is no significant ground state depletion due to the low triplet quantum yield.

As a measure that may indicate the usefulness of a probe for fluorescence depletion experiments, Johnson and Garland (1981) defined the ratio ϕ_F/ϕ_T. The higher this value, the better that particular probe molecule, provided photochemical stability is assured.

Special features The suggested method is a very sensitive one for measuring rotational diffusion, even in single cells. Compared to absorption or phosphorescence measurements this new method is about 10^6 to 10^9 times more sensitive. With tetramethylrhodamine as a probe it is possible to measure usable signals with only about 1,000 molecules.

The only real disadvantage of the method so far discovered is the relatively long bleach period, especially if rotational relaxation times in the order of μsecs are to be measured. However, as most of the proteins studied so far show slower relaxation times, this limitation is of only minor importance.

Fluorescence bleaching depolarisation
This new method, described by Smith *et al.* (1981), is similar to the last one (fluorescence depletion depolarisation) in that it is capable of measuring rotational diffusion in single cells with a high degree of sensitivity due to measurement of prompt fluorescence. Furthermore, it is different to all the methods so far described in that it irreversibly bleaches fluorophores with a short, intense burst of polarised laser irradiation. After the flash, prompt fluorescence is excited with the low intensity observation beam, again of polarised laser radiation. Provided the latter is orientated parallel to the bleaching pulse, fluorescence will increase due to rotation of the remaining fluorescent molecules. Alternatively, the fluorescence signal will decrease due to rotation, if the measuring beam is polarised perpendicular with respect to the bleaching pulse. The main advantage of this

method lies in the possibility of observing rotational relaxation times as slow as several minutes, the measuring time being limited only by the stability of the electronics and the sample. For more details and data evaluation the reader is referred to the original paper by Smith *et al.* (1981).

Lateral diffusion

Basic principles
In contrast to most procedures for rotational diffusion studies (with the exception of the one latterly mentioned) where photochemical stability of the chromophore is advantageous, the ability to bleach irreversibly the chromophores with an intense light pulse is a prerequisite for lateral diffusion measurements. Furthermore, in contrast to rotational diffusion measurements, which can be performed with membranes suspended in solution, it is necessary in lateral diffusion studies to select single cells by the use of a microscope. Two basic approaches are possible to perform lateral diffusion measurements. Firstly, a small spot (some μm^2) on a single cell is irradiated by an intense laser pulse and chromophores present in the spot are irreversibly bleached. The redistribution of unbleached chromophores is followed with the same laser beam attenuated some 10^4-fold. Depending on how the chromophores are characterised, the experimental procedure is called fluorescence or absorption microphotolysis. Synonyms for the former are fluorescence recovery (or redistribution) after photobleaching (FRAP) and fluorescence photobleaching recovery (FPR) (for reviews see Cherry, 1979; Peters, 1981). Secondly, one may allow bleaching and redistribution to occur simultaneously (Peters *et al.*, 1981). Again, a small area of a cell under a microscope is irradiated, this time continuously with an intermediate intensity. The time course of the fluorescence signal originating from the irradiated area depends on the rate of decomposition of the chromophores and on the rate at which unbleached chromophores enter the irradiated area from its surroundings. Methods based on this procedure are called continuous fluorescence (or absorption) microphotolysis.

Fluorescence and absorption microphotolysis
The ability paritally to bleach rhodopsin irreversibly within the disc organelle from the rod outer segment and then follow the redistribution of unbleached molecules via absorption under a microscope, provided the first quantitative lateral diffusion measurements of intrinsic proteins (Poo and Cone, 1974). As yet, this is the only membrane system where absorption studies have been used to determine lateral diffusion. The principles of the method and data evaluation are almost identical to the fluorescence microphotolysis method, however, and therefore we will only discuss this latter method in detail. This method was first performed by Peters *et al.* (1974) and subsequently developed further by a variety of workers (Axelrod *et al.*, 1976a; Smith and McConnell, 1978; Smith *et al.*, 1979a; Koppel, 1979).

The main steps for the fluorescence microphotolysis method are as follows. Firstly, the membrane components, the lateral diffusion of which are to be investigated, are fluorescently labelled (for the method there is almost no difference whether proteins or lipids are used). Next, the sample is placed in a fluorescence microscope and a single cell chosen for measurement. A small area of the cell (typically about 1 per cent of the cell surface) is irradiated with light at low intensity with an appropriate wavelength so as to excite the fluorophores. If there are of the order of 20,000 fluorophores within the irradiated area, it is technically possible to detect a fluorescence signal. This may be used as a measure of the number of unbleached fluorophores. Thirdly, the light intensity is briefly elevated about 10^4- to 10^5-fold (several msec and up to several seconds for lipid and protein lateral diffusion measurements, respectively). This induces a rapid and irreversible photolysis of the fluorophores (about 50 to 80 per cent of the fluorophores present). After the bleaching period the light intensity is attenuated to its previous level; however, the fluorescence signal is now lower due to photolysis of the fluorophores. If neither movement of the whole cell (uniform flow) nor lateral diffusion of the investigated cell components takes place, the fluorescence signal evoked by the measuring beam stays constant. However, if either one or both of these processes occur, then an increase of the fluorescence signal is observed due to nonphotolysed fluorophores entering into the irradiated area from the surroundings. From the time dependence shown in the recovery of fluorescence, firstly, the type of motion (flow or diffusion) and, secondly, the diffusion constant, may be worked out. The simplifying assumptions made in the above are: the intensity being measured is so low that photolysis is negligible during the record of the fluorescence signal; and bleaching destroys the chromophores irreversibly within a time period that is brief compared to the diffusion time being measured. The range of diffusion constants measurable with this technique is approximately 10^{-6} down to $10^{-12}\,\mathrm{cm^2\,s^{-1}}$.

Bleaching and measurement by fixed "spot" geometry This widespread method is easy to perform and a theoretical basis and guidelines for data evaluation have been given by Axelrod *et al.* (1976a). A small spot on the cell surface (about $10\,\mu\mathrm{m^2}$) is photobleached by a brief exposure to an intense laser beam (delivered energy about 10 mJ) and the subsequent recovery is monitored by the same, but about 10^4- to 10^5-fold attenuated, laser beam. The laser beam may have a gaussian profile (most often used) or a uniform circular disc profile (see Kapitza and Sackmann, 1980; Peters and Richter, 1981). The following theoretical treatment for fluorescence recovery curves for the idealised cases of pure two-dimensional diffusion, pure uniform flow and simultaneous diffusion and flow, is taken from Axelrod *et al.* (1976a).

Photobleaching is assumed to be an irreversible first order reaction within the bleaching period t_b. The rate constant for bleaching is given by $\alpha I(r)$, I being the bleaching intensity, and r the position in the x–y plane of the membrane ($r = 0$ corresponds to the centre of the spot). Time t_b is supposed to be short with respect to transport processes under consideration. During the bleach period the concentration of unbleached chromophores $c(r, t)$ in the absence of transport is given by:

$$\partial c(r, t)/\partial t = -\alpha I(r)c(r, t) \tag{22}$$

At the beginning of the recovery phase ($t = 0$) the fluorophore concentration is given by

$$c(r, 0) = c_i \exp\left(-\alpha t_b I(r)\right) \tag{23}$$

where c_i is the initial concentration of fluorophores before bleaching. The extent of bleaching induced in time t_b may be expressed by a parameter K:

$$K = \alpha t_b I(0) \tag{24}$$

For a gaussian beam the intensity profile $I(r)$ is given by

$$I(r) = (2P_0/\pi w^2) \exp\left(-2r^2/w^2\right) \tag{25}$$

where P_0 is the bleaching laser power and w the half width at e^{-2} height.

For a circular disc profile we have

$$I(r) = \begin{cases} P_0/\pi w^2 & \text{for } r \leqslant w \\ 0 & \text{for } r > w \end{cases} \tag{26}$$

where w is the radius of the disc.

For a single species the differential equation for lateral transport with diffusion constant D_l and uniform flow v_x in the x direction is given by:

$$\frac{\partial c(r, t)}{\partial t} = D_l \nabla^2 c(r, t) - v_x \frac{\partial c(r, t)}{\partial x} \tag{27}$$

The boundary condition is $c(r \to \infty, t) = c_i$ and the initial condition $c(r, t = 0)$ is given by equation 23.

The fluorescence $F_K(t)$ observed at time $t \geqslant 0$ is given by

$$F_K(t) = (q/a) \int_{r=0}^{\infty} I(r)\, c_K(r, t)\, d^2 r \tag{28}$$

where $c_K(r, t)$ is the solution of equation 27 for the K-dependent initial condition given in equation 23; q is the product of all quantum efficiencies of light absorption, emission and detection; and a is the attenuation factor of the beam during fluorescence recovery. In the case of a circular disc profile it is sometimes convenient to evaluate the fluorescence recovery curve in fractional form $f_K(t)$, defined as:

$$f_K(t) = [F_K(t) - F_K(0)]/[F_K(\infty) - F_K(0)] \tag{29}$$

A typical fluorescence recovery curve is shown schematically in Figure 5.4a. In order to work out transport parameters from such measured recovery curves,

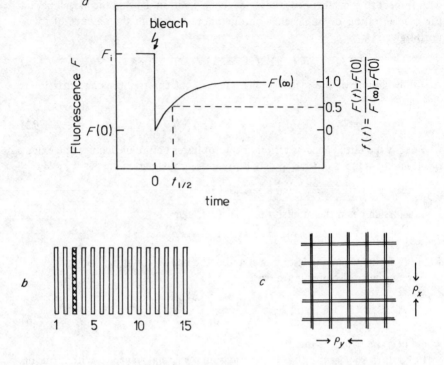

Figure 5.4 *a*, Typical fluorescence recovery curve. *b*, Bleaching (within shaded area at position 3) and subsequent scanning of measuring beam periodically along, say, 15 measuring locations. *c*, Schematic periodic pattern bleaching within stripes of period ρ_x and ρ_y

computer curve fitting procedures may be applied. For this, the solution for equation 28 or 29 is given as series solution, which is more convenient for numerical evaluation than in closed form.

Only diffusion ($v_x = 0$):

$$F_K(t) = (qP_0 c_i/a) \sum_{n=0}^{\infty} [(-K)^n/n!] \; [1 + n(1 + 2t/\tau_D)] \tag{30}$$

for a gaussian beam profile

$$f(t) = 1 - (\tau_D/t) \exp(-2\tau_D/t) \; [B_0(2\tau_D/t) + B_2(2\tau_D/t)]$$

$$- 2 \sum_{k=0}^{\infty} \frac{(-1)^k (2k+2)! \, (k+1)! \, (\tau_D/t)^{k+2}}{(k!)^2 \, (k+2)!^2} \tag{31}$$

for a circular disc profile, where $\tau_D = w^2/4D_1$ is the characteristic lateral diffusion time, and B_0 and B_2 are modified Bessel functions.

Only uniform flow ($D_1 = 0$), for a gaussian beam profile we have:

$$F_K(t) = (qP_0c_i/a) \sum_{n=0}^{\infty} [(-K)^n/(n+1)!] \exp\{[-2n/(n+1)] (t/\tau_F)^2\} \quad (32)$$

and with a circular disc profile:

$$f(t) = (2/\pi) \sin^{-1} (t/\tau_F) + (t/\tau_F) [1 - t^2/4\tau_F^2]^{1/2} \quad (33)$$

Combined flow and diffusion:

$$F_K(t) = (qP_0c_i/a) \sum_{n=0}^{\infty} \frac{(-K)^n \exp\{-2(t/\tau_F)^2 n/[1 + n(1 + 2t/\tau_D)]\}}{n! \, 1 + n(1 + 2t/\tau_D)} \quad (34)$$

for a gaussian beam profile.

With the technique described it is rather difficult to distinguish between combined flow and diffusion (equation 34) and pure diffusion (equations 30 and 31). This may result in a considerable error for D_1 if unexpected membrane flow is occurring in addition to lateral diffusion.

For many practical purposes, diffusion and flow parameters (only if separated) can be obtained from equations 35 and 36, respectively:

$$D_1 = (w^2/4t_{1/2})\beta_D \quad \text{(diffusion)} \quad (35)$$

$$v_x = (w/4t_{1/2})\beta_F \quad \text{(flow)} \quad (36)$$

where $t_{1/2}$ is the time where the fractional fluorescence recovery f is 0.5. In the case of a circular disc profile β_D and β_F are constants with the values

$$\beta_D = 0.88 \quad \text{and} \quad \beta_F = 0.81 \quad (37)$$

For a gaussian beam profile these values depend on the degree of photolysis. β_D Ranges from 1.0 for little photolysis to 1.7 for 90 per cent photolysis. The corresponding range for β_F is between 0.9 and 1.1. If a fraction of the labelled proteins is immobile in the timescale of the experiment, the fluorescence signal $F(\infty)$ will not reach F_i, the initial level it had before bleaching. The mobile fraction of molecules is given by

$$R = [F(\infty) - F(0)]/[F_i - F(0)] \quad (38)$$

It should be noted that equation 38 is based on the model of an infinite two-dimensional plane. In some experiments where cells have a small area, one has to take the finite size of the cell into account, although for most cell systems this model is well approximated. If in practice $F(\infty)$ is smaller than F_i one may perform an easy experiment to see whether this change is simply given by the restrictive cell area or whether an immobile protein fraction is present. If $F(\infty)$ is different from F_i for only the first bleach and all subsequent recovery curves performed on the same spot reveal the same fluorescence both before and a long time after the bleach, the evaluation according to equation 38 may be performed.

Bleaching and subsequent scanning of measuring beam periodically in space This method, invented by Koppel (1979) and called multi-point analysis originally, monitors the fluorescence redistribution after photobleaching with the measuring beam periodically scanning at different locations in, and adjacent to, the bleached area, as shown schematically in figure 5.4b. As will be shown below, the additional spatial information thus obtained firstly provides a sensitivity to systematic flow superimposed on lateral diffusion and, secondly, renders it no longer necessary to make explicit assumptions on beam profiles. In addition, bleaching kinetics do not have to be determined in separate experiments. The following theoretical treatment follows closely the one given by Koppel (1979).

Define $F(\Delta r, t)$ as the fluorescence intensity at time t excited by a measuring beam centred at a position shifted Δr relative to the bleaching beam:

$$F(\Delta r, t) = q \int_{r=0}^{\infty} I(r - \Delta r)c(r, t)d^2r \tag{39}$$

The concentration $c(r, t)$ of fluorescent (nonbleached) fluorophores at time t at position r can be related to $c(r, 0)$, the concentration profile immediately after the bleaching pulse by:

$$c(r, t) = \int_{r'=0}^{\infty} G(r - r', t)c(r', 0)d^2r' \tag{40}$$

where $G(r - r', t)$ is the probability per unit area that a molecule at point r' at time 0 will be at point r at time t. In our case we have

$$G(r'', t) = (4\pi D_1 t)^{-1} \exp\left(-|r'' - vt|^2/(4D_1 t)\right) \tag{41}$$

Combining equations 39 and 40 we have, with $r'' = r - r'$:

$$F(\Delta r, t) = q \int_{r=0}^{\infty} I(r - \Delta r) \int_{r''=0}^{\infty} G(r'', t)c(r - r'', 0)d^2r'' d^2r$$

$$= q \int_{r''=0}^{\infty} G(r'', t)F(\Delta r - r'', 0)d^2r'' \tag{42}$$

In the following, different beam geometries are considered. Firstly, the bleaching and measuring beam are focused to yield a line very much longer than it is wide. Secondly, beam profiles are the usual circular symmetric spots. Finally, lateral motion on a half-bleached sphere is investigated.

LINE GEOMETRY　　Assuming a gaussian beam profile we have

$$F(\Delta r - r'', 0)/F_i = 1 - \alpha \exp\left\{-[e_x(\Delta r - r'')]^2/w_0^2\right\} \tag{43}$$

where α is a constant that characterises the extent of bleaching ($0 < \alpha < 1$); e_x is the unity vector along the x axis, perpendicular to the orientation of the lines;

w_0 is the e^{-1} radius of the gaussian beam; and F_i the initial fluorescence before bleaching.

Combining equations 41 to 43 and integrating over r'' we have

$$F(\Delta r, t)/F_i = 1 - \alpha(t) \exp \left\{ -[e_x(\Delta r - vt)]^2/w^2(t) \right\} \tag{44}$$

where $\qquad \alpha(t) = \alpha/(1 - t/\tau_D)^{1/2}$ and $w^2(t) = w_0^2 (1 + t/\tau_D)$.

In a practical case, if the measuring beam is scanned along the x axis (see figure 5.4b), we have with $(1 - \zeta)$ the immobile fraction of fluorophores

$$F(\Delta x, t)/F_i = 1 - \zeta \alpha(t) \exp \left\{ -(\Delta x - v_x t)^2/w^2(t) \right\} -$$
$$- (1 - \zeta) \alpha \exp \left\{ -(\Delta x - v_x t)^2/w_0^2 \right\} \tag{45}$$

SPOT GEOMETRY   With a gaussian beam profile

$$F(\Delta r - r'', 0)/F_i = 1 - \alpha \exp \left\{ -|\Delta r - r''|^2/w_0^2 \right\} \tag{46}$$

Combining equations 41, 42 and 46 and integrating over r'' gives

$$F(\Delta r, t)/F_i = 1 - \alpha(t) \exp \left\{ -|\Delta r - vt|^2/w^2(t) \right\} \tag{47}$$

where $\alpha(t)$ and $w^2(t)$ are as given before. For the practical case considered before, we get

$$F(\Delta x, t)/F_i = 1 - \zeta \alpha(t) \exp \left\{ -(\Delta x)^2/w^2(t) \right\} -$$
$$- (1 - \zeta) \alpha \exp \left\{ -(\Delta x)^2/w_0^2 \right\} \tag{48}$$

LATERAL MOTION ON A HALF-BLEACHED SPHERE

As a special case for the described method we follow an approach given by Peters *et al.* (1974) for lateral motion of molecules on a sphere. Assume bleaching performed on one half of a sphere. Fluorescence recovery and depletion is measured periodically on the bleached and unbleached hemisphere, respectively. The concentration of fluorophores for the two hemispheres is denoted by $c_-(t)$ and $c_+(t)$, respectively. We define (Schindler *et al.*, 1980):

$$p(t) = \frac{c_+(t) - c_-(t)}{c_+(t) + c_-(t)} = \frac{\Delta c(t)}{c_{tot}} \tag{49}$$

as a normalised measure for fluorophore redistribution ($0 \leqslant p(t) \leqslant 1$). Assuming that all molecules which are labelled move with diffusion coefficient D_1 on the surface of a sphere of radius r, bleached over one hemisphere at $t = 0$, we have (Peters *et al.*, 1974; Huang, 1973):

$$p(t) = \frac{\alpha_+ - \alpha_-}{\alpha_+ + \alpha_-} \sum_{k=0}^{\infty} P_k \exp \left\{ -(2k + 1)(2k + 2)(D_1 t/r^2) \right\} \tag{50}$$

where α_+ and α_- characterise the extent of bleaching for the unbleached and bleached half of the hemisphere, respectively, and

$$P_k = (4k + 3) \left[\frac{(2k)!}{2^{2k+1} k! (k + 1)!} \right]^2 \tag{51}$$

An iterative procedure for determining $p(t)$ and P_k has been given by Peters *et al.* (1974).

Periodic pattern bleaching This method shows its major advantage in the determination of very small and/or anisotropic diffusion constants. The disadvantage with respect to the methods already described is the need for a fairly large cell membrane area (approximately $100 \ \mu m^2$). Smith and McConnell (1978) first invented the method. Fluorophores were photobleached in such a way that a periodic variation of fluorescence intensity as a function of position resulted. This was achieved by placing a Ronchi ruling during bleaching in front of the sample, which consisted of evenly-spaced opaque parallel lines with stripe period ρ on a transparent substrate. This technique was extended to allow simultaneous, independent lateral diffusion measurement in two directions by the use of a photobleached pattern that is periodic in these two directions (Smith *et al.*, 1979a). Fluorescence micrographs are made of the cell at intervals after the photobleaching.

We denote ρ_x and ρ_y as the stripe periods in the two perpendicular directions x and y (see figure 5.4c). The following theoretical analysis takes advantage of the simplicity of the Fourier transform of the diffusion equation and is taken from Smith *et al.* (1979a).

It is assumed that diffusion in an infinite two-dimensional system is characterised by a diffusion tensor D^T, that is, the diffusion constant may be different for particles, diffusing in different directions in the x–y plane. The diffusion equation in this case is given by:

$$\frac{\partial c(x, y, t)}{\partial t} = \left(\frac{\partial}{\partial x}, \frac{\partial}{\partial y} \right) \begin{pmatrix} D_{xx} & D_{xy} \\ D_{yx} & D_{yy} \end{pmatrix} \begin{pmatrix} \dfrac{\partial}{\partial x} \\ \dfrac{\partial}{\partial y} \end{pmatrix} c(x, y, t) \tag{52}$$

The Fourier transform of equation 52 is given by

$$\frac{\partial T(k_x, k_y, t)}{\partial t} = -(k_x, k_y) \begin{pmatrix} D_{xx} & D_{xy} \\ D_{yx} & D_{yy} \end{pmatrix} T(k_x, k_y, t) \tag{53}$$

where (k_x, k_y) is a wave vector with a spatial frequency corresponding to

$$k_x = 2\pi/\rho_x \quad \text{and} \quad k_y = 2\pi/\rho_y \tag{54}$$

Generally, the Fourier transform is a complex function, represented by an amplitude and a phase. As the phase is not affected by diffusion, it is only necessary to deal with the amplitude $T(k_x, k_y, t)$. The solution to equation 53 is given by

$$T(k_x, k_y, t) = T(k_x, k_y, 0) \exp\left\{-(k_x, k_y) \begin{pmatrix} D_{xx} & D_{xy} \\ D_{yx} & D_{yy} \end{pmatrix} \begin{pmatrix} k_x \\ k_y \end{pmatrix} t\right\} \quad (55)$$

where $T(k_x, k_y, 0)$ is the value of the Fourier amplitude as a function of wave vector at time 0. Because D^T is constant (independent of position and time), there exists a choice of coordinates X and Y such that D^T is diagonal, in which case:

$$T(k_x, k_y, t) = T(k_x, k_y, 0) \exp\left\{-(k_x^2 + k_y^2)(D_{XX} \cos^2\theta + D_{YY} \sin^2\theta)t\right\} \quad (56)$$

where θ is the angle between (k_x, k_y) and the positive k_x axis.

Data evaluation becomes particularly easy if a square pattern geometry is chosen and if diffusion is characterised along the two perpendicular directions of the stripes. In this case the solution for diffusion along x and y, respectively, is given by:

$$c(u, t) = a_0 + a_1 \exp\left\{-D_{uu}\rho_u^2 t\right\} \sin(\rho_u u) +$$

$$+ \sum_{k=2}^{\infty} a_k \exp\left\{-D_{uu}(2k - 1)^2 \rho_u^2 t\right\} \sin\left[(2k - 1)\rho_u u\right] \quad (57)$$

where $u = x$ or y (Smith and McConnell, 1978). Equation 57 states that the period of the striped pattern in space remains constant and that the amplitude of the pattern decays with time. Because the terms in the sum decay much more rapidly than the second term, equation 57 may be approximated for times $t > 0.1/D_{uu}\rho_u^2$ by only the first two terms and neglecting the sum. The two diffusion constants can then be calculated from the measured time constants τ_u according to

$$D_{uu} = 1/\rho_u^2 \tau_u \quad (58)$$

In a special application, Owicki and McConnell (1980) used the described stripe pattern method to evaluate lateral diffusion in inhomogeneous membranes.

Continuous fluorescence and absorption microphotolysis

This new method has been applied by Peters *et al.* (1981). As compared to fluorescence microphotolysis, described in the previous section, this method brings about an improvement of data quality and detection limit by some orders of magnitude. In the description thereafter we follow closely the work of Peters *et al.* (1981) and Peters (1981).

The number of molecules available in microscopic membrane studies is naturally limited. For example, the density of membrane proteins varies from a few molecules per μm^2 for example hormone receptors, to about 30,000 molecules per μm^2, as in crystalline arrays. As the measuring light intensity for performing fluorescence microphotolysis measurements has to be so low as not to bleach significantly the fluorophores, it may be appreciated that all these restrictions taken together result in small measuring signals and hence constitute a limitation for sensitivity and data quality.

The experimental procedure for continuous fluorescence microphotolysis (the procedure would be almost the same for continuous absorption microphoto-lysis) is much simpler than for the already described fluorescence microphotolysis measurements. Again, as in the latter studies, a small area of a fluorescently-labelled cell is continuously irradiated with an intermediate intensity of about 10 μW and the fluorescence decay is monitored simultaneously. The time course of the fluorescence signal originating from the irradiated area depends first on the rate of decomposition of fluorophores and second on the rate at which un-photolysed molecules enter the irradiated area from the surroundings.

If the fluorophores were immobile, in the case of a first-order reaction for the bleaching process the fluorescence signal would follow an exponential decay (compare with equation 22). Any mobility of the fluorophores due to diffusion of laminar flow leads to replenishment of unbleached chromophores and, hence, shifts the measured fluorescence signal above this simple exponential decay curve. In this case, the measuring curve initially displays a steep decay (early time regime) and then, without reaching an equilibrium, turns into a slower decay (late time regime). The early time regime is determined by the relaxation time of the bleaching reaction and lateral motion of the chromophores; the late time regime, in addition, is determined by the size and geometry of the area available for diffusion.

Assuming first-order kinetics for the bleaching of the chromophores, the photoreaction may be characterised by the time $\tau_{ph} = (\alpha I(r))^{-1}$, where $\alpha I(r)$ is given as in equation 22. The relevant timescale for a diffusion process is given by $\tau_d = w^2/D_1$ for the fluorophore to cross the irradiated area by diffusion. The accuracy of the method is at its best when $\tau_{ph} \approx \tau_d$. By proper choice of w, the size of the irradiated area and of the light intensity $I(r)$, it is possible to fulfil this condition for diffusion coefficients in the range 10^{-6} to 10^{-12} cm^{2}s^{-1}. A typical signal, also indicative of the sensitivity of the method, is shown in figure 5.5. The average initial number of fluorophores was in the range of only approximately 40 μm^{-2}.

Early time regime The decay in this time regime depends only on the rate constant for bleaching, $\alpha I(r)$, the diffusion constant, D_1, and the size of the irradiated area, w. The concentration $c(r, t)$ of unphotolysed fluorophores at radius r from the centre of the irradiated area at time t is

$$\frac{\partial c(r, t)}{\partial t} = D_1 \left(\frac{\partial^2}{\partial r^2} + \frac{1}{r} \frac{\partial}{\partial r} \right) c(r, t) - k(r)c(r, t) \qquad (59)$$

with

$$k(r) = \begin{cases} I(r) & \text{for } r \leqslant w \\ 0 & \text{for } r > w \end{cases} \tag{60}$$

The functional dependence of $k(r)$ in equation 60 assumes a homogeneous light intensity within the irradiated disc area. The numerical algorithm best suited to obtain $c(r, t)$ is the Crank-Nicholson scheme (Richtmeyer and Morton, 1967).

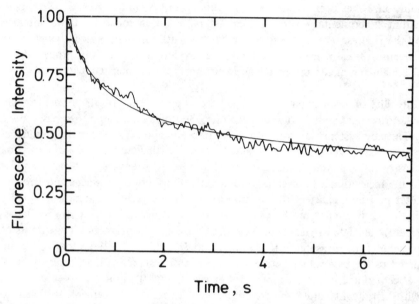

Figure 5.5 Time-dependent fluorescence intensity during the continuous fluorescence microphotolysis of a 35-nM fluorescein-ITC solution (corresponding to about 500 fluorophores within the illuminated area) in a glycerol/water mixture (data from Peters *et al.*, 1981)

Late time regime The slow phase of the decay curve reflects the depletion of fluorophores from more distant parts of the membrane. This process depends on $\alpha I(r), D_1, w$, and, additionally, on the size of the whole system, given by R in the case of a spherical particle. If the slow decay is approximated by a single exponential with time constant τ_s, this value is shown to be given by:

$$\tau_s = \frac{R^2}{D_1} \frac{(w/R)^2 - 3}{8} - \frac{\ln(w/R)}{2(1 - (w/R)^2)} + \frac{1 - (w/R)^2}{4f(x)} \tag{61}$$

with

$$f(x) = x \sum_{i=0}^{\infty} x^i / [i!(i+1)!] / \left\{ \sum_{i=0}^{\infty} x^i / (i!)^2 \right\}$$

$$x = \tau_d / (4\tau_{ph}) = w^2 \, \alpha I(r) / (4D_1)$$

Possible artefacts

Lateral diffusion measurements may be liable to artefacts caused by instrumental factors (Barisas, 1980) or by the intense bleaching light pulse needed for fluorescence microphotolysis measurements. The latter may be due to either membrane heating or photochemical effects (for example crosslinking). This potential source of errors applies as well to continuous fluorescence microphotolysis measurements. However, as was summarised and discussed by Wolf *et al.* (1980a), such effects were shown not to have a significant role in these measurements. In addition, it has been shown with the rhodopsin system (Wey *et al.*, 1981) that, within experimental error, the same lateral diffusion constant can be obtained by the fluorescence microphotolysis method, utilising a fluorescent label, or by the absorption microphotolysis method, exploiting the built-in probe retinal. The main arguments against the above artefacts are summarised below.

Criticality of beam alignment Inadequate superposition of the bleaching and measuring light spot in fluorescence microphotolysis measurements may cause a potentially systematic error as well as irreproducibility, as pointed out in detail by Barisas (1980). This problem becomes particularly important if neutral density filters are mechanically inserted in order to attenuate the bleaching pulse to the measuring light level. Optical imperfections, primarily wedge and errors in filter positioning, affect the superposition of the bleaching and measuring light. If the displacement of the two light spots is equal to the spot size w, Barisas (1980) calculated that, in the case of a gaussian light beam and low extents of bleaching, the measured diffusion constant D_1 will be 3.3 times too small compared to the true value. To measure diffusion constants with an accuracy of 10 per cent this displacement must not exceed $0.3 w$. It should be noted that even with high quality filters the present wedge may cause displacements sufficient to decrease the measured D_1 values by a factor in the range of 3 to 15, relative to the true value.

In order to overcome the described problem, two possibilities have been described, their common feature being the avoidance of any moving filter components in the apparatus. The first method uses an interferometric beam attenuator (Koppel, 1979; Barisas and Leuther, 1979). In this device the laser beam is separated into two components by a beam splitter. One beam is normally blocked by an electronic shutter, while the other beam is greatly attenuated by either neutral density filters or several reflections at the glass-to-air interface, to yield the measuring light for monitoring the fluorescence. Once the shutter is opened, the two beams are recombined by a second beam splitter, providing the bleaching pulse. As no movement or reflective or absorptive optical elements are needed, and the measuring and bleaching spots can be aligned to within 3 arcsec, displacement of these two beams can be neglected. Alternatively, the second method uses an acousto-optic modulator to control the laser intensity (Garland, 1981). This method differs from the first in that the measuring light is no longer a continuous light beam. Instead, the average intensity of the laser beam is changed by variation of the on-off duty cycle of the acousto-optic modulator. For example, to achieve an attenuation of 10^4, the measuring beam is delivered as 10 μsec pulses every 100 msec (10 Hz), compared to an uninterrupted bleaching pulse of 100 msec. Because the bleaching and measuring beam differ only in their duty cycle times, they are expected first to be perfectly aligned and second to have the same power. The latter point is advantageous because the photomultiplier used to measure the weak fluorescence need not be gated out during bleaching; hence, fluorescence of the illuminated area can be measured throughout the bleaching phase.

Cell surface heating by bleaching pulse It is important to know whether the bright bleaching flash or the subsequent attenuated measuring beam induce a significant temperature rise on the cell surface, which could possibly result in damage to the cell surface or distortion of the fluorescence recovery curve. As calculated by Axelrod (1977), the local temperature rise on the cell surface is no more than $0.03°C$, if typical experimental conditions are applied. Although direct measurements on the temperature rise have not been possible so far, thermal artefacts should have shown up as a shift of the main phase transition temperature, T_c, for experiments on artificial lipid membranes; no such changes have been detected (Wu *et al.*, 1977).

Photoinduced cross-linking Exposure of fluorescently-labelled cells to absorbable light does eventually degrade proteins and can induce cross-linking. The phenomenon of cross-linking membrane proteins has been demonstrated for red blood cell ghosts and for plasma membranes from baby hamster kidney cells (Nigg *et al.*, 1979; Lepock *et al.*, 1978; Sheetz and Koppel, 1979) under conditions of low light intensity ($0.1-10$ Wcm^{-2}) and long irradiation times ($1-100$ min). The extent of photodamage is dependent upon various parameters. Nigg *et al.* (1979) noted that deoxygenation drastically reduces photodamage. Different membrane proteins may be cross-linked in a different manner; spectrin was reported to cross-link faster than band 3 protein (Sheetz and Koppel, 1979). Cross-linking could be completely suppressed by the addition (or presence in some living cells) of glutathione, cystamine, or sodium azide at the mM level (Lepock *et al.*, 1978; Sheetz and Koppel, 1979). It was further shown that cross-linking in red cell ghosts was diminished if the same bleaching dose was delivered at higher intensities in shorter times. In this context it is interesting to note that the photolytic decomposition of the fluorophores also depends on the radiation intensity, it being more efficient at lower intensities.

Many experiments have been reported which indicate that photochemical cross-linking and damage is much less than expected from the above results. Jacobson *et al.* (1978) inspected the irradiated area by scanning electron microscopy for possible gross membrane damage; in addition these authors proved that living cells were still impermeable to trypan blue after fluorescence microphotolysis. The effect of fluorescence microphotolysis on fertilisation and early development of sea urchin eggs has been checked (Peters and Richter, 1981). The use of two different dyes to label the same membrane component still provided identical results for lateral diffusion (Schlessinger *et al.*, 1976a). In a more elaborate series of experiments, Wolf *et al.* (1980a) proved by lateral diffusion measurements that the Fc receptor of rat basophil leukaemia cells did not show any tendency for photochemical cross-linking or damage. These authors prepared fluorescein- as well as rhodamine-conjugated immunoglobulin E (f-IgE and r-IgE, respectively) and F_{ab} fragments of fluorescein- as well as rhodamine-conjugated anti-IgE (f-F_{ab} and r-F_{ab}, respectively). Different membrane preparations were prepared (Fc × r-IgE × f-F_{ab} molecules and Fc × f-IgE × r-F_{ab} molecules) and fluorescence microphotolysis measurements performed, using one of the dyes before and after the other dye had been bleached. (This is possible, because fluorescein and rhodamine have sufficiently different absorption spectra.) Bleaching was performed over the entire cell, using different light intensities and exposure times in the range of about 50 Wcm^{-2} and 3–5 min up to 3,200 Wcm^{-2} and 5 sec, respectively. The measured diffusion constant and the extent of the mobile fraction was the same within experimental error for all the different conditions applied. Finally, the lateral diffusion constant for rhodopsin in the rod outer segment was the same for absorption microphotolysis, using the intrinsic probe retinal (Poo and Cone, 1974) and fluorescence microphotolysis, using a fluorescent label attached to rhodopsin (Wey *et al.*, 1981).

In conclusion, it should be recognised that at present no evidence points to radiation artefacts in fluorescence and absorption microphotolysis measurements on living cells. However, as cross-linking was shown to occur at least for isolated membranes, one should always be aware of such effects.

Determination of membrane viscosity from rotational and lateral diffusion coefficients

The problem of rotational and lateral diffusion of protein molecules in biological membranes has been studied by Saffman and Delbrück (1975) by applying the classical analysis of brownian motion to a hydrodynamic model. These authors treated the protein molecules as a cylinder with an axis perpendicular to the plane of the membrane. The membrane was approximated as being an infinite sheet of thickness h. The mean square displacement, $\overline{r^2}$, and the angular rotation in time t, $\overline{\theta^2}$, are related to the diffusion coefficients by

$$\overline{r^2} = 4D_1 t \tag{62}$$

$$\overline{\theta^2} = 2D_r t \tag{63}$$

If the mobility, b, of the molecule is independent of force or torque, the diffusion coefficients are related to the mobilities by the Einstein relations

$$D_1 = k_B T b_1 \tag{64}$$

$$D_r = k_B T b_r \tag{65}$$

Neglecting the viscosity μ' of the surrounding liquid, the rotational mobility b_r was calculated as

$$b_r = (4\pi \mu a^2 h)^{-1} \qquad (66)$$

where a is the radius of the rotating particle and μ the viscosity of the sheet representing the membrane.

In order to be able to apply the Einstein equation 64 for lateral diffusion, additional assumptions have to be made to calculate the lateral mobility b_1. One possibility is to take into account the viscosity μ' of the outer liquid. The lateral mobility in this case was calculated as follows:

$$b_1 = \frac{1}{4\pi \mu h}\left[\ln\left(\frac{\mu h}{\mu' a} \right) - \gamma \right] \qquad (67)$$

where γ is Euler's constant (0.5772). This result should be valid for $\mu h/(\mu' a) \geqslant 1$ which is fulfilled in most applications. As the diameter a of the particle enters equation 67 in a logarithmic factor, the dependence of lateral mobility on particle size is very small in contrast to the rotational mobility.

The above calculations described by Saffman and Delbrück (1975) assume a constant viscosity throughout the membrane sheet. There is evidence in some membrane systems that lipid viscosity near the protein may be different from that at a distance from it. In an interesting new approach, Pink *et al.* (1982) have developed a general model that relates lateral diffusion coefficients for proteins at low concentrations in a lipid bilayer to the static lipid hydrocarbon chain order by using Monte Carlo simulations or mean-field approximations. With this model the lateral diffusion coefficient of some proteins, reconstituted with pure lipids, could be calculated both above and below the main phase transition temperature and shown to be consistent with the measured values.

OPTICAL PROBES

Natural probes

A well-known example for a natural light-sensitive molecule is retinal; the chromophore in both rhodopsin from rod outer segments and bacteriorhodopsin in the purple membrane of *Halobacterium halobium*.

In rhodopsin, 11-*cis*-retinal is attached to a protein, opsin, via a Schiff base linkage. After excitation an irreversible series of dark reactions follows. The main photoproducts determining these reactions are summarised in figure 5.6a. The approximate absorption spectra are taken from Yoshizawa and Horiuchi (1973), Abrahamson and Wiesenfeld (1972), Bensasson *et al.* (1975) and Hoffmann (unpublished data).

In bacteriorhodopsin, retinal is bound to another protein, bacterioopsin, and is present in the dark-adapted state as 11-*trans* retinal. Following light excitation a reversible reaction cycle occurs; the major photoproducts are summarised in

a

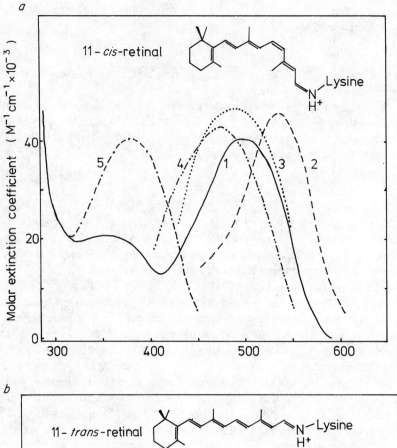

b

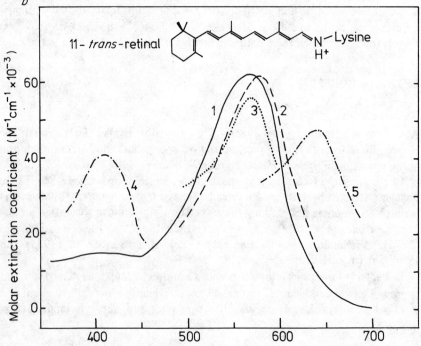

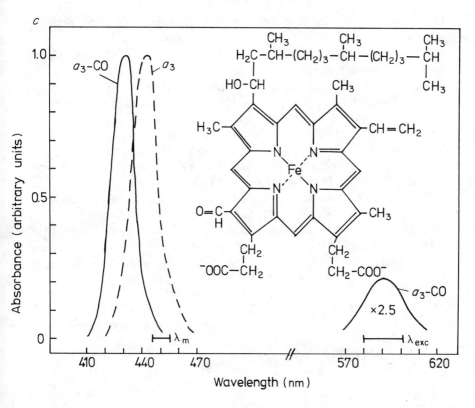

Figure 5.6 *a*, Spectral changes of rhodopsin after light absorption (in brackets the approximate lifetime of the intermediates at room temperature is given): 1, unbleached rhodopsin; 2, prelumirhodopsin (100 nsec); 3, lumirhodopsin (10 μsec); 4, metarhodopsin I (msec); 5, metarhodopsin II (min). *b*, Light-triggered reaction cycle of bacteriorhodopsin: 1, light-adapted bacteriorhodopsin ground state; 2, intermediate *K* (μsec); 3, intermediate *L* (50 μsec); 4, intermediate *M* (msec); 5, intermediate *O* (msec). *c*, Structure for haem a_3 complex and absorption spectrum for a_3 CO complex and after photolysis

figure 5.6*b*. The approximate absorption spectra have been summarised from Lozier *et al.* (1975), Chu Kung *et al.* (1975) and Hoffmann (unpublished data).

Structure and absorption spectra for the haem a_3CO complex, occurring in various cytochromes, are shown in figure 5.6*c*. Excitation is best observed in the α-band region (595 nm or 540 nm (not shown) for cytochrome oxidase or cytochrome P450, respectively). This is a long way from the largest absorbance change due to photolysis of the haem a_3CO complex which is at around 446 nm, the wavelength normally chosen for measuring purposes.

Artificial probes

Only a few membrane proteins have a suitable intrinsic chromophore as described before which allow rotational and lateral diffusion measurements to be made.

In general it is necessary to attach an artificial probe molecule to the protein of interest.

For lateral diffusion measurements probe molecules are used which decompose irreversibly after exposure to a bleaching light pulse of high intensity; they also should possess a high fluorescence quantum yield. These features are best met by fluorescein (see figure 5.7c) and rhodamine.

Most procedures for measuring rotational diffusion need triplet probes. The most useful ones at present are halogenated derivatives of fluorescein; either tetrabromofluorescein (eosin, H = Br in figure 5.7c) or tetraiodofluorescein (erythrosin, H = I in figure 5.7c). These probes are quite stable with regard to photodecomposition and have a high triplet quantum yield.

The absorption spectra for fluorescein, eosin and erythrosin are all similar with absorption peaks at 491 nm, 517 nm and 530 nm, respectively (Zwicker and Grossweiner, 1963; Kasche and Lindqvist, 1965; Garland and Moore, 1979). Upon attachment of a reactive group and binding to a protein there is a red shift of the spectra of about 5 to 10 nm, depending on the protein. As an example, the absorption spectrum for eosin is shown in figure 5.7a.

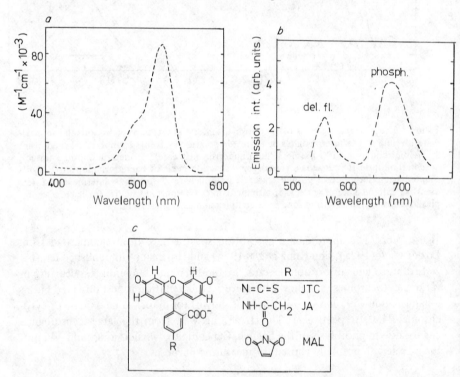

Figure 5.7 a, Absorption spectrum for eosin. b, Delayed emission spectrum for eosin as measured by Garland and Moore (1979). c, Structure of fluorescein and three possible reactive groups: isothiocyanate (IC), iodoacetamido (IA), and maleimide (MAL)

The delayed emission spectra for eosin and erythrosin are also very similar and that of erythrosin is shown in figure 5.7*b*. This is taken from Garland and Moore (1979) and should only indicate the spectral region where delayed fluorescence (550–560 nm region) and phosphorescence (at around 680 nm) is expected. The data are uncorrected for photomultiplier sensitivity (stated to be approximately three-fold lower at 680 nm than at 550 nm) and self absorption by the dye solution.

Another triplet probe, rhodium(III)–protoporphyrin IX, has been used by Vaz *et al.* (1979a). These authors exploited the structural similarity of this metalloporphyrine to replace the native haem group of cytochrome b_5 in order to measure rotational diffusion of this protein.

Reactive groups

In order to bind fluorescein and its derivatives covalently to proteins, a reactive group has to be attached. This may be either an isothiocyanate (SCN), iodoacetamido (IA), or a maleimide (Mal) group, and their respective structures are shown in figure 5.7*c*. The first probe (SCN) binds preferentially to amino groups, while the other two react mainly with sulphydryl residues. Another reactive group which can be used is dichlorotriazin (Peters, 1982).

INVESTIGATED SYSTEMS AND EXPERIMENTAL RESULTS

Rotational diffusion

Intrinsic chromophores

The principal advantage of intrinsic chromophores over artificial ones is that one does not have to worry about probe-induced perturbations. Fortunately, there are several molecules possessing such built-in probes.

Rhodopsin The chromoprotein rhodopsin has been shown to be the molecular photoreceptor in both vertebrate and invertebrate rod cells of the retina. It consists of a membrane-bound protein, opsin (molecular weight about 40,000), and the covalently bound prosthetic group, 11-*cis*-retinal. Following light absorption a series of intermediates have been spectrally defined as discussed earlier. The lipid-to-protein molar ratio for the disc membrane has been estimated to be about 65:1 (Dratz *et al.*, 1979; Nemes *et al.*, 1980), plus an additional 9 cholesterol molecules, depending on the animal species.

From the fact that linearly-polarised light, entering the rod cells in such a way that the propagation vector is perpendicular to the rhodopsin-containing disc membrane, cannot induce any dichroism due to bleaching (Hagins and Jennings, 1959) unless the proteins are cross-linked with gluturaldehyde (Brown, 1972) it has been concluded that rhodopsin may be free to rotate around an axis normal to the plane of the membrane.

Cone (1972) elegantly carried out the first successful investigation of protein rotation in natural membranes. To measure the flash-induced dichroism of rhodopsin by absorption depolarisation, he excited the sample with a 5 nsec laser pulse at 540 nm and followed the transient absorbance changes at 580 nm. The intermediate used within the reaction cascade was lumirhodopsin. A relaxation time of about 20 μsec at 20°C for rotational diffusion of rhodopsin around an axis normal to the plane of the membrane was observed. In the temperature range 0–30°C the relaxation time changes with a Q_{10} of about 3. Rotational diffusion was abolished after fixation by glutaraldehyde.

Taking into account uncertainties in determining the relaxation time and the effective radius of that part of the protein which is inserted into the membrane (20 Å assumed), Cone derived a figure of about 1–7 poise for the membrane viscosity at 20°C.

It should be noted that, in certain conditions, Cone found two relaxation processes. Whether this is due to oligomeric forms of rhodopsin coexisting in the membrane, due to inhomogenetities within the membrane lipid system, or due to two conformationally altered opsin molecules as suggested by Stewart *et al*. (1977) and Hoffmann *et al*. (1978a), has not yet been determined.

The hypothesis that rhodopsin may form aggregates after excitation has been disproved (Downer and Cone, 1978). This indicates that rhodopsin aggregates are not involved in triggering the visual response.

Bacteriorhodopsin   The purple membrane from *Halobacterium halobium* is one of the best characterised natural membrane systems. Only a single protein, bacteriorhodopsin, which spans the membrane bilayer, is present. This protein is capable of undergoing a cyclic photoreaction during which, and/or as a result of, a proton is translocated through the membrane (Stoeckenius *et al*., 1979). The apo-protein, bacterioopsin, contains the chromophore retinal in two different conformations: in the light-adapted state it is present as 11-*trans*-retinal. However, following dark adaptation, which is a very slow process (half-time in the order of minutes), the chromophore is present in the 11-*cis* conformation. Most of the experiments reported so far have used the "light-adapted" state.

The three-dimensional structure of bacteriorhodopsin has been obtained at a resolution of 7 Å from electron diffraction patterns and electron micrographs (Henderson and Unwin, 1975). The protein molecules have been shown to be arranged in a two-dimensional hexagonal lattice structure, P_3 (Blaurock and Stoeckenius, 1971). The lipid-to-protein molar ratio is particularly low in this membrane system. Only 12 to 14 lipid molecules per protein are found (Oesterhelt and Stoeckenius, 1971) and the protein shows no special affinity for any lipid class (Wildenauer and Khorana, 1977). There is good evidence from flash photolysis studies (Hoffmann *et al*., 1978b; Korenstein *et al*., 1978) and an electron spin resonance study (Hoffmann *et al*., 1980b) that bacteriorhodopsin in the purple membrane exists in a temperature-dependent equilibrium between two conformational states.

When purple membrane suspensions are excited with plane-polarised light and the absorption anisotropy is measured, only a very slow rotational diffusion time, attributable to rotation of the whole membrane fragments, is observed (Razi-Naqvi *et al.*, 1973; Sherman *et al.*, 1976). Studies using orientated films of purple membranes and exploiting the very slow light–dark adaptation process showed no decay of the anisotropy parameter over 25 minutes, the conclusion being that bacteriorhodopsin molecules remain fixed and immobile at their lattice points. The transition moment of the 11-*trans* chromophore is reported to form an angle of 70 ± 5° with the normal to the membrane (Razi-Naqvi *et al.*, 1973; Korenstein and Hess, 1978; Ebrey *et al.*, 1977; Sherman *et al.*, 1976).

Halobacterium halobium cells grown in the presence of nicotine lack the chromophore, as retinal synthesis is blocked (Cherry *et al.*, 1977a). The apo-protein in these cells is present in differentiated areas of the membrane, known as the apo-brown membrane. Bacteriorhodopsin is reconstituted after all-*trans* retinal addition, but the rigid purple membrane is not formed as shown by absorption depolarisation measurements (Cherry *et al.*, 1977a).

Bacteriorhodopsin can easily be obtained in large quantities due to the ease of cell culture; the protein is quite stable compared to, say, enzymes. The fact that its structure is known and it has a built-in chromophore suit it well for use in protein–lipid reconstituted systems. Much may be learned from the influence that changes in the lipid phase can have upon the function of intrinsic proteins and the perturbation that these proteins can cause upon the lipid system. The bacteriorhodopsin-phosphatidylcholine reconstituted system has already been studied in great detail (Heyn *et al.*, 1977; Cherry *et al.*, 1977b; 1978; 1980a; Hoffmann *et al.*, 1980c; Heyn *et al.*, 1981; Cherry and Godfrey, 1981). Reconstitution was performed in either of two ways: firstly, the protein was solubilised in Triton X-100, the respective phosphatidylcholine was added and detergent removal was by slow dialysis (Cherry *et al.*, 1978); or, the recombinants were prepared by density gradient centrifugation using sodium cholate as the detergent (Hoffmann *et al.*, 1980c).

Far below the lipid gel to liquid–crystalline phase transition temperature, T_c, bacteriorhodopsin has been shown to crystallise into the same hexagonal lattice as found in the natural purple membrane, leaving areas of protein-free lipid (Cherry *et al.*, 1978). Above this temperature, the proteins rotate as monomers, provided the lipid-to-protein molar ratio is high enough ($\gtrsim 100$, Cherry and Godfrey, 1981). The disaggregation of the protein hexagonal lattice above T_c has been shown by electron microscopy and X-ray diffraction. The latter measurement shows also the change from a 4.1 Å reflex below T_c to a 4.5 Å reflex above T_c, indicative of lipid chain melting (Cherry *et al.*, 1978).

Rotational diffusion measurements in these model systems have been used to determine the orientation of the retinal chromophore with respect to the membrane normal for rotating bacteriorhodopsin molecules (Heyn *et al.*, 1977; Hoffmann *et al.*, 1980c). The first authors obtained for the ratio, m, between residual and flash-induced anisotropy (r_∞/r_0) a value of $m = 0.19$. Based on the rotation around membrane normal model, equation 13 may be used to determine the angle γ. From figure 5.2 it is seen that up to $m = 0.25$ two values of γ are possible. For a value of 0.19 these two values are $38°$ and $78°$. The first value was rejected by Heyn *et al.* (1977) and only the second one, $78°$, was assumed to be appropriate. The values of $m = 0.39$ and 0.42 for dimyristoylphosphatidyl-choline and dipalmitoylphosphatidylcholine, respectively, measured by Hoffmann *et al.* (1980c), do not allow two possible values for γ, and the angles $\gamma = 30 \pm 3°$ and $29 \pm 4°$, respectively, are calculated.

The argument given by Cherry (1979) against additional wobbling diffusion for bacteriorhodopsin need not necessarily be true. The argument was based on the observation that a decrease of the ratio m due to wobbling diffusion (called rocking motion by Cherry, 1979) should decrease the angle γ. As the determined angle γ was even greater than that obtained from static linear dichroism measure-ments for purple membrane, an appreciable wobbling diffusion was believed not to occur. However, this is only true if γ is calculated using the negative sign in equation 13. If γ were calculated from m using the positive sign, a decrease of m is consistent with an increase of the angle γ. There is no *a priori* reason to equate the angle γ for rotating proteins with the one obtained for bacteriorhodopsin immobilised within the purple membrane. If additional wobbling diffusion were to occur in the reconstituted systems at temperatures above T_c, the two different m-values measured by Heyn *et al.* (1977) and Hoffmann *et al.* (1980c) could be due to different wobbling motion, as the morphology of the recombinant systems may be different for the two different reconstitution procedures. It should be noted that in the case of additional wobbling diffusion neither one of the two possible values for γ ($78°$ and $38°$) given by Heyn *et al.* (1977), nor the value of about $30°$ stated by Hoffmann *et al.* (1980c) would be true. The appli-cation of curve-fitting procedures as performed by Cherry and Godfrey (1981) cannot unequivocally rule out one of the possibilities, because the mathematical description becomes too complex in the case of wobbling diffusion superimposed on rotation around membrane normal (see equations 19 and 20).

The temperature dependence for rotational diffusion above T_c of dimyristoyl-phosphatidylcholine ($23°C$) is very weak in the temperature range $25°$ to $37°C$, nor is the dependence of rotational diffusion on the lipid-to-protein molar ratio pronounced (Cherry and Godfrey, 1981). A change in the latter ratio from 51:1 to 250:1 causes a change in the rotational diffusion time only of about $10°$, and that was attributed to protein aggregate effects rather than to changes in the lipid viscosity due to changes in protein concentration.

In a recent study, Cherry *et al.* (1980) investigated the influence cholesterol has on reconstituted bacteriorhodopsin systems. They showed that at cholesterol concentrations greater than about 20 mol% with respect to dimyristoylphospha-tidylcholine there is strong immobilisation of bacteriorhodopsin above T_c (rotational relaxation time increases more than 100 times) due to aggregation of the proteins. This effect is also evident in freeze fracture electron micrographs. Both the aggregation seen in electron microscopy and immobilisation observed by rotational diffusion studies above T_c appeared to be independent on the lipid-to-protein molar ratio in the range 50:1 to 150:1.

Cytochrome oxidase Cytochrome oxidase (complex IV), an integral membrane protein (Henderson *et al.*, 1977; Frey *et al.*, 1978; Ludwig *et al.*, 1979), is the terminal enzyme of the respiratory chain in the mitochondrial inner membrane (Boyer *et al.*, 1977). It accepts electrons from cytochrome *c* and accumulates four reducing species until it reduces oxygen. These reducing species are situated on two haem groups (haem *a* and a_3, respectively) and on two copper ions. Haem a_3 is the binding site for CO. Furthermore, cytochrome oxidase pumps protons from the matrix side across the membrane (Wikström and Krab, 1978; Sigel and Carafoli, 1979). Cytochrome bc_1 complex (complex III) catalyses the transfer of electrons from both complexes I and II to cytochrome *c* (Mitchell, 1966; Hatefi *et al.*, 1979) and proton translocation across the membrane (Mitchell, 1975).

The rotational diffusion of the cytochrome oxidase can be studied by photo-dissociation of the haem a_3CO complex, which provides the necessary long-lived photoproduct (see earlier). The first study with this system was performed by Junge and DeVault (1975). The only relaxation of the photoinduced linear dichroism they observed was attributable to the rotation of the whole mito-chondria and submitochondrial particles, with no dichroic relaxation due to rotational diffusion of the enzyme. Taking into account the approximate circular degeneracy of the dipole moments of the *a* haems, they arrived at two alternative explanations for their results: either the cytochrome oxidase is completely immobilised, or it rotates around a single axis, which is parallel to the symmetry axis of the haem a_3 (for rotation around the membrane normal this would imply that the haem a_3 plane is coplanar to the plane of the membrane). In subsequent studies, Erecinska *et al.* (1977) showed that the symmetry axis of the average haem *a* in cytochrome oxidase is orientated almost perpendicular to the membrane normal, and Kunze and Junge (1977) obtained identical dichroic spectra for isolated and immobilised enzyme as well as for the enzyme in mitochondria. From these studies it was concluded that cytochrome oxidase molecules do not carry out brownian diffusion around any axis in the membrane for times of up to 100 msec.

In a recent study by Kawato *et al.* (1980) rotation of at least half of the cytochrome oxidase molecules was reported to occur in the inner membrane of mitochondria. The authors stated that lack of signal averaging to improve the signal-to-noise ratio and the use of the dichroic ratio ($A_{\parallel}/A_{\perp}$) rather than the anisotropy parameter *r*, where the latter is more sensitive to rotational motion than the former, may have been the main reasons why Junge and DeVault failed to detect this motion. From the time dependence of the anisotropy parameter, together with the above stated fact that the angle between the haem a_3 symmetry axis and the membrane normal is close to $90°$, Kawato *et al.* (1980) concluded that around 60 per cent of the enzyme rotates within approximately 350 μsec, whereas the rest of the molecules are either immobile or rotating very slowly (less than 30 msec relaxation time) at 37°C. The analysis of the data were based on the rotation around the membrane normal model. This is inferred from the fact that cytochrome oxidase maintains a fixed orientation with respect to the membrane plane (Ludwig *et al.*, 1979; Henderson *et al.*, 1977). The rotational diffusion of the enzyme is in accord with the conclusion that there is lateral diffusion of intramembrane particles, based on freeze fracture measurements (Höchli and Hackenbrock, 1976; 1979).

The interaction between cytochrome oxidase molecules and between cytochrome oxidase and cytochrome bc_1 complex has been investigated in reconstituted systems (Kawato *et al.*, 1981). Purified cytochrome oxidase was reconsituted in a phosphatidylethanolamine–phosphatidylcholine–cardiolipin mixture, corresponding to the major phospholipid components in the mitochondrial inner membrane. Two different reconstituted systems were prepared: one had an approximate lipid-to-protein molar ratio of 6,000; the other one about 1,000. In addition, co-reconstitution of cytochrome oxidase with cytochrome bc_1 complex in the same lipid mixture was performed. In vesicles with a high lipid-to-protein ratio nearly all the cytochrome oxidase molecules are rotating with an approximate rotational relaxation time of about 500 μsec at 20°C. In samples with the lower lipid-to-protein ratio, the population of immobile cytochrome oxidase had increased to 17 per cent, while the rotational relaxation time remained unchanged, within experimental error. In both cases the existence of different oligomeric cytochrome oxidase molecules is indicated. In experiments with cytochrome bc_1 co-reconstituted vesicles, both the rotational relaxation time and the immobile fraction of cytochrome oxidase remained unchanged within experimental error. This was found for both high (3,000:1) and low (1,000:1) lipid-to-protein molar ratios.

Cytochrome P450   The monooxygenase system of the endoplasmic reticulum of liver cells has a major role in the metabolism of xenobiotics and steroids. An important question is, how the components of this system are organised in the membrane. The two main components of the liver microsomal hydroxylating system are various molecular forms of cytochrome P450 and the flavoprotein cytochrome P450 reductase.

Studies of rotational diffusion described below used the absorption depolarisation due to photodissociation of the haem–CO complex for this system (excitation at 540 nm, measuring wavelength at 450 nm). The anisotropy decay was analysed in terms of rotation around membrane normal and, because of insufficiently accurate data, the results were evaluated using the simplified equation 12. At 21°C the rotational motion parameter was 270 ± 90 μsec and this value changed between 13 and 37°C with a Q_{10} of about 1.4 (Richter *et al.*, 1979).

In a subsequent study McIntosh *et al.* (1980) used, in addition to rotational diffusion studies, cross-linking experiments to determine whether the interacting cytochromes pre-exist as dimers (or larger oligomers) or whether dimers are formed after random collisions. If the molecules involved pre-exist as stable dimers (or larger oligomers) no change in the rotational mobility is expected when the proteins are exposed to cross-linking agents. If, on the other hand, the cross-linking agents are stabilising dimers, which will form after collisions, a change in the rotational diffusion should result, as the rotational diffusion time depends quadratically on the radius of the rotating particle (see equation 66).

No decay in flash-induced anisotropy at 22°C in liver microsomes from β-naphtoflavone-induced rabbits was observed (in contrast to rat liver microsomes). Hence, cross-linking experiments at this temperature cannot provide further information. However, at 35°C a decay of the anisotropy parameter is observed which is not significantly changed in untreated microsomes and membranes cross-linked at 20°C. This finding supports the view that cytochrome P450 molecules are cross-linked in pre-existing aggregates. At 35°C about two thirds of the cytochrome P450 molecules are rotating with a rotational motion parameter of about 40 μsec.

Reconstituted systems of cytochrome P450 with phospholipids were investigated by Greinhart *et al.* (1979) using the delayed fluorescence depolarisation method. Cytochrome P450 was purified from microsomes of phenobarbital-treated rabbits, labelled with eosin-NCS and reconstituted with egg phosphatidylcholine, egg phosphatidylethanolamine and dipalmitoylphosphatidic acid at a ratio of 2:1:0.06 w/w by the cholate dialysis technique to give a total lipid to protein ratio of 5:1 (w/w). These authors obtained for the extrapolated initial anisotropy r_0, a value of 0.42 ± 0.05 and a rotational relaxation time of 111 μsec at 25°C.

Attached chromophores

Cytochrome b_5   Vaz *et al.* (1979a) reported on measurements with cytochrome b_5 reconstituted with dimyristoylphosphatidylcholine. The protein was isolated and purified from bovine liver microsomal cells. As the triplet state of the haem in this protein is completely quenched, the authors first prepared the apo-cytochrome b_5 and replaced the original haem group by rhodium (III)–proto-porphyrin IX. This metalloporphyrin is expected to produce minimal changes in the protein due to its structural similarity to the original haem. The lipid-to-protein molar ratio was 100:1.

Rotational diffusion measurements were performed as absorption depolarisation, exploiting the singlet depletion at the Soret band or triplet–triplet absorption after excitation (excitation at 500 nm, measurement at 404 nm and 450 nm for singlet depletion and triplet–triplet absorption, respectively).

Cytochrome b_5 is believed to consist of a hydrophobic tail, which is embedded in one half of the lipid bilayer, and a hydrophilic head, containing the metalloporphyrin and protruding from the membrane. From this it can be concluded that, while the lipid protein ratio is 100:1, taking the system as a whole, it is only

50:1 for the outer monolayer of the proteoliposomes, for there is no protein in the inner monolayer. These data, together with the fact that even at $10°C$, which is well below the phase transition temperature for these proteoliposomes (phase transition occurs between $18°$ and $25°C$ with a transition midpoint at $21°C$, Vaz and Füldner, unpublished work, cited in Vaz *et al.*, 1979a), a decrease in the time dependence for anisotropy occurs with the same ratio m as obtained at $35°C$, it is reasonable to assume that the rotational motion for this protein is best described by the wobbling within a cone model. The parameters for this type of motion are for measurements above T_c ($35°C$) and below T_c ($10°C$), respectively: rotational correlation time 0.4 and 9 μsec cone angle in both cases $33°$, ratio r_∞/r_0 in both cases 0.6, and an estimated membrane viscosity of 1.7 and 34 poise.

Band 3 protein from erythrocytes　The human erythrocyte membrane is relatively well characterised in terms of composition and properties. Major constituents are spectrin, a fibrous protein composed of two polypeptides of molecular weights (MW) 220,000 and 240,000, and band 3 (also known as component *a*). Band 3 consists of an intrinsic, hydrophobic protein, comprising about 25 per cent of the total membrane protein. It is responsible for the essential anion and other transport functions. It is a glycoprotein of MW about 100,000 and spans the membrane, probably more than once (for review see Cabantchik *et al.*, 1978). The major sialoglycoprotein, glycophorin, also spans the membrane and has been extensively characterised (Tomita and Marchesi, 1975).

The first investigation of protein rotation in membranes using triplet probes was performed with the erythrocyte membrane (Cherry *et al.*, 1976). The probe eosin-ITC was shown to bind selectively to band 3. The rotational motion parameter was in the order of 500 μsec and was not affected after spectrin depletion of the erythrocyte membrane. Since this early study a number of additional experiments have been performed by Cherry and colleagues, which have already been reviewed by Cherry (1979) and more recently by Cherry and Nigg (1980; 1981). Hence we will only summarise the major results obtained. All measurements reported by the above group have been performed by absorption depolarisation due to ground state depletion of attached triplet probes.

The dimeric association of band 3 was shown by Nigg and Cherry (1979a). This conclusion was based on the result that, within experimental error, the same rotational diffusion coefficient was obtained in intact human erythrocytes and after dimerisation of band 3, achieved by copperphenanthroline-catalysed oxidation of cytoplasmic sulphydryl residues to form disulphide bridges.

The influence of temperature on the rotational diffusion of band 3 was investigated by Nigg and Cherry (1979b). The results were analysed with the rotation around membrane normal model and it was deduced that both fast and slowly rotating forms of band 3 coexist in the membrane. The equilibrium between these two forms was shown to be temperature-dependent, the slowly rotating species becoming more dominant as the temperature is decreased.

The effect of different cholesterol content on the band 3 rotational mobility was reported in the same paper. In normal erythrocyte membranes the molar cholesterol-to-phospholipid ratio is 0.9. This ratio was varied by depletion and enrichment in the range 0.34 to 1.66. Interestingly, the anisotropy-time curves were found to be almost independent of cholesterol concentration over the temperature 15° to 37°C. However, as shown by Hoffmann *et al.* (1981), the effect of cholesterol on a lipid probe shows approximately an exponential dependence: that is, most of the effect is observed at low cholesterol concentration (up to about a ratio of 0.4), whereas at high cholesterol content (the range studied by Nigg and Cherry, 1979b) a saturating behaviour is observed. The same mechanism may apply to band 3 proteins.

The question of whether band 3 is associated with glycophorin *A* was studied by Nigg *et al.* (1980a). The rotational diffusion of band 3 was strongly reduced following cross-linking of glycophorin *A* with divalent antiglycophorin *A* antibodies. As little or no effect on band 3 rotation was observed by monovalent antiglycophorin *A*, F_{ab} fragments and other antibodies, it was concluded that the immobilisation of band 3 is caused by cross-linking of pre-existing band 3-glycophorin *A* complexes. Due to the fact that no significant difference was found for rotational mobility of band 3 in En(a⁻) erythrocyte cells − a rare naturally occurring variant, which completely lacks glycophorin *A* − it was concluded that glycophorin *A* contributes less than 15 per cent to the cross-sectional diameter of the band 3-glycophorin *A* complex in the plane of the membrane normal (Nigg *et al.*, 1980b). Further evidence for a structural association between glycophorin *A* and band 3 comes from measurements on the influence of influenza and Sendai viruses on the rotational mobility of band 3 proteins (Nigg *et al.*, 1980c).

Evidence for the linkage of a band 3 population with the cytoskeleton was investigated by Nigg and Cherry (1980). The result was that up to 40 per cent of band 3 may be associated with the erythrocyte cytoskeleton.

Austin *et al.* (1979) and Jovin *et al.* (1981), measuring the rotational diffusion of band 3 by phosphorescence depolarisation, found a similar two-component anisotropy decay, which they ascribed to a possible binding or environmental heterogeneity of the triplet probe or the existence of excited state equilibria. The decrease in r_∞, also seen by Nigg and Cherry (1979b), was suggested to occur from a change in the distribution of subspecies.

The rotational mobility of band 3 has also been measured by fluorescence depletion depolarisation on single cells (Johnson and Garland, 1981) with similar results as reported above.

Glycophorin reconstituted in dimyristoylphosphatidylcholine The rotational diffusion of glycophorin reconstituted in dimyristoylphosphatidylcholine vesicles was measured by Jovin *et al.* (1981) using phosphorescence depolarisation with erythrosin-ITC as a triplet probe. Two rotational motion parameters were observed (1-2 μsec and 10-20 μsec) which were reported to be consistent with a model, whereby the faster and the slower time constant was attributed to mono-meric and aggregated glycophorin, respectively. The latter aggregation was only observed below the lipid phase transition temperature, T_c. The fact that the initial flash-induced anisotropy r_0 decreased systematically from about 0.11 at $5°C$ down to 0.03 at $30°C$ was tentatively ascribed to an increasing degree of fast segmental motion within the protein with increasing temperature. In contrast, the time-independent anisotropy, r_∞, showed a transition behaviour in the tem-perature range $15°$ to $25°C$, which was correlated with a broadened lipid phase transition.

$(Ca^{2+} + Mg^{2+})$-activated ATPase The $(Ca^{2+} + Mg^{2+})$-activated ATPase (ATP phosphohydrolase, EC3.6.1.3) is the major constituent of sarcoplasmic reticulum membrane (60–90 per cent of the total membrane protein; Meissner, 1975) and plays a dominant part in regulating Ca^{2+} fluxes. Sarcoplasmic reticulum mem-branes have to be in two distinct functional states during the muscle contraction-relaxation cycle. The relaxation is initiated by the ATP-mediated accumulation of Ca^{2+} into the sarcoplasmic reticulum tubules which lowers the cytoplasmic Ca^{2+} concentration below 10^{-7} M (Ebashi *et al.*, 1969). During excitation, the accumulated Ca^{2+} is rapidly released from sarcoplasmic reticulum, giving rise to the contraction of the muscle (for review see Ebashi *et al.*, 1969). Rotational diffusion of the (Ca^{2+})ATPase has been measured both in the native sarco-plasmic reticulum membrane (Hoffmann *et al.*, 1979; Moore *et al.*, 1979; Bürkli and Cherry, 1981) and in reconstituted systems composed of dipalmitoylphos-phatidylcholine vesicles (Hoffmann *et al.*, 1980a).

The rotational diffusion of (Ca^{2+})ATPase in the native sarcoplasmic reticulum membrane gave the following rotational motion parameters at temperatures around $15°C$: 130 μsec, 200 μsec, and 70 μsec, as measured by Hoffmann *et al.* (1979), Moore *et al.* (1979), and Bürkli and Cherry (1981), respectively. It should be noted that Moore *et al.* (1979) obtained their results with the more sensitive phosphorescence depolarisation method using erythrosin-ITC, whereas the other two groups used absorption depolarisation, exploiting ground state depletion from eosin-ITC (Hoffmann *et al.*, 1979) and IA-eosin (Bürkli and Cherry, 1981).

The flash-induced dichroism was relatively small in all of the reported studies and found to be temperature-dependent, varying from about 0.08 at $-10°C$ down to 0.04 at $40°C$ (Bürkli and Cherry, 1981). This small value was ascribed by the latter authors to arise from independent probe motion (occurring in the ns timescale) followed by segmental motion of labelled parts of the ATPase (assumed to occur in the sub-μsec time domain. The following time-resolved anisotropy decay in the μsec time range should then be due to protein rotation and/or wobbling diffusion.

The Arrhenius plot for the rotational motion parameter deserves further comment, as it may be of more general importance in evaluating temperature dependencies for rotational as well as lateral diffusion. In figure 5.8 a schematic

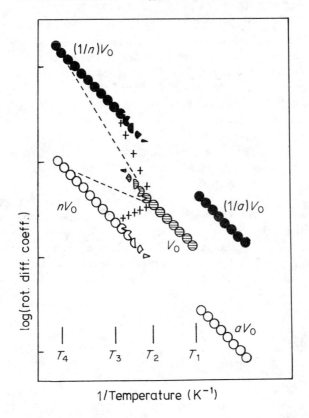

Figure 5.8 Temperature dependence for a reference particle with volume V_0 (●●●●). At T_1 a volume increase (aV_0, ○○○) or a decrease (($1/a)V_0$, ●●●) is assumed to occur. Between T_2 and T_3 a temperature-dependent equilibrium between aggregates (nV_0, ○○○) and monomers (V_0) is assumed (alternatively, a breakdown into n small particles (($1/n)V_0$, ●●●). For more details see text

illustration for rotational diffusion constant as function of temperature for a reference particle with volume V_0 is shown (V_0 denotes only that part of the protein which is embedded in the membrane). A straight line in the Arrhenius plot is expected, if the particle does not change its shape and as long as there is no phase change of the surrounding medium within which the particle is rotating. Once the latter point is checked for the lipid matrix, nonlinearities in the Arrhenius plot for rotational (or lateral) diffusion may then result from the following events. Assume a sudden volume change for the rotating particle at a temperature T_1, either an increase (aV_0) or a decrease ($a^{-1}V_0$, $a > 1$). The result is a jump in the Arrhenius plot at T_1, downwards or upwards, respectively. Note that the further temperature dependence is governed by the same activation energy. Another possibility may be that at a temperature T_2 a temperature-dependent equilibrium begins between the monomeric particle V_0 and aggregates (nV_0, with n the number of monomers to form the aggregate). If there is a finite size for the largest aggregate denoted by n^*, and almost all the molecules are at T_3 in this form n^*V_0, a further temperature change will yield the same activation energy, as obtained below T_2. In the temperature midrange $(T_2 < T < T_3)$ one would expect as many rotational diffusion constants as there are different aggregated particles ($n^* = 2$ in the case of figure 5.8), with the relative contribution from each one varying with temperature as shown schematically by the different size of the particles. In practice, however, it may be difficult to detect this behaviour, especially for small values of n^*, and an average rotational motion parameter will be obtained as indicated by the crosses. Possible other Arrhenius plot shapes are also indicated (equilibrium extending to T_4, breakdown of the particle into n small particles).

The results of Hoffmann *et al.* (1979) were discussed in the light of these considerations and taken as evidence of a temperature-dependent formation of ATPase oligomers. This proposed hypothesis is currently being further investigated by us with improved instrumentation. Preliminary anisotropy curves using phosphorescence depolarisation are shown in figure 5.9. Bürkli and Cherry (1981) inferred from the increase of time-independent anisotropy r_∞ with

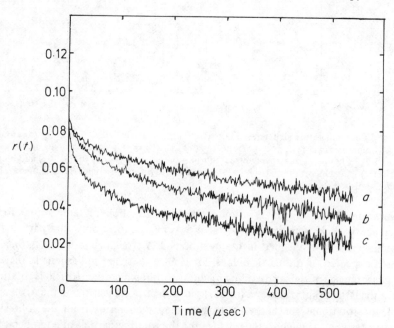

Figure 5.9 Time dependence of the anisotropy parameter, r, for the sarcoplasmic reticulum, $(Ca^{2+} + Mg^{2+})$ATPase at three temperatures: a, $5°C$; b, $15°C$; and c, $25°C$. These data were obtained using sarcoplasmic reticulum labelled with erythrosin isothiocyanate and with the flash photolysis apparatus configured to measure the phosphorescence emission anisotropy. Each signal represents the result after averaging 64 shots. It can be seen that, at each temperature, a decrease of the anisotropy is occurring indicative of protein rotation. However, curve fitting procedures have shown that the time dependence of the anisotropy is complex in the case of this protein and suggests the presence of both fast and slow moving components

decreasing temperature an increase of self aggregation. If these large aggregates with nonresolved rotational motion parameter are not formed spontaneously, it is interesting to note that the slope change observed for their rotational motion parameter is opposite to that one would expect if larger particles with time-resolved relaxation time were formed at lower temperatures.

The rotational diffusion of the ATPase in reconstituted dipalmitoylphosphatidylcholine vesicles was studied by Hoffmann *et al.* (1980a). The anisotropy decay was evaluated with the rotation around membrane normal model and neglecting possible wobbling diffusion. Two decay plots are shown in figure 5.10*a* for two temperatures. At temperatures far below T_c of the pure lipid ($41°C$) the flash-induced anisotropy parameter was not observed to decay with time. This indicates that there is no rotational diffusion of the protein in the timescale of the experiment. At temperatures higher than about $30°C$, which is considerably below the T_c of the pure lipid, the anisotropy first shows a decay and then levels off to yield a time-independent value r_∞. From this decay, the rotational motion parameter is calculated; the Arrhenius plot for this is shown in figure 5.10*b* for a recombinant with a lipid-to-protein molar ratio of 86:1. Also shown is the ratio r_0/r_∞, which shows a significant increase as the temperature is lowered (figure 5.10*c*). Two possible explanations for this change exist. First, there could be a temperature-dependent change of the mean value for $\bar{\gamma}$; or second, there is a fractional increase in proteins that are so large that their associated rotational motion parameter would be too slow to be observed in the timescale of the experiment. The first interpretation yields angles of $26°$ and $19°$ for $\bar{\gamma}$, at $45°C$ and $30°C$, respectively, whereas the second interpretation indicates that, while all proteins are assumed to rotate at $45°C$, the fraction of immobile molecules at $30°C$ is approximately 40 per cent.

Additional studies (wide-angle X-ray diffraction, freeze fracture electron microscopy, and enzymatic activity measurements) all combine to the conclusion that melting of patches which are high in protein content occurs at temperatures around $30°C$. This in turn results in a decrease of hexagonally-packed lipid, start of rotational diffusion of the ATPase, and increase of enzymatic activity at temperatures higher than about $30°C$.

Receptor proteins Living organisms contain a large variety of proteins that possess the ability to bind specifically particular compounds. Important examples are hormone receptors, lectin receptors and antibodies.

Very often the problem arises that a particular membrane component has to be specifically labelled within a membrane of highly complex composition. If the whole membrane is exposed to the reactive group of a label such as those described in the previous section, all molecules possessing the desired binding site will be labelled. In order to have just one protein component labelled we may take advantage of the above described specific binding properties. If antigens, hormones, or lectins are labelled with triplet probes and then incubated

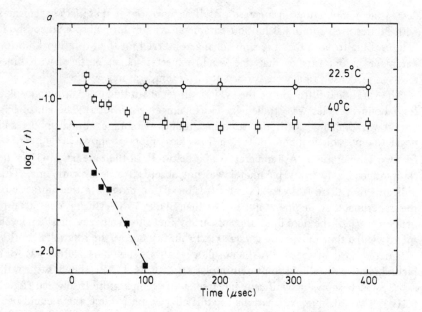

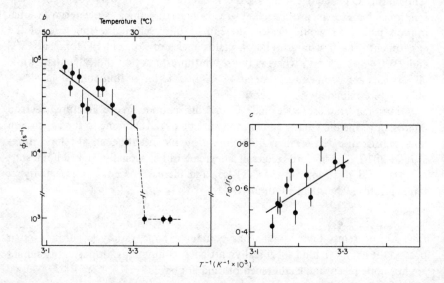

Figure 5.10 Time dependence of the anisotropy parameter, r, for a $(Ca^{2+} + Mg^{2+})$ATPase
—dipalmitoylphosphatidylcholine recombinant, having a lipid: protein molar ratio of 86, at
two temperatures, far below $(22.5°C)$ and near T_c $(40°C)$. At the higher temperature, the
difference between the time-independent anisotropy (– – –) and the measured anisotropy
(□) is shown (□ • – •) and from the slope of the line the rotational motion parameter is
calculated (*a*). An Arrhenius plot of rotational motion parameter of such a recombinant is
shown in *b*; data below 30°C are limited by the lifetime of the triplet probe. *c*, Temperature
dependence of the ratio r_∞/r_0 for the same sample as in *b* (data from Hoffmann *et al.*,
1980a)

with membranes, only those receptor proteins will be labelled which selectively bind that compound.

Hormones, responsible for the communication between cells in our bodies, may be simply classified into long and short range messengers. The former are synthesised by specialised glands, released into the blood and circulated intact to their target molecules; examples are insulin and thyroid. The short range messengers are produced by nerve cells (neurones) and are released only a few angstroms or microns away from their target. They are called neurotransmitters, and an example is acetylcholine (for review see Eldefrawi and Eldefrawi, 1977). Molecules mimicking the effect of acetylcholine are called agonists and drugs which inhibit the effect of the neurotransmitter are termed antagonists. An example of the latter is α-bungarotoxin, which binds strongly to the acetylcholine receptor.

Although hormone receptors are normally only present in minute amounts, the advent of highly sensitive methods like phosphorescence depolarisation has made it feasible to study the rotational diffusion of such molecules. Lo *et al.* (1980) looked for rotational mobility of the acetylcholine receptor of torpedo electric organ to which they attached α-bungarotoxin labelled with erythrosin-ITC. These authors confirmed earlier suggestions obtained by saturation transfer electron spin resonance that rotational diffusion was confined to a time range longer than several msec (limited by the phosphorescence lifetime). There is some evidence that after alkali extraction, which removes mainly a polypeptide of MW 43,000 and some other proteins, but none of the acetylcholine receptors, rotation of the latter is seen to occur.

The rotational motion of the hormone receptor for epidermal growth factor receptor on living human epidermoid carcinoma cells (A431) was measured by phosphorescence depolarisation by Zidovetzki *et al.* (1982). Labelling was by erythrosin-ITC attached to epidermal growth factor. This low molecular weight polypeptide (MW 6,045) stimulates the proliferation of various fibroblasts, epidermal and epithelial cells *in vivo* and *in vitro* after binding to the receptor protein (MW 170,000–190,000). Rotational motion parameters in the range 25 to 90 μsec were reported at 4°C. Prolonged incubation and exposure to higher temperatures (up to 37°C) resulted in an increase of the rotational motion parameter up to 350 μsec. With the results from lateral diffusion measurements obtained on the same system, this was explained by the progressive formation of microclusters, estimated to contain 10–50 hormone receptors. Upon internalisation of the hormone receptor complexes, the rotational motion parameter was shorter, indicating a decrease in size of the rotating unit.

Another class of proteins which bind to specific sites are the lectins which are mainly found in plants. The best known of these are concanavalin A, wheat germ agglutinin, phytohaemagglutinin, and soybean agglutinin (for review see Sela, 1977; Bøg-Hansen, 1981). The main characteristic of lectins are their ability to agglutinate cells and to stimulate lymphocytes. Lectins interact specifically with polysaccharides and glycoproteins to form precipitates. They may be inhibited by low molecular weight "haptens"; these are compounds identical with or derived from the sugar(s) with which the lectins interact. Although lectins have become quite an attractive tool in biological and biochemical research, the role these molecules are thought to have in nature is still only speculative. The rotational mobility of eosin-labelled concanavalin A bound to mouse spleen cells transformed with Friend erythleukaemia virus was reported by Austin *et al.* (1979). These authors failed to detect any measurable decay in the anisotropy versus time curves at either 4 or 37°C, which was interpreted as being due to the absence of significant rotational mobility, at least up to several msec.

Lateral diffusion

Many measurements of lateral diffusion of proteins (and lipids) on cell membranes and lipid model membranes have been performed up to now. In a recent review (Peters, 1981) all relevant data on these various systems have been compiled; furthermore, additional reviews on various aspects of lateral diffusion have been published recently (Webb *et al.*, 1981; Edidin, 1981; Jacobson and Wojcieszyn, 1981). Hence we will only summarise lateral diffusion data for some of the investigated systems and the reader is referred to the review by Peters (1981).

Intrinsic chromophore
Although rhodopsin was the first system where quantitative lateral diffusion measurements were reported, it has remained the only one where an intrinsic chromophore is used. The reason for this is the fact that rhodopsin is the only protein found so far to consist of a bleachable intrinsic chromophore. With the absorption microphotolysis method, Poo and Cone (1974) measured for the lateral diffusion coefficient for rhodopsin within the frog and mudpuppy retina at 20°C a value of $(3.5 \pm 1.5) \ 10^{-9} \ cm^2 s^{-1}$ and $(3.9 \pm 1.2) \ 10^{-9} \ cm^2 s^{-1}$, respectively.

Attached chromophores

Rhodopsin
Fluorescence microphotolysis measurements, applied to membranes other than the disc membrane, most often yielded protein diffusion coefficients much smaller than those obtained for rhodopsin by the absorption microphotolysis method. To help indicate that these smaller values are not artefacts of the fluorescence microphotolysis method, Wey *et al.* (1981) labelled frog rod outer segments with IA-tetramethylrhodamine, which reacted mainly with rhodopsin. The diffusion coefficient at 22°C was $(3.0 \pm 1.2) \ 10^{-9} cm^2 s^{-1}$ if estimated from the rate of recovery of fluorescence in the bleached spot, and $(5.3 \pm 2.4) \ 10^{-9} \ cm^2 s^{-1}$ if estimated from the rate of depletion of fluorescence from nearby regions. The temperature coefficient, Q_{10}, for diffusion was 1.7 ± 0.5 over the range 10-29°C. Taking into account the size of the disc membrane, at least about

66-77 per cent of the rhodopsin molecules were found to be mobile (estimated from the fluorescence recovery). Fissures which are present in the frog disc membrane may account, among other factors, for the remaining immobile fraction.

Integral proteins in erythrocyte membranes The first lateral diffusion measurement with proteins which lack an intrinsic chromophore was performed with the human erythrocyte membrane (Peters *et al.*, 1974). After labelling the haemoglobin-free erythrocyte ghosts with fluorescein-ITC, lateral diffusion was studied by the fluorescence microphotolysis method. In contrast to the result obtained on the rhodopsin system, the lateral diffusion of integral proteins in ghost membranes was found to be severely restricted at around $20°C$ ($D_1 < 3 \times 10^{-12} cm^2 s^{-1}$). In contrast, if lateral diffusion in mouse spherocytic erythrocyte membranes (that is, erythrocyte variants deficient of spectrin) is measured, the lateral diffusion coefficient increases considerably ($D_1 = (2.5 \pm 0.6) 10^{-9} cm^2 s^{-1}$ (Sheetz *et al.*, 1980)) with respect to normal mouse erythrocytes ($D_1 = (4.5 \pm 0.8) 10^{-11} cm^2 s^{-1}$). From this result it may be deduced that the spectrin skeleton restricts lateral movement of intrinsic proteins by direct linkage and/or trapping of proteins within the skeleton network.

Hormone receptors Although the density of hormone receptors in the plasma membrane is very low, it is possible to perform fluorescence microphotolysis measurements on such systems by the synthesis of highly fluorescent hormone derivatives. Lact-albumin, substituted with rhodamine at a molar ratio of 7 (Shechter *et al.*, 1978), has been coupled to the hormones insulin and epithelial growth factor; nerve growth factor could be labelled directly with rhodamine at a ratio of between 8 and 10 (Levi *et al.*, 1980). The receptors for these hormones were found to be diffusely distributed in the plasma membrane of cultured cells, with D_1 values for the hormone–receptor complex at around $5 \times 10^{-10} cm^2 s^{-1}$ with mobile fractions in the range 0.4 to 0.8 (Schlessinger *et al.*, 1978; Levi *et al.*, 1980). The lateral diffusion coefficient of epidermal growth factor–receptor complexes on living human epidermoid carcinoma cells, labelled with tetramethylrhodamin-ITC, was 3×10^{-10}, 6×10^{-10}, and $8.5 \times 10^{-10} cm^2 s^{-1}$ at 4, 23 and $37°C$, respectively, with the fraction of mobile molecules of 0.9 and 0.45 at 4 and $37°C$, respectively (Zidovetzki *et al.*, 1982). Rhodamine-labelled α-bungarotoxin was bound to acetylcholine receptors from rat myotubes and diffusion coefficients of 5×10^{-11} and $1.6 \times 10^{-10} cm^2 s^{-1}$ at 22 and $35°C$, respectively, were reported (Axelrod *et al.*, 1976b). In membrane areas with receptor patches this value decreased to $10^{-12} cm^2 s^{-1}$ at both temperatures.

Lectin receptors The lateral diffusion of concanavalin A receptors from a variety of different cells has been investigated (Schlessinger *et al.*, 1976a; 1977a, b; Axelrod *et al.*, 1976b; 1977; Zagyansky and Edidin, 1976; Zagyansky *et al.*, 1977; Jacobson *et al.*, 1976; Leuther *et al.*, 1979; Smith *et al.*, 1979b; Eldridge *et al.*, 1980). The lateral diffusion coefficients for these different receptor proteins are quite similar and fall in the range $(1-50)10^{-11} cm^2 s^{-1}$, with most measurements between $(3-13)10^{-11} cm^2 s^{-1}$.

Another lectin receptor, wheat germ agglutinic receptor, has been studied by Jacobson *et al.* (1976; 1978). For two different cells the lateral diffusion coefficient was 4×10^{-11} and $8 \times 10^{-11} cm^2 s^{-1}$ at $25°C$, respectively.

Surface antigens and immune receptors As a label for surface antigens and immune receptors, fluorescein- and rhodamine-labelled IgE and F_{ab} fragments were used for a variety of different cells. Most measurements show lateral diffusion coefficients in the range $(2-7)10^{-10} cm^2 s^{-1}$ (Schlessinger *et al.*, 1976b; 1977c; Johnson and Edidin, 1978; Dragsten *et al.*, 1979; de Laat *et al.*, 1979; 1980; Reidler *et al.*, 1981; Eldridge *et al.*, 1980). Some exceptions have been found in specially prepared mast cells ($D_1 < 6 \times 10^{-12} cm^2 s^{-1}$ (Schlessinger *et al.*, 1976b)) and fibroblasts ($D_1 \sim (3 \pm 2) 10^{-11} cm^2 s^{-1}$ (Schlessinger *et al.*, 1977c)).

Other measurements Lateral diffusion measurements on directly-labelled membrane proteins from fibroblast and myoblast cells have been reported (Edidin *et al.*, 1976; Schlessinger *et al.*, 1976a; Wolf *et al.* 1980b). The lateral diffusion coefficient for these measurements is in the range $(2-7) 10^{-10} cm^2 s^{-1}$.

Peters and Richter (1981) found for fluorescein-ITC labelled sea urchin eggs a substantial decrease in protein lateral diffusion after fertilisation. While the diffusion coefficient in unfertilised eggs is $(3.5 \pm 0.7) 10^{-10} cm^2 s^{-1}$, this value is reduced to $(7 \pm 1.5) 10^{-11} cm^2 s^{-1}$ after fertilisation. As lipid analogue lateral diffusion is only reduced about twofold in the same experimental conditions, the authors account for this observation by a different protein-membrane-skeleton interaction before and after fertilisation. This explanation is further strengthened by the fact that large amounts of actin polymerises to microfilaments after fertilisation.

Vaz *et al.* (1979b) reported on measurements with amphipathic apolipoprotein, Apo C-III, bound to phosphatidylcholine bilayers. In the case of dipalmitoylphosphatidylcholine, the lateral diffusion coefficient displayed a transition behaviour at about $30-35°C$, well below the T_c of the pure lipid ($41°C$). The diffusion coefficient is very high for this protein above $35°C$ (about $8 \times 10^{-8} cm^2 s^{-1}$) and even below $30°C$ (10^{-8} and $10^{-9} cm^2 s^{-1}$, at 30 and $15°C$, respectively). Cholesterol was shown to slow down lateral diffusion of this protein in egg phosphatidylcholine–cholesterol recombinants by a factor of about 10 in the temperature range $10-40°C$ with respect to cholesterol-free systems.

The lateral motion of glycophorin in dimyristoylphosphatidylcholine membranes at a molar ratio of $1:4,500$ displayed a sharp transition behaviour at about $15°C$, some $9°C$ lower than for the T_c of the pure lipid ($D_1 \sim 10^{-8} cm^2 s^{-1}$ at $T > 20°C$ and less than $(2-4) 10^{-11} cm^2 s^{-1}$ for $T < 15°C$, Vaz *et al.*, 1981). The experimental result was explained by a so-called "ice-breaker" model, where the protein disorders the gel phase lipid in its immediate environment to such a degree as if it were in a relatively fluid lipid environment. This explanation was contained partly in the theoretical studies by Pink *et al.* (1982).

The lateral diffusion of eosin-labelled bacteriorhodopsin in reconstituted dimyristoylphosphatidylcholine vesicles was studied by Peters and Cherry (1982). The diffusion coefficient of a recombinant at a lipid-to-protein molar ratio of 140:1 was found to be 4.5×10^{-11}, 4.4×10^{-10}, 1.5×10^{-9}, 1.1×10^{-8} and $2.3 \times 10^{-8}\,cm^2 s^{-1}$ at the temperatures of 17, 20, 21.5, 24.5 and 32°C, respectively. Also measured was the diffusion coefficient of a lipid analogue (diO–C_{18}) at the same temperatures with the values 3.7×10^{-11}, 9.4×10^{-10}, 2.1×10^{-9}, 1.4×10^{-8}, and $4.3 \times 10^{-8}\,cm^2 s^{-1}$, respectively.

CONCLUDING REMARKS

Comparison of rotational and lateral diffusion data

The first membrane system where both rotational and lateral diffusion coefficients have been available was the photoreceptor disc membrane. It was in this system that the first quantitative test for the hydrodynamic theory for free rotational and lateral diffusion (Saffman and Delbrück, 1975) was performed. In figure 5.11*a* the temperature dependence for the calculated membrane viscosities derived from rotational and lateral diffusion coefficients, denoted by η_r and η_l, respectively, is shown. In order to calculate these according to equations 64 and 65, we used as parameters $a = 20$ Å, $h = 45$ Å, $D_r^{-1} = 20\,\mu sec$ at 22°C and Q_{10} about 3 (Cone, 1972) and $\eta' = 10^{-2}$ poise, $D_1 = (3 \pm 1.2)\,10^{-9}\,cm^2 s^{-1}$ at 22°C and $Q_{10} = 1.7$ (Wey *et al.*, 1981). In the temperature range 10–30°C the membrane viscosity η_r is in the range 1–25 poise, and 8–50 poise for η_l. The agreement is reasonably good, especially if the large experimental error limits, the simplifying assumptions of the model, the uncertainty regarding the viscosity η' of the surrounding medium and the different animal species (*Rana pipiens* and *Rana catesbiana* in the case of rotational and lateral diffusion measurements, respectively) are taken into account. In addition, the rather low lipid-to-protein molar ratio in the disc membrane may as well contribute to this difference as protein-protein interactions are not considered in the Saffman-Delbrück model.

Another system, bacteriorhodopsin reconstituted with dimyristoylphosphatidylcholine, has been characterised by protein rotational diffusion (Heyn *et al.*, 1981; Cherry and Godfrey, 1981) as well as protein and lipid analogue lateral diffusion measurements (Peters and Cherry, 1982). Rotational diffusion coefficients D_r have been estimated from the figure 4 of Heyn *et al.* (1981) for samples with a lipid-to-protein molar ratio of 111 and 168, and from the figure 8 of Cherry and Godfrey (1981) for samples having a ratio of 179 and 212. Lateral diffusion coefficients D_l are taken from Peters and Cherry (1982) for a recombinant with a ratio of about 140. Additional parameters used to calculate the membrane viscosity η_r according to equation 64 are the bacteriorhodopsin radius ($a = 16.4$ Å according to Henderson and Unwin, 1975) and the height of

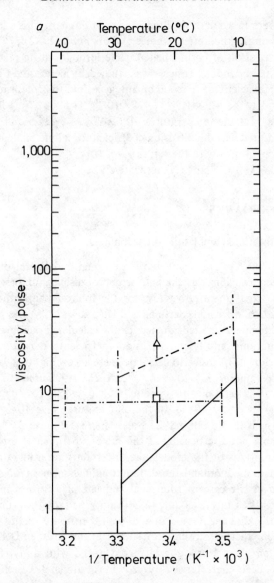

Figure 5.11 Comparison of membrane viscosity derived from protein rotational (η_r) and lateral (η_l) diffusion data. *a*, Temperature dependence for η_r (———, Cone, 1972) and η_l (– · – · –, Wey *et al.*, 1981) for rhodopsin within the photoreceptor disc membrane; erythrocyte membrane viscosity η_l for membranes genetically depleted of spectrin, according to Koppel *et al.* (1981, □) and equation 65 (△); temperature dependence for $\bar{\eta}_r$ for normal erythrocyte membranes (·· – ·· –, Nigg and Cherry, 1979b).

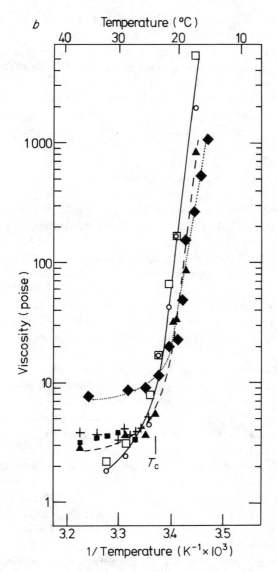

Figure 5.11 *b*, Temperature dependence for η_r for a bacteriorhodopsin-dimyristoylphos-phatidylcholine recombinant with a lipid-to-protein molar ratio of 111 and 168 (♦•••••♦ and ▲ – – –▲, respectively, Heyn *et al.*, 1981) and 179 and 212 (+++ and ■■, respectively, Cherry and Godfrey, 1981); the temperature dependence η_l for bacteriorhodopsin (○——○) and a lipid analogue (□——□) for the same recombinant system with a ratio of about 140, is also shown (Peters and Cherry, 1982). The gel to liquid crystalline phase transition temperature (T_c) for the pure lipid system is indicated

the protein within the membrane (h = 45 Å). A viscosity of 10^{-2} poise is used for η' to calculate the membrane viscosity η_l from equation 65.

As seen in figure 5.11b the agreement for the membrane viscosity η_l when calculated from lipid and protein lateral diffusion coefficients is excellent over the entire temperature range of 17–32°C. This is indicative of free lateral diffusion for both lipid molecules and protein monomers in that range.

In order to discuss the rotational diffusion data and to compare η_r with η_l, we consider two temperature ranges: first, temperatures above T_c (23°C); and second, temperatures $T_{imm} < T < T_c$, where T_{imm} is the temperature where the protein becomes immobilised (about 15°C).

From the rotational diffusion data of Heyn *et al.* (1981) the sample with a ratio of 111 shows an increased viscosity with respect to the sample with a higher ratio (168). This is most probably due to small protein aggregates as Cherry and Godfrey (1981) failed to detect a noticeable dependence of rotational diffusion on the lipid-to-protein ratio in the range 136 up to 212. At all protein concentrations the viscosity η_r is almost insensitive at temperatures above about 25°C. This is in contrast to the temperature dependence of η_l, which does not show such saturating behaviour up to 32°C. Whether this can be explained in a trivial way (different sample preparations, experimental error limits) or is due to an inadequate procedure for calculating diffusion coefficients or membrane viscosity (for example, neglecting possible wobbling diffusion), remains to be seen.

At temperatures below T_c there is rather good correlation between η_r and η_l. From this we may deduce that the proteins are diffusing as monomers (or small aggregates) below T_c and above immobilisation. If the small diffusion coefficient D_r had been due to large aggregates, the calculated viscosity η_r, assuming a monomer in equation 64, would be in reality much smaller (by a factor $1/n^2$ for aggregates with a cross-sectional diameter of n times the one for a monomer). On the other hand, if the measured D_l value had been due to the same aggregates, the difference between true and calculated membrane viscosity would be negligible due to the logarithmic dependence of η_l on the diffusing particle radius (see equation 65). Hence we would have expected a very different temperature dependence for η_r and η_l, if increasingly larger aggregates had been formed with decreasing temperatures below T_c.

Despite the minor inconsistencies described for the two membrane systems (disc membrane and reconstituted bacteriorhodopsin), which both lack an additional network beyond and/or above the plasma membrane, protein and lipid diffusion is reasonably well described by the hydrodynamic model developed by Saffman and Delbrück (1975).

The possibility that cytoskeletal structures may cause restraints on lateral and rotational mobility has been suspected for some time for the erythrocyte membrane (Peters *et al.*, 1974, Nigg and Cherry, 1980). In figure 5.11a we have summarised calculations based on rotational and lateral diffusion data. If the spectrin network is genetically depleted (Sheetz *et al.*, 1980), a viscosity η_l of about 24 poise is obtained from equation 65 (assuming $a = h = 40$ Å). A somewhat smaller value was reported by Koppel *et al.* (1981), based on a model which took into account interactions of the cytoskeleton with the plasma membrane; they reported a value of about 8 poise. These two values are compatible with viscosity data determined from rotational diffusion data for band 3 dimers in the temperature range 15-38°C (Nigg and Cherry, 1979b). If lateral diffusion of band 3 is measured in normal erythrocytes an apparent membrane viscosity of about 2,000 poise results, which is incompatible with the rotational diffusion data. This behaviour may be rationalised such that, as already mentioned by Cherry *et al.* (1976), a proportion of the band 3 dimers, which is not linked to the cytoskeleton, is entrapped within a spectrin network where it rotates (and most probably undergoes microscopic lateral diffusion). Lateral diffusion over large distances is prevented by the network and diffusing particles being confined to skeleton-free membrane areas. It should be emphasised that, in general, rotational diffusion measurements report on the microenvironment of the protein, while lateral diffusion gives insight about displacement over macroscopic distances.

A similar protein–skeleton interaction may be expected for other cells too. Jacobson and Wojcieszyn (1981) pointed out that other possible restrictions to plasma membrane protein mobility may be provided by cells possessing an exoskeleton, for example a glycocalyx matrix.

Possible mechanisms for control of protein diffusion

In summary, lateral and rotational diffusion data have provided good evidence that, from a dynamic point of view, biological membranes are present in all different forms from "rigid", via "intermediate" to "free" systems.

Rigid systems may be characterised by viscosities less than 10^4 poise (corresponding to $D_1 < 10^{-12} \text{cm}^2\text{s}^{-1}$ and $D_r < 50$ msec for a typical membrane protein). Examples are bacteriorhodopsin in the natural purple membrane, acetylcholine receptors of Torpedo electric organ, and integral proteins in reconstituted systems well below T_c, such as bacteriorhodopsin, ($Mg^{2+} + Ca^{2+}$) ATPase, and glycophorin recombinants. In these systems the protein immobility is caused by the surrounding highly viscous gel phase of the lipid.

Intermediate systems may be characterised by additional peripheral molecular assemblies, adjacent to the plasma membrane. The best example is the erythrocyte membrane. The discrepancy, which exists for most measured protein lateral diffusion data compared with lipid diffusion and protein rotational diffusion data can at least be partly explained by such or a similar interaction of membrane proteins with cyto- and/or exoskeletal structures. This may be either by direct linkage or due to compartmentilisation of the plasma membrane, which results in the inhibition of macroscopic lateral diffusion. The described interaction may of course also result in complete inhibition of mobility, leading to rigid membrane systems as described before.

Free and fluid systems may be characterised by the lack of additional membrane structures and a fluid lipid phase (that is, well above T_c). Examples are rhodopsin in the photoreceptor disc membrane, erythrocyte membranes depleted of spectrin, and integral proteins in reconstituted systems at temperatures above the lipid phase transition of the respective lipid. Examples are bacteriorhodopsin and $(Ca^{2+} + Mg^{2+})$ATPase recombinants.

In conclusion, the diffusibility of intrinsic membrane proteins may be controlled by one or more of the following events:

lipid phase transition, resulting in immobilisation of the protein well below T_c;

direct linkage of the proteins to rigid cyto- and/or cytoskeletal structures;

viscous drag imposed on the proteins by highly viscous cyto- and/or exoskeletal structures;

compartmentilisation of the membrane by cyto- and/or exoskeletal structures, resulting in lateral diffusion coefficients not compatible with protein rotational and lipid lateral diffusion data;

aggregation of the proteins within the membrane.

ACKNOWLEDGEMENTS

We thank Dr R. Peters for reading the manuscript. C.J.R. thanks the Muscular Dystrophy Group of Great Britain for support.

REFERENCES

Abrahamson, E. W. and Wiesenfeld, J. R. (1972). In *Handbook of Sensory Physiology* (ed. H. J. A. Dartnall), Springer-Verlag, Vol. VII/1, p. 67.

Albrecht, A. C. (1961). *J. molec. Spectrosc.*, 6, 84.

Albrecht, A. C. (1970). *Prog. React. Kinet.*, 5, 301.

Austin, R. H., Chan, S. S. and Jovin, T. M. (1979). *Proc. natn. Acad. Sci. U.S.A.*, 76, 5650.

Axelrod, D., Koppel, D. E., Schlessinger, J., Elson, E. and Webb, W. W. (1976a). *Biophys. J.*, 16, 1055.

Axelrod, D. *et al.* (1976b). *Proc. natn. Acad. Sci. U.S.A.*, 73, 4594.

Axelrod, D. (1977). *Biophys. J.*, 18, 129.

Badea, M. G. and Brand, L. (1979). *Meth. Enzym.*, 61, 379.

Barisas, G. B. and Leuther, M. D. (1979). *Biophys. Chem.*, 10, 221.

Barisas. G. B. (1980). *Biophys. J.*, 29, 545.

Bensasson, R., Land, E. J. and Truscott, T. G. (1975). *Nature*, 258, 768.

Birks, J. B. (1976). *Photochem. Photobiol.*, 24, 287.

Belford, G. G., Belford, R. L. and Weber, G. (1972). *Proc. natn. Acad. Sci. U.S.A.*, 69, 1392.

Blaurock, A. E. and Stoeckenius, W. (1971). *Nature new Biol.*, 233, 152.

Bøg-Hansen, T. C. (ed.) (1981). In *Lectins*, Vol. 1, W. de Gruyter.

Boyer, P. D. *et al.* (1977). *Ann. Rev. Biochem.*, 46, 955.

Brown, P. K. (1972). *Nature new Biol.*, 236, 35.

Bürkli, A. and Cherry, R. J. (1981). *Biochemistry*, 20, 138.

Cabantchik, Z. J., Knauf, P. A. and Rothstein, A. (1978). *Biochim. biophys. Acta*, 515, 239.

Cherry, R. J., Bürkli, A., Busslinger, M., Schneider, G. and Parish, G. R. (1976). *Nature*, 263, 389.

Cherry, R. J., Heyn, M. P. and Oesterhelt, D. (1977a). *FEBS Lett.*, 78, 25.

Cherry, R. J., Müller, U. and Schneider, G. (1977b). *FEBS Lett.*, 80, 465.

Cherry, R. J. (1978). *Meth. Enzym.*, **54**, 47.
Cherry, R. J., Müller, U., Henderson, R. and Heyn, M. P. (1978). *J. molec. Biol.*, **121**, 283.
Cherry, R. J. (1979). *Biochim. biophys. Acta*, **559**, 289.
Cherry, R. J. and Nigg, E. A. (1980). In *Membrane Transport in Erythrocytes* (eds U. V. Lassen, H. H. Ussing and J. O. Wieth). Munksgaard, Copenhagen, p. 130.
Cherry, R. J., Müller, U., Holenstein, C. and Heyn, M. P. (1980). *Biochim. biophys. Acta*, **596**, 145.
Cherry, R. J. and Nigg, E. A. (1981). In *The Function of Red Blood Cells: Erythrocyte Pathobiology* A. R. Liss, New York 10011, p. 59.
Cherry, R. J. and Godfrey, R. E. (1981). *Biophys. J.*, **36**, 257.
Chuang, T. J. and Eisenthal, K. B. (1972). *J. chem. Phys.*, **57**, 5094.
Chu Kung, M., Devault, D., Hess, D. and Oesterhelt, D. (1975). *Biophys. J.*, **15**, 907.
Cone, R. A. (1972). *Nature new Biol.*, **236**, 39.
Cox, A. and Kemp, T. L. (1971). In *Introductory Photochemistry*, McGraw-Hill, London, p. 36.
Downer, N. W. and Cone, R. A. (1978). *Biophys. J.*, **21**, 135a.
Dragsten, P., Henkart, P., Blumenthal, R., Weinstein, J. and Schlessinger, J. (1979). *Proc. natn. Acad. Sci. U.S.A.*, **76**, 5163.
Dratz, E. A., Miljanich, G. P., Nemes, P. P., Gaw, J. E. and Schwartz, S. (1979). *Photochem. Photobiol.*, **29**, 661.
Ebashi, S., Endo, M. and Ohtsuki, J. (1969). *Q. Rev. Biophys.*, **2**, 351.
Ebrey, T. G., Becher, B., Mao, B., Kilbride, P. and Honig, B. (1977). *J. molec. Biol.*, **112**, 377.
Edidin, M., Zagyansky, Y. and Lardner, T. J. (1976). *Science*, **191**, 466.
Edidin, M. (1981). In *Membrane Structure* (eds Fineau and Michell), Elsevier/North-Holland, Vol 2, p. 37.
Eldefrawi, M. E. and Eldefrawi, A. T. (1977). In *Receptors and Recognition*, ser. A4 (eds P. Cuatrecasas and M. F. Greaves), Chapman and Hall, London, p. 199.
Eldridge, C. A., Elson, E. L. and Webb, W. W. (1980). *Biochemistry*, **19**, 2075.
Erecińska, M., Blasie, J. K. and Wilson, D. F. (1977). *FEBS Lett.*, **76**, 235.
Frey, T. G., Chan, S. H. P. and Schatz, G. (1978). *J. biol. Chem.*, **253**, 4389.
Frye, L. D. and Edidin, M. (1970). *J. Cell Sci.*, **7**, 319.
Garland, P. B. and Moore, C. H. (1979). *Biochem. J.*, **183**, 561.
Garland, P. B. (1981). *Biophys. J.*, **33**, 481.
Greinert, R., Staerk, H., Stier, A. and Weller, A. (1979). *J. biochem. biophys. Meth.*, **1**, 77.
Hagins, W. A. and Jennings, W. H. (1959). *Discuss. Faraday Soc.*, **27**, 180.
Hatefi, Y., Galante, Y. M., Stiggall, D. L. and Ragan, C. I. (1979). *Meth. Enzym.*, **56**, 577.
Henderson, R. and Unwin, P. N. T. (1975). *Nature*, **257**, 28.
Henderson, R., Capaldi, R. A. and Leigh, I. S. (1977). *J. molec. Biol.*, **112**, 631.
Heyn, M. P., Cherry, R. J. and Müller, U. (1977). *J. molec. Biol.*, **117**, 607.
Heyn, M. P., Cherry, R. J. and Dencher, N. A. (1981). *Biochemistry*, **20**, 840.
Höchli, M. and Hackenbrock, C. R. (1976). *Proc. natn. Acad. Sci. U.S.A.*, **73**, 1636.
Höchli, M. and Hackenbrock, C. R. (1979). *Proc. natn. Acad. Sci. U.S.A.*, **76**, 1236.
Hoffmann, W., Siebert, F., Hofmann, K.-P. and Kreutz, W. (1978a). *Biochim. biophys. Acta*, **503**, 450.
Hoffmann, W., Graca-Miguel, M., Barnard, P. and Chapman, D. (1978b). *FEBS Lett.*, **95**, 31.
Hoffmann, W., Sarzala, M. G. and Chapman, D. (1979). *Proc. natn. Acad. Sci. U.S.A.*, **76**, 3860.
Hoffmann, W. *et al.* (1980a). *J. molec. Biol.*, **141**, 119.
Hoffmann, W., Clark, A. D., Turner, M., Wyard, S. and Chapman, D. (1980b). *Biochim. biophys. Acta*, **598**, 178.
Hoffmann, W., Restall, C. J., Hyla, R. and Chapman, D. (1980c). *Biochim. biophys. Acta*, **602**, 531.
Hoffmann, W., Pink, D. A., Restall, C. J. and Chapman, D. (1981). *Eur. J. Biochem.*, **114**, 585.
Huang, H. W. (1973). *J. theor. Biol.*, **40**, 11.
Hyde, J. S. (1978). *Meth. Enzym.*, **49**, 480.
Israelachvili, J. *et al.* (1975). *Biochim. biophys. Acta*, **382**, 125.

Jablonski, A. (1961). *Z. Naturforschung*, **A16**, 1.
Jacobson, K., Wu, E. and Poste, G. (1976). *Biochim. biophys. Acta*, **433**, 215.
Jacobson, K., Hou, Y. and Wojcieszyn, J. (1978). *Expl cell Res.*, **116**, 179.
Jacobson, K. and Wojcieszyn, J. (1981). *Commun. molec. cell. Biophys.*, **1**, 189.
Johansson, L. B. and Lindblom, G. (1980). *Q. Rev. Biophys.*, **13**, 63.
Johnson, M. and Edidin, M. (1978). *Nature*, **272**, 448.
Johnson, P. and Garland, P. B. (1981). *FEBS Lett.*, **132**, 252.
Jovin, T. M., Bartholdi, M., Vaz, W. L. C. and Austin, R. H. (1981). *Ann. N.Y. Acad. Sci.*, **366**, 176.
Junge, W. and DeVault, D. (1975). *Biochim. biophys. Acta*, **408**, 200.
Kapitza, H.-G. and Sackmann, E. (1980). *Biochim. biophys. Acta*, **595**, 56.
Kasche, V. and Lindqvist, L. (1965). *Photochem. Photobiol.*, **4**, 923.
Kasha, M. (1960). *Rad. Res. Suppl.*, **2**, 243.
Kawato, S., Kinosita, Jr, K. and Ikegami, A. (1977). *Biochemistry*, **16**, 2319.
Kawato, S., Sigel, E., Carafoli, E. and Cherry, R. J. (1980). *J. biol. Chem.*, **255**, 5508.
Kawato, S. and Kinosita, K. (1981). *Biophys. J.*, **36**, 277.
Kawato, S., Sigel, E., Carafoli, E. and Cherry, R. J. (1981). *J. biol. Chem.*, **256**, 7518.
Koppel, D. E. (1979). *Biophys. J.*, **28**, 281.
Koppel, D. E., Sheetz, M. P. and Schindler, M. (1981). *Proc. natn. Acad. Sci. U.S.A.*, **78**, 3576.
Korenstein, R. and Hess, B. (1978). *FEBS Lett.*, **89**, 15.
Korenstein, R., Hess, B. and Kuschmitz, D. (1978) *FEBS Lett.*, **93**, 266.
Kunze, U. and Junge, W. (1977). *FEBS Lett.*, **80**, 429.
deLaat, S. W., Van der Saag, P. T., Elson, E. L. and Schlessinger, J. (1979). *Biochim. biophys. Acta*, **558**, 247.
deLaat, S. W., Van der Saag, P. T., Elson, E. L. and Schlessinger, J. (1980). *Proc. natn. Acad. Sci. U.S.A.*, **77**, 1526.
Lepock, J. R., Thompson, J. E., Kruuv, J. and Wallach, D. F. H. (1978). *Biochim. biophys. Res. Commun.*, **85**, 344.
Leuther, M. O., Barisas, B. G., Peacock, J. S. and Krakauer, H. (1979). *Biochim. biophys. Res. Commun.*, **89**, 85.
Levi, A., Shechter, Y., Neufeld, E. J. and Schlessinger, J. (1980). *Proc. natn. Acad. Sci. U.S.A.*, **77**, 3469.
Lipari, G. and Szabo, A. (1980). *Biophys. J.*, **30**, 489.
Lo, M. M. S., Garland, P. B., Lamprecht, J. and Barnard, E. A. (1980). *FEBS Lett.*, **111**, 407.
Lower, S. K. and El-Sayed, M. A. (1966). *Chem. Rev.*, **66**, 199.
Lozier, R. H., Bogomolni, R. A. and Stoeckenius, W. (1975). *Biophys. J.*, **15**, 955.
Ludwig, B., Downer, N. W. and Capaldi, R. A. (1979). *Biochemistry*, **18**, 1401.
McClure, D. S. (1949). *J. chem. Phys.*, **17**, 905.
McGlynn, S. P., Azumi, T. and Kinoshita, M. (1969). In *Molecular Spectroscopy of the Triplet State*, Prentice Hall, Inc. Englewood Cliffs.
McIntosh, P. R., Kawato, S., Freedman, R. B. and Cherry, R. J. (1980). *FEBS Lett.*, **122**, 54.
Meissner, G. (1975). *Biochim. biophys. Acta*, **389**, 51.
Mitchell, P. (1966). *Biol. Rev.*, **41**, 445.
Mitchell, P. (1975). *FEBS Lett.*, **56**, 1.
Moore, C., Boxer, D. and Garland, P. (1979). *FEBS Lett.*, **108**, 161.
Nemes, P. P., Miljanich, G. P., White, D. L. and Dratz, E. A. (1980). *Biochemistry*, **19**, 2067.
Nigg, E. and Cherry, R. J. (1979a). *Nature*, **277**, 493.
Nigg, E. A. and Cherry, R. J. (1979b). *Biochemistry*, **18**, 3457.
Nigg, E., Kessler, M. and Cherry, R. J. (1979). *Biochim. biophys. Acta*, **550**, 328.
Nigg, E. A., Bron, C., Girardet, M. and Cherry, R. A. (1980a). *Biochemistry*, **19**, 1887.
Nigg, E. A., Gahmberg, C. G. and Cherry, R. J. (1980b). *Biochim. biophys. Acta*, **600**, 636.
Nigg, E. A., Cherry, R. J. and Bächi, T. (1980c). *Virology*, **107**, 552.
Nigg, E. A. and Cherry, R. J. (1980). *Proc. natn. Acad. Sci. U.S.A.*, **77**, 4702.
Oesterhelt, D. and Stoeckenius, W. (1971). *Nature new Biol.*, **233**, 142.
Owicki, J. C. and McConnell, H. M. (1980). *Biophys. J.*, **30**, 383.

Parker, R. T., Freedlander, R. S. and Dunlap, R. B. (1980). *Ann. chim. Acta*, 119, 189.
Peters, R., Peters, J., Tews, K. H. and Bähr, W. (1974). *Biochim. biophys. Acta*, 367, 282.
Peters, R. and Richter, H. P. (1981). *Devl Biol.*, 86, 285.
Peters, R. (1981). *Cell Biol. int. Rep.*, 5, 733.
Peters, R., Brünger, A. and Schulten, K. (1981). *Proc. natn. Acad. Sci. U.S.A.*, 78, 962.
Peters, R. and Cherry, R. J. (1982). *Biophys. J.*, 37, 277a.
Peters, R. (1982). personal communication.
Pink, D. A., Lookman, T., MacDonald, A. L., Zuckermann, M. J. and Jan, N. (1982). *Biochim. biophys. Acta*, 687, 42.
Pinto da Silva, P. (1972). *J. Cell Biol.*, 53, 777.
Poo, M. and Cone, R. A. (1974). *Nature*, 247, 438.
Porter, G., Reid, E. S. and Tredwell, C. J. (1974). *Chem. Phys. Lett.*, 29, 469.
Razi-Naqvi, K., Gonzales-Rodriguez, J., Cherry, R. J. and Chapman, D. (1973). *Nature new Biol.*, 245, 249.
Razi-Naqvi, K. and Wild, U. P. (1975). *Chem. Phys. Lett.*, 36, 222.
Reidler, J. A., Keller, P. M., Elson, E. L. and Lenard, J. (1981). *Biochemistry*, 20, 1345.
Richter, C., Winterhalter, K. H. and Cherry, R. J. (1979). *FEBS Lett.*, 102, 151.
Richtmeyer, R. D. and Morton, K. W. (1967). In *Difference Methods for Initial Value Problems*, Wiley, N.Y. p. 189.
Rigler, R. and Ehrenberg, M. (1973). *Q. Rev. Biophys.*, 6, 139.
Saffman, P. G. and Delbrück, M. (1975). *Proc. natn. Acad. Sci. U.S.A.*, 72, 3111.
Schindler, M., Osborn, M. J. and Koppel, D. E. (1980). *Nature*, 283, 346.
Schlessinger, J. *et al.* (1976a). *Proc. natn. Acad. Sci. U.S.A.*, 73, 2409.
Schlessinger, J., Webb, W. W., Elson, E. L. and Metzger, H. (1976b). *Nature*, 264, 550.
Schlessinger, J., Axelrod, D., Koppel, D. E., Webb, W. W. and Elson, E. L. (1977a). *Science*, 195, 307.
Schlessinger, J. *et al.* (1977b). *Proc. natn. Acad. Sci. U.S.A.*, 74, 2909.
Schlessinger, J. *et al.* (1977c). *Proc. natn. Acad. Sci. U.S.A.*, 74, 1110.
Schlessinger, J., Shechter, Y., Cuatrecasas, P., Willingham, M. C. and Pastan, J. (1978). *Proc. natn. Acad. Sci. U.S.A.*, 75, 5353.
Sela, M. (ed.) (1977). In *The Antigens*, Vol. 4, Academic Press.
Shechter, Y., Schlessinger, J., Jacobs, S., Chang, K.-J. and Cuatrecasas, P. (1978). *Proc. natn. Acad. Sci. U.S.A.*, 75, 2135.
Sheetz, M. P. and Koppel, D. E. (1979). *Proc. natn. Acad. Sci. U.S.A.*, 76, 3314.
Sheetz, M. P., Schindler, M. and Koppel, D. E. (1980). *Nature*, 285, 510.
Sherman, W. V., Slifkin, M. A. and Caplan, S. R. (1976). *Biochim. biophys. Acta*, 423, 238.
Sigel, E. and Carafoli, E. (1979). *J. biol. Chem.*, 254, 10572.
Smith, B. A. and McConnell, H. M. (1978). *Proc. natn. Acad. Sci. U.S.A.*, 75, 2759.
Smith, B. A., Clark, W. R. and McConnell, H. M. (1979a). *Proc. natn. Acad. Sci. U.S.A.*, 76, 5641.
Smith, L. M., Parce, J. W., Smith, B. A. and McConnell, H. M. (1979b). *Proc. natn. Acad. Sci. U.S.A.*, 76, 4177.
Smith, L. M., Weis, R. M. and McConnell, H. M. (1981). *Biophys. J.*, 36, 73.
Stewart, J. G., Baker, B. N. and Williams, T. P. (1977). *Biophys. Struct. Mech.*, 3, 19.
Stoeckenius, W., Lozier, R. H. and Bogomolni, R. A. (1979). *Biochim. biophys. Acta*, 505, 215.
Taylor, R. B., Duffus, W. P. H., Raff, M. C. and de Petris, S. (1971). *Nature new Biol.*, 233, 225.
Thomas, D. D. (1978). *Biophys J.*, 24, 439.
Tomita, M. and Marchesi, V. T. (1975). *Proc. natn. Acad. Sci. U.S.A.*, 72, 2964.
Turro, N. J., Liu, K.-C., Chow, M.-F. and Lee, P. (1978). *Photochem. Photobiol.*, 27, 523.
Vaz, W. L. C., Austin, R. H. and Vogel, H. (1979a). *Biophys. J.*, 26, 415.
Vaz, W. L. C., Jacobson, K., Wu, E.-S. and Derzko, Z. (1979b). *Proc. natn. Acad. Sci. U.S.A.*, 76, 5645.
Vaz, W. L. C., Kapitza, H.-G., Stümpel, J., Sackmann, E. and Jovin, T. M. (1981). *Biochemistry*, 20, 1392.
Wahl, P., Kasai, M., Changeux, J. P. and Auchet, J.-C. (1971). *Eur. J. Biochem.*, 18, 332.
Webb, W. W., Barak, L. S., Tank, D. W. and Wu, E. S. (1981). *Biochem. Soc. Symp.*, 46, 191.

Weber, G. (1953). *Adv. Prot. Chem.*, 8, 415.
Weber, G. (1973). In *Fluorescence Techniques in Cell Biology* (Eds A. A. Thaer and M. Sernetz), Springer-Verlag, Berlin, p. 5.
Wey, C.-L., Cone, R. A. and Edidin, M. A. (1981). *Biophys. J.*, 33, 225.
Wikström, M. and Krab, K. (1978). *FEBS Lett.*, 91, 8.
Wildenauer, D. and Khorana, H. G. (1977). *Biochim. biophys. Acta*, 466, 315.
Wolf, D. E., Edidin, M. and Dragsten, P. R. (1980a). *Proc. natn. Acad. Sci. U.S.A.*, 77, 2043.
Wolf, D. E., Henkart, P. and Webb, W. W. (1980b). *Biochemistry*, 19, 3893.
Wu, E.-S., Jacobson, K. and Papahadjopoulos, D. (1977). *Biochemistry*, 16, 3936.
Yguerabide, J. (1972). *Meth. Enzym.*, 26, 798.
Yoshizawa, T. and Horiuchi, S. (1973). In *Biochemistry and Physiology of Visual Pigments* (ed. H. Langer), Springer-Verlag, p. 69.
Zagyanski, Y., Benda, P. and Bisconte, J. C. (1977). *FEBS Lett.*, 77, 206.
Zagyanski, Y. and Edidin, M. (1976). *Biochim. biophys. Acta*, 433, 209.
Zander, M. (1968). In *Phosphorimetry*, Academic Press, N.Y.
Zidovetzki, R., Yarden, Y., Schlessinger, J. and Jovin, T. M. (1982). *Proc. natn. Acad. Sci. U.S.A.*, in the press.
Zwicker, E. F. and Grossweiner, L. J. (1963). *J. phys. Chem.*, 67, 549.

6

Theoretical models of monolayers, bilayers and biological membranes

David A. Pink, Theoretical Physics Institute, St. Francis Xavier University, Antigonish, Nova Scotia, Canada B2G 1CO

INTRODUCTION

The area of two-dimensional and quasi two-dimensional systems and their static structures and phase transitions has become a major field of study. If one restricts oneself to "pure" lipid monolayers and bilayers, one must be prepared to discuss, for example, the various structures that arise at the main, pre- and sub-transitions (Chen *et al.*, 1980) in bilayers, structures in monolayers that give rise to their characteristic isotherms, as well as effects of pH and ionic concentration on their interactions in the polar region. Some of the phenomena apparently involve competition between interactions in the hydrophobic region of bilayers and those in the polar region, while there is considerable disagreement as to the mechanisms that give rise to monolayer isotherms and the location and nature of their critical points. In a mixed system, a great variety of bilayers, ranging from two-component systems (lipid 1-lipid 2, lipid–cholesterol, lipid-protein) to biological membranes, can occur. A brief review such as this could fall between two extremes: either essentially a list of references with a few words added to say what they contain; or a more detailed exposition of only a few topics. Recently there have been several reviews of theoretical work concerned with monolayers (Bell *et al.*, 1981), the physical effects underlying membrane organisation (Israelachvili *et al.*, 1980), the main lipid phase transition at T_c (Nagle, 1980), the methods used and models constructed to study phase changes in one- and two-component bilayers (Pink, 1981), and models of monolayers and bilayers containing intrinsic molecules, such as anaesthetics (Caillé *et al.*, 1980).

320   *Biomembrane Structure and Function*

This review will concentrate on some problems that have arisen in recent years and that remain unsolved; it is directed at both experimentalists and theorists in the field. Some mathematics is included; this is intended to bring readers to the point where they can critically examine theories by themselves. We begin with an outline of equilibrium statistical mechanics and describe some models for lipid phase transitions. Approximation or stimulation schemes are reviewed and examples from current research discussed critically. This is followed by a discussion of recent work on monolayers, bilayers and biological membranes. Topics which are no longer currently researched are only briefly mentioned, while ideas that may be coming into fashion, such as the Landau-Ginzburg theory, are discussed in more detail. Reference will be made to experimental work only if it is directly concerned with applications of the models; there are already several good recent reviews (for example, Chapman, 1980).

This review will not concern itself with phase transitions merely in two-dimensional systems on the grounds that monolayers and bilayers are quasi two-dimensional, possessing interactions in a third dimension with water. Thus, questions of topological long range order (Kosterlitz and Thouless, 1978), or of the existence of the Nelson–Halperin mechanism (Nelson and Halperin, 1979) of two-dimensional melting will be considered only later. There are recent reviews of this by Barber (1980) and Abraham (1981a). Finally, space is too limited to review adequately all recent theoretical work and the selection here reflects the author's interests.

INTRODUCTORY EQUILIBRIUM STATISTICAL MECHANICS

When dealing with phase changes in lipid monolayers or bilayers it is generally assumed that measurements are carried out on a system in thermodynamic equilibrium with its surroundings. When this is the case we may use equilibrium statistical mechanics to calculate thermodynamic functions of interest, and this section gives a brief outline of the quantities which may be calculated (see Heer, 1972; Huang, 1967; Landau *et al.*, 1980; Stanley, 1971).

For given values of external parameters that may be experimentally controlled, such as absolute temperature, T, pressure, P, pH, relative concentration of molecular species and so on, the system will be in that state for which its free energy is a minimum. The Helmholtz free energy is defined:

$$\mathcal{F} = -k_B T \ln Z$$
$$Z = \text{Tr}(e^{-\beta \mathcal{H}}), \quad \beta = 1/k_B T \tag{1}$$

where Z is the partition function, $\mathcal{H}$ is the hamiltonian or, here, the total energy operator for the system and k_B is Boltzmann's constant. Tr (Trace) indicates that one must perform a sum over all diagonal matrix elements of the operator $e^{-\beta \mathcal{H}}$ which is defined by its power series. The matrix elements may be calculated using any convenient complete set of states (see below). If R is some operator then its average value at temperature T is given by:

$$\langle R \rangle = \mathrm{Tr}(Re^{-\beta\mathcal{H}})/Z \qquad (2)$$

Once an expression for the free energy and the appropriate average values are known, all thermodynamic quantities can be calculated. Thus, for example, the entropy, S, enthalpy, Q, specific heat at constant pressure, C_p, or lateral compressibility, κ, are given by

$$S = -\left(\frac{\partial \mathcal{G}}{\partial T}\right)_P,$$

$$Q = -T^2 \frac{\partial}{\partial T}\left(\frac{\mathcal{G}}{T}\right)_P = \langle\mathcal{H}\rangle$$

$$\qquad (3)$$

$$C_P = \left(\frac{\partial Q}{\partial T}\right)_P = (\langle\mathcal{H}^2\rangle - \langle\mathcal{H}\rangle^2)/k_B T$$

$$\kappa = -\frac{1}{\langle A\rangle}\frac{\partial\langle A\rangle}{\partial\Pi} = (\langle A^2\rangle - \langle A\rangle^2)/k_B T\langle A\rangle$$

where $\mathcal{G}$ is the Gibbs free energy, $\mathcal{G} = \mathcal{F} + PV$. Here, $\langle A\rangle$ is the average cross-sectional area of a quantity of interest and Π is the conjugate lateral pressure applied in the plane in which $\langle A\rangle$ is measured. The last two quantities are related to fluctuations in the hamiltonian and the area, and are examples of response functions that describe the response of the system to a change in the respective conjugate parameters T and Π. Because of the appearance of infinitely long-range fluctuations at critical points, these response functions diverge at such points. Many of the pure systems we will look at here seem to undergo phase transitions from one phase to another. Thus, at ~41°C a bilayer of dipalmitoyl phosphatidylcholine (DPPC) in excess water seems to undergo a first-order phase transition, this being manifested by a narrow peak in C_Π, as well as by the observation of a narrow hysteresis loop (Estep *et al.*, 1978; Mabrey *et al.*, 1978; Davis, 1979). The peak shows that a phase change has taken place while the hysteresis loop suggests that it is a first-order phase transition. Mathematically, such a transition manifests itself as a discontinuity in Q at the transition temperature and a δ-function in C_Π, the specific heat at constant lateral pressure; it is referred to as a discontinuous phase transition. The discontinuity in Q is the transition enthalpy or heat of transition. A second-order or continuous phase transition appears, mathematically, as a divergence in C_Π at the transition temperature and with zero heat of transition, that is, Q is continuous.

We thus see that the hamiltonian, the operator that describes all contributions to the energy of the system, determines the phases and the kinds of phase transitions that can appear. The hamiltonian operator is determined by the interactions between the components of the system and must reflect the symmetries which the system possesses. It can generally be written as (ignoring a constant term)

$$\mathcal{H} = \sum_i \mathcal{H}_i + \sum_{ij} \mathcal{H}_{ij} + \sum_{ijk} \mathcal{H}_{ijk} + \dots \tag{4}$$

where $\mathcal{H}_i$ is the energy operator of the ith unit of the system (an atom or a molecule), $\mathcal{H}_{ij}$ describes the interaction energy between the ith and jth units, $\mathcal{H}_{ijk}$ is the interaction energy between units, i, j and $k, \dots \mathcal{H}_i$ contains no terms describing the interaction of the ith unit with any other unit of the system. To see the significance of equation 4 let us consider the case in which all interaction terms in $\mathcal{H}$ are zero. Then the partition function and free energy are

$$Z = \mathrm{Tr}(e^{-\beta \sum_i \mathcal{H}_i}) = \prod_i \mathrm{Tr}_i(e^{-\beta \mathcal{H}_i}) = \prod_i Z_i$$

$$\mathcal{F} = -k_B T \ln (\prod_i Z_i) = -k_B T \sum_i \ln Z_i = \sum_i \mathcal{F}_i \tag{5}$$

Here Z_i is the partition function for the ith unit with $\mathcal{F}_i$ its free energy, and we see that the free energy is a sum of the free energies of each of the units, none of which interact with any other. Now, single units of microscopic size such as atoms or molecules do not in general show phase transitions as described above, therefore, neither will the total system. Thus, a system of non-interacting microscopic units will not in general show phase transitions, though changes of phase can occur over some temperature ranges that have either zero latent heat or no divergence in the specific heat associated with them. First- or second-order phase transitions therefore arise because of the interactions between the units of a system and are examples of cooperative phenomena. Thus, any model which purports to show a phase transition without its hamiltonian containing interaction terms, cannot in fact, do so. Whilst it is often trivial to evaluate $\mathcal{F}_i$ above, it is, in general, a very difficult problem to evaluate $\mathcal{F}$ when $\mathcal{H}$ contains interaction terms. If an exact analytical expression can be obtained for $\mathcal{F}$ for a given hamiltonian characterising the system of interest, then we say that such a model can be solved exactly. There are very few non-trivial models which can be solved exactly and some of these are the Ising model in one and two dimensions, some ferroelectric models, the 8-vertex model, the Potts model and the spherical model (McCoy and Wu, 1973; Lieb and Wu, 1972; Berlin and Kac, 1952; Wu, 1982; Stanley, 1971).

To make some statements about a model that cannot be solved exactly one must resort to approximation schemes or numerical methods, described below. Exactly soluble models of monolayers or bilayers have been constructed by Nagle (1975) and Wiegel (1975, 1976, 1977). These models, however, represent the bilayer as having only one lateral dimension so that their utility to model real systems is limited. They have been discussed by Nagle (1980), Bell *et al.* (1981) and Pink (1981).

SOME MODELS OF SINGLE-COMPONENT MONOLAYERS AND BILAYERS

As an example of a model of a phosphatidylcholine bilayer let us consider one which assumes that the main phase transition in DPPC, occurring at temperature $T = T_c$, is due to the "melting" of the hydrocarbon chains and that molecular rotation and lateral diffusion can be ignored. Each hydrocarbon chain can be in any of a set of conformational states $\{|n>\}$ which are characterised by an internal energy, E_n (dependant on the number of *gauche* conformers), a cross-sectional area, A_n, perpendicular to the local normal to the bilayer, and a degeneracy, D_n, giving the number of states with energy E_n possessing area A_n. We assume that the only effect of the polar region interactions is to bring the bilayer into existence (Tanford, 1979) and to set up an effective internal lateral pressure, Π, acting on the hydrocarbon chains (Marčelja, 1974). Two chains, i and j, in conformational states $|n>_i$ and $|m>_j$ have an interaction energy of $-J_0 I_{ij}(n, m)$. If we define projection operators $\mathcal{L}_{in} = |n>_i \ _i<n|$ (see, for example Messiah, 1967) for the ith chain in state n which possess the property $\sum_n \mathcal{L}_{in} = 1$, then the hamiltonian operator, $\mathcal{H}_{con}$, describing the conformational states of the chains, is

$$\mathcal{H}_{con} = \sum_i \sum_n (\Pi A_n + E_n)\mathcal{L}_{in} - \frac{J_0}{2} \sum_{ij} \sum_{nm} I_{ij}(n,m)\mathcal{L}_{in}\mathcal{L}_{jm} \tag{6}$$

This hamiltonian describes interactions within one half of a bilayer as well as any between the two halves of the bilayer. The operator for the area for the ith chain is

$$A_i = \sum_n A_n \mathcal{L}_{in} \tag{7}$$

The state of the bilayer in which the ith chain is the state n_i is $\prod_i |n_i>_i$ and Z is given by

$$Z = \sum_{\{n_i\}} \prod_i \ _i<n_i| e^{-\beta \mathcal{H}} \prod_i |n_i>_i \tag{8}$$

$$= \sum_{\{n_i\}} D_{\{n_i\}} \exp[-\beta(\sum_i (\Pi A_{n_i} + E_{n_i}) - \frac{J_0}{2} \sum_{ij} I_{ij}(n_i,m_j))]$$

where $\{n_i\}$ denotes the integers labelling the states of all the chains and $\prod_{\{n_i\}}$ denotes a product of single-chain states describing the state of many chains. Our hamiltonian contains no interactions describing the direct transfer of energy from one chain to another. Such a term could look like, for example,

$$\mathcal{H}_{con\ transfer} = -J_0, \sum_{ij} \sum_{nm} t(n,m) |n>_i \ _j<m| \tag{9}$$

This is the analogue of the hopping term in electronic conduction or the off-diagonal terms in the Heisenberg ferromagnet. Note also that the interactions in equations 6 and 9 can arise from both repulsive (hard- or soft-core) and attractive (van der Waals) forces.

Particularly simple forms of this model were used by Doniach (1978), Caillé *et al.* (1978) and Pink and Carroll (1978) who argued that for $T < T_c$, the hydrocarbon chains are predominantly in a low-energy extended state, $|g>$, while for $T > T_c$ the chains are in a melted high-energy state $|e>$. They assumed that the two halves of the bilayer were effectively non-interacting and that each chain has exactly z nearest neighbours in each half of the bilayer. This implies that the chains occupy the sites of a lattice, and if $z = 6$ then the lattice is triangular (and not hexagonal, for which $z = 3$). Only interactions between chains which are nearest neighbours are considered, so that the hamiltonian becomes

$$\mathcal{H}_{con} = \sum_i \left((\Pi A_g + E_g) \mathcal{L}_{ig} + (\Pi A_e + E_e) \mathcal{L}_{ie} \right) - \frac{J_0}{2} \sum_{<ij>} (I(g,g) \mathcal{L}_{ig} \mathcal{L}'_{jg}$$

$$+ I(g,e) \left(\mathcal{L}_{ig} \mathcal{L}_{je} + \mathcal{L}_{ie} \mathcal{L}_{jg} \right) + I(e,e) \mathcal{L}_{ie} \mathcal{L}_{je})$$

(10)

where $<ij>$ denotes an interaction between nearest neighbours i and j. Because of the property $\mathcal{L}_{ig} + \mathcal{L}_{ie} = 1$, we need only one variable, σ_i, which takes on the values ± 1 such that

$$\mathcal{L}_{ig} = \frac{1}{2}(1 + \sigma_i), \quad \mathcal{L}_{ie} = \frac{1}{2}(1 - \sigma_i), \quad \sigma_i = \pm 1 \tag{11}$$

The hamiltonian then becomes, ignoring a term independent of σ,

$$\mathcal{H}_{con} = -\frac{J}{2} \sum_{<ij>} \sigma_i \sigma_j - h \sum_i \sigma_i$$

$$J = \frac{J_0}{4} \left(I(g,g) - 2I(g,e) + I(e,e) \right) \tag{12}$$

$$h = \frac{J_0}{4} z(I(g,g) - I(e,e)) + \frac{1}{2}(E_e - E_g + \Pi(A_e - A_g))$$

This hamiltonian is formally identical to that of a two-dimensional Ising model in an external field h (McCoy and Wu, 1973). It is clear that in order to have extended chains at low temperatures, we must have $J > 0$, from which it follows plausibly that $h > 0$. The difference btween equation 12 and an Ising model is that the states $\sigma_i = +1$ and -1 have degeneracies D_g and D_e and that $D_e \gg D_g$. It is easy to see (for example, Pink *et al.*, 1980a) that the partition function can then be written as

$$Z = (D_e D_g)^{N/2} \operatorname{Tr}(e^{-\beta \mathcal{H}'_{con}})$$

$$\mathcal{H}'_{con} = -\frac{J}{2} \sum_{<ij>} \sigma_i \sigma_j - H \sum_i \sigma_i \tag{13}$$

$$H = h - k_B \frac{T}{2} \ln\left(\frac{D_e}{D_g}\right)$$

where N is the total number of chains in the bilayer. Thus, the effect of the degeneracies is to replace h by H. Furthermore, for small T, $H > 0$, while for large T, $H < 0$, so there is a temperature, $T_c = 2h/k_B \ln(D_e/D_g)$, at which H changes sign. Now, if the term in H is absent the resulting Ising model has a continuous phase transition at $T = T^*$ given by $\tanh(\beta^* J) = (2)^{\frac{1}{2}} - 1$, $\beta^* = 1/k_B T^*$. Hence if $T_c < T^*$, then just below T_c each chain is predominantly in its $|g>$ state and, as T increases through T_c, each chain goes discontinuously to its $|e>$ state, so that the system displays a first-order phase transition at T_c. If $T_c > T^*$ then no phase transition will be obtained, while if $T_c = T^*$, the system has a continuous (second-order) phase transition so that $T_c = T^*$ is the critical point.

If we develop this approach we could assume that there are three important states: the two, $|g>$ and $|e>$, above; and an "intermediate" state $|I>$ where $A_g < A_I < A_e$, $D_g < D_I \ll D_e$ and $E_g < E_I < E_e$. Because the two-state model had one independent variable per chain we were able to map it onto the "spin-half" Ising model. The three-state model will have two such independent variables and we can map it onto the "spin-one" Ising model. The mapping

$$\mathcal{L}_{ig} = \frac{1}{2}(S_i^2 + S_i), \quad \mathcal{L}_{iI} = 1 - S_i^2, \quad \mathcal{L}_{ie} = \frac{1}{2}(S_i^2 - S_i)$$

$$S_i = \pm 1, 0 \tag{14}$$

transforms the hamiltonian so that the partition function is given, analogous to equation 13 by

$$Z = D_I^N \, \text{Tr}(e^{-\beta \mathcal{H}'_{con}})$$

$$\mathcal{H}'_{con} = -\frac{J_0}{2} \sum_{<ij>} (AS_iS_j + B(S_iS_j^2 + S_i^2S_j) + CS_i^2S_j^2)$$

$$\quad - \sum_i (HS_i + KS_i^2)$$

$$H = \frac{J_0}{2} z(I(g,I) - I(I,e)) + \frac{1}{2}(\Pi(A_e - A_g) + E_e - E_g) - \frac{k_B T}{2} \ln\left(\frac{D_e}{D_g}\right)$$

$$K = \frac{J_0}{2} z(I(g,I) + I(I,e) - 2I(I,I)) + \frac{1}{2}(\Pi(2A_I - A_e - A_g) \tag{15}$$

$$\quad + 2E_I - E_e - E_g) + \frac{k_B T}{2} \ln\frac{D_g D_e}{D_I^2} \equiv k + \frac{k_B T}{2} \ln\left(\frac{D_g D_e}{D_I^2}\right)$$

The point to note is that the first two terms in H are, plausibly, positive, while the third is negative. Again then, it is the "effective field", the coefficient of

S_i, that changes sign from positive to negative at some temperature T_c. If the coefficients are chosen so that there is not a transition from $<S^2> \approx 1$ to $<S^2> \approx 0$ (this represents the physical implausibility of a transition from $|g>$ or $|e>$ to $|I>$), then we obtain results as in the two-state model: the main lipid transition occurs at $T_c = 2(h<S_i> + J_O B \sum_\delta <S_i S_i^2 + \delta>)/k_B<S_i>$ in (D_e/D_g) if $T_c < T^*$. We see that this transition is "entropy driven" in that it occurs when $D_e \gg D_g$.

In studying the temperature-dependence of the intensity of the "1,130 cm^{-1}" Raman band which is a hydrocarbon chain C–C skeletal stretch mode (Snyder, 1970), Pink *et al.* (1980b), deduced Raman intensities contributed by hydrocarbon chains in states with many *gauche* bonds by extrapolating the calculations of Snyder (1967, 1970). In constructing a model of chain melting they assumed that the lipid chain conformational states $\{|n>\}$ were those given, by the rotational isomeric model (Flory, 1969), and found that nine low-energy hydrocarbon chain states with cross-sectional area $\lesssim 25 \text{Å}^2$, ranging from the all-*trans* state to states with three *gauche* bonds, contributed significantly to the Raman intensity of the 1,130 cm^{-1} band. The limit on the area per chain was imposed to allow for hard-core steric hindrance in the gel phase, where, it was argued, only conformations with small cross-sectional areas could be thermally excited. With a high energy "melted" state, these 10 states were used in the hamiltonian of equation 6 and, lacking an exact solution, thermodynamic quantities and Raman intensities were calculated in a mean field approximation (below). Good agreement was found between the calculated and measured intensities, and the average number of *gauche* bonds per chain was calculated as a function of temperature. These numbers were 0.75 ($T = 15°C$), 1.3 ($T = 37°C$) 1.5 (just below T_c) and ~5 (just above T_c). Subsequently, the model was used to calculate a phase diagram for a DPPC–cholesterol or DMPC–cholesterol bilayer and Raman intensities were calculated as a function of temperature and cholesterol concentration. Again, good agreement between experiment and theory was found (Pink *et al.*, 1981a).

If we want to model the orientation of the DPPC molecules in the plane of the bilayer (that is, the orientation of the glyceride backbones) we must identify an order parameter. If we consider the molecule to be approximately elliptical with inversion symmetry and ignore the fact that the polar head group defines a direction along the long axis of the backbone, then the interaction between two such molecules i and j can be expanded in even powers of the cosine of the angle $\phi_i - \phi_j$, where ϕ_i and ϕ_j define the orientation of the molecules with respect to an external axis. A suitable molecular orientational order parameter is $Q_i = \cos^2\phi_i - \frac{1}{2}$, because if Q is averaged over ϕ in two dimensions we obtain zero. In three dimensions the order parameter is the zz component of the irreducible tensor $(\frac{3}{2}\cos^2\theta - \frac{1}{2})$ (de Gennes, 1975) which, of course, yields zero when averaged over the azimuthal angle θ. To second order we can write the orientational hamiltonian as

$$\mathcal{H}_{\text{orient}} = -\frac{1}{2} \sum_{ij} W_{ij}(\cos^2(\phi_i - \phi_j) - \frac{1}{2}) + \dots \tag{16}$$

The origin of W_{ij}, which may not be of finite range, lies in the dipole interactions and the stresses set up by boundaries in the bilayer. It should not be forgotten that although we are discussing ordering in a plane, the system is three-dimensional due to coupling to the water region. Thus problems concerned with the lack of long-range order in a two-dimensional system with continuous symmetry and finite-range interactions (Mermin and Wagner, 1966) may not arise. Expanding the cosine in equation 16 we obtain

$$\mathcal{H}_{\text{orient}} = -\sum_{ij} W_i(Q_iQ_j + p_ip_j) + \ldots \tag{17}$$

$$Q_i = \cos^2\phi_i - \frac{1}{2}, \quad p_i = \cos\phi_i\sin\phi_i$$

In the next section we shall study this system in a mean field approximation.

Apart from the lateral motion of a phospholipid molecule in the plane of the membrane, there is also possibly motion in a direction along the local normal to the plane of the bilayer, as well as reorientation of the long axis of the molecule with respect to the local bilayer normal. The first two motions relate to the centre of mass of the molecule while the third involves the motion in three dimensions of a rod possessing a strong interaction (via the water layer) that tries to keep itself orientated with its hydrocarbon chains in the interior of the bilayer. The last-named interaction may be very important for the static structure of phospholipid bilayers set up in the "ripple phase" between the pre-transition, T_p, and T_c (Janiak *et al.*, 1976; Luna and McConnell, 1977a; 1977b; Doniach, 1979).

APPROXIMATION SCHEMES AND SIMULATIONS

Most mathematical models of phenomena cannot be solved exactly; closed analytical expressions cannot be written down for quantities of interest described in previous sections. In statistical mechanics a number of models have been solved in one dimension, a few have been solved in two dimensions and very few in three dimensions. A lipid monolayer or bilayer might be looked on as a system that extends in a third direction, though a much shorter distance than in the other two. In the case of multilayers, however, this is not obviously so, since the stacking of bilayers can extend for distances comparable with the planar dimensions of the bilayers, and the distance between bilayers can be sufficiently small that they cannot obviously be considered in isolation from each other. The interactions are complicated and, in the absence of exact solutions, approximation methods must be used if one desires algebraic expressions for thermodynamic quantities. Here we shall consider variations on the mean field approximation (MFA).

If one does not wish to obtain merely approximate solutions, computer simulations can be performed to obtain numerical values for quantities of interest. Given sufficient computer time and ingenuity in digitising the system which is being modelled, one can study not only the system in equilibrium, but also its approach to that state of equilibrium (Binder, 1979). The advantage of this approach compared to that of using approximation schemes is that one can, in principle, make the model as detailed as one likes and so approach a real system. The disadvantage in obtaining numerical values of functions, rather than an analytical expression for them, is that one must then deduce the general behaviour of the system from a knowledge of these particular numerical values. It is then possible that unsuspected behaviour might be missed. For a discussion concerning the performance and interpretation of computer simulations of true two-dimensional systems that illustrate this point see Abraham (1981a, 1981b) and Frenkel and McTague (1980). Monte Carlo and Molecular Dynamics simulations are, however, essential in the study of lipid mono- and bilayers.

Mean field approximation (MFA)

The method here is to write the free energy, $\mathcal{F}$, as $\mathcal{F} = \mathcal{F}_0 + \Delta \mathcal{F}$, where $\mathcal{F}_0$ can be calculated exactly, and then to try to approximate $\Delta \mathcal{F}$. To this end a hamiltonian, $\mathcal{H}_0$, is chosen that is thought to approximate the hamiltonian of the system, $\mathcal{H}$, in the essentials of the process being studied. In practise, $\mathcal{H}_0$ is made up to sums of single-body operators (see equation 4). For any choice of $\mathcal{H}_0$ the exact free energy, calculated using $\mathcal{H}$, obeys the Bogoliubov inequality:

$$\mathcal{F} \leqslant \mathcal{F}_0 + <\mathcal{H}-\mathcal{H}_0>_0, \quad \mathcal{F}|_0 = -k_B T \ln Z_0$$

$$Z_0 = Tr(e^{-\beta \mathcal{H}_0}), \quad <R>_0 = Tr\,(Re^{-\beta \mathcal{H}_0})/Z_0 \tag{18}$$

where $\mathcal{F}$ is as given in equation 1. In the MFA, $\mathcal{H}_0$ is written as a function of the "mean fields", $\mathcal{H}_0(\lambda)$, where λ denotes the set of mean fields. Expressions are obtained for the set λ by minimising the equality

$$\mathcal{F} = \mathcal{F}_0 + <\mathcal{H}-\mathcal{H}_0>_0 \tag{19}$$

with respect to each of the average values of operators, R, that appear in equation 19.

Let us take, for example, the two-state model of a DPPC bilayer with $\mathcal{H} = \mathcal{H}_{con}$ as in equation 10. As it is not yet possible to evaluate $\mathcal{F}$ exactly, let us take $\mathcal{H}_0$ to be

$$\mathcal{H}_0 = -\sum_i \sum_n \lambda_n \mathcal{L}_{in} + \sum_i \sum_n (\Pi A_n + E_n) \mathcal{L}_{in} \tag{20}$$

when n runs over g and e, and the two-chain interaction term has been replaced by the one-chain mean field term. It is trivial to calculate Z_0 (see equation 5), and we now require that the set λ be chosen such that

$$\frac{\partial \mathcal{F}}{\partial <\mathcal{L}_g>_0} = 0 \quad \text{and} \quad \frac{\partial \mathcal{F}}{\partial <\mathcal{L}_e>_0} = 0 \tag{21}$$

that is, $\mathscr{F}$ is a minimum with respect to the average value of $\mathscr{L}_g$ and $\mathscr{L}_e$. We find that

$$\frac{1}{N}<\mathscr{H}-\mathscr{H}_0>_0 = -\frac{J_0 z}{2}(I(g,g)<\mathscr{L}_g>_0^2 + 2I(g,e)<\mathscr{L}_g>_0<\mathscr{L}_e>_0$$

$$+ I(e,e)<\mathscr{L}_e>_0^2) + \lambda_g<\mathscr{L}_g>_0 + \lambda_e<\mathscr{L}_e>_0 \tag{22}$$

$$\frac{1}{N}\frac{\partial\mathscr{F}_0}{\partial<\mathscr{L}_n>_0} = -\frac{\partial\lambda_n}{\partial<\mathscr{L}_n>_0}<\mathscr{L}_n>_0, n = g, e$$

where N is the number of lipid chains and z is the number of nearest neighbour chains to any given chain. We thus obtain

$$\frac{1}{N}\frac{\partial\mathscr{F}}{\partial<\mathscr{L}_g>_0} = \frac{1}{N}\frac{\partial\mathscr{F}_0}{\partial<\mathscr{L}_g>_0} - J_0 z \left(I(g,g)<\mathscr{L}_g>_0 + I(g,e)<\mathscr{L}_e>_0\right) +$$

$$+ \frac{\partial\lambda_g}{\partial<\mathscr{L}_g>_0}<\mathscr{L}_g>_0 + \lambda_g \tag{23}$$

with a similar expression holding for $\frac{1}{N}\partial\mathscr{F}/\partial<\mathscr{L}_e>_0$. Solving for the mean fields we find

$$\lambda_g = J_0 z(I(g,e)<\mathscr{L}_g>_0 + I(g,e)<\mathscr{L}_e>_0) \tag{24}$$

$$\lambda_e = J_0 z(I(g,e)<\mathscr{L}_g>_0 + I(e,e)<\mathscr{L}_e>_0)$$

The probabilities of any chain being in its $|g>$ or $|e>$ state is $<\mathscr{L}_g>_0$ or $<\mathscr{L}_e>_0$ and these are

$$<\mathscr{L}_n>_0 = D_n e^{\beta(\lambda_n - E_n - \Pi A_n)}/Z_0, n = g, e$$

$$Z_0 = \left[D_g e^{\beta(\lambda_g - E_g - \Pi A_g)} + D_e e^{\beta(\lambda_e - E_e - \Pi A_e)}\right]^N \tag{25}$$

These equations are implicit for $<\mathscr{L}_n>_0$ because λ_n contains these quantities. It can be seen that correlations such as $<\mathscr{L}_{in}\mathscr{L}_{jm}>_0$ factor to give $<\mathscr{L}_{in}\mathscr{L}_{jm}>_0 = <\mathscr{L}_n>_0<\mathscr{L}_m>_0$ so that the MFA ignores correlations between different chains. Recalling that long-range correlations become very important near critical points, we see that near a critical point the MFA will be unreliable. If, however, a phase transition is sufficiently discontinuous that long wavelength fluctuations do not arise, then the MFA will give an acceptable description of it, with the proviso that numerical values of parameters, such as D_n or $I(n,m)$, derived from fitting a calculated first-order transition to an observed one, may be in error. The MFA described here is also known as the Bragg–Williams approximation.

It is evident from equations 20 and 24 that this approximation replaces the details of the interactions between a chain and its surroundings by an average interaction which depends on its state. The unit for which exact expressions in the hamiltonian are retained is thus merely a single chain. For a better approximation a larger unit within which no approximations are made must be taken.

Thus, if we consider two chains as the unit, retaining the exact interaction between them, but replacing their interactions with other chains by mean fields, we obtain the Oguchi approximation (Caillé *et al.*, 1980). If we retain the interaction between a chain and its z nearest neighbours, but replace those between the nearest neighbours and the remaining chains by mean fields, we obtain the Bethe-Peierls-Weiss (BPW) approximation (Domb, 1960; Moraal, 1976). In this case the unit comprises $z + 1$ chains. For a discussion of the BPW approximation, Bethe lattices and Cayley trees see Moraal (1976) and Georgallas (1979). Note that the symmetries of the system will impose conditions on the average values calculated. Thus, if we assume that all chains are equivalent, as we have done in the examples above, then average values of chain variables cannot depend on the position of the chain in the unit. Although in the case of DPPC the chains are not equivalent for $T < T_c$ (Seelig and Seelig, 1975), this does not invalidate the general results obtained here and can easily be taken into account.

The Landau–Ginzburg–DeGennes (LGD) theory

This approach to phase transitions was invented by Landau (Landau, Lifshitz and Pitaevskii, 1980) to bypass the difficulty of calculating the partition function to obtain the free energy. It makes use of the symmetry of the system to argue that the free energy must possess a certain functional form which in turn determines what kind of phase transitions the system may display, and has been used with success to study a variety of solid state and liquid crystal systems (deGennes, 1975; Luban, 1976; Barber, 1980). It has been used to model both pure lipid bilayers and bilayers containing integral proteins (Priest, 1977; Owicki *et al.*, 1978; Owicki and McConnell, 1979; and Jähnig, 1981a, 1981b). This is a phenomenological approach and, unless modified as described below, will give results near critical points similar to those obtained using the MFA. The theory is based on two assumptions: (1) for the system being considered we can identify an order parameter, $u(\vec{r}, t)$, which gives a description of the system at position $\vec{r}$ at time t; and (2) for temperatures near the critical temperature we can define a "free energy", $f(u)$, which is a function of u only, from which all the equilibrium and low-frequency quantities of interest can be calculated. When $f(u)$ is a minimum with respect to u, then the value of u for which this occurs is the value appropriate to the system at that temperature, and $f(u)$ is then equal to the Gibbs free energy. The form of the free energy is assumed to be expanded in a truncated power series in u around $u = 0$, and, as generally used, is of the form

$$f(u) = a_0 + a_1 u + \tfrac{1}{2}a_2 u^2 + \tfrac{1}{3}a_3 u^3 + \tfrac{1}{4}a_4 u^4 + \tfrac{1}{6}a_6 u^6 + \dots \qquad (26)$$

The term in u is due to the presence of any fields which tend to pin the system in some preferred value of u. In general, those terms in even powers of u will be present, and in the case where there is no symmetry relation between states with $+u$ and $-u$, a term in u^3 can occur. In the theory of the nematic–isotropic transition in liquid crystals, for example, u is the zz component of the three-dimensional quadrupole order parameter, $Q(\theta) = \frac{3}{2}\cos^2\theta - \frac{1}{2}$ (deGennes, 1975). Because there is no symmetry between the states with $\pm Q$, $a_3 \neq 0$. In the case of some ferroelectric crystals, $a_3 = 0$ but there is a term in u^6 (Blinc and Žekš, 1974).

It is shown elsewhere (for example Landau *et al.*, 1980) that the coefficient of a_2 can be written as $a_2 = a\epsilon$ where $\epsilon = (T - T^*)/T^*$ and $a > 0$. To have a continuous phase transition at $T = T^*$ it is necessary that $a_1 = 0$, $a_3 = 0$, and $a_4(T^*) > 0$. If $a_3 \neq 0$ then a first-order transition can occur when $a_1 < 0$ and $a_3 < 0$. It is also possible to have a first-order transition if $a_1 = a_3 = 0$, but $a_6 \neq 0$ (see Kittel, 1976). We shall show presently that in certain conditions a first-order phase transition occurs even if $a_3 = a_6 = 0$, as long as a_1 possesses a suitable temperature dependence. Thus, although the conditions for the appearance of a continuous phase transition are restrictive, there are many ways in which a first-order transition can arise. The implication is then that, whereas the LGD free energy expansion of a system possessing a continuous phase transition must have a certain form, the corresponding free energy expansion for a system possessing a first-order transition is by no means unique, and that in order to discover it some thought should be given to the microscopic model from which it is supposed to come.

To illustrate this let us consider the models for lipid hydrocarbon chain melting and lipid rotation described by equations 10 and 17. We shall solve both of these models in the MFA and put the free energy in the form of equation 26 in order to identify the coefficients. Using equations 13 and 25 it follows that the free energy per chain is

$$\frac{\beta \mathcal{F}}{N} = -\ln 2 - \tfrac{1}{2}\ln(D_e D_g) - \ln \cosh \beta(Jz\langle\sigma\rangle + H) + \tfrac{1}{2}k_B TJz\langle\sigma\rangle^2 \quad (27)$$

$$\langle\sigma\rangle = \tanh\beta(Jz\langle\sigma\rangle + H) \quad (28)$$

Expanding equation 27 in powers of $\langle\sigma\rangle$, and noting from equation 28 that $T^* = Jz/k_B$, we obtain

$$\frac{\beta \mathcal{F}}{N} = -\ln 2 - \tfrac{1}{2}\ln(D_e D_g) - \beta H\langle\sigma\rangle + \tfrac{1}{2}\frac{T^*}{T}\epsilon\langle\sigma\rangle^2 + \tfrac{1}{12}\langle\sigma\rangle^4 +$$

$$+ \tfrac{1}{30}\langle\sigma\rangle^6 + 0(\langle\sigma\rangle^8) \quad (29)$$

We see that the coefficient of $\langle\sigma\rangle^2$ is as required and that there is no term in $\langle\sigma\rangle^3$. Despite this, the model does display a first-order transition because the coefficient of $\langle\sigma\rangle$ is temperature dependent. As we saw earlier, H changes sign at T_c. Recalling that $-1 \leqslant \langle\sigma\rangle \leqslant 1$, we see that if $T_c < T^*$, then $\mathcal{F}$ is minimised by $\langle\sigma\rangle$ switching discontinuously from a positive value to a negative value as T increases through T_c.

Let us now consider the model of glyceride backbone orientation mentioned earlier. We shall assume that, because of strains or boundary effects in the bilayer, a symmetry-breaking axis is set up for a domain composed of a sufficiently large number of lipid molecules, and we choose the external axis, with respect to which ϕ_i is measured, to coincide with it. Performing a MFA we obtain

$$\mathcal{K}_0 = -\lambda \sum_i Q_i, \quad \lambda = 2<Q> W(0) \tag{30}$$

where we have made use of $<p> = 0$ and $W(0) = \sum_j W_{ij}$. The partition function corresponding to $\mathcal{K}_0$ is

$$Z_0 = e^{-\beta\lambda/2} \int_0^{2\pi} d\phi e^{\beta\lambda \cos^2 \phi} \tag{31}$$

and we find that (Kirkwood, 1943)

$$Z_0 = 2\pi I_0 \left(\frac{\beta\lambda}{2} \right), \quad <Q>_0 = \tfrac{1}{2} I_1 \left(\frac{\beta\lambda}{2} \right) / I_0 \left(\frac{\beta\lambda}{2} \right) \tag{32}$$

where $I_0(x)$ and $I_1(x)$ are modified Bessel functions (Abramowitz and Stegun, 1970). These possess the expansions, valid for small x,

$$I_n(x) = (\tfrac{1}{2}x)^n \sum_{m=0}^{\infty} \frac{(\tfrac{1}{4}x^2)^m}{m! \, \Gamma(n+m+1)} \tag{33}$$

and it is seen that $I_0(x)$ contains only even powers of x while $I_1(x)$ contains only odd powers. The free energy expansion will thus contain only even powers of $\frac{\beta\lambda}{2}$ and is given by

$$\frac{\beta \mathcal{F}}{N} = -\ln 2\pi + 4 \left(\frac{T^*}{T} \right)^2 \epsilon <Q>_0^2 + \frac{\beta^5 W(0)^4}{32} <Q>_0^4 + \ldots \tag{34}$$

This system thus has a continuous phase transition at $T^* = W(0)/4k_B$ as can be checked by expanding the equation for $<Q>_0$ in powers of $<Q>_0$ and assuming that $<Q>_0$ is infinitesimal but non-zero. A continuous phase transition in this system is in accord with the results of Firpo *et al.* (1981) who allowed the backbone axis to assume only two orientations in the plane: parallel and perpendicular to the symmetry-breaking axis.

Let us now compare the LGD free energies of three models: the two-state model of earlier, the model of Owicki *et al.* (1978), and that of Jähnig (1981a). They are all supposed to describe the main lipid hydrocarbon chain transition at T_c but they ascribe it to different mechanisms. The first associates it with an effective field coupled to the order parameter $<\sigma>$, which changes sign at T_c, while the other two ascribe it to the presence of suitable third-order terms in the order parameters, u, an area term (Owicki *et al.*, 1978, and below), and $<Q(\theta)>$ a quadrupole term (Jähnig, 1981a). The free energy involving u is not associated directly with a microscopic model. Jähnig's microscopic model, however, is that of a flexible chain (Jähnig, 1979), where there is a Maier–Saupe (1959a,b) interaction between nearest-neighbour chains. This model contains a "tension" term, Γ, which represents the steric restrictions that keep the chains parallel to the bilayer normal (this is the analogue of the $\Pi - A$ term), as well as an internal energy term related to the stiffness of the chains. The case of a rigid rod adequately serves to illustrate this model and to identify the differences between the two models. If we write the partition function in a more general form than Jähnig does, then the mean field hamiltonian and partition function for a *single* chain are

$$\mathcal{H}_0 = -W<Q>Q(\theta) - \tau L_0 x(\theta)$$

$$Z_0 = \int_0^{\pi} D(\theta)\sin\theta d\theta e^{-\beta\mathcal{H}_0}, \quad Q(\theta) = \tfrac{3}{2}\cos^2\theta - \tfrac{1}{2}, \quad x(\theta) = \cos\theta \quad (35)$$

where L_0 is the length of the extended chain and τ is the "tension" perpendicular to the bilayer plane trying to keep the chain aligned in the direction $\theta = 0$. The model of Jähnig (1979) has $D(\theta) = 1$, so that the phase space available is simply that of a rigid rod, in this example. His more sophisticated models effectively have $D(\theta) = 1$ for the phase space available to the end of the chain. The phase transition occurring for this choice of $D(\theta)$ thus seems to be similar to that studied by Maier and Saupe (1959b), except that the presence of the term in $x(\theta)$ drives the transition to higher temperatures and eventually to a critical point. This transition seems to be quite different to that taking place in the two-state model.

While it is true that the two-state model and that of Jähnig belong to different universality classes, (for example Kadanoff, 1976), such a comment does not show how they can be related to each other.

Let us assume that as the chain reorientates, there are possibly very many more states available to it, due to *gauche* conformer formation, than those simply described by a phase space density of $\sin\theta$. To give a concrete example let us choose

$$D(\theta) = D_0 e^{-(\cos\theta - C)/\Delta} \quad 0 \leqslant \theta \leqslant \cos^{-1} C \leqslant \pi/2$$
$$= 0 \quad \cos^{-1} C < \theta \leqslant \pi \quad (36)$$

This states that the chain may reorientate itself up to an angle of $\cos^{-1} C$, and, depending on the size of Δ, there can be very many more *gauche* states available at large angles than at small angles. The fact that the effective length of the chain will change with angle θ as *gauche* conformers are excited has been ignored as it will not affect the conclusions. The partition function is

$$Z = D_0 e^{\dfrac{-\beta W<Q>}{2}} \int_0^{\cos^{-1} C} \sin\theta d\theta e^{\beta W<Q>\cos^2\theta + \beta(\tau L_0 - \dfrac{1}{\beta\Delta})\cos\theta} \quad (37)$$

Now, to have many excited states, Δ must be small. If there are D_e excited states available when $\theta = \cos^{-1} C$, then Δ and D_e are related by

$$\frac{1}{\Delta} = (\ln D_e - \ln D_0)/C \tag{38}$$

There is thus an "effective steric" term, analogous to the effective field term, H, (equation 13). If the term in $\cos^2\theta$ does not trigger a Maier-Saupe-type of transition for the temperatures in question, then that term is relatively unimportant because a first-order phase transition will occur at the temperature $T_c = \tau L_0 \Delta/k_B$ where the "effective steric" term, $\tau L_0 - 1/\beta\Delta$ changes sign. The order parameter to describe this transition will be $<x(\theta)>$ rather than $<Q(\theta)>$. Furthermore, it is clear that an expansion of the free energy in powers of $<x(\theta)>$ will contain the "effective steric" term as the coefficient of the linear term. It is probably also true that the discontinuity in the order parameter, which will be related to the transition enthalpy, ΔQ, will be larger than that obtained by Jähnig (1979). The transition in $<Q(\theta)>$ described by Jähnig's model is driven, essentially, by competing interactions, whereas the transitions of two-state and similar models (see earlier) and the rigid (or flexible) chain model modified as described here, which involve the order parameters $<\sigma>$ and $<x(\theta)>$ respectively, depend on a competition between interaction energies and internal energies, and degeneracy (entropy) terms. This is probably why the values of ΔQ calculated by Jähnig are too small. This model has also been criticised by Dill and Flory (1980) on the grounds that when the van der Waals interaction is set equal to zero the flexible chain does not exhibit an order parameter "plateau". This is probably because the "steric hindrance" of that model (Jähnig, 1979, equation 7) allows all conformations to be excited thermally with a relatively "soft" energy barrier proportional to $\cos\theta$. A similar comment is true of the model of Marčelja (1974), though models which explicitly allow for hard-core interactions (Nagle, 1973; Dill and Flory, 1980; 1981) display the "plateau". The ten-state model of Pink *et al.* (1980) includes such steric effects in the gel phase by omitting those conformations which have a cross-sectional area greater than a chosen value, and their model displays a "plateau".

The LGD theory of Owicki *et al.* (1978) and Owicki and McConnell (1979) defines an order parameter $u = (A_f - A)/(A_f - A_s)$, which is undergoing a phase transition, where A_f and A_s are the average cross-sectional areas of lipid molecules in their fluid and solid (gel) states near T_c and A is the average area, with $0 \leqslant u \leqslant 1$. They assume that the free energy can be expanded as a power series around $u = 0$,

$$f(u) = -\Pi(A_f - A_s)u + \tfrac{1}{2}a\epsilon u^2 - \tfrac{1}{3}Bu^3 + \tfrac{1}{4}Cu^4 \tag{39}$$

and ascribe the first-order phase transition at T_c to the presence of the term in u^3. No microscopic model is referred to but to see whether the two state model is the kind of microscopic model which will lead to equation 39 we can define $<v> = (A_e - <A>)/(A_e - A_g)$ so that $0 \leqslant <v> \leqslant 1$ and $<\sigma> = 2<v> - 1$. Substituting this into equation 27 we find

$$\frac{\beta \mathcal{F}}{N} = (-\tfrac{1}{2}k_B T \ln(D_e D_g) + \beta H - \tfrac{1}{2}\frac{T^*}{T}\,\epsilon) + (\frac{2T^*}{T}\,\epsilon - 2\beta H - 1)<v> +$$

$$+ \tfrac{1}{2}\frac{T^*}{T}<v>^2 + \tfrac{1}{6}<v>^3 + \tfrac{1}{12}<v>^4 + \ldots + <v>\ln<v> \tag{40}$$

An inspection of this shows that if $T_c < T^*$ then when $H > 0$, $<v> \simeq 1$, and when $H < 0$ $\beta \mathcal{F}/N$ can be minimised by $<v> \simeq 0$ so that a first-order phase transition occurs at T_c. Note that equation 40 does not look like equation 39, the first-order transition occurring via an entirely different mechanism, and that an expansion in a power series in $<v>$ does not even exist because of the essential singularity in the term $<v> \ln <v>$. Because the three-state model exhibits a first-order transition similar to that of the two-state model, viz, through the change in sign of a temperature-dependent field, H, it seems plausible that a similar result will hold if more states are included. It thus seems unlikely that the free energy described by Owicki *et al.* (1978) corresponds to a microscopic model of this kind. The fact that first-order phase transitions need not arise only from the presence of a third-order term in the expansion of the free energy in powers of the order parameter undergoing the transition, implies that other mechanisms may be overlooked when such a transition is modelled by the inclusion of this term. This being so, the usefulness of simply writing down a LGD free energy expansion without reference to any particular microscopic model from which it may be derived is questionable.

Returning to the free energy expansion for the two-state model, equation 29, if we minimise $\beta \mathcal{F}/N$ with respect to $<\sigma>$ we obtain an equation for $<\sigma>$ valid for sufficiently small ϵ,

$$-\beta H + \frac{T^*}{T}\,\epsilon <\sigma> + \tfrac{1}{3}<\sigma>^3 = 0 \tag{41}$$

A discussion of the solutions are given by Luban (1976). The enthalpy, Q, can be calculated from equations 3 and 29 and is

$$Q = -h <\sigma> - \tfrac{1}{2}k_B T^* <\sigma>^2 \tag{42}$$

where h is given in equation 12. As H changes sign then $<\sigma>$ changes sign but not magnitude. Thus the heat of transition is $\Delta Q = 2h <\sigma>$ evaluated at T_c.

If equation 41 is used to calculate critical exponents (for example Stanley, 1971) we find that when $H \equiv 0$, $<\sigma> = 0$ or $<\sigma> = \pm \left(\frac{3T^*}{T}\right)^{\frac{1}{2}} |\epsilon|^{\frac{1}{2}}$, and when $\epsilon \equiv 0$, $<\sigma> = (3\beta |H|)^{1/3}$. The critical exponents, β and δ, defined by $<\sigma> \sim |\epsilon|^\beta$ or $<\sigma> \sim |H|^{1/\delta}$ (the critical exponent β should not be confused with $\beta = 1/k_B T$) thus take on the values $\beta = 1/2$ and $\delta = 3$ in the MFA. These values are incorrect, the correct ones being $\beta = 1/8$ and $\delta = 15$ for the two-dimensional Ising model. The reason that incorrect critical exponents are obtained in any MFA is that fluctuations in $<\sigma>$ have been ignored. Low-frequency fluctuations can be taken into account in the case of continuous phase transitions by introducing a free energy functional, $F[u(\vec{r})]$, which contains a spatial dependence of $u(\vec{r})$ through a gradient term $\vec{\nabla}u(\vec{r})$. For a D-dimensional system we have (Luban, 1976):

$$F[u(\vec{r})] = f_0 + \int d^D r \; [Hu(\vec{r}) + \tfrac{1}{2}a\epsilon u(\vec{r})^2 + \tfrac{1}{4}Bu(\vec{r})^4 + \tfrac{1}{2}C(\vec{\nabla}u(\vec{r}))^2] \quad (43)$$

By minimising F with respect to $u(\vec{r})$ we obtain

$$H + a\epsilon u(\vec{r}) + Bu(\vec{r})^3 - C\nabla^2 u(\vec{r}) = 0 \quad\quad\quad (44)$$

To delve more deeply into LGD theory for one-order parameter would be out of place and interested readers should refer to Luban (1976) or Barber (1980).

It is likely that the chain-melting main transition is coupled to the onset of reorientations of the glyceride backbone so that the phase transition is described by two-order parameters (Firpo *et al.*, 1981). An extension of Landau's theory when there are two-order parameters, u and v, has been given by Chen (1978). In the case of a continuous phase transition in the variable u we write the free energy $f(u,v)$ as

$$f(u,v) = f_0(v) + \tfrac{1}{2}a(v)\epsilon u^2 + \tfrac{1}{4}B(v)u^4 \quad\quad\quad (45)$$

where u undergoes a continuous phase transition at $T = T^*$ at which $v = v^*$. We now require that $\partial f/\partial u = 0$ and $\partial f/\partial v = 0$, as well as that $B(T^*, v^*) = 0$ together with $\frac{d}{dT}(a\epsilon)_{T=T^*\; v=v^*} = 0$. Chen (1978) has shown that the last condition can be replaced by $u(du/dT)_{T=T^*} < 0$. Note that it must be checked that the state with $u = 0$ and $v = v^*$ has the lowest free energy at T^*.

Monte Carlo methods

Two methods have been applied to large arrays in order to study the phases occurring in two-component lipid bilayers (lipid$_1$–lipid$_2$ or lipid–cholesterol) or phase separation, lipid melting and protein diffusion in lipid–protein bilayers, and phase transitions in lipid monolayers. The former (Freire and Snyder, 1980a, 1980b; Snyder and Freire, 1980; Freire and Snyder, 1982) use a method apparently similar to that of Alexandrowicz (Alexandrowicz, 1971; Meirovitch and Alexandrowicz, 1977), whilst the latter (Pink *et al.*, 1982a; Georgallas and Pink, 1982a) use the Metropolis method (Metropolis *et al.*, 1953). The methods represent ways of approximating $\langle R \rangle$ in equation 2. Let us write $\langle R \rangle$ as

$$\langle R \rangle = \mathrm{Tr}(Re^{-\beta\mathcal{H}})/\mathrm{Tr}(e^{-\beta\mathcal{H}}) \quad\quad\quad (46)$$

$$= \sum_X R(X)e^{-\beta E(X)}/\sum_X e^{-\beta E(X)}$$

where we have chosen a basis in which $\mathcal{H}$ is diagonal with eigenvalue $E(X)$ depending on the set X of variables characterising the system, and the sums are performed over the range of values which the variables take on. In cases where equation 46 cannot be analytically calculated, one could numerically perform the sum over the set X. For sufficiently large systems this method is impractical and one must use sampling methods to evaluate equation 46. The method of random sampling of points in the set X is not suited, however, to systems which undergo phase transitions because the integrand will vary over many orders of magnitude at temperatures of interest. The Monte Carlo method of Metropolis *et al.* (1953) is a sampling algorithm that uses the idea of "importance sampling" (Hammersley and Handscomb, 1964; Shreider, 1966). The points in the set X are not chosen randomly but are selected according to a probability $P(X)$ and equation 46 is approximated by

$$<R> \simeq \sum_X R(X)P^{-1}(X)e^{-\beta E(X)} / \sum_X P^{-1}(X)e^{-\beta E(X)} \tag{47}$$

The method of Alexandrowicz (1971) consists of observing that for systems containing a very large number of units, we can approximate Z in equation 1 by

$$Z = \sum_X e^{-\beta E(X)} \simeq \max(N(X)e^{-\beta E(X)}) \equiv N^*(X)e^{-\beta E^*(X)} \tag{48}$$

where $N(X)$ is the number of states with energy $E(X)$, and $N^*(X)$ and $E^*(X)$ have the property that $N^*e^{-\beta E^*}$ is the largest term of this kind.

The next question is: how are these approximations implemented? In the Metropolis method the energy $E(X)$ of a given configuration is calculated. The N units of the system (for example the hydrocarbon chains) are in states defined by the set $X = \{x_1, \ldots x_N\}$ where x_i defines the state of the ith unit. One unit, say the jth, is "visited" by being selected randomly and its state is changed from x_j to x'_j, where the state x'_j is randomly selected. The energy of the new configuration, $E(X')$, is calculated and if $E(X') < E(X)$ then the visit is completed and another unit is selected randomly to be visited. If $E(X') > E(X)$, then a random number, r, uniformly distributed on the interval $(0,1)$ is selected and we define $\Delta E = E(X') - E(X) > 0$. If $e^{-\beta \Delta E} < r$ then the jth unit is returned to its original state x_j, while if $e^{-\beta \Delta E} > r$ it remains in the new state x'_j. This procedure is repeated until all units have been visited once only. It can be shown (Barker and Henderson, 1976) that this procedure leads to canonical averaging; that is to a distribution of states in accord with the Boltzmann distribution. As an example, consider the two-state model of lipid chain melting given by equation 10. Consider a chain labelled i and let it have n_g and n_e nearest neighbours in their $|g>$ and $|e>$ states. Then the energy of chain i when it is in its $|g>$ or $|e>$ state is

$$\epsilon_{ig} = \Pi A_g + E_g - \tfrac{1}{2}k_B T \ln\left(\frac{D_e}{D_g}\right) - J_0(I(g,g)n_g + I(g,e)n_e)$$
$$\tag{49}$$
$$\epsilon_{ie} = \Pi A_e + E_e + \tfrac{1}{2}k_B T \ln\left(\frac{D_e}{D_g}\right) - J_0(I(g,e)n_g + I(e,e)n_e)$$

Thus, if $\epsilon_{ig} - \epsilon_{ie} > 0$ and if it is in the state $|e>$ and we want to see whether it will change to its $|g>$ state, we define $\Delta \epsilon_i = \epsilon_{ig} - \epsilon_{ie}$, calculate $e^{-\beta \Delta \epsilon_i}$ and compare it with a random number r, as described above. This model of the lipid chain main transition has been used in studies of protein lateral diffusion and phase separation and monolayer isotherms to be described below.

The method used by Freire and Snyder to study, for example, a $lipid_1$–$lipid_2$ bilayer (Freire and Snyder, 1980a) is as follows: initially $lipid_1$ molecules occupy all sites of a (triangular) lattice. Equal probabilities, p_0, are associated with all sites for them to be chosen as the site to replace a $lipid_1$ by a $lipid_2$. Having made this replacement, the probabilities are changed. A probability, p_1, is now associated with each site adjacent to the $lipid_2$, it differs from P_0 associated with all the other sites, and the $lipid_2$ site possesses probability 0. Thus, if $p_1 < p_0$, those adjacent sites are less likely to be selected in replacing a second $lipid_1$ by a $lipid_2$. The probability associated with a site occupied by a $lipid_1$ adjacent to k sites each occupied by a $lipid_2$ is p_k proportional to $e^{k\Delta E}$ where ΔE is an energy of mixing. The procedure is repeated until the desired concentration of $lipid_2$ is reached. This simulation method is similar to some which have been used to study irreversible cluster growth and may not be appropriate for discovering equilibrium properties of two-component bilayers.

Average values in both methods are calculated by generating a number of distributions as described above for a sufficiently large number of units. An average value of the variable R, R_n, is calculated for the nth distribution and the average, equation 46, over M distributions is given by

$$<R> = \frac{1}{M} \sum_{n=1}^{M} R_n \tag{50}$$

In the Metropolis method M must be sufficiently large such that the variance is small and, in practice, the system is allowed to come to thermal equilibrium by generating a sufficient number of distributions before averaging is begun. It has been found useful to quantify cluster formation by calculating the cyclomatic index $C(n_{kk}, n_k)$. If a cluster contains n_k units of the type k with n_{kk} nearest neighbour bonds between pairs of them, then (Domb and Stoll, 1977; Stoll and Domb, 1979):

$$C(n_{kk}, n_k) = n_{kk} - n_k + 1 \tag{51}$$

which is large for a compact cluster and small for a ramified cluster.

Binder (1979) has summarised many of the concerns connected with the accuracy of Monte Carlo simulations and the ability to deduce information about macroscopic systems from simulations done on systems with between 10^2 and 10^4 units. In the neighbourhood of a phase transition where long-range fluctuations begin to appear problems of finite size, finite time averaging, suitable boundary conditions and obtaining representative samples of phase space become important. In addition to periodic, free surface, and "self-consistent field" boundary conditions (Binder, 1974; 1976), Jan (unpublished calculations) has proposed and used a "two-site" boundary condition. Here, the states of the units defined on the first layer outside the boundary of the system are determined by the requirement that the nearest neighbour pair correlation function, with one of the units as a member of the pair, is equal to that calculated from the finite system. The states are chosen randomly consistent with the fluctuations in the pair correlation function.

MONOLAYERS AND BILAYERS – SIMILARITIES AND DIFFERENCES

In recent years studies have been carried out to deduce DPPC monolayer phase diagrams (Albrecht *et al.*, 1978) and a line of first-order phase transitions has been identified. Albrecht *et al.* (1978) have identified a tricritical point as well as a line of continuous transitions on their phase diagram and both they and Cadenhead *et al.* (1980) have studied the dependence of transition enthalpy on the first-order transition temperature that depends on the lateral pressure, Π. Albrecht *et al.* arrived at aspects of their phase diagram by analysing their data in terms of an LGD theory with two-order parameters.

A major point of disagreement in recent years has been the nature of the phase transition from the liquid condensed (LC) state, in which the lipid hydrocarbon chains are, apparently, predominantly extended perpendicular to the substrate surface, to the liquid expanded (LE) state in which the chains are statically disordered. Most theorists (Nagle, 1973; 1975; 1976; Priest, 1977; Marčelja, 1974; Firpo *et al.*, 1981) have ascribed it to hydrocarbon chain melting and calculated it to be a first-order phase transition, in accord with, for example, the interpretation of Albrecht *et al.* (1978). However, Cadenhead *et al.* (1980) have emphasised the fact that the shapes of the measured isotherms in going between the LC and LE phases are unlike typical discontinuous phase transitions. The disagreement has in some cases, been dismissed as being due to kinetic or boundary effects but Cadenhead (1977) has pointed out the reproducibility of the isotherms in different experimental conditions. A discussion of this is given by Bell *et al.* (1981).

Bell *et al.* (1978) developed a theory which assumed that the phase transition was due to the orientational disordering (with only two orientational states available to each molecule) in the plane of the substrate together with the creation of free volume represented as vacant sites on a lattice. As, at the phase transition, the number of vacant sites changes by a small amount (~4 per cent, Zuckermann *et al.*, 1982), although thereafter it increases rapidly with lowering lateral pressure, the transition obtained should be a continuous phase transition as shown above. This was found to be so and isotherms reflecting the observed shapes were obtained, though the theoretical curves have greater slopes than those observed. Dunne and Bell (1980) incorporated the effect of chain melting into their model by assuming that each molecule could be in an additional "dimer" state representing hydrocarbon chains in excited states that possess an entropy determined by the degeneracy of the excited state. They found that the continuous phase transition was converted into a first-order transition at low pressures (~20 mN M^{-1}) for the case of myristic acid on 0.1 N HCl. They thus seem to have a tricritical point at $\Pi \approx 20$ mN M^{-1} and $T \approx 30°C$ which happens to coincide almost exactly with a critical pressure of $\Pi^* = 18.9$ mN M^{-1} and $T^* \approx 30°$C, calculated by Georgallas and Pink (1982a) for palmitic chains representing DPPC from an exact solution of the two-state model discussed previously.

These results differ from the conclusions of Albrecht *et al.* (1978) who deduce values of $\Pi^* \approx 45$ mN M^{-1} and $T_t \approx 40$–45°C for DPPC. Firpo *et al.* (1981) studied this system by using a two-state model for hydrocarbon chain melting, to which is coupled a model describing the orientation of the molecule with respect to the substrate. They assumed that when the chains are in their extended states, the molecule projects an isotropic shape of area A_0 on the surface of the substrate, while when the chains are melted the molecule projects an anisotropic (rectangular) shape of area $(m + 1)A_0$. It was also assumed that the projected rectangle could be orientated in only two mutually perpendicular directions in the plane of the substrate. The anisotropy is thus created when the chains melt, in contrast to the earlier model where the glyceride backbone is always anisotropic. Firpo *et al.* used a LGD theory with two-order parameters, for chain melting and molecular orientation. Their model is thus similar to that of Dunne and Bell (1980) and, like them, they found a low Π region of first-order phase transitions terminating in a tricritical point with a high Π line of continuous phase transitions due to orientational disordering. Unlike Dunne and Bell (1980), however, they identified their tricritical point with that of Albrecht *et al.* (1978).

Despite the success of Bell *et al.* (1978) there are two points to bear in mind: (1) the "kink" points in the isotherms (Adam and Jessop, 1926; Bell *et al.*, 1981) must be explained by a theory, and this is done by that of Bell *et al.* (1978); (2) the non-zero slope of the DPPC isotherms at the phase transitions persist down to pressures well below the critical pressure of ~ 20 mN M^{-1} calculated by Dunne and Bell (1980) (Albrecht *et al.*, 1978; Cadenhead *et al.*, 1980; Gaines, 1966). It is possible that there remains something to be discovered about these isotherms and to this end Georgallas and Pink (1982a) studied the effect of "substitutional impurities" on the first-order phase transition of their two-state model. Using Monte Carlo simulations they found that 4 per cent of such "impurities" could abolish the first-order phase transition and shift the transition to higher pressures with an isotherm slope similar to that reported by Albrecht *et al.* (1978). They suggested that the "impurities" probably represent dislocations and other defects in the LC phase in accord with the idea of a "diffuse" first-order transition (Cadenhead *et al.*, 1980). The possible existence of dislocations suggests that the lipid monolayer is composed of domains at least in the LC phase. To study this, a model has been constructed (Georgallas and Pink, 1982b) which assumes that as the domains melt into the LE phase they combine to form a single large melted domain. The domains are modelled as Cayley trees, each site of which is occupied by a two-state lipid chain (equation 10) with the number of sites in a typical domain given by

$$N_s = N_0 + (N_{\max} - N_0)P(<\sigma>) \tag{52}$$

Here N_0 is the number of sites in a domain at high pressures in the LC phase while N_{max} is the number of sites in a completely melted domain in the LE phase. $P(<\sigma>)$ is a probability related to the average area of a chain for given values of Π and T (equation 11) and both N_s and $<\sigma>$ must be self-consistently solved for. The completely melted domain is assumed to possess the thermodynamic averages of the infinite Cayley tree. They chose

$$P(<\sigma>) = (1 - <\sigma>)/2 \qquad (53)$$

and Figure 6.1 shows typical isotherms. It can be seen that they display the two important characteristics of monolayer isotherms referred to above. The transition in this model is not a continuous phase transition but is a phase change occurring in a finite-sized domain which would display a first-order transition if it was infinitely large. Furthermore, the inclusion of rotational states, which would display a continuous phase transition, would not alter the isotherms, because their shape is typical of those showing continuous phase transitions. Earlier, Scott and Cheng (1977) had suggested that the two important characteristics of monolayer isotherms could be understood by assuming that the hydrocarbon chain region and the lipid polar layer are thermodynamically decoupled. As Bell *et al.* (1981) point out, however, the calculated isotherms of Scott and Cheng might be quite different if their method of applying the Maxwell construction in calculating the chain pressure before adding the contribution from the polar region was applied *after* the contributions from hydrophobic and polar region were added together. The latter method they suggest, would seem to be more reasonable.

Georgallas and Pink (1982a) have also suggested that the critical point of DPPC monolayers on water may not have been correctly identified so that the linear dependence of the apparent transition enthalpy for $T \gtrsim 30°C$, extrapolating to zero at ~45°C, may be an artefact. They suggest that the very sharp phase changes calculated to occur at pressures higher than Π^* and T^* may be mistaken for phase transitions, and that a non-existent transition enthalpy may be deduced from an unjustified use of the Clausius–Clapeyron equation.

Finally, there is the still open question: what is the internal pressure of a lipid bilayer? With the exception of Albrecht *et al.* (1978), all workers have assumed that a bilayer can be considered as two decoupled (or very weakly coupled) monolayers. The difficulty then arises in, for example, the case of DPPC, that for the same value of transition enthalpy, a DPPC monolayer undergoes a phase transition ~11° lower than does a DPPC bilayer. If, on the other hand, the lateral pressure on a monolayer is increased so that it undergoes a transition at $T_c \approx 41°C$, then the transition enthalpy is ~0. Estimates for internal pressure of a bilayer have been 12.5 mN M^{-1} (Albrecht *et al.*, 1978), 14.7 mN M^{-1} (Meraldi and Schlitter, 1981), 20 mN M^{-1} (Marčelja, 1974), 30 mN M^{-1} (Blume, 1979; Pink and Chapman, 1979) and 50 mN M^{-1} (Nagle, 1976). Fulford and Peel (1980) analysed the motion of the fluorescent probe diphenylhexatriene in DPPC bilayers and deduced that Π ranged from ~92

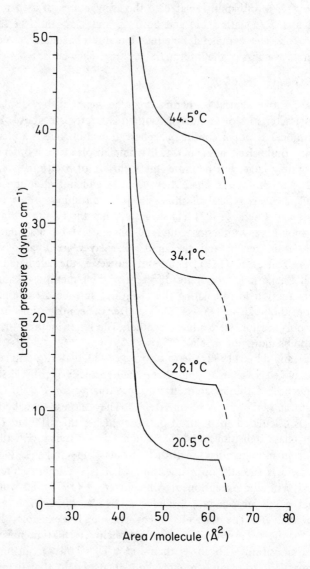

Figure 6.1 Calculated isotherms of a saturated lipid monolayer using the model described in the text and modelling the lipid "domains" as Cayley trees with coordination number = 6. At high pressures the "domains" contain about 100 lipid molecules in the LC phase and as they begin to melt the "domains" grow larger until an infinitely large Cayley tree is obtained in the LE phase. Because the calculation does not include the formation of free volume, no further expansion occurs after melting, so that the range of validity of this calculation lies between 20.4Å^2 and $\sim 65\text{Å}^2$

mN M^{-1} at $5°C$ to ~ 20 mN M^{-1} at $51°C$. In addressing this question Albrecht *et al.* (1978) suggested that a coupling between each half of the bilayer would act like an additional effective pressure, Π_1, on each half, but it can be seen that any addition to the hamiltonian of equation 6 that is linear in the projection operators, as such a $\Pi_1 A_n$ term would be, may raise the transition temperature from that of a monolayer to that of a bilayer but may cause a decrease in transition enthalpy, as pointed out above. If, however, a bilinear interaction term describing the interaction between each half of the bilayer is included in equation 6 then this problem does not arise. The internal pressure of a bilayer can then be demonstrated to be approximately equal to that at which the monolayer displays the same transition enthalpy as the bilayer.

TWO-COMPONENT BILAYERS AND BIOLOGICAL MEMBRANES

In general, to study the thermodynamics of a two-component system one must be prepared to look at whether a separation into two co-existing phases occurs. If one assumes that the bilayer containing intrinsic molecules exhibits only a single homogeneous phase and uses a mean field approximation or a Landau-Ginzburg approach, one will discover a line of first-order lipid phase transitions in the temperature-concentration $(T-c)$ phase diagram beginning at T_c when $c = 0$ and terminating in a critical point of some kind (that is, critical, tricritical, etc. . . . .). For certain kinds of phase diagrams this approach, though incorrect, will yield information concerning the specific heat and transition enthalpy that is sufficiently correct. For two components which are nearly immiscible below T_c, however, a description of the system deduced from this approach can be incorrect. There is good evidence to suggest that some integral proteins behave in this way in bilayers (see below), and thus theories which do not take into account the possibility of phase separation in lipid-protein bilayers below T_c may be incomplete. The impression exists that phase separation in a system composed of components A and B means the coexistence of pure A and pure B. This is not so. Phase separation simply means the coexistence of two phases which differ in their concentration of A and B.

One difficulty that arises in treating mixtures is the problem of how to calculate the combinational term in the partition function which describes the number of configurations available for a given concentration of one component in another. Descriptions of attempts to calculate this can be found in Landau, Lifshitz and Pitaevskii (1980) or other standard texts but, in general, only the mean field approximation suitable for ideal systems has been used in bilayer models. The only exception to this has been the work of Von Dreele (1978) discussed below. In computer simulations this problem does not arise.

Lipid–cholesterol and lipid$_1$–lipid$_2$ bilayers

Although there seems to be a good understanding of the phase diagrams of bilayers composed of two lipids which do not differ too much in chain length, there remain a number of problems concerned with lipid–cholesterol bilayers. Pink and Carroll (1978) successfully predicted that the dependence of transition enthalpy on cholesterol concentration would not obey the linear relationship originally reported (Hinz and Sturtevant, 1972), but would display a more complex behaviour (see also Pink and Chapman, 1979). This was subsequently found to be in agreement with the measurements of Estep *et al.* (1978) and Mabrey *et al.* (1978). Their method of not calculating a phase diagram but rather of simply equating the free energies of homogeneous gel-like and fluid-like phases to calculate a transition enthalpy ΔQ, leads to correct results because the phase diagram of this model exhibits a phase separation region extending over only a few degrees from $c = 0$ to $c \approx 0.15$. This method has been used by other workers, but can be seriously in error when applied to the case of lipid–protein bilayers (below). The presence of a broad peak in the specific heat at higher temperatures than a sharper peak at $T \approx T_c$, however, remains unexplained in terms of a phase diagram. The discovery by Copeland and McConnell (1980) of ripples of apparently cholesterol-rich and lipid-rich regions for $T < T_c$ seems to imply that a description of lipid–cholesterol interactions beyond the mean field theories used to date must be considered. The dependence of lipid lateral diffusion on cholesterol concentration, c, in this phase has been plausibly explained by Owicki and McConnell (1980). The dependence of the lipid lateral diffusion coefficient on cholesterol concentration for $T > T_c$ has been plausibly explained in terms of the formation of critical percolation clusters (Snyder and Freire, 1980), though in the light of the results of Copeland and McConnell (1980) this may not be all the explanation for $T < T_c$ as the cholesterol distributions of Snyder and Freire are random and not in the form of stripes. Pink *et al.* (1981a) have calculated a phase diagram for DPPC–cholesterol and DMPC–cholesterol bilayers and used it, together with a theory of Raman scattering by the hydrocarbon chain C–C skeletal stretch vibrational mode, when the chains are in various conformational states, to calculate successfully the temperature- and concentration-dependence of the "1,130 cm^{-1}" band. Their phase diagram does not, however, account for the high-temperature broad specific heat peak or ripples in DMPC–cholesterol bilayers (Copeland and McConnell, 1980).

Observations of steady state fluorescent polarisation, using the probe DPH, in DMPC–cholesterol bilayers for $T > T_c$ have been interpreted (Hoffmann *et al.*, 1981) in terms of an increase in the probe static order parameter due to its proximity to cholesterol molecules. Making use of the assumption that the presence of one intrinsic molecule adjacent to the probe is sufficient to alter its order parameter, an understanding of the dependence of r_∞ on the concentration of intrinsic molecules was obtained. Other studies of lipid–cholesterol bilayers have been discussed in detail by Pink (1981).

In a study of DMPC-DPPC, DPPC-DSPC and DMPC-DSPC bilayers Von Dreele (1978) used the approximation of Prigogine *et al.* (1952) for the combinational term, $g(N, N_1, N_{12})$ in the partition function. This term describes the number of configurations that N_k units of type k ($k = 1,2$, $N_1 + N_2 = N$), with N_{12} nearest-neighbour pairs of unlike units, can adopt. For ideal mixing, $g(N, N_1, N_{12}) = N!/N_1!N_2!$ and it is this term which leads to the mixing entropy of $N_1 \ln(N_1/N) + N_2 \ln(N_2/N)$ when the N_k are very large. Von Dreele analysed experimental phase diagrams in terms of a non-ideality parameter, v, describing the interaction between the molecules. For each point on a solidus or fluidus curve, a value of v was calculated and quantitative conclusions were deduced about non-ideal interactions in the bilayer.

Freire and Snyder (1980a, 1980b) studied the same systems as Von Dreele using their simulation method described above. They used Von Dreele's non-ideality parameter, v, to generate typical distributions of the components in the bilayers, and from them calculated correlation length and cluster sizes. The procedure used was described above where the probability, p was taken as $e^{\beta \Delta E_m}$, with ΔE_m related to v in the usual way (Von Dreele, 1978). They found that small changes in ΔE_m such as would occur at phase changes would affect the compactedness of clusters of like molecules without significantly affecting the average cluster size. Other recent work, more fully reviewed by Pink (1981), has been by Jacobs *et al.* (1977), Lee (1977, 1978), Cheng (1980), Caillé *et al.* (1980) and Marčelja and Wolfe (1979). Recent experimental work on mixed-chain bilayers (for example Mason *et al.*, 1981) implies that more thought will have to be given to trans-bilayer interactions.

Lipid–protein bilayers without phase diagrams

Marčelja (1976) studied the effect of one isolated protein on the surrounding lipids. The key to understanding his results is that he assumed that each lipid chain interacts with the protein surface via an interaction $V_{lp}S$ where S is the quadrupole order parameter of the chain and takes on values appropriate to the chain state and V_{lp} does not depend on the lipid chain state. He found that chains adjacent to a protein were more statically ordered than chains in the absence of proteins at all temperatures. This is not in accord with ^{2}H-NMR measurements in the fluid phase (Seelig and Seelig, 1978; Oldfield *et al.*, 1978; Jacobs and Oldfield, 1981). This result was obtained probably because the numerical value chosen for V_{lp} is larger than the magnitude of the mean field in the fluid phase, leading to a static ordering of these chains. He also found that there is an effective attractive interaction between pairs of proteins, but this result, though reasonable, must be in doubt because of the incorrect order parameter result. Boothroyd *et al.* (1982) have re-studied this problem by using a 10-state model with protein–lipid interactions which depend on the state of the lipid chains and which yield results in accord with ^{2}H-NMR measurements.

They found that although there is a strong attractive lipid-mediated protein-protein interaction below T_c, the corresponding interaction above T_c is effectively zero. This is because proteins try to keep the hydrocarbon chains at least as fluid as chains in a pure fluid bilayer. The consequence of this would be to induce phase separation for $T < T_c$.

Schröder (1977) used linear response theory to study lipid-mediated protein-protein interactions which has been commented on by Zuckermann and Pink (1980) (below). Owicki *et al.* (1978) used their LGD free energy expansion in $u(r)$, modified by a term in $|\vec{\nabla}u(r)|^2$, to study the dependence of $u(r)$ on distance, r, from an isolated protein. By choosing u_0, the value of $u(r)$ adjacent to the protein, results in accord with experiments (for example Jacobs and Oldfield, 1981) could be obtained. They found that the correlation length is of the order of one lipid diameter but becomes larger when T is near T^* and they showed that two proteins could either attract or repel each other depending on the value of $u_0 - u_\infty$, where $\lim_{r\to\infty} u(r) = u_\infty$. Apart from the points concerning the form of the LGD free energy expansion raised earlier, this approach does not involve a theory of u_0, that is, for each temperature and protein concentration a value of u_0 must be chosen. The approach of Marčelja (1976), Pink and Chapman (1979) and Boothroyd *et al.* (1982) where a protein–lipid interaction, which, of course, does not depend on temperature, could be used to *calculate* u_0 seems to be more fundamental.

Owicki and McConnell (1979) extended this model to consider the case of many proteins which occupied the sites of a triangular lattice. They must necessarily find a line of first-order phase transitions terminating in a critical point, which they do, and they study the dependence of ΔQ on protein concentration, c. The significance of their results must be judged in the light of whether, and what form of, phase separation occurs for $T < T_c$. There is good evidence that, for a variety of integral proteins, in the neighbourhood of and below T_c, there is phase separation into a phase with a high concentration of lipids and one with a high concentration of proteins (see, for example Chapman, 1980 or Overath and Thilo, 1978). If this is so then the model of Owicki and McConnell may be valid only for $c \approx 0$ and for very high c when there is little lipid present so that the proteins are nearly close-packed. We shall see below that there may be important aspects of protein–lipid phase diagrams which this model cannot treat.

Scott and Cheng (1979) modelled gramicidin but did not consider a phase diagram and similar comments apply to that model. Jähnig (1981a) used a LGD free energy expansion to study the effect of proteins assumed to be distributed homogeneously in the plane of the bilayer. In addition to the comments made about this model earlier, it shares the disadvantages of the others mentioned here in not considering a phase diagram. The line of first-order phase transitions and the critical point are not necessarily relevant either to the behaviour of ΔQ or to that of the peak in the specific heat with changing c, except possibly for $c \approx 0$. It should be added, in fairness, that these calculations are stated to be for small c, but the results are extrapolated to finite values of c. The fact that ΔQ decreases linearly with c is merely a consequence of the small c approximation. The model is also used to study lipid–cholesterol bilayers and, although the assumption of no phase separation between $c \approx 0$ and $c \approx 0.15$ may be a satisfactory approximation, the assumption that c is small may be invalid at the concentrations to which the model is extrapolated.

Lipid–protein bilayers—phase diagrams and biological membranes

Pink and Chapman (1979) calculated phase diagrams and studied the behaviour of ΔQ in relation to c for small integral proteins and for cholesterol. A two-state model was used and various kinds of lipid–protein interactions were studied to see what kind of phase diagrams would appear, and the previously-calculated behaviour of ΔQ for lipid–cholesterol bilayers was confirmed. Phase separation was predicted to occur in general for $T < T_c$ and the possibility of eutectic mixtures in lipid–protein bilayers was studied. Cases in which the protein binds lipids to various sites on its surface was shown to lead to short-range orientational ordering of the proteins via a lipid-mediated protein–protein interaction. The calculations showed that for a variety of reasonable lipid–protein interactions no "anulus" of lipid chains in their essentially all-*trans* states could surround a protein and that protein–protein contact would occur. The possibility of polar region perturbation by high local concentrations of proteins was raised.

Pink and Zuckermann (1980) studied a model of the membrane of *Acholeplasma laidlawii* to see whether the interpretation of the temperature dependence of ^{2}H-NMR static order parameters were in accord with the interpretations of the temperature dependence of the "1,130 cm^{-1}" Raman band in DPPC bilayers. They modelled the membrane as a DPPC bilayer containing a suitable concentration of one kind of "average protein" of molecular weight $\sim$65,000. They obtained a phase diagram which showed phase separation into a nearly-pure lipid phase and a protein-rich phase for $T < T_c$, and the melting (or freezing) of a protein-rich phase at temperatures below T_c. They found that the ^{2}H-NMR measurements were in accord with the model for chain melting used in the Raman study and pointed out that a nearly maximal quadrupole splitting does not imply the absence of jogs and kinks near the methyl end of a lipid chain.

Freire and Snyder (1982) used their method to generate protein distributions, as described earlier, for various protein sizes and concentrations and values of ΔE_m. They found that protein-rich domains became connected at a critical concentration and suggest that this is reflected in changes in lateral diffusion coefficient. Although they do not calculate a phase diagram, this is not necessary within the context of their study. By the nature of their model they cannot study dynamical protein and lipid phenomena.

Recently Lookman *et al.* (1982) have studied a computer simulation of a DPPC bilayer containing proteins of molecular weight $\sim$15,000. The lipid chains are modelled by a two-state model (Georgallas and Pink, 1982a) and the proteins are allowed to diffuse laterally, depending to what extent the chains in their neighbourhoods are melted. This is an extension of a model used to study glycophorin in DPPC and DMPC bilayers (Pink *et al.*, 1982). They deduced lipid–protein interactions by requiring that lipid chain order parameter dependence on c above T_c be in accord with ^{2}H-NMR results (Jacobs and Oldfield, 1981). They calculated phase diagrams and found a protein-rich phase which "melted" at a temperature below T_c, in accord with results of Gomez-Fernandez *et al.* (1980) and Hoffman *et al.* (1980). They found that the curve of ΔQ against c could be either linear or concave, depending on how it is measured. This is illustrated in Figure 6.2 where a comparison is made with cholesterol.

Figure 6.2*a* shows the lipid–protein phase diagram. Below T_c the fluid phase (F) becomes more protein-rich as T decreases. Below T_K the system separates into an essentially pure lipid phase (G) and a protein-rich phase (P). The lipids in P remain fluid for temperatures well below T_K where they eventually display non-cooperative freezing. Typical distributions are shown in Figures 6.2*b* ($T < T_K$); c ($T_K \lesssim T$); d ($T \lesssim T_c$); and e ($T > T_c$). The melting of the protein-rich "patch" at T_K is clearly seen. The transition enthalpy, ΔQ, as a function of c depends on how it is calculated. Let us consider first the case of cholesterol. At low concentrations the number of lipids affected is proportional to c (Figure 6.2*f*, A). As c increases configurations of the form ● x x ●, where x are chains and ● are cholesterols, appear and have a greater effect on each chain involved than simply the sum of x ●. This is because cholesterol likes to have chains in "intermediate" states adjacent to it, rather than all-*trans* or melted. The dependence is still approximately linear but now the slope increases (Figure 6.2*f*, B). At high concentrations, because of cholesterol–cholesterol "contacts" saturation is reached (Figure 6.2*f*, C). Let us compare this to the case of the phase diagram shown here. If we measure ΔQ across a region like I in Figure 6.2*a* where the proteins are loosely packed (Figure 6.2*d*), then because the proteins keep the chains adjacent to them essentially fluid there is no change as one goes from configurations like ● x to ● x x ● . Hence what are two distinct sections — A and B — for cholesterol, are now identical. Saturation still occurs at high c, so that a concave shape results (Figure 6.2*g*) as found by Boggs *et al.* (1980). If, however, ΔQ, is measured across the region II in Figure 6.2*a*, where the maximum phase separation has been achieved, then the amount of lipid not in the protein-rich phase is proportional to c so that a linear dependence of ΔQ on c will be seen over a great range of c (Figure 6.2*h*) except possibly at high concentrations, as found by Gomez-Fernandez *et al.* (1980), who included the entire region II in their calculation of ΔQ.

OTHER APPLICATIONS OF THEORETICAL MODELS

Freire and Biltonen (1978) used a non-interacting "droplet" (or "cluster") model to deduce thermodynamic quantities from specific heat measurements.

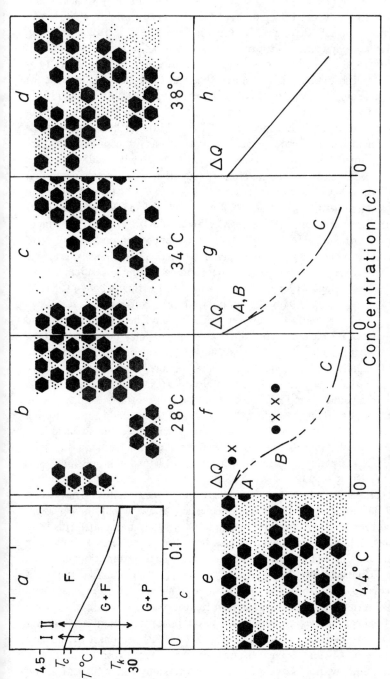

Figure 6.2 *a*, calculated phase diagram of a DPPC bilayer with integral proteins of molecular weight ~15,000 using Monte Carlo simulation. *b–e*, typical instantaneous distributions from the simulation for $c = 0.028$ showing the protein-rich cluster. The $T < T_K$, (*b*), the melting of the cluster for $T_K < T < T_c$ (*c, d*) and the melting of the lipids for $T > T_c$ (*e*). Large hexagons are proteins, dots are "melted" lipid chains and blank areas contain extended lipid chains. *f*, ΔQ against *c* for a lipid–cholesterol bilayer showing the three concentration regions (see text). *g*, ΔQ against *c* for a lipid–integral protein bilayer calculated across the temperature range I of *a* (see text). *h*, ΔQ against *c* for a lipid–integral protein bilayer calculated across the temperature range II of *A* (see text)

Yager and Peticolas (1978) extended the droplet model used by Kanehisa and Tsong (1978) to study the effect of hydrostatic pressure on the 2,880 cm^{-1} C-H Raman band in DPPC vesicles. Their prediction for $T \gtrsim T_c$ fitted very well, but there was poor agreement with their measurements for $T \lesssim 37.5°$C. This is probably due to the fact that only one temperature-independent intensity is associated with each of the F and S states. While this is approximately true for $T \gtrsim T_c$ it is probably not true for $T < T_c$ (see Pink *et al.*, 1980b). Gruen (1980) and Gruen and Haydon (1981) constructed a model of chain melting and calculated quantities for black lipid films. Meraldi and Schlitter (1981) constructed a pleasing model in which steric interactions and van der Waals interactions are present and studied effects of hydrocarbon chain order with and without a cholesterol molecule near it, and the effect of anaesthetics. They calculated that there are about 1.2 *gauche* bonds per DPPC chain at T_c in the gel phase, in essential agreement with Pink *et al.* (1980b) who calculated 1.5 *gauche* bonds per chain at T_c. These numbers are slightly higher but in essential agreement with the results of Snyder *et al.* (1982). In this connection de Verteuil *et al.* (1981) calculated phase diagrams to study the effects of small anaesthetics on lipid bilayers. These provided some understanding of the measurements of Cater *et al.* (1974). Heyn (1979), Jähnig (1980) and Hoffmann *et al.* (1981) all studied the behaviour of DPH probes in lipid bilayers. Hoffmann *et al.* (1981) have also applied their theory to interpret results of spin label measurements and suggested that certain nitroxide spin label measurements may be reporting steric hindrance by intrinsic molecules not characteristic of unlabelled lipids. Dill and Flory (1981) studied hydrocarbon chain order in small vesicles and micelles. Pink *et al.* (1981b) analysed end methyl group ^{2}H-NMR measurements as a function of gramicidin A$'$ and cytochrome oxidase concentration and suggested that two competing effects, a slight ordering due to the proximity of a protein or polypeptide hydrophobic surface and a large disordering due to local high concentrations of the intrinsic molecule, were present. Zuckermann and Pink (1980) studied fluctuations, correlation lengths and lateral compressibilities as well as the relative importance of static (Caillé *et al.*, 1980) and dynamic fluctuation (Doniach, 1978) effects for trans-bilayer ionic permeability. Thayer and Kohler (1981) calculated ^{31}P-NMR lineshapes and showed that there was no necessary correlation between these and lipid packing arrangements. This is an important result because certain lineshapes have been considered as indicating the presence of, for example, a hexagonal phase. The pretransition has been modelled by Doniach (1979) and Chan and Webb (1981), and Day and Willis (1981) calculated the density of states for a single hydrocarbon chain as a function of internal energy and area. Recently, real space renormalisation group methods have been applied to study monolayer phase transitions at air–water and oil–water interfaces (for example, Lavis *et al.*, 1982). Amongst the advantages of this method is that a phase diagram can be deduced from a calculation of the fixed points without having to solve for thermodynamic quantities, and that the method is capable of giving results that take account of critical phenomena (for example, long wavelength fluctuations) and so is better than an MFA (see, for example, Ma, 1977).

Recent papers concerned with theoretical models are:

Edeholm, O. (1981). *Chem. Phys. Lipids*, **29**, 213.
Slater, G. and Caillé, A. (1982). *Biochim. biophys. Acta*, **686**, 249.
Slater, G. and Caillé, A. (1982). *Phys. Lett.*, **86A**, 256.
Gruen, D. W. R. and Wolfe, J. (1982). *Biochim. biophys. Acta*, **688**, 572.
van der Ploeg, P. and Berendsen, H. J. C. (1982). *J. chem. Phys.*, **76**, 3271.
Pace, R. J. and Chan, S. I. (1982). *J. chem. Phys.*, **76**, 4217; 4228; 4241.
Pearce, P. A. and Scott, H. L. Jr, (1982). *J. chem. Phys.*, **77**, 951.
Brown, M. F. (1982). *J. chem. Phys.*, **77**, 1576.

ACKNOWLEDGEMENTS

It is a pleasure to thank Alex Georgallas for many discussions on some of the ideas here and for criticisms of parts of the manuscript, as well as Naeem Jan for advice about a number of topics, Turab Lookman for his work on computer simulations and Martin Zuckermann, Dennis Chapman and Mike Steinitz for their valued collaboration. I would also like to thank Peter Fulde for his hospitality at the Max-Planck-Institut, Stuttgart where part of this was written and where I benefited from discussions with his group. Thanks also to Greta Chisholm who typed the manuscript. This work was supported in part by the Natural Sciences and Engineering Research Council of Canada.

REFERENCES

Abraham, F. F. (1981a). *Phys. Rep.*, **80**, 340.
Abraham, F. F. (1981b). *J. Chem. Phys.*, **75**, 498.
Abramowitz, M. and Stegun, I. A. (1970). *Handbook of Mathematical Functions*, Dover Publications, New York.
Adam, N. K. and Jessop, G. (1926). *Proc. R. Soc.*, **A112**, 364.
Albrecht, O., Gruler, H. and Sackmann, E. (1978). *J. Phys. (Paris)*, **39**, 301.
Alexandrowicz, Z. (1971). *J. Chem. Phys.*, **55**, 2780.
Barber, M. N. (1980). *Phys. Rep.*, **59**, 375.
Barker, J. A. and Henderson, D. (1976). *Rev. Mod. Phys.*, **48**, 587.
Bell, G. M., Mingins, J. and Taylor, J. A. G. (1978). *J. chem. Soc., Faraday Trans. II.*, **74**, 223.
Bell, G. M., Combs, L. L. and Dunne, L. J. (1981). *Chem. Rev.*, **81**, 15.
Berlin, T. H. and Kac, M. (1952). *Phys. Rev.*, **86**, 821.
Binder, K. (1974). *Adv. Phys.*, **23**, 917.
Binder, K. (1976). In *Phase Transitions and Critical Phenomena* (eds C. Domb and M. S. Green), Vol. 5b, Academic Press, London.
Binder, K. (1979). *Monte Carlo Methods in Statistical Physics*, Springer-Verlag, Heidelberg.
Blinc, R. and Žekš, B. (1974). *Soft Modes in Ferroelectrics and Antiferroelectrics*, North-Holland, Amsterdam.
Blume, A. (1979). *Biochim. biophys. Acta*, **557**, 32.

Boggs, J. M., Clement, I. R. and Moscarello, M. A. (1980). *Biochim. biophys. Acta*, **601**, 134.
Cadenhead, D. A. (1977). *Nobel Symp.*, **34**, 63.
Cadenhead, D. A., Müller-Landau, F. and Kellner, B. M. (1980). In *Ordering in Two Dimensions* (ed S. K. Sinha), North-Holland, New York, p. 73.
Caillé, A., Rapini, A., Zuckermann, M. J., Cros, A. and Doniach, S. (1978). *Can. J. Phys.*, **56**, 348.
Caillé, A., Pink, D. A., deVerteuil, F. and Zuckermann, M. J. (1980). *Can. J. Phys.*, **58**, 581.
Cater, B. R., Chapman, D., Hawes, S. M. and Saville, J. (1974). *Biochim. biophys. Acta*, **303**, 54.
Chan, W. K. and Webb, W. W. (1981). *Phys. Rev. Lett.*, **46**, 39.
Chapman, D. (1980). In *Membrane Structure and Function* (ed. E. Bittar) John Wiley, New York, Vol. 1.
Chen, H. H. (1978). *Nuovo Cim.*, **43**, 277.
Chen, S. C., Sturtevant, J. M. and Gaffney, B. J. (1980). *Proc. natn. Acad. Sci. U.S.A.*, **77**, 5060.
Cheng, W. H. (1980). *Biochim. biophys. Acta*, **600**, 358.
Copeland, B. R. and McConnell, H. M. (1980). *Biochim. biophys. Acta*, **599**, 95.
Davis, J. (1979). *Biophys. J.*, **27**, 339.
Day, J. and Willis, C. R. (1981). *J. theor. Biol.*, **88**, 693.
deGennes, P. G. (1975). *The Physics of Liquid Crystals*, Clarendon Press, Oxford.
deVerteuil, F., Pink, D. A., Vadas, E. B. and Zuckermann, M. J. (1981). *Biochim. biophys. Acta*, **640**, 207.
Dill, K. A. and Flory, P. J. (1980). *Proc. natn. Acad. Sci. U.S.A.*, **77**, 3115.
Dill, K. A. and Flory, P. J. (1981). *Proc. natn. Acad. Sci. U.S.A.*, **78**, 676.
Doniach, S. (1978). *J. chem. Phys.*, **68**, 4912.
Doniach, S. (1979). *J. chem. Phys.*, **70**, 4587.
Domb, C. (1960). *Adv. Phys.*, **9**, 149.
Domb, C. and Stoll, E. (1977). *J. Phys, A* **10**, 1141.
Dunne, L. J. and Bell, G. M. (1980). *J. Chem. Soc. Faraday Trans II*, **76**, 431.
Estep, T. N., Mountcastle, D. B., Biltonen, R. L. and Thompson, T. E. (1978). *Biochemistry*, **17**, 1984.
Firpo, J. L., Dupin, J. J., Albinet, G., Baret, J. F. and Caillé, A. (1981). *J. chem. Phys.*, **74**, 2569.
Flory, P. J. (1969). *The Statistical Mechanics of Chain Molecules*, Wiley, New York.
Freire, E. and Biltonen, R. L. (1978). *Biochim. biophys. Acta*, **514**, 54.
Freire, E. and Snyder, B. (1980a). *Biochemistry*, **19**, 88.
Freire, E. and Snyder, B. (1980b). *Biochim. biophys. Acta*, **600**, 643.
Freire, E. and Snyder, B. (1982). *Biophys. J.*, **37**, 617.
Frenkel, D. and McTague, J. P. (1980). *A. Rev. Phys. Chem.*, **31**, 491.
Fulford, A. J. C. and Peel, W. E. (1980). *Biochim. biophys. Acta*, **598**, 237.
Gaines, G. L. Jr (1966). *Insoluble Monolayers at Liquid-Gas Interfaces*, Wiley, New York.
Georgallas, A. (1979). thesis, London.
Georgallas, A. and Pink, D. A. (1982a). *J. Colloid. Interface Sci.*, **89**, 107.
Georgallas, A. and Pink, D. A. (1982b). *Can. J. Phys.*, **60**, 1678.
Gomez-Fernandez, J. C., Goni, F. M., Bach, D., Restall, C. J. and Chapman, D. (1980). *Biochim. biophys. Acta*, **598**, 502.
Gruen, D. W. R. (1980). *Biochim. biophys. Acta*, **595**, 161.
Gruen, D. W. R. and Haydon, D. A. (1981). *Biophys. J.*, **33**, 149; 167.
Hammersley, J. M. and Handscomb, D. C. (1964). *Monte Carlo Methods*, Methuen, London.
Heer, C. V. (1972). *Statistical Mechanics, Kinetic Theory and Stochastic Processes*, Academic Press, New York.
Heyn, M. P. (1979). *FEBS Lett.*, **108**, 359.
Hinz, H-J. and Sturtevant, J. M. (1972). *J. biol. Chem.*, **247**, 3697.
Hoffmann, W. *et al.* (1980). *J. molec. Biol.*, **141**, 119.
Hoffmann, W., Pink, D. A., Restall, C. and Chapman, D. (1981). *Eur. J. Biochem.*, **114**, 585.
Huang, K. (1967). *Statistical Mechanics*, Wiley, New York.
Israelachvili, J. N., Marčelja, S. and Horn, R. G. (1980). *Q. Rev. Biophys.*, **13**, 121.

Jacobs, R. E., Hudson, B. S. and Andersen, H. C. (1977). *Biochemistry*, 16, 4349.
Jacobs, R. and Oldfield, E. (1981). In *Progress in NMR Spectroscopy* (eds J. W. Emsley, J. Feeny and L. H. Sutcliffe), Academic Press, New York, 14, 113.
Jähnig, F. (1979). *J. chem. Phys.*, 70, 3279.
Jähnig, F. (1980). *Proc. natn. Acad. Sci. U.S.A.*, 76, 6361.
Jähnig, F. (1981a). *Biophys. J.*, 36, 329; (1981b). 36, 347.
Janiak, M. J., Small, D. M. and Shipley, G. G. (1976). *Biochemistry*, 15, 4575.
Kadanoff, L. P. (1976). In *Phase Transitions and Critical Phenomena* (eds C. Domb and M. S. Green), Academic Press, London, Vol. 5A.
Kanehisa, M. I. and Tsong, T. T. (1978). *J. Am. Chem. Soc.*, 100, 424.
Kirkwood, J. G. (1943). *Publ. Am. Ass. Advmt Sci. (Surf. Chem.)*, 21, 157.
Kittel, C. (1976). *Introduction to Solid State Physics*, Wiley, New York.
Kosterlitz, J. M. and Thouless, D. J. (1978). In *Progress in Low Temperature Physics* (ed. D. Brewer), North-Holland, Amsterdam, Vol. VIIb.
Landau, L. D., Lifshitz, E. M. and Pitaevskii, L. P. (1980). *Statistical Physics*, 3rd edn, Pergamon Press, Oxford.
Lavis, D. A., Southern, B. W. and Bell, G. M. (1982). *J. Phys.*, C15, 1077.
Lee, A. G. (1977). *Biochim. biophys. Acta*, 472, 237; 285.
Lee, A. G. (1978). *Biochim. biophys. Acta*, 507, 433.
Lieb, E. H. and Wu, F. Y. (1972). In *Phase Transitions and Critical Phenomena* (eds C. Domb and M. S. Green), Academic Press, London, Vol. 1.
Lookman, T., Pink, D. A., Grundke, E. W., Zuckermann, M. J. and deVerteuil, F. (1982). *Biochemistry*, 21, 5593.
Luban, M. (1976). In *Phase Transitions and Critical Phenomena* (eds C. Domb and M. S. Green), Academic Press, London, Vol. 5A.
Luna, E. J. and McConnell, H. M. (1977a). *Biochim. biophys. Acta*, 466, 381.
Luna, E. J. and McConnell, H. M. (1977b). *Biochim. Biophys. Acta*, 470, 303.
Ma, S.-K. (1977). *Modern Theory of Critical Phenomena*, Benjamin, Reading, Mass.
Mabrey, S., Mateo, P. L. and Sturtevant, J. M. (1978). *Biochemistry*, 17, 2464.
Maier, W. and Saupe, A. (1959a). *Z. Naturforsch.* A14, 882; (1959b). 15, 287.
Marčelja, S. (1974). *Biochim. biophys. Acta*, 367, 165.
Marčelja, S. (1976). *Biochim. biophys. Acta*, 455, 1.
Marčelja, S. and Wolfe, J. (1979). *Biochim. biophys. Acta*, 557, 24.
Mason, J. T., Huang, C-h. and Biltonen, R. L. (1981). *Biochemistry*, 20, 6086.
McCoy, B. M. and Wu, T. T. (1973). *The Two-dimensional Ising Model*, Harvard University Press, Cambridge, Mass.
Meirovitch, H. and Alexandrowicz, Z. (1977). *J. statist. Phys.*, 16, 121.
Meraldi, J-P. and Schlitter, J. (1981). *Biochim. biophys. Acta*, 645, 183; 193.
Mermin, N. D. and Wagner, H. (1966). *Phys. Rev. Lett.*, 17, 1133.
Messiah, A. (1967). *Quantum Mechanics*, North-Holland, Amsterdam, Vol. I, Ch. 8.
Metropolis, N., Rosenbluth, A. W., Rosenbluth, M. N., Teller, A. H. and Teller, E. (1953). *J. chem. Phys.*, 21, 1087.
Moraal, H. (1976). *Physica*, 85A, 457.
Nagle, J. F. (1973). *J. chem. Phys.*, 58, 252.
Nagle, J. F. (1975). *J. chem. Phys.*, 63, 1255.
Nagle, J. F. (1976). *J. Membrane Biol.*, 27, 233.
Nagle, J. F. (1980). In *A. Rev. Phys. Chem.*, 31, 157.
Nelson, D. R. and Halperin, B. I. (1979). *Phys. Rev.*, B19, 2457.
Oldfield, E. *et al.* (1978). *Proc. natn. Acad. Sci. U.S.A.*, 75, 4657.
Overath, P. and Thilo, L. (1978). In *Biochemistry of Cell Walls and Membranes II.* (ed. J. C. Metcalfe), University Park Press, Baltimore, Vol. 19, p. 1.
Owicki, J. C., Springgate, M. W. and McConnell, H. M. (1978). *Proc. natn. Acad. Sci. U.S.A.*, 75, 1616.
Owicki, J. C. and McConnell, H. M. (1979). *Proc. natn. Acad. Sci. U.S.A.*, 76, 4750.
Owicki, J. C. and McConnell, H. M. (1980). *Biophys. J.*, 30, 383.
Pink, D. A. and Carroll, C. E. (1978). *Phys. Lett.*, A66, 157.
Pink, D. A. and Chapman, D. (1979). *Proc. natn. Acad. Sci. U.S.A.*, 76, 1542.
Pink, D. A., Georgallas, A. and Zuckermann, M. J. (1980a). *Z. Physik*, 40, 103.

Pink, D. A., Green, T. J. and Chapman, D. (1980b). *Biochemistry*, **19**, 345.
Pink, D. A. and Zuckermann, M. J. (1980). *FEBS Lett.*, **109**, 5.
Pink, D. A. (1981). In *Biological Membranes* (ed. D. Chapman), Academic Press, London, Vol. 4, 131.
Pink, D. A., Green, T. J. and Chapman, D. (1981a). *Biochemistry*, **20**, 6692.
Pink, D. A., Georgallas, A. and Chapman, D. (1981b). *Biochemistry*, **20**, 7152.
Pink, D. A., Lookman, T., MacDonald, A. L., Zuckermann, M. J. and Jan, N. (1982). *Biochim. biophys. Acta*, **687**, 42.
Priest, R. G. (1977). *J. chem. Phys.*, **66**, 722.
Prigogine, I., Mathot-Sarolea, L. and van Hove, L. (1952). *Trans Faraday Soc.*, **48**, 485.
Scott, H. L. Jr and Cheng, W-H. (1977). *J. Colloid. Interface Sci.*, **62**, 125.
Scott, H. L. and Cheng, W-H. (1979). *Biophys. J.*, **28**, 117.
Schröder, H. (1977). *J. chem. Phys.*, **67**, 1617.
Seelig, A. and Seelig, J. (1975). *Biochim. biophys. Acta*, **406**, 1.
Seelig, A. and Seelig, J. (1978). *Hoppe-Seyler's Z. Physiol. Chem.*, **359**, 1747.
Shreider, Yu, A. (1966). *The Monte Carlo Method*, Oxford University Press, Oxford.
Snyder, B. and Freire, E. (1980). *Proc. natn. Acad. Sci. U.S.A.*, **77**, 4055.
Snyder, R. G. (1967). *J. chem. Phys.*, **47**, 1316.
Snyder, R. G. (1970). *J. molec. Spectrosc.*, **36**, 222.
Snyder, R. G., Cameron, D. G., Casal, H. L., Compton, D. A. C. and Mantsch, H. H. (1982). *Biochim. biophys. Acta*, **684**, 111.
Stanley, H. E. (1971). *Introduction to Phase Transitions and Critical Phenomena*, Oxford University Press, New York.
Stoll, E. and Domb, C. (1979). *J. Phys.*, **A12**, 1843.
Tanford, C. (1979). *Proc. natn. Acad. Sci. U.S.A.*, **76**, 4175.
Tiessier-Lavigne, M., Boothroyd, A., Zuckermann, M. J. and Pink, D. A. (1982). *J. chem. Phys.*, **76**, 4587.
Thayer, A. M. and Kohler, S. J. (1981). *Biochemistry*, **20**, 6831.
Von Dreele, P. H. (1978). *Biochemistry*, **17**, 3939.
Wiegel, F. W. (1975). *J. statist. Phys.*, **13**, 515; (1976). *Phys. Lett.*, **57A**, 393; (1977). *Physica*, **89A**, 397.
Wu, F. Y. (1982). *Rev. mod. Phys.*, **54**, 235.
Yager, P. and Peticolas, W. L. (1980). *Biophys. J.*, **31**, 359.
Zuckermann, M. J. and Pink, D. A. (1980). *J. chem. Phys.*, **73**, 2919.
Zuckermann, M. J., Pink, D. A., Costas, M. and Sanctuary, B. C. (1982). *J. chem. Phys.*, **76**, 4206.

7

The Ca^{2+} dependent ATPase of sarcoplasmic reticulum

G. Inesi and M. Kurzmack
Department of Biological Chemistry, University of Maryland, Baltimore,
Maryland

INTRODUCTION

The sarcoplasmic reticulum (SR) of striated muscle has an important role in the control of contractile activity by providing an intracellular sink for calcium during relaxation and a source for calcium release upon membrane excitation. SR and excitation–contraction coupling have been the subjects of several detailed reviews (Caputo, 1978; deMeis and Vianna, 1979; Ebashi and Endo, 1968, Endo, 1977; Fabiato and Fabiato, 1979; Fuchs, 1974; Hasselbach, 1964; 1978; Ikemoto, 1982, Inesi, 1979; 1981; MacLennan and Holland, 1975; Martonosi, 1972; Tada *et al.*, 1978; Weber, 1966; Yamamoto *et al.*, 1979).

Structural and functional studies of SR membranes have been greatly aided by the isolation of a microsomal fraction obtained by differential centrifugation of muscle homogenates and identified with vesicular fragments of SR according to ultrastructural and functional criteria (Muscatello *et al.*, 1961). The original preparation methods (Portzehl, 1957; Ebashi, 1958; Nagai *et al.*, 1960) have been refined by the use of sucrose gradient centrifugation and separation of "light" and "heavy" fractions of somewhat different protein composition (Meissner *et al.*, 1973; Meissner, 1975).

STRUCTURE

The protein component of the SR membrane

The protein component accounts for approximately 60 per cent of the SR membrane dry weight. Following membrane solubilisation in strong detergents, such as sodium dodecylsulphate, most of the protein migrates on electrophoretic gels as a band with a mobility corresponding to approximately 110,000 molecular weight (MW). This band has been identified with the Ca^{2+}-activated ATPase (Martonosi and Halpin, 1971; McFarland and Inesi, 1971), which was first purified by MacLennan (1970). Good SR preparations are deprived of phosphory-lase (Figure 7.1) which may be suspected of migrating with the ATPase band in SDS gels owing to a similar molecular weight. In fact, the 110,000-MW protein behaves homogeneously with respect to tryptic digestion (Thorley-Lawson and Green, 1973; Migala *et al.*, 1973; Stewart and MacLennan, 1974; Inesi and Scales, 1974), indicating that the entire band is composed of ATPase in the form of identical polypeptide chains, or of closely related isozymes.

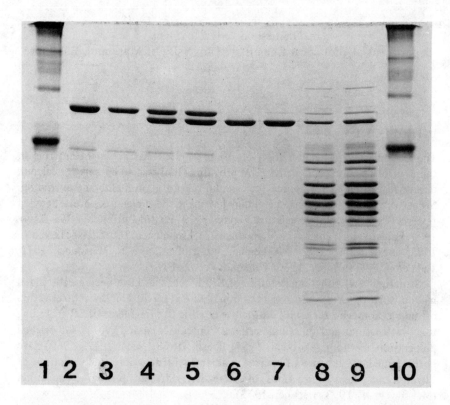

Figure 7.1 SDS gel electrophoresis of solubilised SR vesicles (2 and 3), vesicles with added phosphorylase (4 and 5), phosphorylase (6 and 7), supernatant obtained from homogenated muscle during the preparation of SR vesicles (8 and 9), and crosslinked serum albumin used as a molecular weight marker (1 and 10). The experiment shows that the principal protein component (ATPase) of SR vesicles is not associated with phosphorylase; the latter can be clearly separated if added to the SR sample. In fact, phosphorylase is removed during the SR preparation and is found in the supernatant which is obtained after centrifugation. The ATPase migration velocity is consistent with a molecular weight slightly larger than that of phosphorylase (92,000) and considerably smaller than that of the albumin dimer (136,000)

In addition to the prominent ATPase band, gel electrophoresis of solubilised SR vesicles shows other minor components (Figure 7.1) such as "calsequestrin" (MacLennan and Wong, 1971), and a "calcium-binding protein" (Ostwald and MacLennan, 1974). These minor bands are easily discernible in microsomal preparations obtained from rabbit muscle, but are barely detectable in preparations from lobster muscle (Malan *et al.*, 1975). A proteolipid fraction and a glycoprotein are also associated with SR vesicles (MacLennan *et al.*, 1973; Michalak *et al.*, 1980).

Disposition of the ATPase protein in the SR vesicles

As the ATPase protein is the predominant component of the membrane mass, it also contributes to prominent ultrastructural details of the SR vesicles. The ATPase polypeptide chains behave as amphiphylic units and are inserted into the membrane with a non-polar portion penetrating the lipid bilayer (Deamer and Baskin, 1969), while a hydrophylic portion protrudes from the surface of the vesicles into the medium (Ikemoto, 1968; Inesi and Asai, 1968). The hydrophylic portions of the ATPase chains can be seen by electron microscopic techniques with negatively-stained preparations, or with thin sections (Figure 7.2*a*). In addition, thin sections prepared with tannic acid (Figure 7.2*a*) even show the corresponding non-polar segments intruding into the bilayer and aligned within the cross section of the membrane.

Another view of the ATPase protein is obtained by freeze fracturing the vesicles along the plane of the bilayer. In this case, protein particles are present almost exclusively on the concave and, very rarely, on the convex freeze fracture faces (Figure 7.2*b*). This indicates a predominant association of the ATPase protein with the outer, as opposed to the inner, monolayer. Therefore, the distribution of the ATPase with respect to the perpendicular axis of the membrane is assymmetric, and nearly all the vesicles obtained in SR preparations display homogeneous orientation with the ATPase protein exposed to the medium. This conclusion is also supported by low angle X-ray diffraction studies (Dupont *et al.*, 1973; Herbette *et al.*, 1977) which have provided profiles of electron density distribution across the membrane (Figure 7.3).

Another ultrastructural feature which becomes apparent when comparing electron micrographs of outer granules with those of inner particles is that the density of the particles in freeze fracture preparations is lower than the density of the outer granules (Scales and Inesi, 1976). While the ATPase chains retain their individuality on the outer surface of the vesicles, they may aggregate into oligomeric structures within the bilayer. This suggestion is reinforced by images produced with rotary shadowing techniques (Figure 7.2*d*), which show irregular size and substructure of particles, seemingly due to the confluence of a variable number of subunits.

The close spatial proximity of the ATPase chains in the SR membrane, and their tendency to polymerise, is also supported by studies on crosslinking

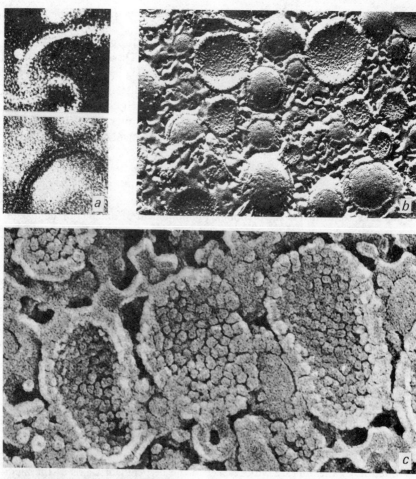

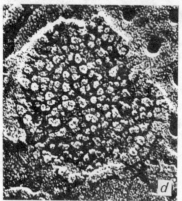

Figure 7.2 SR ATPase in its membrane environment as viewed by electron microscopy. *a*, Ca-ATPase polypeptides appear as hydrophilic surface projections in negatively-stained preparations (top) or in ultra-thin sections of plastic-embedded microsomes (bottom) (both ×258,000). The thin-section view, prepared with tannic acid, also shows lipophilic portions of the ATPase that appear as regularly spaced processes that span the bilayer. *b*, Suspension of vesicles that were frozen, fractured and then coated with platinum at an angle of 45° show that intramembranous particles are associated predominantly with concave fracture faces. Each particle corresponds to several polypeptides of Ca-ATPase (shadows printed white; ×77,800). *c*, Rotary shadowed preparations of freeze-fractured SR vesicles give a variety of details depending on the shadowing angle. At 38° the concave fracture faces are populated with a high density of platinum-coated particles that are sometimes difficult to distinguish from background lipid-rich areas (shadows printed black). Stereo microscopy is needed to recover the three-dimensional character of the specimens (×271,000). *d*, Specimens that are rotary shadowed at 24° show distinct particles with a variety of sizes and shapes (shadows printed black; ×271,000)

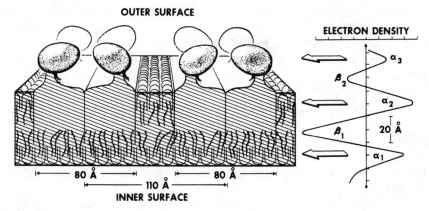

Figure 7.3 Summary of experimental findings related to the structure of the SR membrane. The ATPase outer granules are those revealed by electron microscopy on negatively-stained or deeply etched preparations. The 90 Å ATPase protein units are those revealed by electron microscopy on the concave faces of freeze-fracture vesicles. The diagram reflects a greater density of outer granules relative to the inner particles and suggests that the non-polar portions of the amphiphilic ATPase chains aggregate within the membrane bilayer, while the polar ends retain their individuality on the membrane surface (Scales and Inesi, 1976). On the right side of the figure an electron-density profile obtained by low-angle X-ray diffraction (Dupont *et al.*, 1973) is drawn in a position corresponding to the protein and phospholipid units

(Bailin, 1980; Louis *et al.*, 1977; Louis and Holroyd, 1978; Murphy, 1976), fluorescence energy transfer (Vanderkooi *et al.*, 1977) and EPR spectroscopy of spin labels (Andersen *et al.*, 1981). On the other hand, monomer preparations retaining ATPase activity have been obtained in the presence of detergents (Dean and Tanford, 1978). To what extent oligomerisation is necessary for vectorial transport and/or enzyme regulation is the subject of current studies.

A relatively rapid and temperature-dependent anisotropic rotation of the ATPase protein within the bilayer was demonstrated by measurements of nuclear spin relaxation times for bound nucleotide (Manuck and Sykes, 1977), saturation transfer EPR of spin-labelled preparations (Thomas and Hidalgo, 1978) and decay of laser flash-induced dichroism with the covalently attached triplet probe eosin isothiocyanate or 5-iodoacetamidoeosin (Hoffmann *et al.*, 1979; 1980; Burkli and Cherry, 1981).

Purification and structure of SR ATPase

Using solubilisation with deoxycholate and precipitation with salt, MacLennan (1970) achieved the first purification of the Ca^{2+}-dependent ATPase. Other methods include Triton X-100 (Ikemoto *et al.*, 1971; McFarland and Inesi, 1971), extraction with octylglucoside (Banerjee *et al.*, 1979) and sequential solubilisations with deoxycholate (Martonosi, 1968; Meissner *et al.*, 1973) or octaoxyethylene dodecyl monoether (Dean and Tanford, 1977).

The molecular weight of the solubilised chains is 115,000–119,000 (LeMaire *et al.*, 1976; Rizzolo *et al.*, 1976) as determined by analytical centrifugation. Studies on the primary structure of the ATPase protein indicate that the molecular weight of the polypeptide chains is around 100,000. This is more in line with gel electrophoresis determinations (Louis and Shooter, 1972; MacLennan, 1970; McFarland and Inesi, 1971; Thorley-Lawson and Green, 1973).

Due to the amphiphilic character of the polypeptide chains, most ATPase preparations acquire a membranous state of aggregation in their final form. This property can be exploited when reconstituting membranes of selected lipid composition (Knowles *et al.*, 1976; Peterson and Deamer, 1977; Warren *et al.*, 1974) and vesicular preparations displaying both transport and ATPase activity (Chiesi *et al.*, 1978; Racker, 1972; Wang *et al.*, 1979).

When native SR vesicles are subjected to mild trypsin digestion, the ATPase polypeptide chains are cleaved into two complementary fragments of approximately 45,000 and 55,000 MW (Inesi and Scales, 1974; Migala *et al.*, 1973; Thorley-Lawson and Green, 1973; Stewart and MacLennan, 1974). This initial cleavage is not accompanied by any significant loss of protein or reduction in Ca^{2+} transport activity, indicating that the two fragments are intimately associated and stabilised by multiple weak interactions (Rizzolo *et al.*, 1976). After solubilisation in SDS, dissociation of the fragments can be demonstrated by gel electrophoresis. Subsequent tryptic digestion causes further cleavage of the 55,000-MW fragment into 24,000 and 33,000-MW subfragments.

Fragmentation of the ATPase with proteolytic enzymes and cyanogen bromide has led to sequencing work (Allen and Green, 1976; Allen *et al.*, 1980; Klip *et al.*, 1980; Tong, 1980) and to clarification of the primary structure of three large fragments of the ATPase chain, as well as the 31 residue N-terminal peptide, and the C-terminal octapeptide. The relationship between the five known sequences and the initial tryptic fragments is shown in Figure 7.4. Note that a significant portion of the ATPase chain is not amenable to sequencing due to low solubility. The segments of undetermined sequence are also shown in Figure 7.4. The insoluble segment corresponds to polypeptide folds that intrude into the hydrophobic portion of the membrane bilayer. The amino acid composition of sequenced and non-sequenced regions of the ATPase protein is given in Table 7.1.

The functionally important Asp^{26} of segment 3 is phosphorylated by ATP during the catalytic cycle. Segment 3 also contains 11 cystein residues. This feature may explain the sensitivity of enzymic activity to −SH reagents, as well as the sensitivity of −SH directed probes to catalytic events (Coan and Inesi, 1977; Hasselbach and Seraydarian, 1966; Ikemoto *et al.*, 1978; Murphy, 1976; Thorley-Lawson and Green, 1977; Yamada and Ikemoto, 1978). Another important feature is the presence of a lysine in close proximity to the phosphorylation site. This lysine is likely to be the residue which reacts with pyridoxal-5′-phosphate, causing enzyme inactivation (Murphy, 1977).

Table 7.1 Amino acid composition of sequenced and non-sequenced regions of the ATPase protein (Allen *et al.*, 1980)

Amino acid	No. of residues			
	Total in sequences	Total in other known sequences	Total in ATPase (mol/110 kg)	Non-sequenced residues by difference
Lys	40	10	51	1
His	3	8	13	2
Arg	37	8	51	6
Asp	57	21	87	9
Thr	40	14	60	6
Ser	40	13	64	11
Glu	60	25	107	22
Pro	21	14	49	14
Gly	39	20	73	14
Ala	51	21	85	13
Cys	15	6	24	3
Val	52	17	79	10
Met	20	13	34	1
Ile	33	18	59	8
Leu	35	36	98	27
Tyr	14	6	22	2
Phe	17	10	42	15
Trp	1	0	19	18
Total residues	575	260	1017	182
Polar residues (Lys, His, Arg, Asx, Thr, Ser, Glx)	277	99	433	57
Polar residues (%)	48	38	43	31

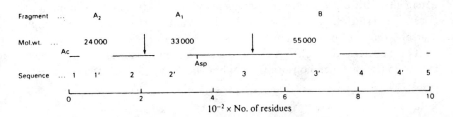

Figure 7.4 Linear map of the ATPase amino acid sequence. The relationship between the known sequences and the tryptic fragments A_2, A_1 and B is shown. The four gaps have been numbered 1′, 2′, 3′ and 4′. Their location is approximate to the extent that the molecular weights of the fragments are approximate and the exact position of sequence 4 in the second half of fragment B is unknown (Allen *et al.*, 1980)

The electron microscopic observations, as well as the studies on tryptic cleavage, indicate that the active site is on the outer surface of the vesicles and is contained in the outer granules protruding from the SR membrane.

The lipid component

Lipids constitute approximately 40 per cent of the membrane dry weight, 90 per cent of those being phospholipids (Drabikowski *et al.*, 1966; Fiehn and Hasselbach, 1970; Fiehn and Peter, 1971; MacLennan *et al.*, 1971; Martonosi *et al.*, 1968; Meissner and Fleischer, 1971; Tagaki, 1971). Phosphatidylcholine (50-70 per cent) and phosphatidylethanolamine constitute the largest portion of the phospholipids, but sphyngomyelin, phosphatidylserine, phosphatidy-linositol and plasmologen compounds (Marai and Kuksis, 1973; Owens *et al.*, 1972; Waku *et al.*, 1971) are also present. Neutral lipids include cholesterol, cholesterol esters, triacylglycerols. Small amounts of free fatty acids have also been detected.

It was recognised even in early studies (Kielly and Meyerhof, 1950) that phospholipids are required for the enzymatic activity of the muscle microsomes which were later identified with vesicular fragments of SR membrane (Ebashi and Lipman, 1962). Subsequent studies demonstrated that phospholipase treatment and removal of the digestion products interferes with the hydrolytic activity of Ca^{2+}-ATPase (Fiehn and Hasselbach, 1970; MacLennan *et al.*, 1971; Martonosi *et al.*, 1968). Addition of phospholipid to the depleted vesicles restores the hydrolytic activity (Martonosi *et al.*, 1971; Meissner and Fleischer, 1972).

Another approach to the study of the lipid requirement of the SR ATPase is the technique introduced by Warren *et al.* (1974a, 1974b) and Hesketh *et al.* (1976). This method consists of lipid exchange in the presence of cholate and subsequent gradient centrifugation of the vesicles. Using this technique, it was found that the phospholipid requirement is not specific. This was also demonstrated by Knowles *et al.* (1976), and LeMaire *et al.* (1976). Quantitatively the requirement is limited to approximately 30 phospholipid molecules per ATPase chain. All, or nearly all, of these phospholipids can be replaced by nonionic detergents with a preference for detergents with a polar moiety of limited size (Dean and Tanford, 1978). The affinity of the enzyme for native phospholipids is greater than for the detergents.

It is apparent that Ca^{2+}-ATPase, an amphiphilic molecule itself, requires interaction with other nonspecific amphiphilic molecules to acquire an active conformation.

FUNCTION

ATPase and Ca^{2+} transport

Their ability to accumulate Ca^{2+} in the presence of ATP is the most specific and important functional feature of SR vesicles (Ebashi and Lipman, 1962;

Hasselbach and Makinose, 1961; 1963). The vesicles constitute a uniquely advantageous system for studies of Ca^{2+} transport coupled to ATP utilisation due to the very high content and homogeneous orientation of the ATPase protein in nearly all vesicles obtained by differential centrifugation of muscle homogenates.

When ATP is added to SR vesicles in a medium containing $MgCl_2$, KCl and a neutral buffer, the vesicles take up calcium from the medium, reaching an asymptotic level within 60 to 90 seconds (Figure 7.5). Such an ATP-dependent Ca^{2+} uptake leads to formation of a transmembrane Ca^{2+} gradient that can be

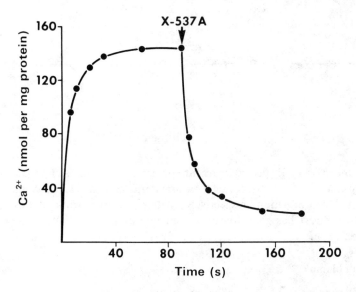

Figure 7.5 Ca^{2+} uptake and subsequent release following addition of ATP and then the ionophore X-537A to SR vesicles (Scarpa *et al.*, 1972)

readily collapsed by the addition of appropriate ionophores which increase the passive permeability of the membrane and leakage of accumulated Ca^{2+} (Figure 7.5). The energy required for Ca^{2+} transport and establishment of the gradient is derived from utilisation of ATP (Ebashi and Lipman, 1962; Hasselbach and Makinose, 1961; 1963; Martonosi and Feretos, 1964; Weber, 1966). Comparative experiments on SR preparations prepared from different animal species and containing different protein contaminants in addition to ATPase (Malan *et al.*, 1975), as well as reconstitution experiments with purified ATPase reassembled into phospholipid vesicles (Chiesi *et al.*, 1978; Racker, 1972; Wang *et al.*, 1979), indicate that the ATPase protein is the sole operator of the calcium pump.

The catalytic and transport cycle of SR ATPase includes enzyme activation by calcium, transfer of the ATP terminal phosphate to form a phosphorylated enzyme intermediate (Makinose, 1969; Yamamoto and Tonomura, 1967), calcium translocation and hydrolytic cleavage of the phosphate from the intermediate. The main features of the cycle are shown in the following scheme which is nearly identical to that originally proposed by deMeis and collaborators (Carvalho *et al.*, 1976):

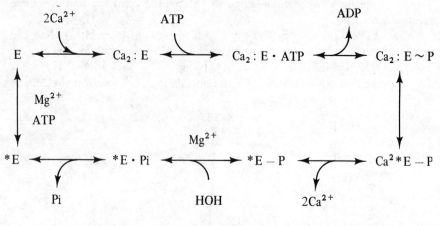

Scheme I

where the E and *E species represent enzyme states with calcium sites in high affinity and outward orientated conformation, and low affinity and inward orientated conformation, respectively. Within the framework of this scheme, significant effort has gone towards characterisation of partial reactions in the catalytic cycle.

Calcium binding

Calcium binding to SR ATPase is an absolute requirement for activation of the enzyme. Binding of the divalent cation (in the absence of ATP) can be measured in equilibrium conditions and several investigators (Carvalho, 1966; Chevalier and Buton, 1971; Chiu and Haynes, 1977; Fiehn and Migala, 1971; Ikemoto, 1974; 1975; Inesi *et al.*, 1980; Meissner *et al.*, 1973) have described the presence of various classes of binding sites which differ in their affinity for Ca^{2+} (Figure 7.6). The highest affinity ($K_d \cong 1 \times 10^{-6}$ M at neutral pH) class includes the specific sites involved in enzyme activation, as indicated by a similar dependence of site titration and ATPase activity on Ca^{2+} concentration.

It should be pointed out that control of Ca^{2+} concentrations within and below the micromolar region requires the use of Ca^{2+} buffers in reaction mixtures of relatively high total calcium content. In this case the actual concentration of free Ca^{2+} is controlled by experimental manipulation of a chelating agent such as EGTA (ethyleneglycol-bis-(β-aminoethyl ether)N,N'-tetraacetic acid), which is used because it has much higher affinity for Ca^{2+} than for Mg^{2+}.

Calculations of the free Ca^{2+} concentration are based on the total concentrations and association constants of calcium, EGTA and any other competing

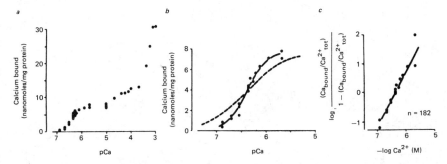

Figure 7.6 Calcium binding to SR vesicles in the absence of ATP (pH 6.8, in the presence of Mg^{2+}). The graph on the left shows various classes of binding sites, while the cooperative character of the high affinity binding is demonstrated by the other two graphs. The dotted line is a theoretical curve representing non-cooperative binding to independent sites (Inesi et al., 1980a)

cations and anions (see Fabiato and Fabiato (1979) for a review). Although several values may be found in the literature for the Ca · EGTA binding constant, such that some doubt may exist about the absolute free Ca^{2+} concentration, the use of EGTA has facilitated the demonstration of the dependence of several biological processes on very low Ca^{2+} concentrations. As long as a single value for the Ca · EGTA constant is used, all experiments and analyses will be internally consistent. Absolute values for free Ca^{2+} may be checked further with the more reliable and sensitive electrodes which are now available (Owen, 1976; Berman and Aderem, 1981).

Equilibrium measurements of calcium binding to SR ATPase in the absence of ATP reveal a maximal number of 8-9 nmol of high affinity ($K_{obs} \cong 1 \times 10^6$ M^{-1} at pH 6.8) sites per mg of SR protein (Inesi *et al.*, 1980; Figure 7.6). These are the specific sites the occupancy of which by calcium leads to enzyme activation, and whose transformation following utilisation of ATP leads to inward Ca^{2+} release against a concentration gradient. It is of interest that calcium binding to SR in the absence of ATP displays a cooperative behaviour (Inesi *et al.*, 1980) and a pronounced pH dependence (Watanabe *et al.*, 1981). The effect of pH on both binding affinity and cooperativity (Figure 7.7) can be explained satisfactorily with a model, assuming competition of one H^+ for one Ca^{2+} at each binding site, as well as conformational interactions among protein domains containing the binding sites (Hill and Inesi, 1982). H^+ release upon calcium binding has been measured directly (Chiesi and Inesi, 1980) and H^+ binding curves derived from calcium binding analysis (Hill and Inesi, 1982) display negative cooperativity, indicating that the protein domains interact differently (for example possess different conformational states) depending on the identity of the ligand.

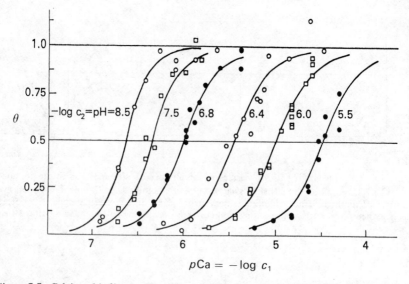

Figure 7.7 Calcium binding to SR ATPase in the absence of ATP as a function of pH. In addition to 5 mM pH buffer, 10 mM $MgCl_2$, and 80 mM KCl were present. Temperature was 25 °C. Binding was measured following equilibration of SR vesicles with radioactive calcium. $\theta = 1$ corresponds to 8–9 nmol calcium per mg of SR protein (Hill and Inesi, 1982)

Nucleotide binding

Direct measurements of nucleotide binding are difficult in equilibrium conditions, as the nucleotides are rapidly used as substrates. Measurements made in the absence of Ca^{2+}, or with nucleotide analogues that bind, but undergo hydrolysis very slowly, have revealed the presence of 3–4 nmol of high affinity sites ($K_d = 10^{-6} - 10^{-5}$ M) per mg protein in SR vesicles (Dupont, 1977; Pang and Briggs, 1977). These sites correspond to the catalytic sites of the ATPase, as activation of the enzyme also occurs at this concentration of nucleotides.

Recently, nucleotide binding sites in SR vesicles were conveniently titrated by measuring both the optical signal and radioactivity (^{32}P) of the ATP analogue $2',3'\text{-}O\text{-}(2,4,6\text{-trinitrocyclohexadienylidine})$adenosine 5'-triphosphate (TNP-ATP) (Watanabe and Inesi, 1982). In agreement with the phosphorylation levels observed with ATP, it is possible, in SR vesicles, to titrate 4 nmol of high affinity TNP-ATP binding sites, demonstrating a competitive behaviour with ATP. In addition, an approximately equivalent number of low affinity nucleotide sites are revealed by TNP-ATP binding studies. Presently, it is uncertain whether these low affinity sites in excess of the phosphorylation sites should be considered as regulatory sites or should be attributed to nonspecific binding.

Enzyme phosphorylation by ATP

The earliest event noted following the addition of ATP to SR ATPase in the presence of Ca^{2+} is the transfer of the ATP terminal phosphate onto an aspartyl residue of the enzyme protein (Bastide *et al.*, 1973; Degani and Boyer, 1973; Makinose, 1969; Yamamoto and Tonomura, 1967). As demonstrated by kinetic studies, the phosphorylated enzyme is an intermediate in the ATPase reaction (Froehlich and Taylor, 1975; Inesi *et al.*, 1970; Makinose, 1969; Verjovski-Almeida *et al.*, 1978; Yamamoto and Tonomura, 1967; 1968).

The maximal levels of phosphoenzyme obtained following addition of ATP to SR vesicles in the presence of Ca^{2+} are approximately 4 nmol per mg protein. In principle, this level is determined by the steady state behaviour of the enzyme, for example by the reverse and forward fluxes of the intermediate. However, such fluxes can be minimised by reducing the amount of ADP present (thereby preventing reversal) and by adding high levels (mM) of Ca^{2+} and/or lowering the temperature (thereby minimising forward fluxes). Even following these experimental manipulations the maximal levels of phosphoenzyme remain the same, indicating that all available sites are saturated. This is in agreement with nucleotide binding experiments showing an equivalent number of sites.

Stoichiometric ratios of calcium sites, phosphorylation sites and ATPase chains in SR vesicles

Equilibrium and kinetic experiments yield values of 8-9 nmol calcium sites and 4.0-4.5 nmol phosphorylation sites per mg protein in SR vesicles. These numbers explain satisfactorily the $2 : 1$ stoichiometric ratio between calcium transport and ATP utilisation which is observed in most experimental conditions. However, a discrepancy is apparent between the phosphorylation sites and the number of ATPase chains (7.5-8.5 nmol per mg SR protein) expected to be present in SR vesicles based on the predominance of the 110,000-MW band in electrophoretic gels (80-90 per cent of the total protein; compare Figure 7.1). It is possible that some of this material corresponds to an inactive isozyme or inactivated protein. Alternatively, the native enzyme may be a dimer. Comparison of site stoichiometries in ATPase that has been purified by various procedures would be helpful in this regard. If preparations of purified ATPase are obtained which yield levels of active sites that account for all ATPase chains, it will be very important to identify what is discarded during the purification procedure.

Steady state calcium transport and P_i production

Early measurements of Ca^{2+} transport and P_i production (Hasselbach and Makinose, 1961; 1963; Martonosi and Feretos, 1964; Weber *et al.*, 1967) were obtained in steady state conditions. In these experiments rapid inhibition due to build-up of high intravesicular concentrations ($\sim$mM) of free Ca^{2+} was avoided by the use of calcium-precipitating anions such as oxalate or phosphate. Formation of calcium oxalate or phosphate complexes with low solubility reduces the high concentration of free Ca^{2+} inside the vesicles and prevents back inhibition of the pump, allowing steady state activity to be measured for several minutes. In these conditions, calcium transport and P_i production (that is, ATP hydrolysis) proceed at a $2:1$ ratio, indicating that two calcium ions are transported per ATP molecule hydrolysed.

ATPase activity can also be studied in steady state conditions if the permeability of the membrane is increased with calcium ionophores (Scarpa *et al.*, 1972). In this case, calcium accumulation is prevented and ATPase activity proceeds at a constant velocity for the time sufficient to allow steady state measurements.

This type of experimentation was used to establish the Ca^{2+} and ATP concentration dependences of SR ATPase. It was found that the enzyme is activated by micromolar concentrations of Ca^{2+} and the activation curve displays a sigmoidal shape (deMeis, 1971; Neet and Green, 1977; Thé and Hasselbach, 1972; Vianna, 1975). These features are consistent with the equilibrium measurements of Ca^{2+} binding which show a cooperative behaviour (Inesi *et al.*, 1980). It should be pointed out that the Ca^{2+} concentration dependence of enzyme activity would reveal stoichiometric cooperativity, even in the absence of cooperative binding interactions, if activation of each enzyme cycle depends on the occupancy of two calcium sites.

The ATP concentration dependence of the ATPase reaction is complex. A first activation at ATP concentrations between 0.5 and $50\,\mu M$ is followed by a further rise of activity at higher concentrations (deMeis, 1971; deMeis and deMello, 1973; Dupont, 1977; Froehlich and Taylor, 1975; Inesi *et al.*, 1967; Ribeiro and Vianna, 1978; Scofano *et al.*, 1979; Shikegawa *et al.*, 1978; Taylor and Hattan, 1979; Thé and Hasselbach, 1972a; 1972b; Vianna, 1975; Yates and Duance, 1976; Yamamoto and Tonomura, 1967). The observed dependence cannot be fitted with simple Michaelis–Menten kinetics. However, it is possible that the effect of high ATP is related to activation of partial reactions which follow the initial enzyme phosphorylation with ATP and contribute to limitations in the rate of enzyme turnover. Consistent with this suggestion, it was found that the ATP concentration dependence of the initial enzyme phosphorylation is limited to the lower concentration range (Froehlich and Taylor, 1975; Kanazawa *et al.*, 1971; Scofano *et al.*, 1979; Verjovski-Almeida *et al.*, 1978), but that hydrolytic cleavage of the phosphoenzyme formed in the initial part of the reaction is activated by high ATP concentrations (deMeis and deMello, 1973; Froehlich and Taylor, 1975; Verjovski-Almeida and Inesi, 1979).

In addition to ATP, other nucleotides such as ITP, GTP, CTP and UTP (Hasselbach, 1964; Makinose, 1966; Makinose and Thé, 1965) and other phosphorylated compounds such as acetylphosphate, *p*-nitrophenyl phosphate, carbamylphosphate, methylumbelliferulphosphate and furylacryloylphosphate (deMeis, 1969a; 1969b; Friedman and Makinose, 1970; Inesi, 1971; Kurzmack *et al.,* 1980; Nakamura and Tonomura, 1978; Rossi *et al.,* 1979), can be used as substrates for SR ATPase. ATP is the most specific substrate, in that it is used at very low concentrations and high rates. All of these substrates are utilised through the formation of a phosphorylated enzyme intermediate.

A most important feature of the SR ATPase is that even though most substrates produce similar levels of enzyme intermediate, the velocity of P_i production varies greatly with the substrate used. This indicates that the turnover of the phosphoenzyme is highly dependent on the nature of the substrate present in the reaction mixture. In addition to its role as a phosphoryl donor, the substrate has a regulatory role. This can only be accomplished if the nucleotide is bound to the enzyme, not only during the phosphorylation reaction, but also during phosphoenzyme turnover. As we know that ADP is released soon after utilisation of ATP for the phosphorylation reaction (Froehlich *et al.,* 1980), another molecule of nucleotide must bind either to the phosphorylation site or to an alternative regulatory site.

In fact, this can be demonstrated in reaction mixtures containing appropriate concentrations of ATP and TNP-ATP which binds to SR ATPase, but does not phosphorylate the enzyme. The phosphorylation reaction is followed by a large increase in the fluorescence of bound TNP-ATP (Figure 7.8), demonstrating that a structural change produced by the phosphorylation reaction affects the environment of another nucleotide molecule bound to the same ATPase unit (Watanabe and Inesi, 1982).

Kinetic resolution of Ca²⁺ transport and P_i production in the transient state

Time resolution of the early phase of calcium transport and substrate utilisation following addition of ATP requires rapid kinetic instrumentation. The earliest measurements of the initial velocity of calcium transport in stopped flow experiments (Inesi and Scarpa, 1972) were made by dual wavelength detection of optical changes of metallochromic indicators (Figure 7.9). It was found that the initial pump turnover is approximately $10 \, s^{-1}$ at $25\,^{\circ}C$.

Metallochromic indictors that can be used for measurements of Ca²⁺ transients (that is, changes in the Ca²⁺ concentration in the medium as a consequence of transport or release of Ca²⁺ by SR) include murexide (Inesi and Scarpa, 1972; Ohnishi and Ebashi, 1963), arsenazo III (Dipolo *et al.,* 1976; Inesi and Kurzmack, 1977), tetramethylmurexide (Ohnishi, 1978) and antipyrylazo III (Scarpa *et al.,* 1978). The structure and absorption spectra of the four indicators are shown in Figures 7.10 and 7.11.

Comparisons of the four indicators have been made by Ogawa *et al.* (1980) and Scarpa (1982). Murexide has the disadvantage of low sensitivity. Tetramethylmurexide is twice as sensitive as murexide, but may penetrate the vesicles. Antipyrylazo III has the advantage of higher sensitivity to Ca²⁺, but it is also sensitive to Mg²⁺ and, above $20\,\mu M$ Ca²⁺, does not show a linear response. Arsenazo III is the most sensitive Ca²⁺ indicator, but it is also sensitive to

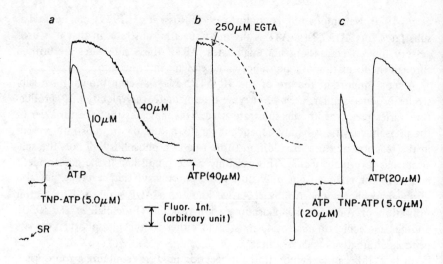

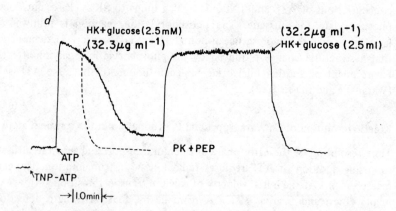

Figure 7.8 Fluorescence changes induced by various ligands on bound TNP–ATP. The concentrations of SR protein and TNP–ATP were 0.25 mg m⁻¹ and 5 mM, respectively. *a*, Enhancement by ATP. *b*, 0.25 mM EGTA was added to chelate Ca²⁺ and prevent ATP utilisation by SR ATPase; dotted line is a control without EGTA. *c*, No fluorescence enhancement is detected if ATP is added in the absence of TNP–ATP, but the effect is readily observed upon addition of ATP. An immediate effect of TNP–ATP is noted if ATP is present. *d*, Effects of ATP trapping and regenerating systems. Reaction mixture: 20 mM Tris–maleate (p H 8.0), 80 mM KCl, 5 mM MgCl₂, 50 μM CaCl₂, 20 per cent glycerol, pyruvate kinase (10.3 μg ml⁻¹), hexokinase (32.3 μg ml⁻¹), 0.125 mM phosphoenolpyruvate, 2.5 mM glucose, 40 μM ATP. The SR concentration was 1.37 mg protein ml⁻¹. Excitation, 410 nm; emission, 515 nm (Watanabe and Inesi, 1982b)

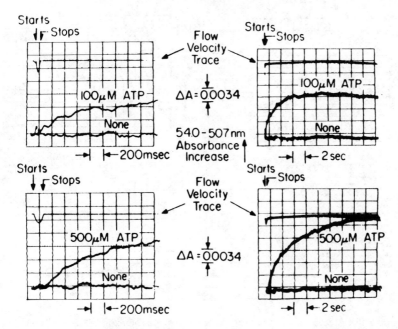

Figure 7.9 Ca^{2+} uptake by SR vesicles. The reaction was started by addition of ATP in a stopped-flow apparatus and detected by double wavelength spectrophotometry (508 and 545 nm) in the presence of murexide. Reaction mixture: 20 mM Tris-maleate (pH 6.8), 50 mM KCl, 0.14 mM $CaCl_2$, 0.1 mM $MgCl_2$ and 0.7 mg SR protein ml^{-1}. Temperature 25°C (Inesi and Scarpa, 1972)

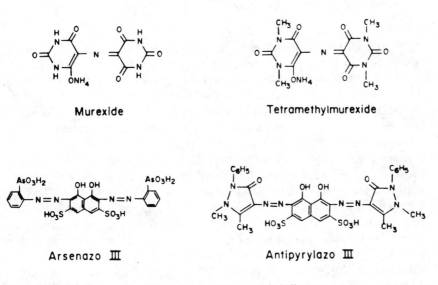

Figure 7.10 Structures of commonly used metallochromic indicators

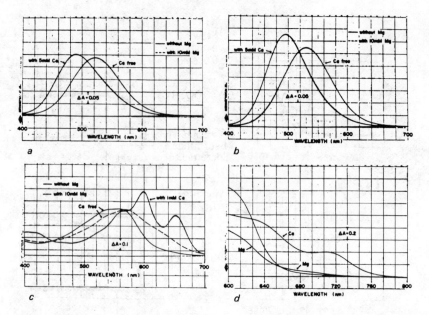

Figure 7.11 Absorption spectra of the four indicators. *a*, Murexide. "Ca free" solution contained 100 mM KCl, 20 mM imidazole (*p*H 6.8) and 20 μM murexide in the absence (—) or presence (– –) of 10 mM magnesium. Calcium was added at a final concentration of 5 mM. The temperature was 20°C. *b*, Tetramethylmurexide. The solution was similar to that in *a* expect for 20 M tetramethylmurexide instead of murexide. *c*, Arsenazo III. The solution was similar to that in *a* except for 14.1 μM arsenazo III and 1 mM Ca instead of 5 mM. *d*, Antipyrylazo III. The solution was composed of 100 mM KCl, 20 mM Tris-maleate (*p*H 6.8) and 54 μM antipyrylazo III. Calcium or magnesium was added to the solution at a final concentration of 10 mM (Ogawa *et al.*, 1980)

Mg^{2+}. At high Ca^{2+} concentrations, the dye no longer gives a linear response due to a change in the stoichiometric ratio of the Ca $\cdot$ arsenazo complex (1 : 1 to 2 : 1). In addition, arsenazo III seems to inhibit transport in certain conditions.

The sensitivity of the indicators to Ca^{2+} can be much improved through the use of differential spectrophotometry (Chance, 1972). This also reduces any interference caused by light scattering. Differential spectra (presence against absence of Ca^{2+}) of two indicators are shown in Figure 7.12. From such spectra it is possible to select pairs of wavelengths which give optimal sensitivity. As shown in Figure 7.13, arsenazo III responds linearly to micromolar Ca^{2+} changes in appropriate conditions and allows the detection of Ca^{2+} uptake by SR vesicles following addition of ATP. Kinetic resolution can then be obtained by stopped flow mixing in instruments permitting simultaneous detection of absorption changes at the two selected wavelengths. An example of such measurements is given in Figure 7.14 which also shows that arsenazo III gives a better signal to noise ratio than murexide (Figure 7.9).

A general disadvantage of the metallochromic indicators is that they do not

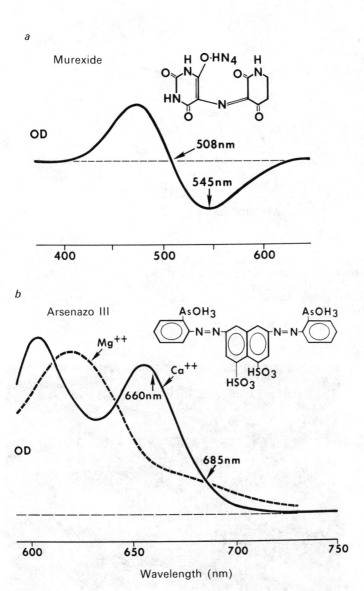

Figure 7.12 Differential light absorption spectra of Ca · murexide (*a*) and Ca · arsenazo (*b*) relative to free murexide and free arsenazo. The dotted line in *b* corresponds to the differential spectrum of Mg · arsenazo. The wavelengths indicated on the spectra correspond to the pairs most commonly used for dual wavelength measurements of Ca²⁺ transients (Inesi and Kurzmack, 1977)

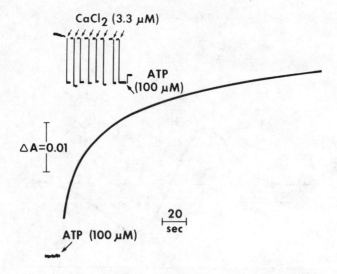

Figure 7.13 Ca²⁺ uptake by SR vesicles detected by double wavelength (660 and 685 nm) photometry in the presence of arsenazo. Reaction mixture: 20 mM MOPS (pH 6.8), 80 mM KCl, 5 mM MgCl₂, 40 μM CaCl₂, 40 μM arsenazo III and 0.7 mg SR protein ml⁻¹. Reaction was started by the addition of ATP to a final concentration of 0.1 mM (Inesi and Kurzmack, 1977)

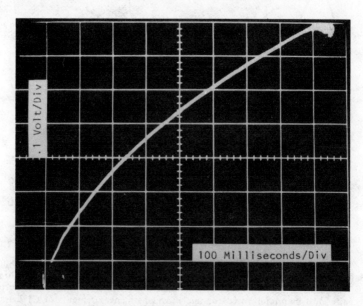

Figure 7.14 ATP-dependent calcium uptake by SR vesicles measured by double wavelength (660 vs 690 nm) photometry in a stopped-flow apparatus. The reaction was followed by monitoring light absorption changes undergone by the calcium-sensitive dye arsenazo III

permit the use of Ca · EGTA buffers, as shifts of Ca^{2+} from EGTA to SR are detected only partially (or not at all). This is a serious limitation in the range of free Ca^{2+} concentration which may be studied, as the total calcium concentration must be maintained at levels high enough to sustain transport activity throughout the course of the experiment.

Stopped flow mixing and optical measurements have also been useful in measurements of H^+ production (Inesi *et al.*, 1978; Chiesi and Inesi, 1980) and utilisation of chromogenic substrates (Kurzmack *et al.*, 1981) by the Ca^{2+}-dependent ATPase of SR vesicles.

Another very useful technique for time resolution of the early phase of the ATPase reaction and associated Ca^{2+} transport is rapid quenching. The instruments used for these experiments consist of two pneumatically or stepping motor driven forced flow syringes which are used to push two reagents through a first mixing chamber and a delay line. A third syringe is used to add a quenching reagent which is mixed with the reaction mixture in a second mixing chamber (Figure 7.15). The reaction time is dependent on the transit time of the reaction mixture through the delay line between the two mixing chambers and may be regulated by changing the length of the delay line or the flow rate (that is, regulated by changing the pressure). In practice reaction times of between 6 and 250 ms are obtained by continuous flow mixing. In some instruments reaction times may be extended to several seconds by filling the delay line, stopping the flow and allowing the reaction mixture to "age" in the delay line, and then resuming flow, at the same time quenching the reaction at the second mixer.

Whilst stopped flow experiments allow the generation of an entire kinetic curve from a single mixing, rapid quenching yields only a single time point from each "push", requiring multiple "pushes" to obtain a complete progress curve. Furthermore, whilst stopped flow experiments are monitored optically and

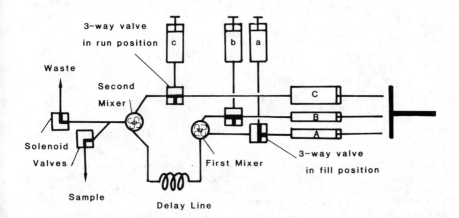

Figure 7.15   Diagram of Dionex rapid mixing apparatus

require the use of a suitable indicator, rapid quenching permits collection of quenched samples which may be analysed optically, by chemical methods and/or by using radioactive tracers. This constitutes an extremely powerful and sensitive technique for rapid kinetic studies of SR and other ATPase enzymes.

In rapid quench experiments, formation of the phosphorylated enzyme intermediate and production of P_i can be measured using $[\gamma - {}^{32}P]$ ATP and acid quenching (Froehlich and Taylor, 1975; Verjovski-Almeida *et al.*, 1978). Calcium translocation can be measured by the use of ^{45}Ca, quenching with EGTA (Kurzmack *et al.*, 1977) or with lanthanum (Chiesi and Inesi, 1979), and filtration of the quenched samples.

It was established using these techniques that formation of the phosphorylated intermediate is the first measurable event following the addition of ATP to SR vesicles. The initial velocity of enzyme phosphorylation with ATP can be measured by rapid quench methods (Figure 7.16), as the phosphoenzyme is stable in acid. This allows the reaction to be rapidly quenched using solutions of perchloric acid or trichloroacetic acid. The rate constant of phosphorylation is approximately $100\,s^{-1}$ at $25\,°C$ (Froehlich and Taylor, 1975; Verjovski-Almeida *et al.*, 1978). In some cases, a small overshoot was noted in the phosphoenzyme level in the early part of the reaction (Froehlich and Taylor, 1975; Figure 7.17). Formation of phosphoenzyme is rapidly followed by translocation of two moles of calcium per mole of intermediate from the outer surface of the

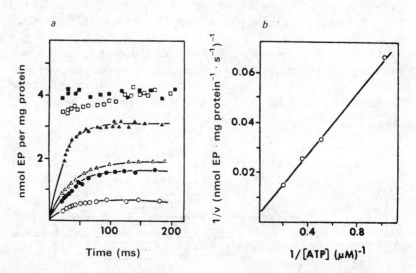

Figure 7.16 Phosphorylation of SR ATPase with ATP. Time curves in *a* were obtained in the presence of $\circ$, 1; $\bullet$, 2; $\triangle$, 2.9; $\blacktriangle$, 5; $\square$, 100; and $\blacksquare$, 1,000 mM ATP in a reaction mixture containing 40 mM MOPS (pH 6.8), 5 mM $MgCl_2$, 80 mM KCl, 0.1 mM $CaCl_2$, 3 mM PEP and 20 units of pyruvate kinase ml^{-1}. Temperature was $25\,°C$. In *b* initial velocities are plotted as a function of [ATP] to obtain a maximal velocity of phosphorylation extrapolated to infinite [ATP]. The maximal velocity was then divided by the number of phosphorylation sites to obtain a first order rate constant (Verjovski-Almeida *et al.*, 1978).

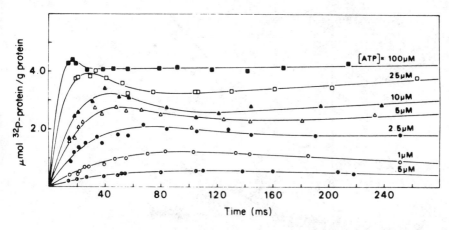

Figure 7.17 ATP concentration dependence of SR ATPase phosphorylation following the addition of ATP in the presence of Ca^{2+} (Froehlich and Taylor, 1975)

membrane to a position within the membrane which is not accessible to EGTA in the medium (Kurzmack *et al.*, 1977). Then, following a rate-limiting step, steady state P_i production and calcium transport begin with a stoichiometric ratio of two calcium ions per mole of P_i (Figure 7.18). The sequence of these events has been demonstrated independently by Sumida and Tonomura (1974), Inesi *et al.* (1978), Dupont (1977; 1980), Takakuwa and Kanazawa (1979) and others. Enzyme phosphorylation, calcium site translocation and hydrolytic cleaveage of P_i are represented in scheme I by $E \sim P \cdot Ca_2$, $*E - P \cdot Ca_2$, and $*E + P_i$, where $*E - P \cdot Ca_2$ is a phosphoenzyme state with low affinity and inward orientation of the calcium sites.

Calcium translocation and release into the vesicles

A basic requirement for the vectorial character of active transport is that the calcium sites undergo a change in orientation and a reduction in affinity ($E \sim P \cdot Ca_2 \leftrightarrow *E - P \cdot Ca_2$ in scheme I) to allow release of calcium into the lumen of the vesicles before the phosphoenzyme is hydrolysed and a new cycle begins.

We have seen that soon after phosphorylation by ATP, two Ca^{2+} ions per enzyme unit are transferred from the outer surface of the vesicles to a location which does not allow rapid equilibration with EGTA in the medium. The question is then whether it is possible to demonstrate if Ca^{2+} is actually released into the lumen of the vesicles. This question must be studied in leaky vesicles to prevent the interference of net Ca^{2+} accumulation with the detection of Ca^{2+} release. Using an enzyme prepared by solubilisation of native vesicles with Triton X-100, Ikemoto (1975; 1976) observed a release of bound calcium following phosphorylation with ATP. On the other hand, Takakuwa and Kanazawa (1979) and Dupont (1980) reported experiments indicating that the bound calcium is not

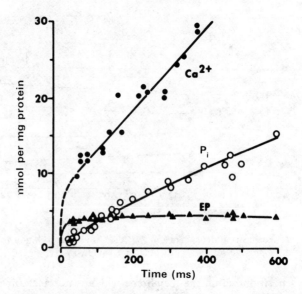

Figure 7.18 Phosphoenzyme formation (▲), calcium uptake (●) and P_i production (○) following addition of 0.1 mM ATP to SR vesicles in the presence of 20 mM MOPS (pH 6.8), 5 mM $MgCl_2$, 80 mM KCl and 50 μM $CaCl_2$. Rapid mixing and quenching were obtained with the aid of a Dionex rapid mixing apparatus. Temperature was 25 °C. The quenching medium was 0.25 M PCA and 1.0 mM P_i for phosphoenzyme and P_i measurements, or 20 mM MOPS (pH 6.8), 80 mM KCl and 20 mM EGTA for calcium uptake measurements. Phosphoenzyme and P_i were obtained by following the distribution of $^{32}P_i$ (5). Calcium uptake was determined by filtering 0.1 ml of reaction mixture through the Millipore filter (Type HATF 0.45 μm) soon after quenching, washing with cold quenching medium and counting the ^{45}Ca associated with the vesicles on the filter

released immediately upon phosphorylation, but is retained in an occluded form which is not accessible from either side of the membrane. In this case, the occluded form would be prevalent in the steady-state operation of the enzyme.

In our laboratory, we have been able to demonstrate Ca^{2+} release from the enzyme upon phosphorylation with ATP when dimethylsulphoxide was added to a reaction mixture containing purified ATPase protein. It is shown in Figure 7.19 that at zero time approximately 10 nmol of calcium are bound per mg of purified ATPase protein, demonstrating a saturation of the high affinity sites (Figure 7.6). A barely detectable amount of calcium is released upon addition of ATP in the absence of dimethylsulphoxide. In the presence of dimethylsulphoxide, however, release of up to 60–70 per cent of the bound calcium can be detected. A parallel reduction of P_i production is also observed in accordance with the inhibition of hydrolytic activity produced by increasing amounts of dimethylsulphoxide.

An important feature of these experiments is that, when the ATP in the medium is consumed, calcium binds to the ATPase again. In fact the duration of the release is proportional to the concentration of ATP added. It is clear

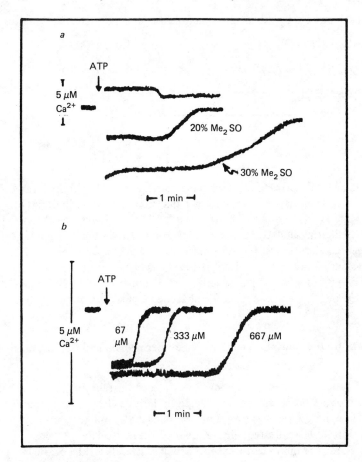

Figure 7.19 Spectrophotometric determination of calcium release from ATPase following addition of ATP. *a*, Effect of dimethylsulphoxide concentration. The reaction mixture consisted of 0.4 mg of ATPase (MacLennan, 1970) per ml, 20 mM Mes (pH 6.1), 45 μM CaCl$_2$, 80 mM KCl, 5 mM MgCl$_2$, 50 μM arsenazo III and various concentrations of dimethylsulphoxide. ATP (0.333 mM) was added at time zero. The base line is normalised to the absorption levels obtained after exhaustion of ATP and the specific absorption change due to the calcium standard is normalised for the different absorption noted at different dimethylsulphoxide concentrations; temperature was 25 °C. *b*, ATP concentration dependence of calcium release from ATPase. Conditions as in *a*, except for an ATPase concentration of 0.71 mg ml⁻¹ and a dimethylsulphoxide concentration of 20 per cent

that release and rebinding of calcium are due to changes in affinity of the binding site related to phosphorylation and dephosphorylation of the enzyme. The requirement for dimethylsulphoxide in order to detect the release is probably due to its property as an inhibitor of the hydrolytic cleavage of the phosphoenzyme (Thé and Hasselbach, 1977; Shigekawa and Akowitz, 1979; Inesi *et al.*, 1980) and the increase in the lifetime of the phosphoenzyme following Ca²⁺ release.

This can be better explained by the following reaction scheme:

1. $Ca_2 \cdot E + ATP \quad \longrightarrow \quad Ca_2 \cdot E \sim P(\cdot ADP)$

2. $Ca_2 \cdot E \sim P(\cdot ADP) \quad \longrightarrow \quad Ca_2 \cdot {}^*E - P + ADP$

3. $Ca_2 \cdot {}^*E - P \quad \longrightarrow \quad {}^*E - P + 2Ca^{2+}$

4. ${}^*E - P \quad \longrightarrow \quad E + P_i$

5. $E + 2Ca^{2+} \quad \longrightarrow \quad Ca_2 \cdot E$

Scheme II

where E and *E correspond to enzyme states with high affinity sites and low affinity sites, respectively. As it is known that step 1 is not rate limiting (Froehlich and Taylor, 1975; Verjovski-Almeida *et al.*, 1978), we conclude that steps 2 or 3 are rate limiting in native enzyme preparations, while step 4 which is normally fast, becomes rate limiting in the presence of dimethylsulphoxide. Therefore, the prevalent steady-state species in the two sets of conditions are $[Ca_2 \cdot E \sim P + Ca_2 \cdot {}^*E - P]$ or $[{}^*E - P]$, respectively. Accumulation of ${}^*E - P$ allows detection of the net Ca^{2+} release from the phosphoenzyme during the steady state.

Evolution of the phosphorylated enzyme intermediate and hydrolytic cleavage of P_i

Optimal coupling of the enzyme cycle with calcium transport requires that the phosphoenzyme be permitted to undergo hydrolytic cleavage only after unloading calcium inside the vesicles. Loss of phosphate and reacquisition of high affinity for Ca^{2+} before reorientation would prevent calcium release inside the vesicles and cause inefficient transport activity. Therefore, one of the last partial reactions of the catalytic cycle is hydrolytic cleavage of the phosphorylated enzyme intermediate. A transient state kinetic pattern consisting of phospho-enzyme formation and calcium translocation followed by P_i release and recycling of the enzyme, and maintenance of a high level of phosphoenzyme (Figure 7.18), suggests that the hydrolytic cleavage is the rate limiting step of the transport cycle.

However, when the hydrolytic rate constant is measured directly (Masuda and deMeis, 1973) by first phosphorylating the enzyme with $^{32}P - P_i$ in the absence of Ca^{2+} (reversal of $E - P \rightleftharpoons E \cdot P_i$ in Scheme I) and then monitoring the decay of the ^{32}P-phosphoenzyme following dilution with non-radioactive P_i (Figure 7.20), a value of $60\,s^{-1}$ is obtained at $25°C$, pH 6.8, and in the presence of K^+ (Inesi *et al.*, 1982a and 1982b). This value is much higher than the turnover number of the enzyme $(10\,s^{-1})$. Therefore, the rate-limiting step of the catalytic and transport cycle must be a transformation of the phosphoenzyme preceding its hydrolytic cleavage.

The kinetic evolution of the phosphorylated enzyme intermediate following

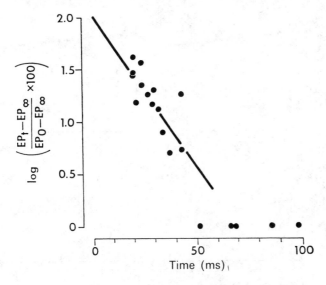

Figure 7.20   Kinetics of phosphoenzyme cleavage at *p*H 6.8 in the presence of 80 mM KCl and conditions commonly used in studies of SR ATPase. The phosphoenzyme was first formed by equilibration of SR vesicles with 1.0 mM ^{32}P-P$_i$, 10.0 mM MgCl$_2$, 0.5 mM Tris-maleate (*p*H 6.0), and 0.5 mM EGTA in the absence of K$^+$ and Ca^{2+} to ensure a high yield of phosphoenzyme. This mixture was then diluted with an equal volume of a medium containing a 12-fold excess of non-radioactive P$_i$, 50 mM MOPS (*p*H 6.8), 20 mM MgCl$_2$, and 160 mM KCl. Sequential quenching was obtained with the aid of a Dionex rapid mixing apparatus. Temperature was 25°C (Inesi *et al.*, 1982a)

its formation by the initial reaction of the enzyme with ATP in the presence of Ca^{2+} can be studied by first quenching the phosphorylation reaction with EGTA (thereby removing the activating Ca^{2+}) and then quenching the phosphoenzyme decay with acid at serial times. When first used at 2°C with mixing by hand, this double quenching technique demonstrated that the phosphoenzyme formed with ATP is a transient species undergoing decay within a timescale compatible with a role as a reaction intermediate (Inesi *et al.*, 1970). It was then found that the phosphoenzyme formed with ATP includes at least two sequential states, only one of which is sensitive to added ATP and can be used to form ATP (Shigekawa and Dougherty, 1978a; 1978b; Shigekawa and Akowitz, 1979; Takisawa and Tonomura, 1979).

These experiments were also carried out at 25°C using rapid mixing devices adapted for a double quench. It was found that when SR vesicles are exposed to ATP for 500 ms (permitting the vesicles to accumulate large amounts of Ca^{2+}) and then quenched with EGTA to stop the phosphorylation reaction, most of the enzyme decays with very slow kinetics (Figure 7.21*a*). This indicates that the high internal Ca^{2+} concentration produces a "back inhibition". A surprising finding is that even when the exposure of the vesicles to ATP is limited to 20 ms (permitting only a single enzyme cycle), approximately 50 per cent of the

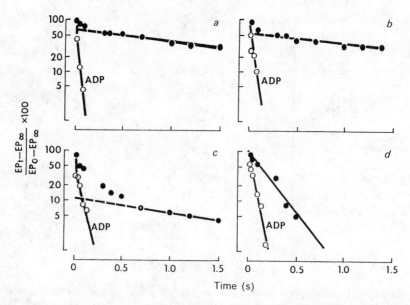

Figure 7.21 Decay of phosphoenzyme formed from ATP in vesicles sustaining net calcium uptake (a, b) and in vesicles rendered permeable with the ionophore X537A (c, d). SR vesicles were first incubated with $25\,\mu M$ ^{32}P-ATP in a medium containing 20 mM Tris-maleate (pH 6.8), 80 mM KCl, 5 mM $MgCl_2$, $50\,\mu M$ $CaCl_2$, 0.66 mM phosphoenolpyruvate and $60\,\mu g$ pyruvate kinase ml^{-1}. After 500 (a, c) or 20 (b, d) ms, the phosphorylation reaction was quenched with an equal volume of the same medium, except for the replacement of $CaCl_2$ by 15 mM EGTA and, when indicated, 3 mM ADP. A second quenching with PCA and P_i was then carried out at serial time intervals. Temperature was 25°C (Inesi *et al.*, 1982b)

enzyme is already "back inhibited" (Figure 7.21b). This may be due to the small internal volume of the compartment receiving the released Ca^{2+}, thus causing a build up of high internal Ca^{2+} following transport of 8 nmol Ca^{2+} per mg protein as a consequence of only one enzyme cycle. It is possible that Ca^{2+} is first released into a microcompartment from which a diffusion step is required to reach the lumen of the vesicles. If the preparation is treated with a calcium ionophore, thereby causing a leak of accumulated Ca^{2+}, nearly all of the phosphoenzyme decays with a rate constant of about $10\,s^{-1}$, the turnover rate of the phospho-enzyme in the absence of "back inhibition". This may be seen especially well if the vesicles are exposed to ATP for only 20 ms before the EGTA quench (Figure 7.21d).

"Back inhibition" is thus a limiting kinetic factor caused by high internal Ca^{2+}. This inhibition may be due to interference with unloading of transport sites in the low affinity inward state, but it may also be related to calcium binding to other low affinity cation sites and/or intravesicular pH perturbations.

Addition of ADP with the EGTA quench accelerates the disappearance of phosphorylated intermediate in all cases (Figure 7.21a–d). This causes reversion of a considerable amount of phosphoenzyme to ATP and non-phosphorylated enzyme (Takakuwa and Kanazawa, 1979; Dupont, 1980). The prominent reactivity of the phosphoenzyme to ADP shown in Figure 7.21 indicates that in these conditions (25°C), most of the phosphoenzyme retains calcium, as the phosphoenzyme would not be reactive to ADP following Ca^{2+} dissociation (Nakamura and Tonomura, 1982). This is in agreement with the experiments shown in Figure 7.19.

It is of interest that the pool of phosphoenzyme reactive to ADP is not homogeneous, but contains at least two interconvertible forms of which only one yields ATP very rapidly (Froehlich *et al.*, 1980). This rapid ATP yield is likely related to reversal of

$$ATP \cdot E \cdot Ca_2 \rightleftharpoons E \sim P \cdot Ca_2 + ADP$$

in Scheme I, while the slower yield is due to sequential reversal of

$$ATP \cdot E \cdot Ca_2 \rightleftharpoons E \sim P \cdot Ca_2 + ADP \rightleftharpoons {}^*E - P \cdot Ca_2 .$$

If, as is shown in Figure 7.21*d*, the phosphoenzyme species retaining calcium in the low affinity inward orientated configuration ($^*E - P \cdot Ca_2$ in scheme I) decays with a rate constant of $10 s^{-1}$ (approximately equal to the enzyme turnover in the absence of back inhibition) and the hydrolysis of the last species of phosphoenzyme ($^*E - P$ in scheme I) occurs with a rate constant of $60 s^{-1}$ (Figure 7.20), the rate limiting step for the reaction cycle in the absence of "back inhibition" must be a phosphoenzyme isomerisation related to Ca^{2+} release inside the vesicles and preceding hydrolytic cleavage. It is apparent that such a slow isomerisation is linked to structural constraints, as a significantly higher turnover is obtained when the enzyme is solubilised with detergents (Figure 7.22).

Following hydrolytic cleavage of P_i, the enzyme seems to recycle without delay, as indicated by chase experiments with radioactive ATP in which the kinetics of phosphorylation of the recycling enzyme match the kinetics of dephosphorylation of phosphoenzyme in the preceding cycle (Figure 7.23).

The $Ca^{2+} \cdot H^+$ exchange

The pH dependence of Ca^{2+} binding to the activating (transport) sites of SR ATPase (Beil *et al.*, 1977; Meissner, 1973; Verjovski-Almeida and deMeis, 1977; Watanabe *et al.*, 1981) and the detection of H^+ release upon calcium binding in the absence of ATP (Chiesi and Inesi, 1980) indicate that a protein residue dissociating H^+ with a pK near neutrality participates as a ligand for calcium binding. The dependence of binding on H^+ concentration can be accounted for by a mechanism based on competition for the binding site between one H^+ and one Ca^{2+} (Hill and Inesi, 1982). The question then is whether H^+ has a role in the transport mechanism supported by ATP.

H^+ fluxes during ATP dependent Ca^{2+} accumulation by SR vesicles were first

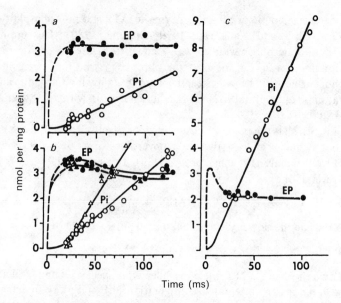

Figure 7.22 Phosphoenzyme formation and P_i production following addition of ATP to native vesicles (*a*), vesicles rendered leaky with the ionophore X537A (▲, △) or 0.1% Triton X-100 (●, ○) (*b*), and ATPase solubilised with the detergent $C_{12}E_8$ (*c*). The experiments were carried out with a rapid mixing device. Several samples were collected for each reaction time to obtain a large volume of quenched reaction mixture for analysis. The large volumes were necessary to offset the very low protein concentration used in these experiments. The medium contained 25–50 g SR protein ml^{-1} 80 mM KCl, 5 mM $MgCl_2$, 50 μM $CaCl_2$ and 20 mM MOPS (pH 7.0) or Tris (pH 7.5, *c*). Where indicated, 20 μM X537A, 0.1% Triton X-100, or 1.0 mM $C_{12}E_8$ were present. The reaction was started by adding 10 μM ^{32}P-ATP and stopped by acid quenching at serial times. Temperature was 25°C

noted by Carvalho (1972) and Madeira (1978). Madeira inferred that the SR ATPase is a primary H^+ pump and that Ca^{2+} translocation is secondary to formation of a H^+ gradient. Chiesi and Inesi (1980) confirmed that during active transport of Ca^{2+}, H^+ ejection from SR vesicles occurs in excess of the H^+ production caused by dissociation of the ATPase reaction products. However, they demonstrated that this phenomenon cannot be attributed to a primary H^+ pump, as neither H^+ ejection nor Ca^{2+} uptake is reduced by increasing the passive permeability of the membrane to H^+ with FCCP. Yet, both phenomena are reduced by increasing the membrane permeability to Ca^{2+} with a divalent cation ionophore. Therefore, in SR vesicles, H^+ fluxes are secondary to a primary Ca^{2+} pump.

Ca^{2+} uptake and H^+ ejection occur with parallel kinetics (Figure 7.24) and involve approximately 1 H^+ per Ca^{2+} in the first second of the reaction at pH 6.1. The charge equivalent ratio of the H^+/Ca^{2+} exchange depends on the pK of the binding (transport) site and the intravesicular pH, but tends to be less than 1.0 near neutrality. Therefore, Ca^{2+} transport produces net charge displacement if not compensated for by K^+ and Cl^- fluxes through independent

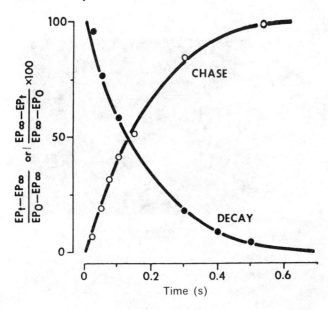

Figure 7.23 Phosphoenzyme formation following addition of ^{32}P-ATP chase to phosphoenzyme formed with non-radioactive ATP. The phosphoenzyme was first formed by incu-
bating leaky vesicles with 25 μM cold ATP, 20 mM Tris-maleate (pH 7.0), 80 mM KCl,
5 mM MgCl$_2$ and 20 μM X537A for 20 ms. A pulse of ^{32}P-ATP was then added (without
significantly changing the ATP concentration) and the reaction was quenched at serial
times with acid. In a parallel experiment, the decay of the phosphoenzyme formed during
the first 20 ms was measured as for Figure 7.21d

channels or by K$^+$ counter transport. Note that the SR membrane is quite
permeable to H$^+$ and, after an initial H$^+$ gradient is formed, protons drift
back inward, thereby avoiding an excessive pH rise inside the vesicles.

The observed H$^+$ ejection during Ca^{2+} transport is probably due to a Ca^{2+} ·
H$^+$ antiport mechanism whereby the initial Ca^{2+} binding to the transport site
outside the vesicles displaces one proton, then Ca^{2+} is translocated inward, and
released inside the vesicles in exchange for one internal proton which is then
transported outward by the recycling site. However, it should be ruled out that
outward H$^+$ fluxes may be simply the result of binding of accumulated Ca^{2+}
to nonspecific sites inside the vesicles, thereby displacing H$^+$ ions which leave
the vesicles through independent channels. This question may be answered if
it can be demonstrated that the partial reactions within a catalytic and transport
cycle are influenced by variations of pH in a manner which is consistent with
the Ca^{2+} · H$^+$ antiport mechanism as, in fact, turns out to be the case.

It is shown in Figure 7.25 that, in the presence of saturating Ca^{2+} and ATP,
equal levels of phosphorylated enzyme intermediate are formed independent
of the H$^+$ concentration (pH 6.0 to 8.0). In all cases phosphorylation of the
enzyme is followed by translocation of two calcium ions. However, Ca^{2+} release

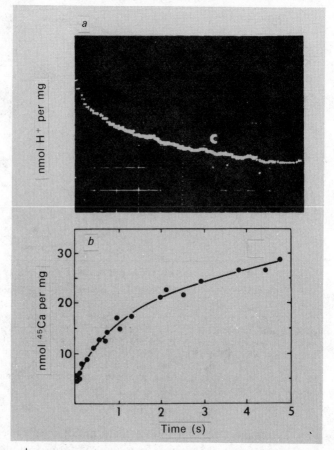

Figure 7.24 H$^+$ (*a*) and Ca^{2+} (*b*) movements through SR membranes upon addition of ATP. The reaction medium contained 80 mM KCl, 5 mM MgCl$_2$, 1.5 mM Mes (*p*H 6.1), 40 μM chlorphenol red, 0.1 mM CaCl$_2$ and 1 mg SR per ml. Final ATP concentration was 0.25 mM. Proton fluxes were obtained with the aid of a Dionex D-137 dual detector stopped-flow spectrophotometer (577 and 630 nm). ^{45}Ca uptake measurements were performed on a Dionex D-133 rapid mixing apparatus using 10 mM EGTA as the quencher (Chiesi and Inesi, 1980)

inside the vesicles, which must precede P$_i$ cleavage and recycling of the enzyme, is obtained only at sufficiently high H$^+$ concentrations (*p*H 6.0 to 6.8). At low H$^+$ concentrations (*p*H 8.0), release of Ca^{2+} inside the vesicles is prevented by the lack of exchanging H$^+$, and steady state P$_i$ release and Ca^{2+} uptake (that is, recycling of the enzyme) are inhibited.

It can be demonstrated in independent experiments that the inhibition of steady state P$_i$ release is not due to actual inhibition of the hydrolytic reaction, which, in fact, is faster at alkaline *p*H (Figure 7.26). Therefore, the inhibition is due to a preceding step, that is the Ca^{2+} dissociation from the inward orientated

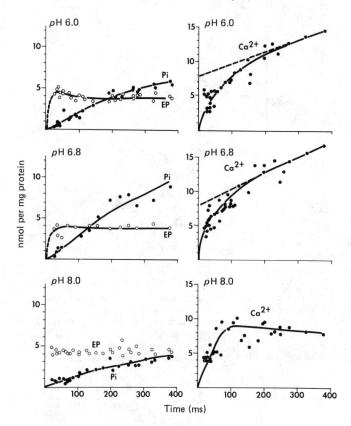

Figure 7.25 Phosphoenzyme formation (○), calcium uptake (●) and P$_i$ cleavage (●) follow-ing addition of ATP to SR vesicles at various H$^+$ concentrations. Rapid mixing was obtained with a Dionex rapid mixing apparatus and the reaction was quenched with acid (for phospho-enzyme and P$_i$ measurements) or with EGTA (for calcium measurements). Temperature was 25 °C

sites of the phosphoenzyme. Ca^{2+} release from these sites is caused by a reduc-tion in their affinity for Ca^{2+} as a consequence of enzyme phosphorylation. With regard to proton effects, it was found that the affinity of the phosphoenzyme for Ca^{2+} remains significantly higher in the presence of low H$^+$ concentrations (Figure 7.27). All these experiments are supportive of a direct role for H$^+$ in the transport mechanism, whereby both the enzyme and the phosphoenzyme reside in specific states depending on whether the transport sites are occupied by H$^+$ or Ca^{2+}, or are unoccupied.

Reversal of the Ca^{2+} pump

Addition of ADP and P$_i$ to calcium-loaded vesicles results in an efflux of calcium and synthesis of ATP (Bargolie *et al.*, 1971; Makinose and Hasselbach, 1971). In

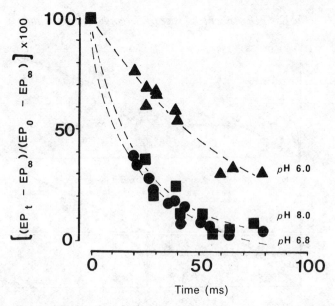

Figure 7.26 Kinetics of phosphoenzyme cleavage at various H^+ concentrations. The phosphoenzyme was first formed by equilibration of SR vesicles with 1.0 mM $^{32}P_i$, 10 mM $MgCl_2$, 0.5 mM Tris-maleate (pH 6.0) and 0.5 mM EGTA. No K^+ or Ca^{2+} was added to ensure a high yield of phosphoenzyme. The mixture was then diluted with an equal volume of a medium containing a 12-fold excess of non-radioactive P_i, 50 mM Tris-maleate (pH indicated), 10 mM $MgCl_2$, 160 mM KCl and 1.0 mM ATP. Sequential quenching was obtained with the aid of a Dionex rapid mixing apparatus. Temperature was 25°C

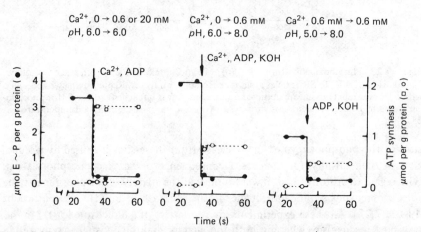

Figure 7.27 pH dependence of the phosphoenzyme affinity for Ca^{2+}. The phosphoenzyme was first obtained by equilibration of ATPase protein with $^{32}P_i$ at pH 5.0 or 6.0 in the presence of high (20 mM) Mg^{2+} and low Ca^{2+} to avoid occupancy of calcium sites. ATP synthesis was then obtained by addition of ADP and variable Ca^{2+} (occupancy of the low affinity sites is a requirement for acquisition of ADP sensitivity by the phosphoenzyme formed with P_i). If the pH is low (pH 6.0), 0.6 mM Ca^{2+} is not sufficient and 20 mM Ca^{2+} is necessary to occupy the phosphoenzyme sites. On the other hand, if the pH is increased to 8.0, it is possible to obtain ATP synthesis without changing the Ca^{2+} concentration. This is due to the relatively low Ca^{2+} affinity of the *non-phosphorylated* enzyme at pH 6.0 (preventing binding of Ca^{2+} and thereby permitting phosphorylation with P_i in the presence of 0.6 mM Ca^{2+}), and the relatively high Ca^{2+} affinity of the *phosphorylated* enzyme at pH 8.0 (permitting Ca^{2+} binding and acquisition of ADP sensitivity by the phosphoenzyme in the presence of 0.6 mM Ca^{2+}) (deMeis and Tume, 1977)

analogy to the forward ATPase cycle, the reverse reaction includes formation of a phosphorylated intermediate. This can be observed by reacting radioactive phosphate with loaded vesicles after addition of EGTA to the outside medium (Makinose, 1972; Yamada and Tonomura, 1972).

The stoichiometry of this reaction involves efflux of 2 calcium ions per ATP formed, and the reaction continues for repeated cycles as long as the Ca^{2+} concentration inside the vesicles remains high and the Ca^{2+} concentration outside is kept low (Figure 7.28). The dependence of the reversal of the pump on the presence of a transmembrane Ca^{2+} gradient suggests that the chemical and/or osmotic potential associated with the gradient provides the free energy required

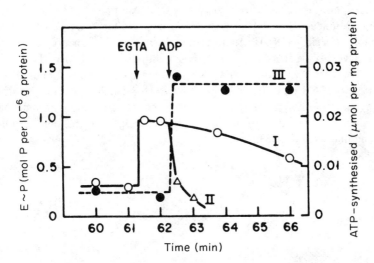

Figure 7.28 Reversal of the catalytic and transport cycle of SR ATPase. SR vesicles were equilibrated in high Ca^{2+} and $^{32}P_i$. Then, EGTA was added to lower the free Ca^{2+} concentration in the outside medium (EGTA does not enter the vesicles) and form a transmembrane Ca^{2+} gradient in the absence of ATP or other "high energy" substrates. At this point phosphorylation of the enzyme with $^{32}P_i$ was obtained and, upon addition of ADP, ATP was formed by phosphoryl transfer from the phosphoenzyme to ADP (Makinose, 1972)

for enzyme phosphorylation with P_i and subsequent ATP synthesis (Makinose 1971; 1972; Yamada and Tonomura, 1973; Yamada *et al.*, 1972). On the other hand, it was found subsequently that phosphorylation of SR ATPase with P_i can take place even in the absence of a gradient as long as the Ca^{2+} concentration in the medium is kept very low ($<10^{-7}$ M) so as to prevent occupancy of the high affinity sites (deMeis and Masuda, 1974; Masuda and deMeis, 1973). Optimal conditions for enzyme phosphorylation with P_i were found to be moderately acid (pH 6.0), in the presence of mM P_i and EGTA, and in the absence of K^+ or Na^+. Phosphorylation with P_i in the absence of a transmembrane gradient has been studied with intact vesicles, leaky vesicles and purified

ATPase (Beil *et al.*, 1977; Boyer *et al.*, 1977; deMeis, 1976; deMeis and Masuda, 1974; Hasselbach, 1978; Kanazawa, 1975; Knowles and Racker, 1975; Kolassa *et al.*, 1979; Masuda and deMeis, 1973; Prager *et al.*, 1979; Punzengruber *et al.*, 1978; Rauch *et al.*, 1977; Verjovski-Almeida *et al.*, 1978).

Enzyme phosphorylation with P_i

Enzyme phosphorylation with P_i is the reversal of the reaction which cleaves P_i from the phosphoenzyme and completes the ATPase cycle in the forward direction. Due to the strong tendency of ATP to undergo hydrolysis, enzyme phosphorylation with ATP can only be studied in transient or steady state conditions, but enzyme phosphorylation with P_i can be studied at equilibrium.

As mentioned above, the phosphorylation reaction with P_i occurs more favourably at acid pH (pH 6) and in the absence of K^+. For this reason most studies have been carried out in these conditions, even though they do not strictly correlate with conditions generally prevailing during studies of ATP utilisation (pH 6.8 and 80 mM K^+). At any rate, detailed equilibrium studies of enzyme phosphorylation with P_i were interpreted with a scheme based on random complexation of P_i (substrate) and Mg^{2+} (activator), as follows (Punzengruber *et al.*, 1978):

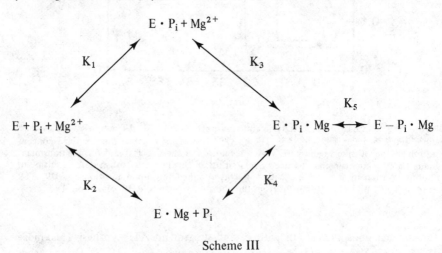

Scheme III

where $E - P$ is the covalently reacted phosphoenzyme, and $E \cdot P_i \cdot Mg$ is the ternary complex preceding the covalent reaction.

Based on this scheme, $E - P$ values at variable ligand concentrations are determined by:

$$\frac{[E - P \cdot Mg]}{\epsilon} = \frac{[Mg^{2+}]\ [P_i]\ K_5}{(K_2 K_4)^{-1} + ([Mg^{2+}]/K_4) + ([P_i]/K_3) + (1 + K_5)\ [Mg^{2+}]\ [P_i]}$$

Experimentally, equilibrium levels of $E - P$ at fixed $[P_i]$ or $[Mg^{2+}]$ display a first order dependence on $[Mg^{2+}]$ or $[P_i]$ (Figure 7.29). Appropriate analysis of these data yields value for K_1, K_2, $K_3(1 + K_5)$, $K_4(1 + K_5)$ and $E - P_{max}$ (Punzengruber *et al.*, 1978; Martin and Tanford, 1981).

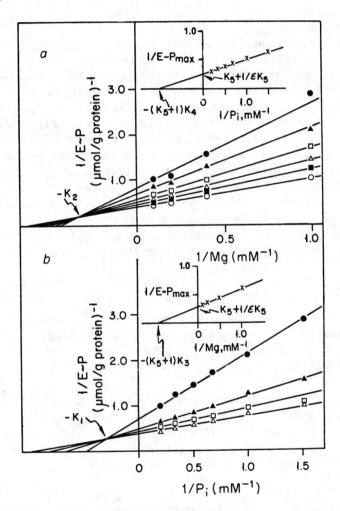

Figure 7.29 Double reciprocal plots of phosphoenzyme formation at various P_i and Mg^{2+} concentrations. The assay medium contained 40 mM Tris-maleate (*p*H 6.0), 1.0 mM EGTA, $^{32}P_i$ and $MgCl_2$ as indicated below. The reaction was started by the addition of SR vesicles to a final concentration of 0.7 mg ml^{-1}, and stopped after 1 minute by the addition of perchloric acid. The experiments shown were performed at 15 °C. *a*, Dependence of the phosphoenzyme levels on magnesium concentration. Orthophosphate concentrations: •, 0.66 mM; ▲, 1.0 mM; □, 1.5 mM; △, 2.0 mM; ■, 3.0 mM; ○, 5.0 mM. *b*, Replot of the same data as a function of reciprocal orthophosphate concentrations. Magnesium concentrations: •, 1.0 mM; ▲, 2.5 mM; □, 5.0 mM; △, 10.0 mM. Insets: intercepts on the $1/E \sim P$ ordinate against the reciprocals of fixed ion concentrations. (Adapted from deMeis *et al.*, 1982)

A disappointing limitation of this analysis is that the equilibrium constant K_5 can only be calculated if the total number of phosphorylation sites (ϵ) is known:

$$E - P_{max} = \frac{\epsilon K_5}{1 + K_5}$$

This number was assumed to be 7–8 nmol per mg protein (Punzengruber *et al.*, 1978; Martin and Tanford, 1981) as electrophoretic analysis indicates that ATPase chains of approximately 100,000 MW account for 80 per cent of the SR protein. Based on an experimental value of 4 nmol per mg protein for $E - P_{max}$, K_5 was estimated to be nearly 1 (Martin and Tanford, 1981; Punzengruber *et al.*, 1978; Watanabe *et al.*, 1981). In this analysis only K_1 and K_2 were obtained directly while K_3 and K_4 were derived with calculations including K_5 which, in turn, was based on an assumed value for ϵ. It was found that the values for K_3 and K_4 estimated in this manner are one order of magnitude higher than K_1 and K_2, suggesting synergistic binding of P_i and Mg^{2+}, as outlined in scheme I.

With the intention of determining K_5 directly and independently of the number of phosphorylation sites, we have subsequently endeavoured to measure the rate constants for phosphorylation of the enzyme and hydrolysis of the phosphoenzyme in rapid quench experiments, thereby deriving K_5 as in

$$K_5 = \frac{k_{phosph}}{k_{hydrol}}.$$

In these experiments the hydrolytic rate constant is obtained from the exponential decay of $[^{32}P]$phosphoenzyme following dilution of the reaction mixture with a medium containing non-radioactive P_i. It can be assumed that following a sufficiently large isotope dilution, formation of radioactive phosphoenzyme is negligible and therefore $k_{obs} = k_{hydrol}$.

Experiments of this type show that the decay of phosphoenzyme is exponential and independent of $[Mg^{2+}]$ (Figure 7.30). In kinetic experiments on phosphoenzyme formation, however, the observed phosphorylation rate constant is a function of the enzyme saturation (s) with P_i and Mg^{2+}, the true phosphorylation rate constant and the hydrolytic rate constant, as in

$$k_{obs} = s \cdot k_{phosph} + k_{hydrol},$$

where s is the fraction of enzyme participating in the ternary complex with P_i and Mg^{2+}. It is clear that only when the enzyme is totally saturated ($s = 1$) will

$$k_{obs} = k_{phosph} + k_{hydrol}.$$

Our initial experiments on phosphorylation kinetics (Watanabe *et al.*, 1981) were conducted in the presence of 2 mM P_i and 10 mM Mg^{2+} with the assumption that the enzyme was nearly saturated at these substrate concentrations, as indicated by equilibrium measurements (Martin and Tanford, 1981; Masuda and

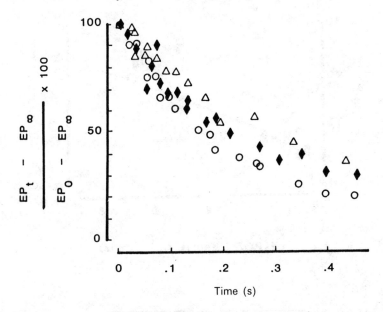

Figure 7.30 Kinetics of phosphoenzyme cleavage at different Mg^{2+} concentrations. The phosphoenzyme was first formed by equilibration of SR vesicles with $1.0\,mM\ ^{32}P_i$, $10\,mM$ $MgCl_2$, $50\,mM$ Tris-maleate ($pH\ 6.0$) and $0.5\,mM$ EGTA. This mixture was then diluted with an equal volume of a medium containing a 12-fold excess of non-radioactive P_i and $50\,mM$ Tris-maleate ($pH\ 6.0$). The concentration of Mg^{2+} in the diluted mixture was controlled by addition of $MgCl_2$ or EDTA to give: ◆, $2.6\,mM$; △, $8.7\,mM$; or ○, $26.6\,mM$ Mg^{2+}. Sequential quenching with acid was obtained with the aid of a Dionex rapid mixing apparatus. Temperature was $25\,°C$. Analysis of these decay curves yields single exponentials with rate constants $k_{hyd} = 2\text{-}4\,s^{-1}$ (Inesi *et al.*, 1982b). This experiment shows that the actual hydrolytic cleavage of the phosphoenzyme *is not* dependent on Mg^{2+}. On the other hand, it was previously shown (Inesi *et al.*, 1970) that evolution of the phosphoenzyme formed with ATP in the presence of Ca^{2+} *is* dependent on Mg^{2+}. Therefore, the Mg^{2+} effect is likely associated with intermediate steps preceding actual hydrolytic cleavage of the phosphorylated enzyme intermediate

deMeis, 1973; Punzengruber *et al.*, 1978). However, inspired by the fluorescence experiments of Lacapere *et al.* (1981), we have recently extended our measurements of phosphorylation kinetics in conditions testing their Mg^{2+} and P_i concentration dependence.

We find (Inesi *et al.*, 1982b) that the observed phosphorylation rate constants have not yet reached their maximal values at Mg^{2+} and P_i concentrations at which maximal equilibrium levels of phosphoenzyme are already reached (Figure 7.31). Therefore, a correct value for the phosphorylation rate constant must be derived from extrapolation to substrate concentrations higher than those yielding maximal equilibrium levels of phosphoenzyme.

The values obtained for k_{phosph} and k_{hydrol} in our experiments (at $pH\ 6$, no K^+) are $40\text{-}50\,s^{-1}$ and $3\text{-}4\,s^{-1}$, respectively. Therefore, $K_5 \geqslant 10$, which is a value quite different from those previously estimated ($K_5 \approx 1$ in Martin

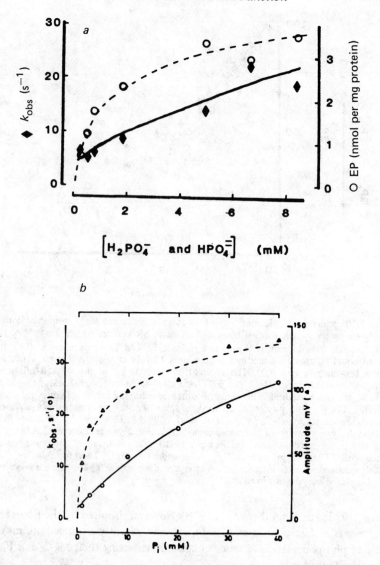

Figure 7.31 *a*, Observed rate constants of enzyme phosphorylation with P_i (Inesi *et al.*, 1982b). The reaction was started by mixing SR vesicles with 50 mM Tris-maleate (pH 6.0), 0.5 mM EGTA, 18 mM Mg^{2+} and variable P_i. Rapid mixing and quenching were obtained with the aid of a Dionex rapid mixing apparatus. Temperature was 25 °C. The rate constants (♦) obtained by analysis of kinetic curves are compared to the equilibrium levels of phosphoenzyme (○) obtained in the same experiments. The equilibrium levels are fitted with a curve (dotted line) expressing a first order dependence on the P_i concentration. Since $k_{obs} = s \cdot k_{phosph} + k_{hydrol}$, extrapolation of k_{obs} to zero $[P_i]$ or $[Mg^{2+}]$ corresponds to k_{hydrol} and yields values consistent with those derived from the experiments of Figure 7.30. *b*, Changes in intrinsic fluorescence measured by Lacapere *et al.* (1981) in similar conditions. It is apparent that the amplitudes and the rates of fluorescence changes are proportional to the phosphoenzyme levels and phosphorylation rates, respectively. These experiments indicate that the phosphorylation reaction with P_i in the absence of calcium is accompanied by a conformational change of the enzyme

and Tanford, 1981; Masuda and deMeis, 1973; Punzengruber *et al.*, 1978). If $K_5 \geqslant 10$, $E - P_{max}$ observed at equilibrium (Figure 7.29) is nearly equal to the total number of phosphorylation sites. Thereby a value of 4.0–4.5 nmol per mg SR protein is obtained for the sites available for phosphorylation with P_i, in agreement with the number obtained in phosphorylation experiments with ATP in SR vesicles.

Note that if a correct value for K_5 is used, K_3 and K_4 are found to be approximately equal to K_1 and K_2 ($\sim 100\,M^{-1}$), indicating that Mg^{2+} and P_i bind independently with no appreciable synergisitic effect.

The equilibrium and kinetic constants obtained through this analysis for the reaction of SR ATPase with P_i in the absence of Ca^{2+} are summarised in Table 7.2. The two sets of constants were obtained at pH 6.0 in the absence of K^+ (the conditions most commonly used in this study), and at pH 6.8 in the presence of K^+ (conditions identical to those commonly used to study the ATPase reaction

Table 7.2 Equilibrium and rate constants for the partial reactions leading to enzyme phosphorylation with P_i in the absence of Ca^{2+}

Constant	pH 6.0; no KCl	pH 6.8; 80 mM KCl
K_1	~ 100	~ 200
K_2	~ 100	~ 200
K_3	~ 100	~ 200
K_4	~ 100	~ 200
K_5	10–17	~ 1.6
k_{phosph}	40–50 s^{-1}	~ 100 s^{-1}
k_{hydrol}	3–4 s^{-1}	60 s^{-1}

See text for experimental conditions and analysis

with ATP as a substrate). Both sets were obtained at 25 °C. Note that in studies of enzyme phosphorylation with P_i, this reaction is commonly considered to be in the forward direction, while it should actually be a reverse reaction when the entire ATPase cycle is considered. Therefore, the equilibrium constants in Table 7.2 must be converted to their reciprocal form when applied to the entire ATPase cycle.

ATP synthesis

The finding that the calcium pump can be completely reversed (deMeis, 1976; Makinose, 1971, 1972; Yamada *et al.*, 1972) demonstrates that the phosphoenzyme formed with P_i in the presence of a transmembrane Ca^{2+} gradient is able to react with ADP and yield ATP. On the other hand, the phosphoenzyme formed with P_i in the absence of Ca^{2+} does not react with ADP. These experiments clearly show the existence of two enzyme species differentiated by their reactivity to ADP (deMeis, 1976; deMeis and Sorenson, 1975; Knowles and

Racker, 1975). It is obvious that the presence of Ca^{2+} is what makes the difference and the important question is whether a transmembrane Ca^{2+} gradient or merely calcium binding to the phosphoenzyme is necessary to form the ADP reactive phosphoenzyme.

This question was answered (deMeis and Tume, 1977; Knowles and Racker, 1975) when net synthesis of ATP was obtained in the absence of a Ca^{2+} gradient by adding millimolar amounts of Ca^{2+} and ADP to the phosphoenzyme formed by incubation of leaky vesicles or purified ATPase with P_i in the absence of Ca^{2+} (Figure 6.32). Therefore, the enzyme is reactive to orthophosphate in the absence of Ca^{2+}, and the phosphoenzyme so obtained can be made reactive to ADP when low affinity Ca^{2+} binding sites are occupied. The presence of Ca^{2+} gradient is necessary to obtain repeated cycles of ATP synthesis, which require alternate exposure of the Ca^{2+} binding sites to the outer medium (to unload Ca^{2+} and allow phosphorylation) and to the inner medium (to acquire Ca^{2+} and ADP sensitivity).

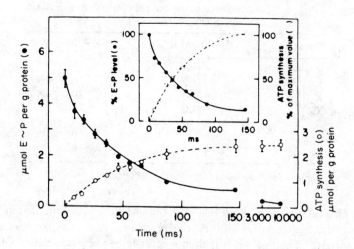

Figure 7.32 ATP synthesis following addition of ADP and Ca^{2+} to phosphoenzyme formed with P_i in the absence of Ca^{2+}. ATP synthesis is limited to a single enzyme cycle as the added Ca^{2+} prevents further phosphorylation of the enzyme with P_i (deMeis and Tume, 1977)

In the absence of a membrane permeability barrier permitting coexistence of high Ca^{2+} ($> mM$) inside the vesicles and low Ca^{2+} ($< 10^{-7} M$) outside the vesicles, ATP synthesis is limited to only one enzyme cycle consisting of the enzyme reaction with P_i in the absence of Ca^{2+}, and equilibration of other sequential states (including $ATP \cdot E \sim P \cdot Ca_2$) when Ca^{2+} and ADP are added. Following addition of Ca^{2+} and ADP, however, further utilisation of P_i by the enzyme is absolutely prevented. It is clear that this reaction requires destabilisation of the enzyme by removal of Ca^{2+} from high affinity sites. This is accomplished experimentally by addition of EGTA.

An illustration of the related enzyme interconversions can be obtained in the following diagram, which is a simplified version of scheme I:

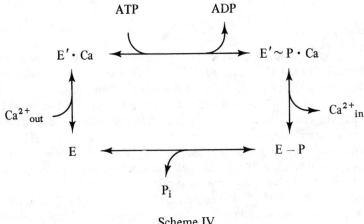

Scheme IV

This brief scheme postulates that the phosphoenzyme resides in equilibrium between a state with high phosphorylation potential and high affinity for Ca^{2+} ($E' \sim P \cdot Ca$) and a state with low phosphorylation potential and low affinity for Ca^{2+} ($E - P$). The enzyme must be able to attain at least two alternative states: one that is able to react with ATP in the presence of Ca^{2+} and another that is able to react with orthophosphate in the absence of Ca^{2+}. In the phosphorylated form the two states are distinguished by their reactivity or non-reactivity to ADP. Following P_i cleavage, the enzyme regains its high affinity for Ca^{2+}.

It is of interest that protons have a role in these interconversions, inasmuch as the affinity of the calcium binding sites on the phosphoenzyme, as well as the Ca^{2+} concentration dependence for acquisition of ADP sensitivity, is higher at low proton concentrations (deMeis and Tume, 1977, Verjovski-Almeida and deMeis, 1977). With suitable conditions, the phosphoenzyme can be made reactive to ADP simply by a pH jump, that is, by causing calcium binding by increasing the affinity of the sites with no need for an increase in Ca^{2+} concentration (deMeis and Tume, 1977; Ratkje and Shamoo, 1980).

Other interesting experimental manipulations involve the use of organic solvents (deMeis *et al.*, 1980) which markedly favour the phosphorylation reaction of the enzyme with P_i. The reaction mixture must then be diluted with water for the phosphoenzyme to acquire reactivity to ADP. These observations led to the suggestion that solvation of substrates and appropriate residues at the active site is involved in determining free energy changes in phosphorylation reactions (deMeis *et al.*, 1980). The effects of experimental manipulations of Ca^{2+} and H^+ concentrations, temperature, and organic solvents on the phosphorylation of SR ATPase with P_i, and on the transformation of the phospho-enzyme to an ADP reactive form have recently been discussed in detail by deMeis and Inesi (1982).

Roles of Mg^{2+} and K^+

A role of Mg^{2+} in the SR ATPase reaction mechanism is revealed by an apparent dependence of the Ca^{2+}-activated ATPase velocity and of the rates of phospho-enzyme formation (Vianna, 1975; Weber *et al.*, 1966; Yamada and Ikemoto, 1980; Yamamoto and Tonomura, 1967) on the concentration of ATP · Mg complex, rather than the concentration of ATP. Therefore, the ATP · Mg complex would seen to be the true substrate for the Ca^{2+}-activated ATPase. In this capacity, Mg^{2+} can be replaced by Ca^{2+} or Mn^{2+} (Chiesi and Inesi, 1981; Yamada and Ikemoto, 1980), although the reaction proceeds at much slower rates when ATP is complexed with these cations.

Another role of Mg^{2+} was pointed out by Inesi *et al.* (1970) who found that the evolution of the catalytic cycle following enzyme phosphorylation with ATP is also dependent on Mg^{2+}. In this case, Mg^{2+} produces this effect by binding directly to the enzyme (Garrahan *et al.*, 1976; Makinose and Boll, 1978). It was also found that the reaction with P_i in the absence of Ca^{2+} is dependent on Mg^{2+} (Masuda and deMeis, 1973; Martin and Tanford, 1981; Punzengruber *et al.*, 1978). This requirement is again satisfied by Mg^{2+} binding directly to the enzyme (see scheme III).

At present, there is no reason to believe that Mg^{2+} is alternatively bound to and dissociated from the enzyme during the catalytic and transport cycle. Experiments using radioactive Mn^{2+} in place of Mg^{2+} indicate that Mg^{2+} counterfluxes do not occur during Ca^{2+} transport (Chiesi and Inesi, 1980). It is rather probable that the Mg · enzyme complex is the native enzyme which is maintained throughout the catalytic cycle, which is capable of acquiring differ-ent states in the presence of Ca^{2+} and substrates. Experimental manipulations producing dissociation of Mg^{2+} from the enzyme reveal a different conformation of the enzyme in the absence, as opposed to the presence, of Mg^{2+} (Guillain *et al.*, 1982).

K^+ is another cation which is required to obtain maximal velocity of ATPase activity and Ca^{2+} transport (Chiu and Haynes, 1980).

Exchange of isotopes and stereochemical specificity

A number of exchange reactions have been used in studies of the SR ATPase reaction mechanism.

1. ATP $\rightleftharpoons$ ADP exchange was demonstrated by addition of ^{14}C-ADP to ATPase using ATP in the presence of Ca^{2+}. It was found that ^{14}C-ATP is rapidly formed (Ebashi and Lipman, 1962; Hasselbach and Makinose, 1962). This exchange of the adenosine moiety indirectly indicates the presence of a phosphorylated

enzyme intermediate which is formed with ATP and is capable of transferring its phosphate back to ADP.

2. ATP $\rightleftharpoons$ P_i exchange was demonstrated by adding ^{32}P-P_i to ATPase using ATP in the presence of Ca^{2+}. It was found that $[\gamma$-$^{32}P]$ATP is rapidly formed (Carvalho *et al.*, 1976; deMeis and Carvalho, 1974; Makinose, 1971). This exchange shows that P_i can react with the enzyme during steady state activity, and the entire cycle can flow simultaneously in the forward and reverse directions if appropriate concentrations of P_i and Ca^{2+} are present.

3. P_i $\rightleftharpoons$ HOH oxygen exchange has been used to reveal the occurrence, and define the kinetics, of the enzyme reaction with P_i (deMeis and Boyer, 1978; Kanazawa and Boyer, 1973).

4. Measurements of the patterns of ^{18}O-P_i species formed from highly ^{18}O-labelled ATP during the ATPase reaction in H_2O, were used to demonstrate the extent of reversal of the phosphoenzyme hydrolysis before actual release of P_i into the medium. It was found that an increase in the ATP concentration reduces the probability of reversal of the hydrolytic reaction (Ariki and Boyer, 1980).

5. The stereochemistry of phosphoryl group transfer was studied using ATP-γ-S stereospecifically labelled in the γ position with both ^{17}O and ^{18}O. Using this substrate for a hydrolytic reaction, the two possible phosphate species that can be formed are the two enantiomers of inorganic (^{16}O, ^{17}O, ^{18}O) thiophosphate. In fact, as a consequence of enzyme-catalysed reactions, stereochemical inversion is produced if the reaction occurs in one step, while stereochemical retention (that is, double inversion) is produced if two steps with an intermediate phosphoryl transfer are involved (Bagshaw *et al.*, 1974). It was then shown that SR ATPase exhibits retention of configuration at the γ-phosphorous atom (Webb and Trentham, 1981). This observation is consistent with a role of the phosphoenzyme as a reaction intermediate.

Conformational changes

Important features of the catalytic and transport cycle of SR ATPase, such as cooperative phenomena, enzyme activation by calcium and changes in orientation and affinity of the calcium sites, suggest that protein conformational changes are involved in the mechanism of the cycle. Presently, at least two types of conformational changes have been shown by spectroscopic measurements.

Effect of Ca²⁺ and substrate binding

Calcium binding to SR ATPase is an absolute requirement for ATP utilisation by the enzyme. The cooperative character of calcium binding and the resulting enzyme activation can be most simply explained with two different conformational states of the ATPase protein, in the absence and in the presence of calcium. In fact, an effect of calcium on protein conformation has been shown by measurements of intrinsic fluorescence (Dupont and Leigh, 1978; Ikemoto *et al.*, 1978), fluorescence of a fluorescein probe (Pick and Karlish, 1980), and —SH reactivity (Murphy, 1978). On the other hand, the relevance of such a conformational change with respect to enzyme activation can be demonstrated by the calcium requirement for a substrate-induced effect on the EPR spectra (Figure 7.33) of SR ATPase labelled with an —SH directed spin label (Coan and Inesi, 1977). The Ca^{2+} concentration dependence of the substrate effect on the spin label parameter is nearly identical to that of ATPase velocity (Figure 7.34), consistent with a direct relationship between the calcium-induced conformational change and the calcium effect on enzyme activation. It is clear from Figure 7.33*b* that Ca^{2+}-dependent spectral changes are observed on addition not only of substrates sustaining enzyme phosphorylation (for example ATP, ITP and AcP), but also of inactive analogues (for example ADP, AMP-PNP). Therefore, phosphoryl transfer from the substrate to the enzyme is not strictly required for the spectral effect. It seems rather that the Ca^{2+}-induced conformational change results specifically in an adjustment of the enzyme · substrate interaction, which is permissive of the phosphorylation reaction.

In the presence of Ca^{2+}, P_i does not produce any spectral change (Figure 7.33*b*). However, it was recently observed that in the absence of Ca^{2+} and in media containing dimethylsulphoxide (for example in conditions favouring

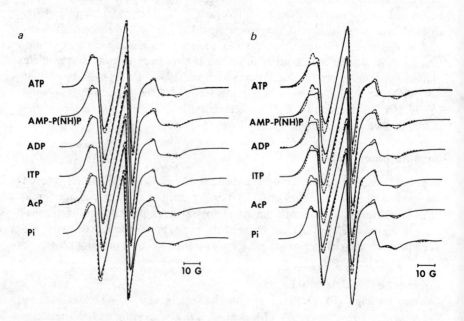

Figure 7.33 EPR spectra of spin-labelled SR (1 mol of 2,2,6,6-tetramethyl-4-amino (*N*-iodoacetamide)piperidine-1-oxyl per mole of ATPase chains) in the absence (dashed lines) or in the presence (solid lines) of various substrates: *a*, in the absence of Ca^{2+} (EGTA present); or *b* in the presence of Ca^{2+}. All media contained 20 mM MOPS (*p*H 6.8), 80 mM KCl and 20 mM MgCl$_2$ (Inesi *et al.*, 1982b)

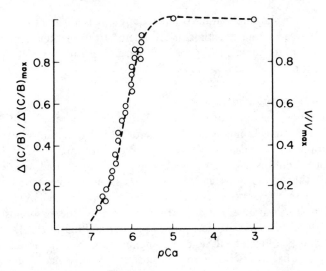

Figure 7.34 Ca^{2+} concentration dependence of the effect of Ca^{2+} on an empirical spectral parameter of spin-labelled SR (o) and on activation of ATPase velocity (dashed line) (Inesi *et al.*, 1982b)

the phosphorylation reaction of SR ATPase with P_i), marked spectral change is produced by P_i (Figure 7.35). In these conditions, ATP is not effective.

In conclusion, spectral changes of spin-labelled SR ATPase are obtained when the catalytic site is occupied by the substrate to which the enzyme is specifically reactive: nucleotide in the presence of Ca^{2+}, or P_i in the absence of

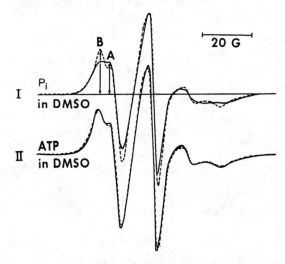

Figure 7.35 Effect of P_i (solid line) on the EPR spectra of spin-labelled SR (control is the dotted line) in the absence of Ca^{2+} (EGTA present) and in the presence of 30% (v/v) dimethylsulphoxide. ATP has no effect in these conditions (Inesi *et al.*, 1982b)

Ca^{2+}. As actual phosphorylation is not required, it is apparent that the spectral changes observed in our experiments are related to formation of an "activated" enzyme · substrate complex (Figure 7.35) which is permissive of the phosphory-lation reaction.

Effect of ATPase phosphorylation

From the functional point of view, the phosphorylation reaction of SR ATPase with ATP is extremely important, as it is followed by translocation and reduc-tion in affinity of the calcium sites as required for active transport of the divalent cation. One would expect this phenomenon to be associated with a structural change of the translocating enzyme and/or its immediate membrane environ-ment. In fact, it was previously shown that phosphorylated ATPase displays different —SH titration kinetics when compared to the non-phosphorylated enzyme (Murphy, 1978). We find now (Watanabe and Inesi, 1982) that addition of ATP to suspensions of SR vesicles containing low concentrations of a deter-gent ($C_{12}E_8$), that by itself does not produce major vesicular disruption, is fol-lowed by a transient change in light scattering (Figure 7.36). The effect is Ca^{2+}-

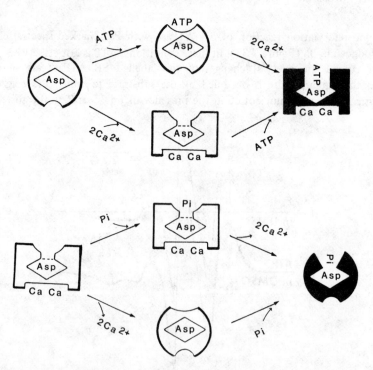

Figure 8.36 Diagram suggesting that binding and dissociation of Ca^{2+} from SR ATPase produce conformational states adjusting the interaction of ATP or P_i with the active site. Only the shaded states generate a spin label effect (Figure 7.34 and 7.35) and are permis-sive of aspartyl residue phosphorylation (Inesi *et al.*, 1982b)

dependent, proceeds in parallel with utilisation of ATP and reverses upon exhaustion of the nucleotide. In this case, ADP and AMP–PNP are not effective.

In addition to light scattering, the effect of ATP can be detected in studies of fluorescence energy transfer between ATPase chains using the technique of Vanderkooi *et al.* (1977). For this purpose, ATPase chains are labelled separately with *N*-iodoacetyl-*N'*-(5-sulpho-1-napthyl) ethylenediamine (IAEDANS) and 6-iodoacetamidofluorescein (IAF). Samples of vesicles uniformly labelled with either IAEDANS or IAF, mixtures of two populations of vesicles uniformly labelled with either fluorophore and vesicles containing randomised chains labelled with either fluorophore are then used as experimental systems. In the last system, significant energy transfer from IAEDANS (donor) to IAF (acceptor) is revealed by fluorescence spectra, and measurement of donor fluorescence intensity and lifetime. This is attributed to close interactions between ATPase chains within the membrane bilayer. It is then found that in the presence of low detergent concentrations, ATP changes the extent of energy transfer between labelled ATPase chains (Figure 7.37), consistent with destabilisation of chains interaction.

These observations indicate that enzyme phosphorylation favours interaction of the ATPase with the detergent, producing an increase in the average distance among the ATPase chains leading to membrane fragmentation. These reversible effects are evidently related to structural transitions concomitant with enzyme phosphorylation by ATP in the presence of Ca^{2+}.

CONCLUSIONS

The most important features of the catalytic and transport cycle of SR ATPase may be summarised by the following sequence of partial reactions which is derived from scheme I, and from various experimental findings described above:

$$ATP \cdot E + 2Ca^{2+}_{out} \rightleftharpoons ATP \cdot E' \cdot Ca_2 \qquad K_a \cong 10^6 \ M^{-1} \qquad (1)$$

$$ATP \cdot E' \cdot Ca_2 \rightleftharpoons ADP \cdot E' \sim P \cdot Ca_2 \qquad \begin{aligned} &k_f \cong 100 \ s^{-1}; \\ &k_{rev} > 400 \ s^{-1} \end{aligned} \qquad (2)$$

$$ADP \cdot E' \sim P \cdot Ca_2 \rightleftharpoons E' \sim P \cdot Ca_2 + ADP \qquad K_d < 10^{-5} \ M \qquad (3)$$

$$ATP + E' \sim P \cdot Ca_2 \rightleftharpoons ATP \cdot E' \sim P \cdot Ca_2 \qquad K_a > 10^5 \ M^{-1} \qquad (4)$$

$$ATP \cdot E' \sim P \cdot Ca_2 \rightleftharpoons ATP \cdot {}^*E' - P \cdot Ca_2 \qquad K \cong 1 \qquad (5)$$

$$ATP \cdot {}^*E' - P \cdot Ca_2 \rightleftharpoons ATP \cdot {}^*E - P + 2Ca^{2+}_{in} \qquad K_d \sim 10^{-3} - 10^{-2} \ M \quad (6)$$

$$2H^+_{in} + ATP \cdot {}^*E - P \rightleftharpoons ATP \cdot E - P + 2H^+_{out} \qquad (7)$$

$$H_2O + ATP \cdot E - P \rightleftharpoons ATP \cdot E \cdot P_i + H^+ \qquad \begin{aligned} &k_{hyd} = 60 \ s^{-1}; \\ &k_{phosp} \cong 100 \ s^{-1} \end{aligned} \qquad (8)$$

$$ATP \cdot E \cdot P_i \rightleftharpoons ATP \cdot E + P_i \qquad K_d \cong 10^{-2} \ M \qquad (9)$$

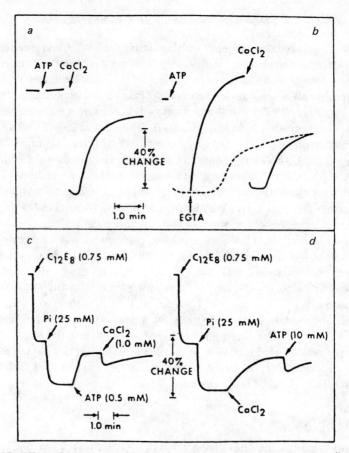

Figure 7.37 Effect of enzyme phosphorylation with ATP (in the presence of Ca^{2+}) or with P_i (in the absence of Ca^{2+}) on light scattering by a suspension of SR vesicles (Watanabe and Inesi, 1982). a, In a reaction mixture containing EGTA, addition of Ca^{2+} is necessary to obtain the ATP effect; b, addition of EGTA to a reaction mixture containing Ca^{2+}, produces reversal of the ATP effect (solid line) which would normally last until all the ATP is used (dashed line); c and d, clearing effect produced by phosphorylation of the enzyme with P_i; in this case, Ca^{2+} must be removed to permit the P_i reaction to occur

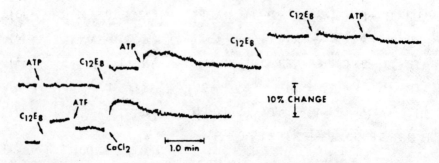

Figure 7.38 Effect of $C_{12}E_8$ and ATP on donor (IAEDANS) fluorescence (Watanabe and Inesi, 1982). The samples contained a 3:7 mixture of IAEDANS- and IAF-labelled SR vesicles which were treated with DOC for reconstitution of vesicles with randomly labelled ATPase chains. Ca^{2+} is required for the ATP effect

The first step of this sequence is Ca^{2+} binding which involves 2 moles of calcium per enzyme unit and is accompanied by a conformation change ($E \rightleftharpoons E'$) related to the activation and the cooperative behaviour of the enzyme (Dupont, 1982; Inesi *et al.*, 1980).

The second step is the Ca^{2+}-dependent phosphorylation of the enzyme by ATP. The forward rate constant for this reaction has been measured (Froehlich and Taylor, 1975; Verjovski-Almeida *et al.*, 1978). A minimal value for the reverse constant is estimated by the rapid ADP–ATP exchange (Verjovksi-Almeida *et al.*, 1978) and the immediate disappearance of a fraction of the phosphoenzyme upon addition of ADP (Froehlich *et al.*, 1980). The intermediate which is formed in this reaction has a high phosphorylation potential ($E \sim P$).

The third step is the ADP dissociation from the catalytic site. ADP dissociation must occur with an off constant somewhat higher than the reverse rate constant of reaction 2 to avoid net reversal of the phosphorylation reaction (at low ADP concentrations).

The fourth step is binding of ATP. This step is required to explain the dependence of phosphoenzyme turnover on the type of substrate present in the reaction mixture. The presence of an ATP molecule on the phosphoenzyme is demonstrated by a fluorescence enhancement exhibited by TNP-ATP as a consequence of enzyme phosphorylation by ATP (Watanabe and Inesi, 1982).

The fifth step is the transformation of the phosphoenzyme from a state with high affinity to one with low affinity for Ca^{2+} ($E' \sim P \rightleftharpoons {}^*E' - P$). Such a transformation is a most important link in free energy transduction, inasmuch as the phosphorylation potential lost as free energy is utilised for a conformational change producing a drastic reduction in affinity for Ca^{2+}. The calcium sites must also acquire an inward orientation to satisfy the vectorial requirements of calcium transport. The equilibrium constant for this reaction is small as, in most experimental conditions, the two species are present in significant concentrations as demonstrated by the diphasic kinetics of phosphoenzyme decay on addition of ADP.

Reaction 6 is the release of Ca^{2+} inside the vesicles. Here the dissociation constant must be between 10^{-3} and 10^{-2} M to explain the build-up of a Ca^{2+} concentration gradient which is observed under operation of the pump. This step is complex and includes reversal of the conformational state acquired in step 1 (${}^*E' - P \rightleftharpoons {}^*E - P$). It is apparent that rate limitation for the entire cycle is related to the establishment of microequilibria among phosphoenzyme states within this step.

Reaction 7 corresponds to the acquisition of H^+ by the transport sites (see preceding sections), reverse of the enzyme to a state with outward orientated calcium sites, and release of H^+ to the outside medium.

Reaction 8 is the hydrolytic reaction. The hydrolytic rate constant is $60\,s^{-1}$ (Inesi *et al.*, 1982a and 1982b) and the equilibrium is nearly unity. These values observed at $pH\,6.8$ should be attributed to the average behaviour of a mixed population of protonated and non-protonated phosphoenzyme. The latter species undergoes faster hydrolysis than the former.

Reaction 9 is the dissociation of P_i from the catalytic site.

It is clear that the most important feature of the pump is the transformation of the transport sites from a state of high affinity for Ca^{2+} to a state of low affinity for Ca^{2+}. The free energy involved in this transformation is approximately 5 kcal mol^{-1}, and 10 kcal per catalytic cycle which handles two moles of calcium per mole of ATP. Therefore the calcium pump requires that ATP (or any suitable substrate) and its products be present at concentration ratios yielding sufficient free energy to meet this requirement. It should be understood that the enzyme can only acquire two discrete states with specific affinities for Ca^{2+} ($K_a = 10^6$ M^{-1} or $10^3 - 10^2$ M^{-1}), and can only operate with a fixed stoichiometry of $2Ca^{2+}$ per ATP. Most experimental observations indicate that, in comparable conditions, the enzyme cannot acquire a calcium affinity different from those corresponding to either of the two possible states; neither can it operate with shifting stoichiometry (that is, varying Ca^{2+} : ATP ratios). Therefore, the free energy which is used to change the enzyme from the high to the low affinity state is the same, independent of the concentration gradient.

Hence the pump operates inefficiently when the Ca^{2+} concentration gradient is low, and is most efficient when the gradient is high. Furthermore, the maximal gradient that can be generated by the pump is determined by the minimal concentration of Ca^{2+}_{out}, which is necessary to saturate the enzyme in the high affinity state, and the maximal concentration of Ca^{2+}_{in} permitting dissociation of calcium from the phosphoenzyme in the low affinity state. The maximal gradient cannot be raised by increasing the chemical potential of the substrate beyond the requirements for the enzyme transition from one to the other of the two discrete states. It is of interest that in the physiological environment of the muscle cell, a nearly ideal match is found between the chemical potential generated by the concentration ratios of ATP and its products, and the Ca^{2+} gradient maintained by the SR membrane (Tanford, 1981) — undoubtedly an extraordinary accomplishment of biological adaptation.

REFERENCES

Allen, G. and Green, N. (1976). *FEBS Lett.*, **63**, 188.

Allen, G., Trinnaman, B. and Green, N. (1980). *Biochem. J.*, **187**, 591.

Andersen, J., Fellmann, P., Moller, J. and Devaux, P. (1981). *Biochemistry*, **20**, 4928.

Ariki, M. and Boyer, P. (1980). *Biochemistry*, **19**, 2001.

Bagshaw, C., Eccleston, J., Eckstein, F., Goody, R., Gutfreund, H. and Trentham, D. (1974). *Biochem. J.*, **141**, 351.

Bailin, G. (1980). *Biochim. biophys. Acta*, **624**, 511.

Banerjee, R., Epstein, M. Kandrach, M., Zimniak, P. and Racker, E. (1979). *Membrane Biochem.*, **2**, 283.

Bargolie, B., Hasselbach, W. and Makinose, M. (1971). *FEBS Lett*, **12**, 267

Bastide, F., Meissner, G., Fleischer, S. and Post, R. L. (1973). *J. biol. Chem.*, **248**, 8385.

Beil, F., Chak, D. and Hasselbach, W. (1977). *Eur. J. Biochem.*, **81**, 151.

Berman, M. and Aderem, A. (1981). *Analyt. Biochem.*, **115**, 297.

Boyer, P., deMeis, L. and Carvalho, M. (1977). *Biochemistry*, **16**, 136.

Burkli, A. and Cherry, R. (1981). *Biochemistry*, **20**, 138.

Caputo, C. (1978). *A. Rev. Biophys. Bioengng*, 7, 63.
Carvalho, A. (1966). *J. cell. Physiol.*, 67, 73.
Carvalho, A. (1972). *Eur. J. Biochem.*, 27, 491.
Carvalho, M., de Souza, D. and deMeis, L. (1976). *J. biol. Chem.*, 251, 3629.
Chance, B. (1972). *Meth. Enzym.*, 24, 322.
Chevallier, J. and Buton, R. (1971). *Biochemistry*, 10, 2733.
Chiesi, M. and Inesi, G. (1979). *J. biol. Chem.*, 254, 10370.
Chiesi, M. and Inesi, G. (1980). *Biochemistry*, 19, 2912.
Chiesi, M. and Inesi, G. (1981). *Archs Biochem. Biophys.*, 208, 586.
Chiesi, M., Peterson, S. and Acuto, O. (1978). *Archs Biochem. Biophys.*, 189, 132.
Chiu, V. and Haynes, D. (1977). *Biophys. J.*, 18, 3.
Chiu, V. and Haynes, D. (1980). *J. membrane Biol.*, 56, 219.
Coan, C. and Inesi, G. (1977). *J. biol. Chem.*, 252, 3044.
Deamer, D. and Baskin, R. (1969). *J. Cell Biol.*, 42, 296.
Dean, W. and Tanford, C. (1977). *J. biol. Chem.*, 252, 3551.
Dean, W. and Tanford, C. (1978). *Biochemistry*, 17, 1683.
Degani, C. and Boyer, P. (1973). *J. biol. Chem.*, 248, 8222.
deMeis, L. (1969). *Biochim. biophys. Acta*, 172, 343.
deMeis, L. (1969). *J. biol. Chem.*, 244, 3733.
deMeis, L. (1971). *J. biol. Chem.*, 246, 4764.
deMeis, L. (1976). *J. biol. Chem.*, 251, 2055.
deMeis, L. and Boyer, P. (1978). *J. biol. Chem.*, 253, 1556.
deMeis, L. and Carvalho, M. (1974). *Biochemistry*, 13, 5032.
deMeis, L. and deMello, M. C. F. (1973). *J. biol. Chem.*, 248, 3691.
deMeis, L. and Inesi, G. (1982). In *Membrane Transport of Calcium* (ed. E. Carafoli), Academic Press, New York, 141.
deMeis, L., Martins, O. and Alves, E. (1980). *Biochemistry*, 19, 4252.
deMeis, L. and Masuda, H. (1974). *Biochemistry*, 13, 2057.
deMeis, L., Otero, A. Martins, O., Alves, E., Inesi, G. and Nakamoto, R. (1982). *J. biol. Chem.*, 257, 4993.
deMeis, L. and Sorenson, M. (1975). *Biochemistry*, 14, 2739.
deMeis, L. and Tume, R. (1977). *Biochemistry*, 16, 4455.
deMeis, L. and Vianna, A. (1979). *A. Rev. Biochem.*, 48, 275.
Dipolo, R., Requena, J., Brinley, F., Mullins, L., Scarpa, A. and Tiffert, T. (1976). *J. gen. Physiol.*, 67, 433.
Drabikowski, W., Dominas, H. and Dabrowska, M. (1966). *Acta biochim. Pol.*, 13, 11.
Dupont, Y. (1977). *Eur. J. Biochem.*, 72, 185.
Dupont, Y. (1980). *Eur. J. Biochem.*, 109, 231.
Dupont, Y. (1982). *Biochim. biophys. Acta*, 688, 75.
Dupont, Y., Harrison, S. and Hasselbach, W. (1973). *Nature*, 244, 555.
Dupont, Y. and Leigh, J. (1978). *Nature*, 273, 396.
Ebashi, S. (1958). *Archs Biochem. Biophys.*, 76, 410.
Ebashi, S. and Endo, M. (1968). *Prog. Biophys. molec. Biol.*, 18, 125.
Ebashi, S. and Lipman, F. (1962). *J. Cell Biol.*, 14, 389.
Endo, M. (1977). *Physiol. Rev.*, 57, 71.
Fabiato, A. and Fabiato, F. (1979). *J. Physiol., Paris*, 75, 463.
Fabiato, A. and Fabiato, F. (1979). *A. Rev. Physiol.*, 41, 437.
Fiehn, W. and Hasselbach, W. (1970). *Eur. J. Biochem.*, 13, 510.
Fiehn, W. and Migala, A. (1971). *Eur. J. Biochem.*, 20, 245.
Fiehn, W., Peter, J., Mead, J. and Gan-Elepano, M. (1971). *J. biol. Chem.*, 246, 5617.
Friedman, Z. and Makinose, M. (1970). *FEBS Lett.*, 11, 69.
Froehlich, J., Heller, P. and Passioneau, J. (1980). *Fedn Proc.*, 39, 2951.
Froehlich, J. and Taylor, E. (1975). *J. biol. Chem.*, 250, 2013.
Fuchs, F. (1974). *A. Rev. Physiol.*, 36, 461.
Garrahan, P., Rega, A. and Alonso, G. (1976). *Biochim. biophys. Acta*, 448, 121.
Guillain, F., Gingold, M. and Champeil, P. *J. biol. Chem.* (in the press).
Hasselbach, W. (1964). *Prog. Biophys. Biophys. Chem.*, 14, 167.
Hasselbach, W. (1978). *Biochim. biophys. Acta*, 515, 23.
Hasselbach, W. and Makinose, M. (1961). *Biochem. Z.*, 333, 518.

Hasselbach, W. and Makinose, M. (1962). *Biochem. biophys. Res. Commun.*, **7**, 132.
Hasselbach, W. and Makinose, M. (1963). *Biochem. Z.*, **339**, 94.
Hasselbach, W. and Seraydarian, K. (1966). *Biochem. Z.*, **345**, 159.
Herbette, L., Marquardt, J., Scarpa, A. and Balsie, J. (1977). *Biophys. J.*, **20**, 245.
Hesketh, T., Smith, G., Houslay, M., Birdsall, N., Metcalfe, J. and Warren, G. (1976). *Biochemistry*, **15**, 4145.
Hill, L. and Inesi, G. *Proc. natn. Acad. Sci. U.S.A.* (in the press).
Hoffmann, W., Sarzala, M. and Chapman, D. (1979). *Proc. natn. Acad. Sci. U.S.A.*, **76**, 3860.
Hoffmann, W., *et al.* (1980). *J. molec. Biol.*, **141**, 119.
Ikemoto, N. (1974). *J. biol. Chem.*, **249**, 649.
Ikemoto, N. (1975). *J. biol. Chem.*, **250**, 7219.
Ikemoto, N. (1976). *J. biol. Chem.*, **251**, 7275.
Ikemoto, N. (1982). *A. Rev. Physiol.*, **44**, 297.
Ikemoto, N., Bhatnager, G. and Gergely, J. (1971). *Biochem. biophys. Res. Commun.*, **44**, 1510.
Ikemoto, N., Morgan, T. and Yamada, S. (1978). *J. biol. Chem.*, **253**, 8027.
Ikemoto, N., Sreter, F., Nakamura, A. and Gergely, J. (1968). *J. Ultrastruct. Res.*, **23**, 216.
Inesi, G. (1971). *Science*, **171**, 901.
Inesi, G. (1979). In *Membrane Transport in Biology* (eds G. Giebisch, D. Tosteson and H. Ussing), Springer-Verlag, Berlin, 357.
Inesi, G. (1981). In *Cell and Muscle Motility* (eds R. Dowben and J. Shay), Plenum, New York, **1**, 63.
Inesi, G. and Asai, H. (1968). *Archs Biochem. Biophys.*, **126**, 469.
Inesi, G., Goodman, J. J. and Watanabe, S. (1967). *J. biol. Chem.*, **242**, 4637.
Inesi, G. and Kurzmack, M. (1977). In *Membranous Elements and Movement of Molecules* (Methodological Surveys of Biochemistry Volume 6), (ed. E. Reid), Horwood, Chichester, 97.
Inesi, G., Kurzmack, M., Coan, C. and Lewis, D. (1980a). *J. biol. Chem.*, **255**, 3025.
Inesi, G., Kurzmack, M., Kosk-Kosicka, D., Lewis, D., Scofano, H. and Guimaraes-Motta, H. (1982a). *Z. Naturforsch.* **C** (in the press).
Inesi, G., Kurzmack, M., Nakamoto, R., deMeis, L. and Bernhard, S. (1980b). *J. biol. Chem.*, **255**, 6040.
Inesi, G., Kurzmack, M. and Verjovski-Almeida, S. (1978). *Ann. N.Y. Acad. Sci.*, **307**, 224.
Inesi, G., Maring, E., Murphy, A. and McFarland, B. (1970). *Archs Biochem. Biophys.*, **138**, 285.
Inesi, G. and Scales, D. (1974). *Biochemsitry*, **13**, 3298.
Inesi, G. and Scarpa, A. (1972). *Biochemistry*, **11**, 356.
Inesi, G., Watanabe, T., Coan, C. and Murphy, A. (1982b). *Ann. N.Y. Acad. Sci.* (in the press).
Kanazawa, T. (1975). *J. biol. Chem.*, **250**, 113.
Kanazawa, T. and Boyer, P. (1973). *J. biol. Chem.*, **248**, 3163.
Kanazawa, T., Yamada, S., Yamamoto, T. and Tonomura, Y. (1971). *J. Biochem. (Tokyo)*, **70**, 95.
Kielley, W. and Meyerhof, O. (1950). *J. biol. Chem.*, **183**, 391.
Klip, A., Reithmeier, R. and MacLennan, D. (1980). *J. biol. Chem.*, **255**, 6562.
Knowles, A., Eytan, E. and Racker, E. (1976). *J. biol. Chem.*, **251**, 5161.
Knowles, A. and Racker, E. (1975). *J. biol. Chem.*, **250**, 1949.
Kolassa, N., Punzengruber, C., Suko, J. and Makinose, M. (1979). *FEBS Lett.*, **108**, 495.
Kurzmack, M., Inesi, G., Tal, N. and Bernhard, S. (1981). *Biochemistry*, **20**, 468.
Kurzmack, M., Verjovski-Almeida, S. and Inesi, G. (1977). *Biochem. biophys. Res. Commun.*, **78**, 772.
Lacapere, J., Gingold, M., Champeil, P. and Guillain, F. (1981). *J. biol. Chem.*, **256**, 2302
LeMaire, M., Moller, J. and Tanford, C. (1976). *Biochemistry*, **15**, 2336.
Louis, C. and Holroyd, J. (1978). *Biochim. biophys. Acta*, **535**, 222.
Louis, C., Saunders, M. and Holroyd, J. (1977). *Biochim. biophys. Acta*, **493**, 78.
Louis, C. and Shooter, E. (1972). *Archs Biochem. Biophys.*, **153**, 641.
MacLennan, D. (1970). *J. biol. Chem.*, **245**, 4508.
MacLennan, D. and Holland, P. (1975). *A. Rev. Biophys. Bioengng*, **4**, 377.

MacLennan, D., Seeman, P., Iles, G. and Yip, C. (1971). *J. biol. Chem.*, **246**, 2702.
MacLennan, D. and Wong, P. (1971). *Proc. natn. Acad. Sci., U.S.A.*, **68**, 1231.
MacLennan, D., Yip, C., Iles, G. and Seeman, P. (1973). *Cold Spring Harb. Symp. quant. Biol.*, **37**, 469.
Madeira, V. (1978). *Archs Biochem. Biophys.*, **185**, 316.
Makinose, M. (1966). *Biochem. Z.*, **345**, 80.
Makinose, M. (1969). *Eur. J. Biochem.*, **10**, 74.
Makinose, M. (1971). *FEBS Lett.*, **12**, 269.
Makinose, M. (1972). *FEBS Lett.*, **25**, 113.
Makinose, M. and Boll, W. (1979). In *Cation Flux Across Biomembranes* (eds Y. Mukohata and L. Packer), Academic, London, 89.
Makinose, M. and Hasselbach, W. (1971). *FEBS Lett.*, **12**, 271.
Makinose, M. and Thé, R. (1965). *Biochem. Z.*, **343**, 383.
Malan, N., Sabbadini, R., Scales, D. and Inesi, G. (1975). *FEBS Lett.*, **60**, 122.
Manuck, B. and Sykes, B. (1977). *Can. J. Biochem*, **55**, 587.
Marai, L. and Kuksis, A. (1973). *Can. J. Biochem.*, **51**, 1365.
Martin, D. and Tanford, C. (1981). *Biochemistry*, **20**, 4597.
Martonosi, A. (1968). *J. biol. Chem.*, **243**, 71.
Martonosi, A. (1972). In *Metabolic Pathways* (ed. L. Hokin), Academic, New York, Vol. 6, 317.
Martonosi, A., Donley, J. and Halpin, R. (1968). *J. biol. Chem.*, **243**, 61.
Martonosi, A., Donley, J., Pucell, G. and Halpin, R. (1971). *Archs Biochem. Biophys.*, **144**, 529
Martonosi, A. and Feretos, R. (1964). *J. biol. Chem.*, **239**, 648.
Martonosi, A. and Halpin, R. (1971). *Archs. Biochem. Biophys.*, **144**, 66.
Masuda, H. and deMeis, L. (1973). *Biochemistry*, **12**, 4581.
McFarland, B. and Inesi, G. (1971). *Archs Biochem. Biophys.*, **145**, 456.
Meissner, G. (1973). *Biochim. biophys. Acta*, **298**, 906.
Meissner, G. (1975). *Biochim. biophys. Acta*, **389**, 51.
Meissner, G., Conner, G. and Fleischer, S. (1973). *Biochim. biophys. Acta.*, **298**, 246.
Meissner, G. and Fleischer, S. (1971). *Biochim. biophys. Acta*, **241**, 356.
Meissner, G. and Fleischer, S. (1972). *Biochim. biophys. Acta*, **255**, 19.
Michalak, M., Campbell, K. and MacLennan, D. (1980). *J. biol. Chem.*, **255**, 1317.
Migala, A., Agostini, B. and Hasselbach, W. (1973). *Z. Naturforsch.* **C28**, 178.
Murphy, A. (1976a). *Biochem. biophys. Res. Commun.*, **70**, 160.
Murphy, A. (1976b). *Biochemistry*, **15**, 4492.
Murphy, A. (1977). *Archs Biochem. Biophys.*, **180**, 114.
Murphy, A. (1978). *J. biol. Chem.*, **253**, 385.
Muscatello, U., Andersson-Cedergren, E., Azzone, G. and von der Decken, A. (1961). *J. Biophys. Biochem. Cytol.*, **10**, 201.
Nagai, T., Makinose, M. and Hasselbach, W. (1960). *Biochim. biophys. Acta*, **43**, 223.
Nakamura, Y. and Tonomura, Y. (1978). *J. Biochem. (Tokyo)*, **83**, 571.
Nakamura, Y. and Tonomura, Y. (1982). *J. Biochem. (Tokyo)*, **91**, 449.
Neet, K. and Green, N. (1977). *Archs Biochem. Biophys.*, **178**, 588.
Ogawa, Y., Harafuji, H. and Kurebayashi, N. (1980). *J. Biochem. (Tokyo)*, **87**, 1293.
Owen, J. (1978). *Analyt. Biochem.*, **85**, 165.
Ohnishi, T. and Ebashi, S. (1963). *J. Biochem. (Tokyo)*, **54**, 506.
Ostwald, T. and MacLennan, D. (1974). *J. biol. Chem.*, **249**, 974.
Owen, J. (1976). *Biochim. biophys. Acta*, **451**, 321.
Owens, K., Ruth, R. and Weglicki, W. (1972). *Biochim. biophys. Acta*, **288**, 479.
Pang, D. and Briggs, F. (1977). *J. biol. Chem.*, **252**, 3262.
Peterson, S. and Deamer, D. (1977). *Archs Biochem. Biophys.*, **179**, 218.
Pick, U. and Karlish, S. (1980). *Biochim. biophys. Acta*, **626**, 255.
Portzehl, H. (1957). *Biochim. biophys. Acta*, **26**, 373.
Prager, R., Punzengruber, C., Kolassa, N., Winkler, F. and Suko, J. (1979). *Eur. J. Biochem.*, **97**, 239.
Punzengruber, C., Prager, R., Kolassa, N., Winkler, F. and Suko, J. (1978). *Eur. J. Biochem.*, **92**, 349.
Racker, E. (1972). *J. biol. Chem.*, **247**, 8198.

Ratkje, S. and Shamoo, A. (1980). *Biophys. J.*, **30**, 523.
Rauch, B., Chak, D. and Hasselbach, W. (1977). *Z. Naturforsch.* **C32**, 828.
Ribeiro, J. and Vianna, L. (1978). *J. biol. Chem.*, **253**, 3153.
Rizzolo, L., LeMaire, M., Reynolds, J. and Tanford, C. (1976). *Biochemistry*, **15**, 3433.
Rossi, B., Leone, F., Gache, C. and Lazdunski, M. (1979). *J. biol. Chem.*, **254**, 2302.
Scales, D. and Inesi, G. (1976). *Biophys. J.*, **16**, 735.
Scarpa, A. (1982). In *Techniques in Cellular Physiology* (ed. P. Baker), Vol. P127, Elsevier, Ireland, 1.
Scarpa, A. Baldassare, J. and Inesi, G. (1972). *J. gen. Physiol.*, **60**, 735.
Scarpa, A., Brinley, F. and Dubyak, G. (1978). *Biochemistry*, **17**, 1378.
Scofano, H., Vieyra A. and deMeis, L. (1979). *J. biol. Chem.*, **254**, 10227.
Shigekawa, M. and Akowitz, A. (1979). *J. biol. Chem.*, **254**, 4726.
Shigekawa, M. and Dougherty, J. (1978). *J. biol. Chem.*, **253**, 1451.
Shigekawa, M. and Dougherty, J. (1978). *J. biol. Chem.*, **253**, 1458.
Shigekawa, M., Dougherty, J. and Katz, A. (1978). *J. biol. Chem.*, **253**, 1442.
Stewart, P. and MacLennan, D. (1974). *J. biol. Chem.*, **249**, 985.
Sumida, M. and Tonomura, Y. (1974). *J. Biochem. (Tokyo)*, **75**, 283.
Tada, M., Yamamoto, T. and Tonomura, Y. (1978). *Physiol. Rev.*, **58**, 1.
Takagi, A. (1971). *Biochim. biophys. Acta*, **248**, 12.
Takakuwa, Y. and Kanazawa, T. (1979). *Biochem. biophys. Res. Commun.*, **88**, 1209.
Takisawa, H. and Tonomura, Y. (1979). *J. Biochem. (Tokyo)*, **86**, 425.
Tanford, C. (1981). *J. gen. Physiol.*, **77**, 223.
Taylor, J. and Hattan, D. (1979). *J. biol. Chem.*, **254**, 4402.
Thé, R. and Hasselbach, W. (1972a). *Eur. J. Biochem.*, **28**, 357.
Thé, R. and Hasselbach, W. (1972b). *Eur. J. Biochem.*, **30**, 318.
Thé, R. and Hasselbach, W. (1977). *Eur. J. Biochem.*, **74**, 611.
Thomas, D. and Hidalgo, C. (1978). *Proc. natn. Acad. Sci. U.S.A.*, **75**, 5488.
Thorley-Lawson, D. and Green, N. (1973). *Eur. J. Biochem.*, **40**, 403.
Thorley-Lawson, D. and Green, N. (1977). *Biochem. J.*, **167**, 739.
Tong, S. (1980). *Archs Biochem. Biophys.*, **203**, 780.
Vanderkooi, J., Ierokomas, A., Nakamura, H. and Martonosi, A. (1977). *Biochemistry*, **16**, 1262.
Verjovski-Almeida, S. and deMeis, L. (1977). *Biochemistry*, **16**, 329.
Verjovski-Almeida, S. and Inesi, G. (1979). *J. biol. Chem.*, **254**, 18.
Verjovski-Almeida, S. and Kurzmack, M. and Inesi, G. (1978). *Biochemistry*, **17**, 5006.
Vianna, A. (1975). *Biochim. biophys. Acta*, **410**, 389.
Waku, K., Uda, Y. and Nakazawa, Y. (1971). *J. Biochem. (Tokyo)*, **69**, 483.
Wang, C., Saito, A. and Fleischer, S. (1979). *J. biol. Chem.*, **254**, 9209.
Warren, G., Toon, P., Birdsall, N., Lee, A. and Metcalfe, J. (1974). *Biochemistry*, **13**, 5501.
Warren, G., Toon, P., Birdsall, N., Lee, A. and Metcalfe, J. (1974). *Proc. natn. Acad. Sci. U.S.A.*, **71**, 622.
Watanabe, T. and Inesi, G. (1982a). *Biochemsitry* (in the press).
Watanabe, T. and Inesi, G. (1982b). *J. biol. Chem.* (in the press).
Watanabe, T., Lewis, D., Nakamoto, R., Kurzmack, M., Fronticelli, C. and Inesi, G. (1981). *Biochemistry*, **20**, 6617.
Webb, M. and Trentham, D. (1981). *J. biol. Chem.*, **256**, 4884.
Weber, A. (1966). In *Current Topics in Bioenergetics* (ed. D. Sanadi), Academic, New York, 203.
Weber, A., Herz, R. and Reiss, I. (1966). *Biochem. Z.*, **345**, 329.
Weber, A., Herz, R. and Reiss, I. (1967). *Biochim. biophys. Acta*, **131**, 188.
Yamada, S. and Ikemoto, N. (1978). *J. biol. Chem.*, **235**, 6801.
Yamada, S. and Ikemoto, N. (1980). *J. biol. Chem.*, **255**, 3108.
Yamada, S., Sumida, M. and Tonomura, Y. (1972). *J. Biochem. (Tokyo)*, **72**, 1537.
Yamada, S. and Tonomura, Y. (1972). *J. Biochem. (Tokyo)*, **71**, 1101.
Yamada, S. and Tonomura, Y. (1973). *J. Biochem. (Tokyo)*, **74**, 1091.
Yamamoto, T., Takisawa, H. and Tonomura, Y. (1979). In *Current Topics in Bioenergetics* (ed. D. Sanadi), Academic, New York, **9**, 179.
Yamamoto, T. and Tonomura, Y. (1967). *J. Biochem. (Tokyo)*, **62**, 558.
Yamamoto, T. and Tonomura, Y. (1968). *J. Biochem. (Tokyo)*, **64**, 137.
Yates, D. and Duance, V. (1976). *Biochem. J.*, **159**, 719.

Index